PROSE AND POETRY JOURNEYS

PROSE AND POETRY

JOURNEYS

DONALD MACLEAN TOWER
CORA J. RUSSELL
CHRISTINE W. WEST

ILLUSTRATIONS · GUY BROWN WISER

SYRACUSE NEW YORK

THE L. W. SINGER COMPANY

The Prose and Poetry Series

PROSE AND POETRY OF ENGLAND
PROSE AND POETRY OF AMERICA
PROSE AND POETRY FOR APPRECIATION
PROSE AND POETRY FOR ENJOYMENT
PROSE AND POETRY ADVENTURES
PROSE AND POETRY JOURNEYS
PROSE AND POETRY OF TODAY
PROSE AND POETRY OF THE WORLD

CONTENTS

JOURNEYS INTO LEGEND AND FANCY

≍ ▌▌▌ ≍

CONTENTS BY TYPES

JOURNEYS

ACROSS AMERICA

H

Observing animal life.

THE MOST DANGEROUS
ENEMY OF ALL

HAROLD MC CRACKEN ·

Two hundred years ago sea otters swarmed in great numbers among the Aleutian Islands and along the western coast of Alaska. Then Russian explorers, discovering that huge profits could be made from the sale of the rich fur, forced the Aleutian natives to kill the sea otters by the score. Within a hundred years the animals were nearly exterminated. Today, however, they are protected by government laws and are gradually increasing in number.

Baby otters, called by the early Russians, "Medviedki," are cared for by their mothers until they are almost full grown. They are taught to swim, to be alert, and to be cautious. Usually their home is a small cave having a narrow entrance. The male sea otter is known as "Bobri Morski" or "Sea Beaver." The mother otter is called "Matka."

MEDVIEDKI [1] grew quite rapidly. His long, woolly, straw-colored hair had begun to shed in spots, exposing the rich brown fur that was underneath. This shedding caused him to itch all over and he repeatedly crawled out of the water to scratch himself, first with one hind flipper and then the other, wherever he could reach. The calloused little pads near the tips of his toes gradually combed out the woolly yellow hair.

Each day he became more expert as a swimmer and already he could glide through the water with speed and grace.

He had also begun to lose his baby habits, such as crying impatiently when Matka left him to dive in prolonged under-

"The Most Dangerous Enemy of All" is reprinted by permission of the publishers, J. B. Lippincott from *The Last of the Sea Otters* by Harold McCracken, copyright 1942 by Harold McCracken.

[1] MEDVIEDKI—Pronounced měd-vē-ĕd′kĭ.

3

water searches for food.   Instead, he dived down to join her.
But he still could not quite manage to balance a flat rock on his
chest or crack a clam or large mussel upon it.   He had learned
to crack sea urchins,[2] without getting his mouth filled with
spines; and to eat thin-shelled mussels.   But he still preferred
the milk which his mother provided.

Nor did he now insist upon sleeping on his mother's chest.
He slept alone, on his back in the water, with all four feet stuck
up in the air, and frequently wagging his triangular tail and
purring aloud to himself.   He didn't wag his tail from side to
side, as might be expected, but up and down; and he always
tried to keep pretty close to Matka's side.   When he finally
quieted down to go to sleep, he folded his hind flippers and tail
up over his stomach and pulled his forepaws over his head to
cover his eyes.

But Medviedki had a very strong desire to find out what was
beyond the entrance to their little cove.   Each time that his
father came in and went out, this desire became stronger.   It
was impossible to see out through the entrance, because the
channel was very narrow, curved sharply and had high rocky
cliffs on either side.   He knew there were other places besides
this little cove, because Bobri Morski went out there and sometimes stayed for several days.   Also the puffins and other birds
flew over the top of the cliffs and were gone a long time; once
a seal swam in, looked around and then swam out again; and
he had heard the thunder of the waves outside when the wind
blew and it was very stormy.

More than once he had started to swim out through the entrance, but Matka always stopped him.   She would swim rapidly to overtake him and push herself right up against his neck
to turn him around.   Nor would she leave him until he had
returned to swim in their own little private pool.   But more
and more he felt that it was high time he found out what else
there was to see.

[2] SEA URCHINS—Small sea animals having thin brittle shells covered with
sharp spines.

One day when Bobri Morski came in to see them, Medviedki determined to follow his father when he went away. So he immediately set out to show Bobri Morski all his swimming tricks, in an effort to impress him with the fact that he was quite grown up and quite ready to become his companion in the adventures which lay in the mysterious world outside. Even before his father and mother had ended their usual visit of greeting, he went gliding speedily through the water around them, jumping forward to dive head first and come out with a leap that took him clear into the air. He rolled on his side and then on his back while he was swimming, and without losing speed; then making a long dive, he came up right beside his parents with such ease that there was scarcely a ripple on the surface. But Bobri Morski didn't seem to show the slightest sign of being impressed.

While the old folks were busy enjoying a feast on the shellfish and other things that the low tide had laid before them, Medviedki suddenly got an idea. He would slip through the entrance and wait for his father outside.

He took a very long breath and then dived, keeping under water until he had swum quite a distance into the deep narrow channel. Then he came to the surface to look around.

High walls of rock rose close on either side, but ahead spread a wide expanse of sky. A current of the outgoing tide carried him slowly along. He hardly had to swim. The water also rolled in quite big swells which gave him a new thrill as he slowly approached the last point of rock. Standing straight up in the water as high as he could, he stared excitedly to get his first glimpse of the great outside world.

Almost before he knew it he was riding the big ground swell well out in the open Pacific. The sea and sky stretched so far and seemed so big that they startled him. He looked back towards the opening through which he had just come. He could hardly see where it was. It was almost lost from view in the wall of cliffs. As he looked around, he could see other great masses of rock rising out of the sea. Some of these were many times larger and higher than the one which sheltered his own home pool. Others were mere points of rock that disappeared from sight when the big waves rolled over them.

As he stood there in the water looking inquiringly about and not knowing just what to do, a flock of big king eider ducks came flying low over the waves. They lit right in front of him, so close that he could plainly see the pretty pale green cheeks on the sides of their blue-gray heads, the black V-shaped marks on their clean white throats and their breasts of creamy buff. For a moment he was on the verge of diving and trying to swim clear back into the protection of his own peaceful cove. He remembered the attack by the eagle and wondered if these big gay-colored ducks were as dangerous. They didn't seem even to notice him, however . . . just sat fat and lazy, letting the rolling sea swing them up and down. So he swam away, watching them suspiciously as he went.

There was so very much water to swim in that he wanted to go speeding across it as fast as he could, just to see where it would take him. He was so fascinated that he had quite forgotten he had come out here to wait for his father. He loved the way the big waves carried him first up on their crests, where he could see a long way off, and then let him slide down their sides into the deep blue-green troughs. He also liked to watch the big waves roll in and burst into noisy spray against the jumble of massive rocks on the shore. It really was a wonderful world and he was very glad he had come out to see it.

He swam along very happily for quite a long time, always keeping quite close to the shore so he could dash in and climb out on one of the rocks if any unfamiliar enemy should suddenly appear in the sea, as well as swim back to find the entrance of his own private cove.

After a while he saw something very strange floating on the sea. It was coming around a point of the rocky shore ahead of him. He stopped and watched it very intently. It was long

6

and narrow. Two parts stuck up out of it and dipped long wooden paddles rhythmically into the water to make it move along. The instinct with which he had been born insisted that he should flee from anything of whose good intentions he was uncertain; but it moved so slowly that he felt confident it could not be very dangerous to such a fast swimmer as himself, and it was such a curious looking thing that he decided to get a closer look at it. As this was, of course, the first time he had ever seen any Aleut [3] native hunters in a skin boat, he could not realize that they were the most dangerous of all the several enemies which he would ever be called upon to escape. Had he been wiser in experience, or had Matka or Bobri Morski been along to warn him, he could have quickly slipped beneath the surface and swum away without being seen by them.

Just about that time his keen eyes also noticed something moving up on a big ledge of rock just out of reach of the spray from the waves that broke at their base. Then he saw that there were several of them. They were sea lions, the largest living creatures he had ever seen and, although he did not know it at the time, one of the most dangerous natural enemies he might be called upon to escape. But they were way up there and he was down in the water, so he just stared at them. It seemed that they were all asleep. Most of them sat up with their great heads thrown back and their monster necks bulging out as if they were about to burst. He noticed that they looked quite a little like his mother and father, except that they had flippers for front feet as well as in back and they were many, many times larger than both Matka and Bobri Morski put together.

When he looked back towards the funny floating thing, it had come quite a bit closer. It moved faster than he had thought. Now he could see that the parts which stuck up were both moving. They each had heads and each was pushing a paddle back and forth through the water. Yes, each was a

---

[3] ALEUT (ăl′ê ōōt)—An Eskimo tribe.

separate creature and they were riding in the long thing that floated on the water.

If Medviedki had been a little closer to this baidar [4] or sea lion skin boat, and had been able to understand the language of the two Aleutian [5] Island natives who were in it, he would have heard one of them say: "I think we are close enough. We better shoot before they dive into the water."

Then there was the most sudden and loudest noise Medviedki had ever heard, followed almost instantly by another blast of the same kind. It scared him so badly that his heart completely stopped and he even forgot to dive. At practically the same time the big monsters up on the rocks all came to life and began letting out such roars that the cliffs seemed to tremble with the noise. They started plunging down off the rocks, and when they hit the water the splashes and spray went up almost as high as the waves that broke against the cliffs. They came up quickly and went right on roaring and bellowing as they swam rapidly out to sea, pushing waves ahead of them as they traveled.

As nothing had attacked him and since he was quite overcome by his childish curiosity, Medviedki just stood up in the water and stared in bewildered amazement.

Soon the sea lions were quite a distance away and the two natives were paddling their baidar in towards the rocks to skin the animals they had shot. The canoe was suddenly turned in Medviedki's direction. Then there was another of those sudden and terrific noises, followed almost instantly by a splash so close to him and so violent that he was almost thrown out of the water. He dived in a flash and swam under the water until he was compelled to come to the surface to breathe. Rising up to look around, he had just located the natives and their baidar when another rifle shot crashed and once more the bullet struck so close to him that he dived without waiting to fill his lungs with air.

[4] BAIDAR—Pronounced bī′där.   [5] ALEUTIAN—Pronounced a-lū′shăn.

The two natives were paddling their baidar as fast as they could to overtake him, for they knew that by keeping close enough to shoot as quickly as he came to the surface they would cause him to dive immediately without taking another breath; and this would soon tire him out so they could get close enough for the kill.

Medviedki's only thought now was to get back to the little cove with his mother; but all the excitement had so confused him that he did not remember which was the right way to go.

He swam as far and as fast as he could, but soon had to come to the surface again. He had taken only a few quick breaths of air, however, when there was another loud crash followed by one of those terrible splashes in the water close beside him. He was now so frightened and beginning to get so tired that he knew he could not keep on doing this very much longer. So he dived and swam right in towards where the waves were breaking in clouds of spray on the jumbled mass of broken rocks at the base of the high cliffs.

He kept right on going under the water until the sea became so rough and broken up that he could not see where he was going and was just thrown helplessly about. When the waves rolled back he found himself in a tiny pool with big rocks all around him. He could not look out over the sea; but neither could he see that awful baidar with the native hunters.

He had just managed to cough out some of the water he had swallowed and gasp a few breaths of fresh air when the next big wave came crashing in to smother him under its thundering weight. But he did not try to swim out. When it rolled back again, he got another few breaths of air.

This was certainly the most unpleasant place he had ever been in, but he decided to stay here as long as he was safe from the new enemy.

The two natives in the baidar paddled back and forth, searching the sea for another glimpse of the most prized of all the trophies they could hope to take home with them. So determined were they to get the sea otter, that they stayed there until it was almost dark . . . hoping that if he had gone in among the rocks where they dared not follow him, he might come out while it was still light enough for them to shoot him. They had almost forgotten the two sea lions which they had killed for skins to make a new baidar . . . because the skin of one sea otter, even a young one such as Medviedki's, would bring enough money from the fur traders to buy a good many fine baidars.

"A fine pair of hunters we are . . ." said one of the natives in a very disappointed tone, "to let a small sea otter get away from us in open water! I'll be ashamed to tell father about it when we get home."

"Oh, well," grumbled the other, "that little sea otter may have gotten away from us this time . . . but let's go home before it gets too dark, and come back tomorrow. The old one is sure to be around here somewhere. There are probably others, too. We'll get all of them, before we are through."

A DUCK'S BEST FRIEND

JOHN BURTON TIGRETT

A LITTLE Indian hunter named Justo Montero was poling his homemade boat through the water hyacinths in the Magdalena River, in Colombia, one day not long ago, when he spotted five teal ducks bobbing in an open patch just ahead. The ducks heard him and started up. Montero quickly raised a long-barreled hammer gun and fired, and one of the ducks fell. Attached to one of its legs was a peculiar silvery band bearing an inscription: "Write Jack Miner, Kingsville, Ont., Canada. Let us consider one another. Heb. 10:24."

Fortunately, Montero did not understand English, or he might have thought he was having a hallucination. Instead, inhaling the thick aroma of Colombian coffee from the fields, he made haste to consult a lawyer in Barranquilla [1] who spoke English.

Paternally, in the manner of his calling, the lawyer explained to his visitor that the band had been placed on the duck's leg by a man who lived about 3000 miles from Barranquilla and who was simultaneously engaged in the scientific study of bird migration and in spreading Biblical texts.

"Come," the lawyer told Montero, "sit down, and let us write this Jack Miner."

This story of Justo Montero and the teal duck is only one of about 30,000 that have been written to Jack Miner since 1909, when he first scratched his address on a small piece of metal and wrapped it around the leg of a black duck named Katie. In 1910, a hunter killed Katie near Anderson, South Carolina, and established Miner as the pioneer bird bander of the North American continent.

Today, at seventy-eight, Jack Miner probably knows more about migratory birds than any other man. At his modest home near Kingsville, Ontario, he has seen his winged visitors' list grow from one stray duck to 50,000 expected guests annually. Some of them stop for only a few days on their flights between Hudson Bay and the warm southern waters, but many like the accommodations so well that they stay for several weeks. In return for his food and care, they have left enough knowledge of their habits and trails to make him a leading lecturer, the author of several books, a friend of the famous, and one of the best-known men in all Canada. Last year, King George conferred on him the Order of the British Empire. For one of ten children born of very poor parents, having no public education and unable for many years even to read or write, Miner has achieved a remarkable prominence.

Miner started out as a meat hunter—his home was the woods and his living came through decoying and killing the wary Ca-

[1] BARRANQUILLA (bär-rän-kēl'yä)—A town in Colombia.

11

nadian game. There was always a sale for the wild delicacies to the "rich folks 'cross the river" in Detroit. But as he became more skilled in luring the big geese and ducks out of the skies to within gun range, he also became more curious about them—curious as to how they lived from season to season, where they flew, how often they mated, how long they lived, and many other points in their behavior.

When the little band from Katie's leg was returned, Jack knew one of his questions had been answered and his career as a naturalist had begun. As his bird-banding methods improved, his enthusiasm over its success increased. Even now, after banding nearly 100,000 geese and ducks, it is still exciting business to Miner.

Up before dawn, Jack pulls on mud-spattered boots, slips on an old raveling gray sweater and, with a well-worn knitted cap covering his big red ears, wakes one of his three sons to go down with him for a look at the trap where the birds are caught for banding. Frequently, all his sons, Jasper, Ted, and Manly, will follow him the 100-odd yards down the pine-needled path to the lookout house. This little structure, built some fifteen feet off the ground and completely enclosed except for a small slit through which to view the lake, contains the mechanism for working the trap.

The trap itself was designed primarily for geese, since they have gradually driven the ducks to other parts of Miner's place, reserving the lake for their own breed. It stretches across the lake, a simple homemade affair consisting of a frame made out of water pipes. The top, sides and ends are covered with chicken wire. The two sides within the lake are hinged to raise and lower, and the trick is to let them close at that moment when the most birds are feeding underneath. When Jack first built the trap, he used decoys to lure the wild birds under the framework. Now there are usually so many geese crowded onto the two-acre lake that it looks like Coney Island on a hot Sunday, so luring them is no longer a problem.

How a goose flying hundreds of miles from Hudson Bay to Louisiana through all sorts of weather can, year after year, find a little two-acre lake is one thing not even Jack Miner has been able to figure out.

"All I can tell you," he says, "is that the fellow who remarks that somebody is 'silly as a goose' is talking through an empty head. I haven't yet seen a human I thought was as smart as a Canada goose."

When Jack is ready to spring the trap, he gives a low quiet trill that rises up to a shrill whistle, causing every goose to stop feeding and raise its head. In a split second, the sides are released and fall to the water with a splash. Once the trap is sprung, the men go back to the house for one of Mamma Miner's delicious hot breakfasts, and then wait for daylight. They return to the lake with gunny sacks and plenty of energy, for it takes a stout heart to drive the usual morning catch of 300 fighting, honking and hissing birds into the small pen at one end of the trap and get them into the sacks where they can be checked and banded.

"Then comes the best part," says Jack, his bright blue eyes blinking. "Mamma and I go down in the basement, where we cut the bands and put on them the Bible verses our friends will carry on their way."

In their little basement workshop, Mrs. Miner holds the bands on top of an old piece of railroad iron while Jack cuts in the dies that give their name and address, the season and year of the catch, and finally, the day's Bible quotation.

They put on a different Bible quotation each day of the season, and it is the key to the exact date of the catch.

"Putting on that word out of the Bible was the thing that made my bird banding unique and successful," he will tell you. "It came to me one afternoon while Mamma was reading a calendar I had bought in Kingsville from a Salvation Army lassie. I got to thinking about their work and the missionaries all around the world, and then of my birds and the strange places they fly to. I decided that between us they could become winged missionaries and provide food for both the body and the soul."

When the bands are ready, the birds are taken out of the sacks, then carefully checked for injuries and for other Miner bands. These other bands are important, for more than 20 per cent of Jack's visitors are repeat guests. If a goose in the morning's catch has one of the Miner bands that has been carried five years, it is given another band on the other leg. By adding a new band for every five-year period, he can tell with reasonable accuracy the age of the birds. The oldest duck, to Jack's knowledge, was shot in West Virginia when it was twenty-three years old. The oldest Canada goose was a favorite named Jack Johnson who lived to the remarkable age of twenty-nine.

The acutal banding takes only a few seconds, with one boy holding the bird while another bends the inch-wide piece of aluminum around its leg with a pair of pliers. Usually, their work is finished in the big yard, so the many visitors who throng the Miner sanctuary can see how it is done. Once banded, the birds are set free to go their way.

After the banding is finished, the boys act as guides to show interested guests the great variety of wild bird life which Jack entertains on the place. But Jack himself slips into the house, takes off his boots and warms his stockinged feet before the fire while Mrs. Miner opens the day's mail.

Stacks of letters come from everywhere—a doctor in South Dakota, a fur trader in Labrador, a farmer in Tennessee—all writing to tell how they have got a Jack Miner band and asking what he knows about their particular bird. To each one, his son, Manly, writes a personal note telling them when they banded it. From the 30,000 bands that have been returned and his many years of studying birds' habits, Jack can trace their migratory routes pretty accurately. In the Miner back yard is a big map of the North American continent on which a dot records each spot where a goose or duck wearing his band has been reported killed. It lays out as carefully as an engineer's transit the two broad well-defined Atlantic flyways the birds follow year after year.

"Geese are more reliable than ducks," says Jack. "They come down from Hudson Bay or Labrador and fly from here either direct to the North Carolina coast or to Louisiana by way of Illinois. Often, where they go depends on whom they meet here. I've seen some families come in annually for four or five years on their way to Louisiana. Then one day the old lady will strike up a friendship with some of the North Carolina crowd, and before you know it, she'll have papa and the brood heading off in that direction. But no matter which way they go from here, they're always weather-wise enough to arrange for a good tail wind to help them along. In all the years I've been watching geese I've never seen one making a migratory flight against a headwind. They mosey along at about fifty miles an hour and have great endurance. My returned bands have proved that some families fly all the way from Kingsville to Baffin Island—more than sixteen hundred miles —without making a stop."

15

Ask Jack how he knows they fly non-stop, and son Manly speaks up: "In the years dad has been banding Canadas, he has had thousands of bands returned from the territory which borders Central and Upper Hudson Bay. But between this area and our home at Kingsville only six bands have been returned, all of which, the accompanying letters indicated, were killed by a lucky shot from out of a large group of geese in flight."

One of the principal sources of returned Miner bands is the Jesuit and Anglican missionaries who preach the Gospel in the cold, desolate, northern wastes from Hudson Bay to Baffin Island. These northwest territories are inhabited mostly by Indians and Eskimos, who shoot the geese during the summer as their principal source of food. The first Miner band known in this north country was brought to Reverend J. W. Walton, some years ago, on the eastern shore of Hudson Bay. The Eskimos, believing it was some ill omen, had not removed the band. They laid the dead bird before the missionary's feet in fear.

When Doctor Walton had translated the band for them and explained what it was, the natives grabbed the goose, tore it apart and ate it raw. They had decided that God sent them that particular bird. It caused such a commotion in the territory that Doctor Walton packed his things and made the long journey down to Kingsville to see the man who had been introduced to him by a Canada goose. From then on, whenever a bird with a band was killed, the Indians or Eskimos would bring it in to the missionary in the area and ask, "What has God said this time?" The quotation on the band became the text for next Sunday's sermon.

In recent years, when the bands became more commonplace, the Eskimos started holding them for trading purposes. Now, each year, Jack sends a large bundle of brightly colored Bible scenes to the various Hudson Bay and Revillon fur-trading posts. There the missionaries have a standing offer—one Bible picture for one band. There's hardly an igloo in those north-ern wilds whose interior isn't decorated with some of Jack's scenes.

While his small lake and the surrounding acres now play to standing room only from November to May, Jack's place has not always been so popular with the wild birds. Ducks had been stopping at his place for several years on their way south when he decided to try to get some geese to call. He prepared the mud pond near his home and put out seven tame geese as decoys. Then he proudly announced to the neighborhood that the geese would be in any day.

This was in the spring of 1904, and his confident announce-ment created so much interest that for several weeks thereafter watching parties were held. But no geese arrived. In 1905 and 1906 none came either. When none came in 1907, he was the town's best joke. As his friend Doc Sloan will tell you, "His neighbors got to where they no longer spoke to Jack; they honked at him." For four long years he watched and waited. Then one day in April, 1908, eleven Canada geese dropped in and vindicated him. He fed them, and after about three weeks they continued on their flight. The next year they returned and brought fifteen friends with them. In the following year more than 400 arrived. They have been increasing ever since.

Today, through the help of the Canadian government and his many sportsman friends, Jack is able to devote the entire 400 acres of his sanctuary solely to the raising of corn for his visitors. Standing with him one afternoon, watching the birds feed, I asked him which were his favorites, ducks or geese.

"Well, I'll tell you," said Jack. I love them both, but ducks are like New York playboys—only out for a good time. The males of every breed can hardly make up to one girl for look-ing at another. Geese are different, and particularly Canada geese. They're my favorite, for they are a model to everyone. They conduct themselves with dignity and accept their responsibilities. They're always peaceful and they never fight unless it's absolutely necessary. When they are forced to battle, their wrath is something terrible.

"And there never was a better family man than a Canada goose. He protects his wife and children from all dangers and will fight to the death to save them. He takes only one mate in a lifetime, and I have never known one to make application for a divorce."

After we had walked a short distance along the lake's edge, Jack continued, "One of the finest characters I ever knew was a big Canada gander. . . . Some of the boys were out shooting back of the pond one day, and they shot into a family of five geese. They killed three and broke the pinion of one gander, and the other one flew away. I got them to give me the one with the broken pinion, and I took him in the house, tied up the severed arteries with some thread and then amputated a part of his wing. I put him out a little while later, and as I did, I noticed another goose circling the house, honking as if his heart would break. When my patient got out toward the pond, where there were maybe a thousand geese, making all sorts of noise, he raised his head toward the sky, gave one weak honk, and this gander that had been circling dropped down right by his side.

"The newcomer was an unusually large and powerful gander. He looked as though he had been the leader of his flock for a long time. Yet, from that moment until his death, he never left the side of his crippled brother. In fact, he never flew again. He gave up all the liberties of this great North American continent to live voluntarily in captivity. We named them David and Jonathan."

Jack's work in mending broken bones has been so successful that he now operates a bird hospital. On an old ironing board which he uses for an operating table, he puts splints on shattered legs, repairs injured wings, removes shot from bodies and does many other things that will make his friends whole again.

Usually, he has forty or fifty patients under treatment or con-valescing in the green-grassed yard that adjoins the hospital. There is no sign on the little shed that says "hospital" in goose language, but the birds know its location well. Nearly every morning during migratory season there will be three or four in-jured geese that have come in during the night, waddled their way up through the pines and are found outside the fence, try-ing to get into the hospital yard. It is a convincing demonstra-tion that geese can talk to one another rather well, for only a very few of the daily patients have ever been inside the enclo-sure before.

Recently, one of Jack's friends injured a big gander and trailed him as he walked more than five miles over rough coun-try to end up at the hospital gate. In two cases, geese flew in out of season for treatment. One, with an ugly gunshot wound in his breast, had evidently flown from Northern Canada through hundreds of miles of stormy weather. Almost on the Miner back porch he dropped from the sky with a splash of blood, stone dead. He hadn't quite made it in time.

Jack Miner's stories of his friends give convincing support to the chain of Miner-like refuges recently established by the Department of the Interior from Canada to the Gulf. As he walks about his place, pockets full of corn for his pets, his strong, red, leathery face and neck aglow from the cold Cana-dian wind, he can already see most of his life's dream come true. One unfilled hope is that his sanctuary at Kingsville may be endowed by some of his sportsman friends, so it can con-tinue after his passing as the great international home of the birds.

"Refuges are so much better than the game-warden system," he says. "For here you protect the birds while they live; the other way they're already dead. Between our new sanctuaries and the true American sportsmen, we should have a bountiful supply of game on this continent for many, many years to come."

TOBY GOES TO MARKET

LEW SARETT

B
(All boys in conversational tone)

WE SHIPPED the calf to the market—
   Toby, the brindle-bull,
With his face of perpetual wonder,
   And his tail like stuck-out wool.

1B
(One boy— owner of Toby)

5 Toby, who wallowed in mischief:
   Who squirmed through the pasture-rails,
Trampled my garden of melons,
   Battered my milking-pails.

Toby, who cried in the downpour,
10   Too frugal of brindle brain
To dash from the storm into shelter,
   Or rump himself to the rain.

B
(All boys)

We tried to corral him for market:
   He blatted, his fear intense,
15 Straddled his legs on a railing,
   And hung himself on the fence.

We cornered him and roped him,
   He flung out his legs and sprawled;
We dragged him into the cow-pen,
20   And there bewildered he bawled.

1B
(One boy)

I drove him into the runway
   That leads to the cattle-cars;
He rattled his heels on the pickets
   And battered his head on the bars.

25 Pierre jammed him in with the cattle,
   Beside his bellowing cow;

25. PIERRE—Pronounced pyĕr.

20

She lowed to her suckling gently
And licked the blood from his brow.

B
(All boys)
30   And Toby trembled beside her,
Fear in his big brown eyes,
As he heard the thunder and tumult.
Of clamoring cattle rise.

A lurch of the snorting engine
Flung him beneath the feet
35   Of steers that trampled him earthward;
And Toby began to bleat.

1B
(One boy)
He was on his way to the market,
Toby, the neighborhood pet,

CHORAL READING

Throughout this book you will find poems marked in the margin with letter symbols such as those used with "Toby Goes to Market." These form a guide to choral reading, one of the best ways of enjoying poetry. The meaning of the markings is as follows:

U—Unison, or all reading together
B—All boys
G—All girls
1B—One boy
1G—One girl

If two or three different boys or girls are to read different lines, the different characters will be represented by numerals:

1B(#1)—First boy
1B(#2)—Second boy
1B(#3)—Third boy, etc.

In "Toby Goes to Market," all boys together read the first four lines. Then one boy alone begins at line 5 and continues through line 12. At line 13, all boys read, and continue through line 20. At line 21 the single boy picks up again.

Further explanation of choral reading may be found in Part II of this book.

Who had licked the salt from my fingers
40   And slavered my hands with wet.

He was off on the big adventure;
He was reluctant to go
On a jaunt that had no returning—
Oh, Toby, how did you know!

RUNAWAY

FRANCES FROST

Awake in the moonlit summer's night
I saw the old barn's silver roof,
I saw the meadows glimmer white
And heard an unfamiliar hoof
5   Striking a pebble in my road.
I hurried to the mapled sill.
The strange light cantering had slowed
And stopped. And there, as taut and still
As he were carven moonlight, stood
10   A white colt with a silver mane.
He snuffed the faint gust from the wood;
Ears pricked and motionless again,
He breathed and listened. Well I knew
He was my neighbor's wayward colt
15   Who, cropping moonlight with the dew,
Had known a sudden urge to bolt,
But his heart was beauty, beat on beat.
He flung his head up, saw me there,
Whickered and whirled. I heard his feet
20   Fly down far roadways of the air.

A DOZEN ROSES AND
A BALE OF HAY

RANDOLPH BARTLETT

"A DOZEN roses, please, and a bale of hay." It hardly sounds like a grocery order, but those items will be found every day on the shopping list of the biggest boarding house in the world, the New York Zoological [1] Park. Every day twenty-five hundred animals must be fed, and no housekeeper in the world has a more complicated problem. Some of the beasts and birds are as picky as a baby with a cold in the head. Some have an idea that they can eat only one thing, and they will sulk if they don't get it. Some want just a tiny bit of food, and others want bales. Some will guzzle anything they can get to their mouths and others will nose their food contemptuously while the keeper is watching, but gobble it quickly when his back is turned.

To Dr. Leonard J. Goss, who is the veterinarian at the Zoo,

"A Dozen Roses and a Bale of Hay" is reprinted by permission of Mrs. Randolph Bartlett and of *The American Girl,* a magazine for all girls published by the Girl Scouts.

[1] ZOOLOGICAL—Pronounced zō-ô-lŏj'ĭ-kăl.

23

they are just so many children. He is the man they send for
when a lion has a tummy-ache, or a giraffe has a sore throat,
or when Alice, the dowager [2] elephant, has an extra bad attack
of rheumatism, or Pete, the big hippo, won't eat his hay. Dr.
Goss nurses the animals when they're sick, and controls their
diet so they won't get that way.

Rule One is to try to give the animal the same food it would
eat if it were running wild in its native land. This is not always
possible, either because the supply is not available, or because
it is too expensive. Then substitutes must be found. The
chemists analyze the animal's native food, and provide it with
something that has the same values.

For example, there was the problem of the *Myrmecophaga
tridactyla,* sometimes called the giant anteater. As may well
be imagined from its name, this creature's preference in food is
a nice dish of raw ants, or ant eggs, and in its native Brazil it
was able to find plenty just by digging up ant hills. But to get
enough ants to satisfy an anteater as big as a large dog was beyond the resources of the kitchens at the Zoo. So the cooks
prepared a mixture of hamburger, canned milk, and tomatoes.
You wouldn't think that when these were added together they
would make ants, but it seems they do. The dish was placed
before Miss Myrmecophaga and she sniffed it. There was
nothing objectionable about the smell, she seemed to be re-
marking, but it wasn't ants. So she turned away.

Then came a fine example of the understanding of animal
psychology, an everyday occurrence at the Zoo but always having for outsiders a little touch of sleight of hand. Since the
anteater obviously was rejecting the mixture because it was unfamiliar, the average person would have thought that to humor
her right then would only encourage her in holding out for more
of her customary fare. Not so, the animal-wise Zoo attendants
think. They tossed a handful of ant eggs into the cage, the
lady recognized them, appreciated the friendly gesture, lapped

[2] DOWAGER (dow'a-jĕr)—A dignified, elderly woman.

24

up the eggs, felt she was among friends, and then ate the hamburger mixture enthusiastically. She is thriving on the diet, and now if you were to offer her an ant egg she would probably be insulted.

The fact is that animals just don't want changes in their food, and sometimes it has to be forced upon them, or disguised. Every now and then, for economic and other reasons, a switch is made from beef to horse meat, in feeding the lions, tigers, and their relatives. The first day they sniff and turn away, but hunger soon brings them back and they eat the strange meat, but without their usual gusto. Later, when the keepers again provide the original menu of beef, the protest is repeated and they want what they had yesterday, horse meat.

There is one cage whose inmates will accept no substitutes. All they ask of life is a bouquet of roses every twenty-four hours. These are the parasol ants, as strange a colony as ever Dr. Raymond L. Ditmars picked up in Trinidad. *Atta Cephalotes* is what Dr. Ditmars calls them, and they raise their own mushrooms. Working only at night, for reasons best known to themselves, they cut semicircular pieces out of the rose petals. Each ant puts one of these pieces over his head, like a parasol, and takes it home. They all sit around and chew the rose leaves into a pulp, and this they make into little garden plots. In these plots they plant the spores of a tiny fungus, and when the fungus comes up they eat it. And that's all they do.

The queen of the colony always keeps an extra supply of these spores on hand, for the population of the colony grows at last to a point where some of the younger and more ambitious members think it would be nice to move out and start a new village of their own, where they could have more privacy and perhaps room for a two-car garage. So the queen gives a little handful of seed to the new queen the pioneers have elected, pats them on the head, tells them not to take any wooden money and to drop in any time. The colonizers then find themselves another rosebush, and so it goes.

For some time after the parasol ants were brought to the Zoo, visitors had no opportunity to see them at work, as they harvested their rose leaves only at night. This was gradually remedied, however, by lighting their cage after dark, dimly at first and then with increasing brightness. This confused the ants, as they do not carry wrist watches, and finally they apparently lost all track of time and gathered roses whenever they were in the mood, to the great entertainment of spectators.

One of the greatest specialists in food is the panda, which wants nothing but bamboo shoots. Some readers may recall a series of pictures of Pandora, the glamour girl of the World's Fair in New York, licking the last drop of something from a dish—but that wasn't food, it was slightly sweetened water. Again, like almost all children, almost all animals like sugar, and it is occasionally given to them for the sake of their morale, or to coax them into good humor when they need a change in diet. But the panda, sugar or no sugar, demands bamboo shoots.

In its native China this was no problem at all, but in the New York Zoo it ran into money. Pandora finally compromised on tender sprouts of sugar cane plants, and went so far as to eat baby food and even gain weight on it. Her untimely death has never been explained, and the most exhaustive post-mortem examination showed no recognizable trace of any disease, or any organic trouble. Certainly there was no lack of nutrition. Neither did the broken-heart theory, so popular with newspaper reporters, seem to apply, for Pandora gave every sign of being perfectly happy. Madame Chiang Kai-shek,[3] wife of the Chinese general, has sent two pandas to the Zoo, and arrangements have been made to have a constant supply of bamboo shoots on hand. A species of bamboo has been found which thrives in the States around the Gulf of Mexico, and it is the identical variety upon which the panda feeds in its native haunts.

But if you think the panda and the parasol ant are particular about what they eat, take a look at the hummingbird. In the outside world it merely sips the nectar from flowers. In captivity however, the problem of feeding is not nearly so difficult as those presented by less dainty eaters. The hummingbirds at the New York Zoo are fed on honey and Mellin's Food. But these tiny birds are able to take their food only through the long bills with which nature has supplied them in order that they may sip from the very bottom of flowers, so their substitute diet is placed in long vials for their convenience.

In proportion to their size, however, hummingbirds are tremendous gluttons. They eat, or sip, almost constantly. A shipment of them was coming to the Zoo on one occasion, and was sent from the docks to the Bronx in a taxicab. When they arrived, one was dead and the others prostrated because they had had nothing to eat during the unloading from the ship and the trip uptown, a little more than an hour.

The prize glutton of the Zoo, at present, is the Galapagos [4] tortoise. It will eat as long as there is a scrap of anything edible in sight. Its menu includes lettuce, apples, oranges, ba-

[3] CHIANG KAI-SHEK—Pronounced chäng kī-shĕk'.
[4] GALÁPAGOS (gä-lä'på-gōs)—The Galápagos Islands are in the Pacific Ocean about on the equator.

nanas, and watermelons. The oldest specimen has been known to eat a barrel of lettuce in a day, and this colony at one time was the outlet for the discarded outer leaves from the New York hotels.

While most animals are very decided about what they will eat and what they will not, there are exceptions. Many members of the sheep family will eat practically anything that is not too big to be swallowed. An aoudad [5] (North African wild sheep) was showing obvious signs of distress recently, and Dr. Goss, after an X-ray examination, removed from its interior a woman's glove, three deflated balloons, and five rubber balls. You could hardly say that the aoudad had eaten them, but at least it had swallowed them.

This is just a sample of the difficulties that thoughtless visitors create wherever animals are on exhibition. No matter how many signs, *"Please do not feed the animals,"* are displayed, children—and older persons who should know better—seem to be determined to throw things, some edible and many not, into the pens and cages. It was for this reason that the Zoological Society installed a number of vending machines from which two ounces of animal food can be obtained for a nickel.

The packages contain pellets about the size of large peas, made of calf meal, alfalfa, oats, bran, and corn. The hoof animals soon became very fond of them. A bear will collect a handful or so before he gulps them down, a single pellet being beneath his consideration. An elephant will hold out his trunk, the end upturned like a cup, while the visitor tosses in one after another of the pellets; when he has captured a dozen or so, he will stick his trunk in his mouth and blow the collection inside. The vending machines have very largely solved the problem of feeding by visitors, and on an average Sunday more than a thousand packages are sold. The ingredients are such that they cannot be harmful to any living creature that is willing to eat them, and the quantities are small enough not to cause any

[5] AOUDAD—Pronounced ä′o͞o-dăd.

danger of overfeeding. The fact is, there is less danger with animals of overfeeding than of wrong feeding, and now that onlookers are using the packages from the machines, the situation is pretty well under control.

An exception, some time ago, did not involve visitors. A long time ago when Alice, the big elephant, was only a girl, she was employed at the Zoo giving rides to children. As she was led back to her quarters every day, past the service building, her keeper would take a loaf of bread from a barrel that stood in the doorway, and give it to Alice as a reward for good behavior.

Years passed, and Alice was relieved of her duties with the children. One night the drain pipe in her cage became blocked, and to escape the cold water that backed up and flooded the stall Alice broke down the back door leading to her private enclosure, found the gate unlatched, and wandered forth into the night. She recalled the bread box, which she had not seen for twenty-five years, went to it and emptied it, gorging herself on several dozen loaves. Then, instead of going home the way she had come, she followed the path along which she used to be led, arrived at the front door of the elephant house and, finding it locked, simply walked in, pushing the doors ahead of her. When she was offered her breakfast, some hours later, she made uneasy and uninterested motions, and her pilfering was discovered. Apparently the only consequence was temporary loss of appetite.

On another occasion, the refusal of an animal to eat as advertised was somewhat embarrassing. In the absence of Dr. Goss, who has made a study of dietary whims, some of the people at the Zoo decided it would be nice to give a birthday party for Pete, the big hippopotamus—a native New Yorker, who had reached the age of thirty-eight. A "cake" was concocted of all the nice things they thought Pete would like, with thirty-eight carrots, one of his great delights, for candles. Photographers were summoned from the newspapers, and with the crowd singing, "Happy birthday, dear Peter," the two-and-a-quarter-ton guest of honor was led in. He snooted the entire proceeding. He wouldn't even nibble a carrot. Of course, as Dr. Goss pointed out when he heard the details, the mistake was in not making Pete a cake of food he was used to and would recognize. Not being especially hungry, he was confused by the festivities, the crowd, and the strange-looking cake, and refused to eat.

Many who think of undomesticated animals as entirely devoid of the finer feelings will be surprised to know that their digestive processes, as well as their appetites, are often seriously disturbed by unusual incidents or excitement. I was frankly flabbergasted when Earl Chase, the keeper at the reptile house, assured me that snakes are among the most sensitive of living beings. In fact, if you listen to Chase long enough, you will feel a slight impulse to go to the cage where the huge python drapes itself around the branch of a tree and beg his pardon for misjudging him. Rejecting the impulse, you learn with amazement that the keeper always tries to avoid feeding the reptiles on Sundays or holidays when there are big crowds present. Many of the larger snakes are fed only every two weeks, and others usually in ratio to their sizes, so this is not difficult to arrange. If, on the other hand, there is a crowd watching while the big serpents are dining, they will not digest their food, and the next day they will disgorge it.

To be sure that all of the twenty-five hundred boarders at the Zoo will receive the right food at the right time requires a big organization, which has developed with the growth of the institution. The busy day begins at 6:30 A.M. sharp, with the arrival of the cook, and it is well after 3 P.M. before he has time to turn away from his chopping block and pressure cooker and take a little rest.

The bears are the first to demand breakfast, and their keeper is on hand at 7 A.M. filling baskets with bread, vegetables, fish, and meat. Trucks are soon rumbling about with grain and hay for the deer, and suchlike vegetarians.   More trucks come rumbling in with the supplies, and in the course of a year the boardinghouse uses up approximately the following quantities of food:

170 baskets of apples; 1,350 bunches of bananas; 40 boxes of huckleberries; 51½ tons of beef; 20½ tons of bread; 135 bushels of carrots; 1,300 chameleons; 500 pounds of cottage cheese; 260 pounds of chicken; 30 tons of corn; 31,200 hen eggs; 22½ tons of scratch feed; 15¼ tons of fish; 1,600 frogs; 150 pounds of grapes; 290 tons of hay; 18 cans of honey; 6,300 pounds of zwieback meal; 1,200 pounds of milk powder; 75 pounds of Brazil nuts; 100 pounds of mixed nuts; 7,000 bushels of oats; 80 boxes of oranges; 600 pounds of oyster shells; 160 pounds of raisins; 200 white rats; 1,300 pounds of brown rice; 800 pounds of broken rice; 500 pounds of rock salt; a ton of hemp seed; 1¼ tons of sunflower seeds; 300 pounds of dried shrimps; 9,000 pounds of wheat; 50 pounds of dried flies.

The Zoo used to import about two hundred and twenty pounds of ant eggs annually, but since the war began they have no longer been available, ship cargo space being required for more serious purposes.

Smaller quantities of about a hundred other foods are required, and even these do not complete the list.   The keepers grow very fond of the animals under their charge, even when the affection is not noticeably returned, and they often forage for delicacies that are not to be had on the market.   Certain birds are extremely fond of wild strawberries and elderberries, and many a keeper spends his days off in spring and summer, gathering all of these he can find, just to please his boarders.

A greater variety of items is required for the birds than for any other section of the Zoo.   The following list of necessities for the bird house, aviary, and enclosures for the feathered tribe is only partial and subject to change with brief notice, should a new arrival be announced:

Apples, pears, grapes, raisins, sultanas, currants, bananas, oranges, figs, wild cherries, elderberries, wild strawberries, ink-berries, huckleberries, milo maize, oats, ground maple peas, hemp seed, flax seed, poppy seed, teazle seed, rock salt, water cress, green corn, cottage cheese, barley, cod-liver oil, dandelion seed, sunflower seed, ant eggs, hen eggs, ground eggshells, cuttlefish bone, oyster shells, Indian nuts, bone meal, alfalfa meal, quartz grit, nannyberries, tomatoes, carrots, potatoes, beets, peas, string beans, lettuce, cabbage, spinach, wild chick-weed, whole corn, cracked corn, wheat, dried milk, dried flies, mealworms, grasshoppers, spiders, cockroaches, condensed milk, honey, fruit flies, butterfish, shrimp, herrings, smelts, beef, horsemeat, rats, mice, guinea pigs, rabbits, chickens, frogs, snakes, bread, rice, game food, peanuts, pecans, wal-nuts, Brazil nuts, and dates.

Few of these articles are required in large quantities. A nightingale which is out of sorts will perk up quickly if it is fed a few common spiders, easily enough obtained, but it does not expect them as daily fare. The secretary bird appreciates an occasional little snake. Ant eggs are imported from the tropics, dried waterflies from Mexico. Crickets and grasshoppers are found in fair quantity right in the meadows of the Zoo itself, but dried locusts are still occasionally to be had from Africa and are imported whenever an occasion offers.

As if conscious of its reputed similarity to the human race, the monkey tribe refuses to be satisfied with a monotonous bill of fare. Their demand for change is almost as definite as that of mankind. Three times a week they get a meat mixture, every night at closing time they have milk and eggs, and for the rest of their meals the rotation is as follows:

Monday: Bananas, boiled potatoes, oranges.
Tuesday: Carrots, lettuce, bananas, apples, oranges.
Wednesday: Rice pudding, cabbage.
Thursday: Monday night's dinner again.
Friday: Tuesday's dinner.

Saturday: Wednesday's dinner.

Sunday: Nothing but bananas—and the peanuts, popcorn, coughdrops, candy, cigarette butts, and chewing gum that thoughtless and sometimes downright vicious visitors throw to the monkeys when the keepers are not at hand.

Among the interesting details that crop up, in this business of feeding the animals, are the quaint tricks many of them develop. The kinkajou [6] likes grapes so well that in eating them he lies on his back, so any juice will drip into his mouth. The ratel,[7] or honey-badger, is allowed an occasional lump of sugar which he has learned to soften by dropping into his drinking cup, and he has also discovered the exact stage at which to remove it before it melts away. The sloth earns his name (or was the word slothfulness derived from his habits?) for he lives a life of almost complete motionlessness except on Sunday when he is fed, and then he shifts himself a bit, ever so slowly, in the branches where he hangs forever downward, to nibble a leaf.

One of the most amusing discoveries in the history of the Zoo, concerning strange appetites of animals, happened one day when the lion keepers tossed a bunch of catnip into the African Plains section where a few lions were roaming about. What followed was the most unleonine behavior imaginable. Everyone knows that a cat will have a lot of fun with a catnip ball, but no one would expect a great, big, ferocious lion to go practically crazy over the herb. But that is what they did! They tossed the sprigs in the air, rolled over on them, turned somersaults, and were as undignified as a bank president on a roller coaster. As a result the lions now get their catnip periodically.

When winter comes, the diet of all the animals in the Zoo is watched still more carefully. Cod-liver oil, carefully disguised with more palatable things, is administered regularly, to make

[6] KINKAJOU (kĭng'kȧ-jōō)—A South American cat-like animal about three feet long.
[7] RATEL—Pronounced rā'tĕl.

up for the decreased sunlight which is the result of closer confinement. Food rations are adjusted to indoor living for the animals which have been enjoying summer freedom.

And every day there is a bale of hay for the elephants and a dozen roses for the parasol ants.

THE CLEANLYS

SAMUEL SCOVILLE, JR.

ALL winter long the Barrens[1] had slept still and white. Rows and regiments of low pitch-pine trees, whose blue-green needles grow in threes instead of the fives of the white or the twos of the Virginia pines, marched for miles and miles across the drifted snow. Through their tops forever sounded the far-away roar of the surf of the upper air, like the rushing of mighty wings, while overhead hung a sky whose cold blue seemed flecked with frost. The air tingled with the spicery of

[1] THE BARRENS—A wooded tract of land in Virginia.

myriads of pine trees. Grim black buzzards, on fringed, motionless wings, wheeled and veered over this land of silence.

Then, with the suddenness of the South, spring came. The woods became a shimmering pool of changing greens. The down-folded leaves of the little lambskill stood erect again, like rabbits' ears, over claret-colored [2] flowers, and the soft warm air was sweet with the heavy perfume of cream-white magnolia blossoms. On jade-green pools gleamed the buds of yellow pond lilies, like lumps of floating gold, and the paler golden-club, whose blossoms look like the tongues of calla lilies. Everywhere, as if set in snow, gleamed the green and gold of the Barrens' heather above the white sand, which had been the bed of some sea, forgotten a million years ago. In the distance, at the edges of the Barrens, were glimpses of far-away meadows, all hazy with blue toadflax and rimmed with the pale gold of narrow-leaved sundrops with their deep orange centers.

Through the woods wound a deep creek, whose water was stained brown and steeped sweet with a million cedar roots. Unlike the singing streams of the North, this brook ran stilly, cutting its deep way through gold-and-white sand, and meeting never rock nor stone to make it murmur. On its bank in the deepest part of the woods grew a vast sweet-gum tree, covered with star-shaped leaves. Tangles of barbed greenbrier set with fierce curved thorns, and stretches of sphagnum [3] bogs guarded the tree from the land side. In the enormous hollow trunk, some fifty feet above the ground, a black hole showed.

There, one May afternoon, as the sun was westering far down the sky, a small face appeared suddenly, framed in the dark opening. It was a funny little face, surmounted by broad, pricked-up, pointed ears, and masked by a black band, which stretched from above a pair of twinkling golden eyes clear down to a small pointed muzzle. As the owner of the face came out of the hollow and began to creep slowly and cau-

[2] CLARET-COLORED—Deep red.
[3] SPHAGNUM (sfăg′nŭm)—A kind of moss.

tiously down the side of the great tree, his fur showed in the sunlight a dull brownish-gray, with black-tipped hairs on the back, while those on the round little belly had white ends. Last of all appeared the black-ringed, cylindrical tail which is the hall mark of the aracoun, raccoon, or coon, as red, white, and black men have variously named the owner of said tail.

This particular little coon was the youngest of four fuzzy, cuddly, blind babies, which had appeared in the old den-tree early in March. His father was a wary, battle-scarred giant among his kind, who weighed thirty pounds, measured three feet from the tip of his pointed nose to the end of his ringed tail, and was afraid of nothing that crawled, ran, swam, or flew.

As the little coon walked carefully, headfirst, down the tree, he showed his kinship to the bears by setting the naked black soles of his little hind feet flat, instead of walking on his toes as most of the flesh-eaters do. His forepaws were like tiny black hands, with a very short little finger and the thumb the same length as the other three long, supple fingers.

It was the first time that this particular youngster had ever ventured out of the home nest. A great bump in the middle of the trunk was his undoing. He crept over the edge, but in reaching down for a safe grip beyond, lost his hold and, with a wail of terror, fell headlong. Fortunately for him, the gum was surrounded on three sides by shallow pools of standing water. Into one of these the young climber fell with a splash, and a second later was swimming for dear life back to his family tree.

At the very first sound of that little SOS the head of Mother Coon appeared in the opening, with three other small heads peering out from behind her. Seeing the little coon struggling in the water, she hurried down the tree, followed in procession by the rest of the family, who had evidently resolved not to miss anything. By the time she came to the bump, however, the small adventurer had reached the trunk from which he had fallen. Fixing his sharp claws into the bark, he climbed up the tree, bedraggled, wet, and much shocked at the manifold dangers of life.

Seeing him safe, Mrs. Coon at once turned back. The three little coons turned with her, and the reversed procession started up to the hole. The littlest of the family climbed slowly and painfully as far as the bump, whimpering all the time. There his feelings overcame him. He was positive that never had any little coon suffered so before. He was wet and shaken and miserable and—his mother had deserted him.

"Err, err, err," he began to cry, softly, but exceeding sorrowfully.

It was too much even for Mother Coon's stern ideals of child training. Once again she crept down the tree and, stopping on the bump, fixed her claws firmly into the bark. Stretching far over the edge, she reached down and gripped the little coon firmly but gently by the loose skin of his neck and, turning around, swung him safely up in front of her between her forepaws. Then, urging him on with little pokes from her pointed nose, she convoyed him up the tree toward the den, from which three little heads looked down. At times the memory of his grief would be too bitter to be borne, and he would stop and whimper and make little soft, sobbing noises. Then Mother Coon would pat him comfortingly with her slim, graceful paws and urge him on until at last he was safely home again. So ended well, after all, the first journey into the world of any of this little family.

By this time the sun was set, and the old coon climbed down the tree to the nearest pool, for a bit of supper. As she approached, there were squeaks and splashes, and several cricket frogs dived into the water ahead of her. Wading in, she looked around at the woods and the tree tops in the darkening light, in a vacant way, as if frogs were the very last thing she had in mind; but under the water her slim fingers were exploring every inch of the oozy bottom with such lightning-like speed, that in less than a minute three frogs had been caught, killed by a skillful nip, and thrown up on the dry bank. Convinced that there were no more left in the pool, she approached her supper table; but before she would eat came the ceremony and ritual of her tribe and blood.

No raccoon, in winter or summer, by night or by day, at home or in captivity, will willingly eat any unwashed food except green corn. One by one the dead frogs were plunged under the water from which they had just been taken, and were washed and re-washed and rubbed and scrubbed, until they were clean enough to suit Mrs. Coon. Then, and not until then, were they daintily eaten. Thereafter soft little chirring calls from the tree top said that her babies were ready for their supper, too; and she climbed back to the nest, where they snuggled against her and nuzzled and cuddled and drank of the warm milk which would not flow much longer for them, since mother raccoons wean their children early.

While they were still at supper, there sounded from the black depths of the pine forest a long whickering "Whoo-oo-oo-oo," much like the wailing call of the screech owl. It was Father Coon on his way home from where he had been spending the night in one of his outlying hunting lodges, of which he had several within a radius of a few miles; and a little later he joined the family. He brought Mother Coon a little tidbit in the shape of a fresh-water mussel, which, although the shell was still dripping, she climbed down and washed before she cracked and ate it like a nut.

After supper, the two started off on a hunting trip, while the babies curled up in a round ball, to sleep until they came back. The gray hour just before dawn found the hunters crouched in the long marshy grass at the very tip of a point of land that ran into a little pond, which was ringed around with the stunted pines of the Barrens. Just as the first light showed in the sky, a flock of mallards, headed by a magnificent drake with a bright green head, swung in to feed. Never a sign nor sound betrayed the presence of the ambushers until the drake reached the edge of the shore. The startled bird had not even time for one quack before there was a splash, and old Father Coon had twisted that gay and gallant neck and was back on the shore again, with the quivering body thrown over his shoulder.

Part of the duck was washed and eaten then and there, and the rest was carried back to the den-tree, where the four little coons were taught to tear off little strips of the rich, dark meat, and to wash them repeatedly before eating. That first taste of flesh and blood forever barred them from the warm milky fountain which had been theirs before. From this time on, they had to hunt for themselves.

The very next night their education began. In the warm fragrant dusk, the whole family trotted in a long, leisurely procession through the underbrush, until they came to a broad bank of warm, white sand that overhung the deep waters of the stream which wound its silent way like a brown snake through the Barrens. Here, in a half-circle, the whole family crouched and dozed comfortably, with their pointed, striped noses on their forepaws, while the dusk deepened into the soft-scented, velvet blackness of a summer night. For long they stayed there, in the still patience which only the wild folk possess.

At last, over the tips of the pointed cedars the moon rose, and turned the white beach to silver. All at once, from where a sand spit sloped gradually into the water, sounded a tiny splash, and out into the moonlight crawled a monstrous, mis-shapen object. From under a vast black shell ridged with dull yellow a snaky neck stretched this way and that, surmounted by a fierce head, with a keen, edged beak and gleaming, cruel eyes which stared up and down the whole beach. It was a snapper, one of the largest of its kind, which weighed perhaps half-a-hundred pounds and would have filled a small washtub.

As the great turtle crawled slowly up the bank, the little coons crouched tensely, and turned their heads to see how the veteran hunters of the family proposed to attack this demon of the stream. As if asleep, both of them crouched motionless; for long ago they had learned that watchful waiting is the best policy when Mrs. Snapper comes out of the water of a spring night. Back and forth the monster crawled heavily, stopping to look and listen for minutes at a time. Satisfied at last that no danger threatened her on that lonely beach, she chose a little ridge of loose sand not ten feet from the raccoon family, and scrabbling with her hind legs and thrusting with her thick, strong tail in the warm sand, dug herself in. There she stayed all the night through, until she had laid a couple of hundred parchment-covered, cylindrical eggs, the greatest delicacy on the whole bill of fare of the hunting folk.

Just before dawn, she pulled herself heavily out of the hole she had dug, and the loose sand poured in after her, filling the cavity and covering the eggs that were hidden there. Not until the turtle had smoothed over the displaced sand and waddled back into the stream did the head of the raccoon family make a movement. He was no coward, but he knew too much to trust his slim paws or his pointed nose anywhere near Mrs. Snapper's shearing jaws. When the brown water at last closed over her monstrous body, Father Coon led his waiting family to the bank and deftly uncovered the newly laid eggs, on which they feasted until sunrise sent them back to bed.

As the freshness of spring melted into the hot, green sweetness of summer, the education of the little Cleanlys went on rapidly. They soon became experts in breakfast botany, and learned to dig for the nutty tubers of the wild bean, with its brown purple blossoms, the spicy roots of the wild sarsaparilla, with its five ashlike leaves and fuzzy ball of white blossoms, the wild ginger, the spatterdock, and a score or so of other pleasant-tasting wild vegetables. They learned, too, how to hunt frogs, and to grub up mussels, and to catch those little fresh-water lobsters, the crawfish, without getting their fingers nipped.

The Cleanly children made few mistakes, and hardly ever

disobeyed their parents. There was a reason. Disobedience among the wild folk means death, and he who makes one mistake often never gets a chance to make another. The sister of the littlest coon was a sad example of this fact. She decided to become a reformer. It seemed to her that it would be pleasanter to hunt by daylight than after dark, so she tried it—once. On her first (and last) trip she met old Sam Carpenter, who always carried a shotgun with him.

Of course, accidents will happen in wild-folk families just as among us humans, only in a wild-folk family, an accident is more apt to be fatal. It was the oldest of the three little Cleanlys, after the reformer had gone, who suffered first. He had been hunting in the wildest part of the five-mile circle, which the family used, and it was after sunrise when he scrambled out of the shallow pool where he had been frogging.

Suddenly from a dry dense thicket near by, there was a fierce hiss like escaping steam, and from a tangle of fern darted the mottled brown-and-white length of a great pine snake. Its curious pointed head, with its golden, unwinking eyes, shot for-

ward, and the next second a set of sharp teeth closed on the soft nose of the small coon. Unlike the poison people, the pine snake has no fangs, and its teeth are used only to hold its prey for the grip of its choking, crushing coils. This particular snake was nearly eight feet long, and as thick around as a big man's wrist. Luckily for the little coon, the thick bushes guarded him for an instant against the smothering coils.

Dragging back from the dreadful glare of the fixed, lidless eyes, he tried to tear loose, and squalled with all his might for his mother. Fortunately for him, she was not far away. Anyone who had ever watched Mrs. Coon climb carefully down a tree trunk, or move deliberately through the thickets, would never have identified her with the furious figure which flashed through the bushes at the very first cry of the little coon. Before the great snake had time to draw its coils clear of the branches, or even to disengage its head to meet the attack, the raccoon was upon it, and sank her sharp teeth through the reptile's spine just back of its head. At once the shut jaws gaped, and the little coon sprang back from the heavy body, which writhed and twisted and beat the bushes horribly in its death agony.

Mother Coon was always practical, with an open mind in regard to matters of diet, and while her cub whimperingly licked, with a long, pink tongue, a much-abused little nose, she began to strip off the speckled skin of her late opponent, and to convert it into lengths of firm, white meat on which the whole raccoon family fed full that night.

It was the youngest of the family who was the next victim. Again it was Mother Coon whose love and wisdom and courage outweighed chance on the scales of life and death. He had been exploring the shallows of the stream near a deserted cranberry bog. All the raccoon people like to follow the shallows of a stream, on the chance of picking up frogs, mussels, crawfish, and other water food. A solitary rock off a tiny island, in shallow water close to the bank, is always a favorite spot for a hunting coon.   Old Sam Carpenter knew all about raccoon habits, and also about one of their weaknesses.

On this night the latest born of the family came splashing down the warm shallows, and half waded and half swam out to a tiny sandbar some six feet from the bank.   There he crouched and scanned the water in the moonlight, on the chance that he might catch a sluggish, red-finned sucker as it winnowed the water through its long wrinkled tube of a mouth. Suddenly, against the yellow sand, he saw three or four gleaming, silver disks, brighter even than the silver-scaled shiners which he had often tried vainly to catch.   Old Sam had begged from a traveling tinker a few scraps of bright tin and strewn them near the little islet.

No raccoon can help investigating anything that glistens in the water, and this one felt that he must have his hands on that treasure-trove.   Wading carefully out into the shallows, he dabbled in the sand with his slim forepaws, trying to draw some of the shining pieces in to shore.   Suddenly there was a snap that sent the water flying, a horrible grinding pain, and the slender fingers of his right forepaw were caught between the wicked jaws of a hidden steel trap.

"Oo-oo-oo-oo!" he cried, with the sorrowful wail of a hurt baby coon.

But this time Mother Coon was far away, around two bends of the crooked stream, investigating a newly found mussel bed. The little coon tried in vain to pull away from the cruel jaws, but they held him unrelentingly.   Then he attempted to gnaw his way loose, but only broke his keen little teeth on the stubborn iron.

At first, he was easily able to keep himself above the water; yet, as the minutes went by, the unremitting weight of the trap forced him under more and more often, to rest from the weary, sagging pain.   Each time that he went down, it seemed easier and easier to stay there, and to slip into oblivion under the glimmering water and forget the torture that racked every nerve in his struggling little body. Yet, in spite of his funny face and quiet ways, the little coon came of a battling breed which never gives up. Once more he struggled up from the soothing coolness of the water, and for the last time his cry for help shuddered faintly across the Barrens. At last and at last, far away down the stream, he heard the snap of a broken branch, and a minute later the rapid pad-pad of flying feet along the sand, as he fought weakly to stay above the surface, sure that the coming of his mother meant rescue from all the treacheries that beset him.

In another minute she had reached the bank, and with a bound, her fur bristling, was beside her cub, ready to fight for him to the last drop of blood in her lithe, powerful body. Fortunately for her cub, the years had brought to Mother Coon wisdom as well as courage. Once certain as to what had happened, she decided instantly upon the stern and only answer which the wild folk have for the snares of their cruel human brethren. She waded out so that her back was under the exhausted little body of her cub, and, ducking under, gripped the trap with one of her flexible hands, strained the little paw away from it with the other and with a few quick slashes of her sharp teeth severed the three black, slim little fingers that the bitter jaws held fast.

As she cut off one after the other, she could feel the warm furry body that rested upon hers thrill and quiver with the pain; but never a sound nor a struggle came from the littlest of the coons. Another minute, and slowly and limpingly he was creeping back to the den-tree. Better, alas, for any child of the wild folk to go maimed and halt through life than to fall alive into the hands of us humans!

The weeks went by. Summer waxed, until the Barrens were green waves, starred and spangled with flowers, and echoing with bird songs. All through the long, warm, flower-scented nights the raccoon family feasted and frolicked, and the little ones grew apace. One velvety warm night, when the crescent moon had sunk in the west, Father Coon led his family toward the farm lands, which year by year crept farther into the Barrens. Beyond the woods they came to a field of towering stalks, whose rustling leaves overshadowed plump ears of creamy corn, swathed in green husks and wound with soft silk. At the sight the leaders for once seemed to forget all their caution.

Into the field they rushed, like mad things, and pulling down stalk after stalk, they stripped off the husks from an ear, and took a bite or so of the angelfood beneath, only to cast it aside and grasp another. The little coons followed their parents' example, and pulled and hauled and tore and chanked among the standing corn, until it looked as if a herd of hungry cows had been there. The feasting kept on until every coon, big and little, was brimming full of melting, creamy corn.

As they ambled contentedly back toward the dense woods, there came a sound which made Father Coon hurry them forward. Scarcely had they reached the edge of the first thicket, when across the field dashed three mongrel hounds, which belonged to Sam Carpenter, and were out hunting tonight on their own account. There was no time to gain the shelter of the trees. Just ahead of them one edge of the stream touched the cleared country, while its farther bank was deep in the Barrens. Following their leader, the whole family took to the water. They had hardly reached the middle of the wide stream when, with a splash, the dogs plunged in, only a few yards behind. Immediately Father Coon dropped back, for when it comes to matters of life and death, it is always Father Coon who fights first. Tonight, in spite of numbers, the odds were all in his favor; for the raccoon is the second cousin of those great water-weasels, the mink and the otter, and it is as dangerous to attack him in the water as to fight a porcupine in his tree or a bear in his den.

The first of the pack was a yellow hound, who looked big and fierce enough to tackle anything. With a gasping bay, he ploughed forward, open-mouthed, to grip that silent, black-masked figure which floated so lightly in front of him—only to find it gone. At his plunge the raccoon had dived deep, a trick which no dog has yet learned. A second later, from behind, a slim sinewy hand closed like a clamp on the dog's foreleg, too far forward to be reached by his snapping jaws. As the hound lowered his head, vainly trying to bite, the raccoon reached across with his other paw, and gripped his opponent smotheringly by the muzzle.

Slowly, inexorably, he threw his weight against the dog's head, until it sank below the surface. As the other dogs approached, the coon maneuvered so that the struggling body was always between himself and his attackers. Never for an instant did he allow his prisoner's head to come to the surface. Suddenly he released it, and flashed back into the shadows. The body of the great hound floated on the surface, with gaping jaws and unseeing eyes.

Once more the coon dived and dragged down, with the same deadly grip, the smaller of his remaining opponents. This time he went under water with him. The dog struggled desperately, but paws have no chance against hands. Moreover, a raccoon can stay under water nearly five minutes, which is over a minute too long for any dog. When the coon at last appeared on the surface, he came up alone.

At that moment old Sam, aroused by the barking and baying of his dogs, hurried to the bank and called off his remaining hound, who was only too glad to swim away from the death in the dark, which had overtaken his pack mates.

Half an hour later, and half a league farther, from a great gum tree on the edge of a black silent stream, came the sound of soft, welcoming love notes.

Father Coon was home again.

ᚻ

Re-living American history.

THE SIEGE OF BOONESBOROUGH

JAMES DAUGHERTY

Rolling across America in search of a home, Squire Boone and his family came upon North Carolina and found it good. There in the days before the Revolution, young Daniel became a man. There he learned the cunning of the red man and the ways of the backwoodsman. But freedom and the land beyond the mountains ever called to Daniel. Soon he too was moving his family westward—ever westward, into the glorious wilderness of Kentucky. His glowing tales stirred the hearts of his neighbors and soon the pilgrimage began—the westward trek that ended with the building of the fort at Boonesborough. The Indians had given ground before the advance of the white man, but the destiny of Boonesborough had not yet been determined.

A PATTERN of fur-clad hunters and long-eared hounds and pack horses carrying iron salt-kettles, trailing among the black leafless trees, made a silhouette on the blue-white snow that lay deep over the winter world of Kentucky. They were going to French Lick to boil thousands of gallons of water at the salt springs in order that desperate Boonesborough might have the salt that kept the meat from putrefying so Boonesborough could eat and live.

In the dead of winter the salt-camp at French Lick felt safe from the Indians, whose custom was to take the warpath only in the spring or summer. But one gray evening in February as Boone was coming back to camp after a long day's hunt, he was completely surprised by an ambush of four Indian warriors. He tried to run for it but in the deep snow it was useless. The Old Fox of Kentucky was caught again. They were the very Shawnees from whom he had escaped years ago on the

Finley expedition. It was a tough heartbreaking moment but he had been there more than once before and had come through. Now it was a quick shift of tactics from physical action to a game of wits and bluff.

The Indians were a large war party under Chief Black Fish headed for a surprise attack on Boonesborough. Suddenly to have caught the great chief of the white men so excited them that Boone was able shrewdly to persuade them to change their plan. The silent white hunter must have turned eloquent and impressive as he stood in the midst of the savage council that was to give the tomahawk vote of life or death for the unsuspecting salt camp. Fantastic as it sounds, nevertheless the war party agreed to leave Boonesborough till the spring, when Boone promised he would arrange a peaceable moving of the settlers farther north where they might live as adopted Shawnees. For the present the Indians would return to Chillicothe [1] with the unscalped salt-boilers as their prisoners. All this was argued out in talk and translated back and forth by a Negro named Pompey.

[1] CHILLICOTHE (chĭl-ĭ-kŏth′ē)—A settlement in what is now Ohio.

Though Boone had saved the fort on the Kentucky and the salt-camp from bloody butchery by his courage and wits alone, some of the men were bitter and resentful against him as they marched half-starved and frozen into the winter encampment of the Shawnees at Chillicothe. After a while Black Fish led a party with the white captives to Detroit to exhibit them and perhaps sell them to General Hamilton.

Detroit in 1776 was a British fort and trading post perched on the open waterway of the Great Lakes. The rich fur trade of a vast area of wild North America passed through there on the way to make fortunes in far-off King George's England. Now there was a revolution in the colonies. It would be bad for the fur business. Inside the fort the red-coated British soldiers went through their daily drill. They dreamed in their barracks of English lanes and ale houses and rosy English sweethearts.

Outside the fort the red tribes came and went at will. They traded and treated with the English soldiers and traders after their quick-changing fashion. White trappers, wild and savage as the Indians, drifted in with their fur packs to swap for ammunition and to liquor up. A trader coming in with a keg of French brandy would leave town with great bales of fine furs, and a wild drunken orgy of whooping and fighting would follow. The Indians brought in from the border raids white captives, men, women, and children, as well as scalps. For these General Hamilton, the British commander, paid fixed prices in money, Indian finery, and war paint. The black faces of African Negroes mingled in the fantastic pageant. Around these wilderness outposts surged a drama of fierce passions and violent deeds.

It was a grand show-off when Black Fish's party stalked out of the forest with the great Daniel and ten of his men as captives. The whole town thrilled to see the legendary hero of the border in the flesh. Boone was as persuasive with the British as with the Indians. He showed his commission as a captain in His British Majesty's army and told of his fictitious plan to

49

capture Boonesborough in the spring. Hamilton was delighted with him. But when it came to selling his prisoners, Black Fish insisted that Boone was his personal property and he was not for sale, even though the general raised the price to the fabulous sum of one hundred pounds.

Boone took a long look at Detroit as he rode back into the forest with the returning Indians. It might be the last time he would ever see white faces.

The naked Indian children stared in wonder at Daniel Boone, and the lean wolf dogs snarled and snapped, not liking his strange white smell as he sat squinting at the fire in the smoky huts of Chillicothe. He was thinking his white man's thoughts as he watched the tall idle warriors and the bronze squaws grinding corn, scraping the skins, kneading the buffalo robes to make them soft. He had done very well pretending he was an Indian, pretending he was happy and satisfied, and pleasing the great chieftain Moluntha with his clever hunting. He looked wistfully at the fat Indian ponies, thinking of a dash for freedom when the right moment came. They had washed away his white blood in the river, pulled out half his hair, and painted him with strange symbols that meant he was the adopted son of the chief Black Fish. He knew by heart the strange rhythms of the mysterious ceremonial songs and dances. He was quick to share in the red laughter or laments.

One evening he came back tired from tedious labor at the salt licks to find the braves in war paint dancing to the pounding drums and shrill war chants. Sitting in his familiar place, he watched the wild frenzies rise and sway around the flickering campfires. There were five hundred warriors preparing for a surprise attack on Boonesborough. He knew how few were the defenders and that the fort was in bad repair. The whole settlement would be utterly unprepared. His hour had come and he was ready. Before dawn he slipped out like a shadow and was gone. Now again he was the hunted fox of the wilderness with the red dogs in close pursuit.

"On the 16th I departed before sunrise in the most secret manner and arrived at Boonesborough on the 20th, after a journey of one hundred and sixty miles, during which I had but one meal." Brief autobiography. How did he know the way all the four days and nights with the Shawnee pack one jump behind?

He was not so young as he used to be but tough and long-winded. When he came at last to the Ohio at full spring flood, he remembered he could not swim. It was the desperate tight spot he had known so often, but the angel of the wilderness showed him a leaky canoe stranded on a sand bar and he made a swift down-stream crossing on the yellow waters to the Kentucky shore that he knew like the back of his hand. Familiar landmarks cheered him. He shot a buffalo and cooked his first meal in four days. He was in sight of Boonesborough. He had kept his rendezvous with destiny.

It was a strange figure that came across the clearing into Boonesborough and said he was Daniel Boone. For weeks they had said Daniel Boone was a goner for sure this time. Even Rebecca's [2] faith had failed and she had returned with the family to the settlements. Boone was sorry, yet glad, too, for she was safe. His brother Israel and Jemima, his beloved daughter who had married Dick Calloway, were there to give him a warm welcome. But it was no wonder Rebecca had gone. Many a husband and father had never come back across the clearing.

The news of the coming Indian raid roused the settlers to action. The neglected log walls were repaired and everything made ready for an attack, the swift short Indian attack with which the borderers were familiar. But weeks passed and no Indians were seen. Then another escaped white man brought in news that Boone's flight had delayed the Indians. Boone then took a raiding expedition across the Ohio and burned an Indian village, getting back just a few hours ahead of the great war party of over four hundred Indians with some forty French

---

[2] REBECCA—Boone's wife.

Canadians under the direction of their officer De Quindre.[3]

There were about fifty men and boys, besides the women and children, behind the log stockade when the Indians surrounded the clearing of Boonesborough. Instead of the usual sudden attack, an Indian came out of the woods with a white flag and by calling back and forth arrànged for a parley. Every hour of delay meant a nearer hope of reinforcements coming in from Harrodsburg. Three of the defenders met Black Fish, Moluntha, and Catahecassa [4] near the fort for a powwow. There was talk of friendship and peaceful surrender. The chief promised that the whites would be taken safely on horses to Detroit if they surrendered peaceably. There need be no bloodshed if the Americans would agree to abandon the fort.

Boone said he would explain to his people and in two days give an answer. He was glad to find that the Indians had heard from a white captive that there were several hundred defenders in the fort. The Indians believed their offer of safety was sure to be accepted.

Inside the fort the chances were talked over and argued and weighed after the democratic way of the backwoods. The odds were ten to one and worse against defense, and not a man, woman, or child would be spared if—But the tough cantankerous spirit of the frontier urged: "Go ahead or bust." They would not have been where they were if they had not been stubborn survivors of a rough, tough, restless race who lived and died in their own independent way by the rifle, the ax, the Bible, and the plow. So they sent back the eagle's answer: "No surrender," the answer of the sassy two-year-old baby democracy, the answer of Man the Unconquerable to the hosts of darkness—"No surrender."

The iron-faced chiefs and the ornery Frenchman De Quindre took the answer grimly back to their council, while the settlers got in their cows, corn, and water from the spring without in-

---

[3] DE QUINDRE—Pronounced dê kĭn′drä.
[4] CATAHECASSA—Pronounced kä-tä-hĕ-kä′så.

terference from the Indians. The next move was an Indian trick which was perfectly transparent to Boone, but he took the chances of playing it to win time.

The Indians proposed a grand council of nine on each side to sign a treaty of peace, after which they would depart, they said, like lambs. The council sat under the sycamore trees within rifle shot of the fort. At a wave of the hat from the delegates the riflemen in the fort were to open fire and cover the nine men's dash back when trouble started.

All day they sat in the shade and smoked, talked, and ate while a fancy treaty of peace, including a sworn allegiance to the British Crown, was agreed on, to be signed tomorrow at the same place. In the night an ambush of Indians was set around the treaty tree. The next day when the nine appeared from the fort, Black Fish met them with eighteen powerful young braves. After the signing came the two-to-one hand-shaking. Two Indians grabbed for each white man and a mob jumped from the laurel to finish the job. Then the nine Kentucky wildcats let loose with teeth and claws, and the fur flew. Shooting began and the nine raced for the fort. They had won the first round.

Next day there was a great hubbub in the forest, bugles blowing and orders for retreat bawled out, and the pack horses were seen crossing the river at the ford. But the old border fox in the fort was not fooled. The gates of Boonesborough remained shut and the Indian trick failed. The real danger was an Indian rush on the gates under a heavy fire from all sides. This was what kept the riflemen waiting and watching at the portholes day and night.

But to charge across the clearing under the fire of Kentucky rifles was so contrary to the Indian way of fighting that all of De Quindre's urging for a mass attack was useless. Instead, the savages remained under cover of the woods, firing continu-ously. Day and night under the heavy encircling fire of the enemy, the riflemen stuck to their posts, blazing away whenever an inch of Indian hide was exposed to view. The women passed out the scant rations and scarce water, loaded guns when the firing was fast, molded bullets, comforted the children, and prayed the prayers of the pioneer faith. Each slow day under the burning sun was an eternity; each night they thanked the God of their Fathers that some protecting angel had kept the gates.

From high up in a distant tree a sniper began sending bullets inside the fort and Jemima Boone was hit. Boone drew a bead at two hundred yards on the sniper as he was reloading, and put a bullet through his head. The figure that pitched from the high tree was black Pompey. Colonel Calloway, of the old school, became irritated at Boone's cautious tactics and contrived an impressive wooden cannon. The roar and smoke of her first shot scared the Indians for about a mile out of range, but when the smoke cleared from her second blast she had burst wide open and was permanently disabled. But she was the wonder of the wilderness as long as she lasted.

More serious was the tunnel which the enemy was driving toward the fort. It carried to the defenders the sinister fear of exploding mines that would breach the wooden walls. Day by day they could hear the digging come nearer. It wore on their strained nerves like the gnawing of a rat in the night.

Hour by hour a week dragged on. In the inky blackness of the seventh night a bright flame suddenly shot across the clearing in a long arc and dropped on a cabin roof. It was the dreadful flaming arrow. Now they were dropping fast on the pine roofs of the cabins. Worse yet, the savages had crept across the clearing in the darkness and started fagot fires against the log palisade on all sides. The spreading glow lit up the clearing as the hungry little flames ran along the shingles. Against the glow the frantic silhouettes of the defenders trying to beat out the flames drew stinging gunfire from the enemy. Suddenly a figure leaped up on a burning roof and in a fury of flame and bullets beat out the fire. When he had finished he calmly jumped down to safety. But the fires along the stockade were taking hold and the last remaining buckets full of precious water would be of no avail. The riflemen were standing at their posts holding their fire, waiting for the final mass attack, and women stood clutching their children. To Boone it seemed the last card had been played and lost. As the red light flickered over his set face, suddenly he felt a drop of water strike the back of his hand, and as he looked up heavy drops struck his face. In a few minutes the God-sent rain streamed down in drenching sheets. The burning stockade hissed, steamed, glowed, and went out. Something beyond human power had saved Boonesborough by the skin of its teeth.

Still the firing from the forest kept up incessantly. No one knew how near the tunnel was, but it seemed almost under their feet. The September pouring rain had soaked everyone to the bone. They would soon be passing around the last ration of food. Hope held desperately to ever slimmer chances. No Indian attack on a fort had ever been known to keep up so long.

Utter darkness of a night of lashing rain set in on the ninth day of the siege. In the fierce movement of the storm it seemed as though the savage demons of all the wild valley had come down for vengeance. It was a blind night when a man could not see the end of his rifle barrel. Nothing now could stop the mass rush of the savages' across the clearing. The riflemen stood grimly at their posts in the pouring rain and waited. In the darkness time stopped. They shifted and growled, trying to keep their powder dry, and muttered to each other. At long last the night lifted. Out of the shapeless grayness the world was taking form. The morning came with no firing from the enemy, and the lookouts reported no signs of Indians in the forest. It looked like another false retreat. A scout or two came back with the news that the Indians were on the march this time for sure.

Then two white men crossed the clearing shouting and waving. One was Simon Kenton who had not been able to get
through the lines. It was true that the Indians had gone.
The white medicine was too strong. The spirits of the forest
were beaten and the white gods prevailed. A surge of wild joy
was in the hearts of Boonesborough when the log gates swung
open and let out the starved cattle. There was whooping and
firing to welcome eighty backwoodsmen from Harrodsburg,
riding in too late for a rescue but in time for the celebration.

PAUL REVERE'S RIDE

HENRY WADSWORTH LONGFELLOW

The time is just before the outbreak of the Revolutionary War.
The colonists had become more and more incensed over the unjust
taxes being levied upon them, and they had gone so far as to collect
ammunition and arms in the little town of Concord near Boston. To
put down the growing spirit of rebellion, the British commander in
Boston determined to capture and imprison Samuel Adams and John
Hancock, who were leaders of the patriots, and to capture the supplies which were in Concord. They accordingly planned an expedition to accomplish these purposes, but the patriots learned of their
plans and prepared for resistance. The man chosen to warn the
Minute Men and the countryside was Paul Revere of Boston.

U   LISTEN, my children, and you shall hear
           Of the midnight ride of Paul Revere,
           On the eighteenth of April, in Seventy-five;
           Hardly a man is now alive
5   Who remembers that famous day and year.

B   He said to his friend, "If the British march
           By land or sea from the town tonight,
           Hang a lantern aloft in the belfry arch
           Of the North Church tower as a signal light—
10   One, if by land, and two, if by sea;
           And I on the opposite shore will be,
           Ready to ride and spread the alarm
           Through every Middlesex village and farm,
           For the country-folk to be up and to arm."
15   Then he said, "Good night!" and with muffled oar
           Silently rowed to the Charlestown shore,
           Just as the moon rose over the bay,
           Where swinging wide at her moorings lay
           The *Somerset*, British man-of-war;
20   A phantom ship, with each mast and spar
           Across the moon like a prison bar,
           And a huge black hulk, that was magnified
           By its own reflection in the tide.

G   Meanwhile, his friend, through alley and street,
25   Wanders and watches with eager ears,
           Till in the silence around him he hears
           The muster of men at the barrack door,
           The sound of arms, and the tramp of feet,
           And the measured tread of the grenadiers,
30   Marching down to their boats on the shore.
           Then he climbed to the tower of the church,
           Up the wooden stairs, with stealthy tread,
           To the belfry chamber overhead,

And startled the pigeons from their perch
35 On the somber rafters that round him made
Masses and moving shapes of shade—
Up the trembling ladder, steep and tall,
To the highest window in the wall,
Where he paused to listen and look down
40 A moment on the roofs of the town,
And the moonlight flowing over all.

U   Beneath, in the churchyard, lay the dead,
In their night encampment on the hill,
Wrapped in silence so deep and still
45 That he could hear, like a sentinel's tread,
The watchful night wind, as it went
Creeping along from tent to tent,
And seeming to whisper, "All is well!"
A moment only he feels the spell
50 Of the place and the hour, and the secret dread
Of the lonely belfry and the dead;
For suddenly all his thoughts are bent
On a shadowy something far away,
Where the river widens to meet the bay—
55 A line of black that bends and floats
On the rising tide, like a bridge of boats.

B   Meanwhile, impatient to mount and ride,
Booted and spurred, with a heavy stride
On the opposite shore walked Paul Revere.
1B(#1) 60 Now he patted his horse's side,
1B(#2) Now gazed at the landscape far and near,
1B(#3) Then, impetuous, stamped the earth,
And turned and tightened his saddle girth;
B But mostly he watched with eager search
65 The belfry tower of the old North Church,
As it rose above the graves on the hill,

Lonely and spectral and somber and still.
And lo! as he looks, on the belfry's height
A glimmer, and then a gleam of light!
70 He springs to the saddle, the bridle he turns,
But lingers and gazes, till full on his sight
A second lamp in the belfry burns!

G   A hurry of hoofs in a village street,
A shape in the moonlight, a bulk in the dark,
75 And beneath, from the pebbles, in passing, a spark
Struck out by a steed flying fearless and fleet;
That was all!   And yet, through the gloom and the
    light,
The fate of a nation was riding that night;
And the spark struck out by that steed, in his flight,
80 Kindled the land into flame with its heat.

B   He has left the village and mounted the steep,
And beneath him, tranquil and broad and deep,
Is the Mystic, meeting the ocean tides;
And under the alders, that skirt its edge,
85 Now soft on the sand, now loud on the ledge,
Is heard the tramp of his steed as he rides.
It was twelve by the village clock
When he crossed the bridge into Medford town.
He heard the crowing of the cock,
90 And the barking of the farmer's dog,
And felt the damp of the river fog,
That rises after the sun goes down.

G   It was one by the village clock,
When he galloped into Lexington.
95 He saw the gilded weathercock
Swim in the moonlight as he passed,
And the meetinghouse windows, blank and bare,
Gaze at him, with a spectral glare,

As if they already stood aghast
100   At the bloody work they would look upon.

B   It was two by the village clock,
When he came to the bridge in Concord town.
He heard the bleating of the flock,
And the twitter of birds among the trees,
105   And felt the breath of the morning breeze
Blowing over the meadows brown.
And one was safe and asleep in his bed
Who at the bridge would be first to fall,
Who that day would be lying dead,
110   Pierced by a British musket ball.

G   You know the rest. In the books you have read,
How the British Regulars fired and fled—
How the farmers gave them ball for ball,
From behind each fence and farmyard wall,
115   Chasing the redcoats down the lane,
Then crossing the fields to emerge again
Under the trees at the turn of the road,
And only pausing to fire and load.

U   So through the night rode Paul Revere;
120   And so through the night went his cry of alarm
To every Middlesex village and farm—
A cry of defiance and not of fear,
A voice in the darkness, a knock at the door,
And a word that shall echo forevermore!
125   For, borne on the night wind of the Past,
Through all our history, to the last,
In the hour of darkness and peril and need,
The people will waken and listen to hear
The hurrying hoof beats of that steed,
130   And the midnight message of Paul Revere.

GRANDMOTHER'S STORY OF THE BATTLE OF BUNKER HILL

OLIVER WENDELL HOLMES

'Tis like stirring living embers when, at eighty, one remembers
All the achings and the quakings of "the times that tried men's
  souls";
When I talk of *Whig* and *Tory,* when I tell the *Rebel* story,
To you the words are ashes, but to me they're burning coals.

5   I had heard the muskets' rattle of the April running battle;
Lord Percy's hunted soldiers, I can see their red coats still;
But a deadly chill comes o'er me, as the day looms up before
  me,
When a thousand men lay bleeding on the slopes of Bunker's
  Hill.

'Twas a peaceful summer's morning, when the first thing gave
  us warning
10 Was the booming of the cannon from the river and the shore:
"Child," says grandma, "what's the matter, what is all this
  noise and clatter?
Are those scalping Indian devils come to murder us once
  more?"

Poor old soul! my sides were shaking in the midst of all my
  quaking
To hear her talk of Indians when the guns began to roar:
15 She had seen the burning village, and the slaughter and the
  pillage,
When the Mohawks killed her father, with their bullets
  through his door.

Then I said, "Now, dear old granny, don't you fret and worry
  any,
For I'll soon come back and tell you whether this is work or
  play;
There can't be mischief in it, so I won't be gone a minute"—
20 For a minute then I started. I was gone the livelong day.

No time for bodice-lacing or for looking-glass grimacing;
Down my hair went as I hurried, tumbling half-way to my
  heels;
God forbid your ever knowing, when there's blood around her
  flowing,
How the lonely, helpless daughter of a quiet household feels!

25 In the street I heard a thumping; and I knew it was the
  stumping
Of the Corporal, our old neighbor, on that wooden leg he wore,
With a knot of women round him,—it was lucky I had found
  him,—

So I followed with the others, and the Corporal marched
  before.

They were making for the steeple,—the old soldier and his
  people;
30 The pigeons circled round us as we climbed the creaking stair,
Just across the narrow river—O, so close it made me shiver!—
Stood a fortress on the hilltop that but yesterday was bare.

Not slow our eyes to find it; well we knew who stood behind it,
Though the earthwork hid them from us, and the stubborn
  walls were dumb:
35 Here were sister, wife, and mother, looking wild upon each
  other,
And their lips were white with terror as they said, *The hour
  has come!*

The morning slowly wasted, not a morsel had we tasted,
And our heads were almost splitting with the cannons' deafening thrill,
When a figure tall and stately round the rampart strode
  sedately;
40 It was Prescott, one since told me; he commanded on the hill.

Every woman's heart grew bigger when we saw his manly
  figure,
With the banyan buckled round it, standing up so straight and
  tall;
Like a gentleman of leisure who is strolling out for pleasure,
Through the storm of shells and cannon-shot he walked around
  the wall.

45 At eleven the streets were swarming, for the red-coats' ranks
  were forming;
At noon in marching order they were moving to the piers;

How the bayonets gleamed and glistened, as we looked far
down and listened
To the trampling and the drum-beat of the belted grenadiers!

At length the men have started, with a cheer (it seemed faint-
hearted),
50 In their scarlet regimentals, with their knapsacks on their
backs,
And the reddening, rippling water, as after a sea-fight's
slaughter,
Round the barges gliding onward blushed like blood along
their tracks.

So they crossed to the other border, and again they formed in
order;
And the boats came back for soldiers, came for soldiers, soldiers still:
55 And the time seemed everlasting to us women faint and
fasting,—
At last they're moving, marching, marching proudly up the hill.

We can see the bright steel glancing all along the lines advancing—
Now the front rank fires a volley—they have thrown away
their shot;
For behind the earthwork lying, all the balls above them flying,
60 Our people need not hurry; so they wait and answer not.

Then the Corporal, our old cripple (he would swear sometimes, and tipple),—
He had heard the bullets whistle (in the old French War)
before,—
Calls out in words of jeering, just as if they all were hearing,—
And his wooden leg thumps fiercely on the dusty belfry
floor:—

65 "Oh! fire away, ye villains, and earn King George's shillin's,
But ye'll waste a ton of powder afore a 'rebel' falls;
You may bang the dirt and welcome, they're as safe as Dan'l
Malcolm
Ten foot beneath the gravestone that you've splintered with
your balls!"

In the hush of expectation, in the awe and trepidation
70 Of the dread approaching moment, we are well-nigh breathless all;
Though the rotten bars are failing on the rickety belfry railing,
We are crowding up against them like the waves against a wall.

Just a glimpse (the air is clearer), they are nearer,—nearer,—
nearer,
When a flash—a curling smoke-wreath—then a crash—the
steeple shakes—
75 The deadly truce is ended; the tempest's shroud is rended;
Like a morning mist it gathered, like a thunder-cloud it breaks!

O the sight our eyes discover as the blue-black smoke blows
over!
The red-coats stretched in windrows as a mower rakes his hay;
Here a scarlet heap is lying, there a headlong crowd is flying,
80 Like a billow that has broken and is shivered into spray.

Then we cried, "The troops are routed! they are beat—it can't
be doubted!
God be thanked, the fight is over!"—Ah! the grim old soldier's
smile!
"Tell us, tell us why you look so?" (we could hardly speak, we
shook so),—
"Are they beaten? *Are* they beaten? ARE they beaten?"—
"Wait a while."

85 O the trembling and the terror! for too soon we saw our error:
They are baffled, not defeated; we have driven them back in
vain;
And the columns that were scattered, round the colors that
were tattered,
Toward the sullen silent fortress turned their belted breasts
again.

All at once, as we are gazing, lo the roofs of Charlestown
blazing!
90 They have fired the harmless village; in an hour it will be
down!
The Lord in heaven confound them, rain his fire and brimstone
round them,—
The robbing, murdering red-coats, that would burn a peaceful
town!

They are marching, stern and solemn; we can see each massive
column
As they near the naked earth-mound with the slanting walls so
steep.
95 Have our soldiers got faint-hearted, and in noiseless haste departed?
Are they panic-struck and helpless? Are they palsied or asleep?

Now! the walls they're almost under! scarce a rod the foes
asunder!
Not a firelock flashed against them! up the earthwork they will
swarm!
But the words have scarce been spoken, when the ominous
calm is broken,
100 And a bellowing crash has emptied all the vengeance of the
storm!

So again, with murderous slaughter, pelted backward to the
water,
Fly Pigot's running heroes and the frightened braves of Howe;

And we shout, "At last they're done for, it's their barges they
 have run for:
They are beaten, beaten, beaten; and the battle's over now!"

105 And we looked, poor timid creatures, on the rough old soldier's
 features,
Our lips afraid to question, but he knew what we would ask:
"Not sure," he said; "keep quiet,—once more, I guess, they'll
 try it—
Here's damnation to the cut-throats!"—then he handed me his
 flask,

Saying, "Gal, you're looking shaky; have a drop of old
 Jamaiky;
110 I'm afraid there'll be more trouble afore this job is done";
So I took one scorching swallow; dreadful faint I felt and
 hollow,
Standing there from early morning when the firing was begun.

All through those hours of trial I had watched a calm clock dial,
As the hands kept creeping, creeping,—they were creeping round to four,
115 When the old man said, "They're forming with their bayonets fixed for storming:
It's the death grip that's a coming,—they will try the works once more."

With brazen trumpets blaring, the flames behind them glaring,
The deadly wall before them, in close array they come;
Still onward, upward toiling, like a dragon's fold uncoiling—
120 Like a rattlesnake's shrill warning the reverberating drum!

Over heaps all torn and gory—shall I tell the fearful story,
How they surged above the breastwork, as a sea breaks over a deck;
How, driven, yet scarce defeated, our worn-out men retreated,
With their powder-horns all emptied, like the swimmers from a wreck?

125 It has all been told and painted; as for me, they say I fainted,
As the wooden-legged old Corporal stumped with me down the stair:
When I woke from dreams affrighted the evening lamps were lighted,—
On the floor a youth was lying; his bleeding breast was bare.

And I heard through all the flurry, "Send for *Warren!* hurry! hurry!
130 Tell him here's a soldier bleeding, and he'll come and dress his wound!"
Ah, we knew not till the morrow told its tale of death and sorrow,
How the starlight found him stiffened on the dark and bloody ground.

Who the youth was, what his name was, where the place from
    which he came was,
Who had brought him from the battle, and had left him at our
    door,
35 He could not speak to tell us; but 'twas one of our brave
    fellows,
As the homespun plainly showed us which the dying soldier
    wore.

For they all thought he was dying, as they gathered 'round him
    crying,—
And they said, "O, how they'll miss him!" and, "What will his
    mother do?"
Then, his eyelids just unclosing like a child's that has been
    dozing,
40 He faintly murmured, "Mother!"—and—I saw his eyes were
    blue.

—"Why, grandma, how you're winking!"—Ah, my child, it
    sets me thinking
Of a story not like this one. Well, he somehow lived along;
So we came to know each other, and I nursed him like a—
    mother,
Till at last he stood before me, tall, and rosy-cheeked, and
    strong.

45 And we sometimes walked together in the pleasant summer
    weather;
—"Please to tell us what his name was?"—Just your own, my
    little dear,—
There's his picture Copley painted: we became so well ac-
    quainted,
That—in short, that's why I'm grandma, and you children all
    are here!

THE BOY PATRIOT

ROBERT D. HENRY AND JAMES M. LYNCH, JR.

CHARACTERS

ANNOUNCER, *clear authoritative voice. Can be female, if few male voices are obtainable.*

VOICE I AND 2, *girls' voices*

READER, *good reader of poetry, preferably female voice*

WASHINGTON, *mature voice*

NATHAN HALE, *youthful voice*

STEPHEN JONES, *mature, but hard, voice*

GUARD, *rough, soldier's voice*

SERGEANT, *same as guard*

BRITISH GUARD, *harsh voice with cockney accent*

DRIVER, *mature voice*

OFFICER, *mature kindly voice*

MUSIC. *Some patriotic air of American origin. Up and fade.*

ANNOUNCER. Heroes! American heroes! What would this

"The Boy Patriot" is reprinted by permission of Row, Peterson & Company, from their collection of radio plays, *History-Makers*.

70

great country of America have done without her Revolutionary War heroes! Her star-studded past would have been
drab indeed, if it weren't for the names of such men and
women as:

VOICE 1. James Otis, who first dared to dub King George III
a tyrant.

VOICE 2. Samuel Adams, the firebrand of the American
Revolution.

VOICE 1. Patrick Henry, whose "Give me liberty or give me
death" was the rally cry for thousands of patriots.

VOICE 2. John Paul Jones, the father of the United States
Navy.

VOICE 1. George Rogers Clark, the conqueror of the British
in the Northwest.

VOICE 2. Mollie Pitcher, the heroine of the Battle of Mon-
mouth.

ANNOUNCER. And on and on. One might name hundreds
more if one took the time. But high on every list of American
heroes, the name of Nathan Hale appears. Why is he so honored? Why is he alone enshrined as the Boy Patriot, when he
failed? Because he died? Because his task was so great?
Yes, but mainly because he had the true American spirit and
courage. The courage to try against impossible odds, and
thus point the way for others to follow. . . . (*Pause.*)

MUSIC. *Up and cut.*

FANFARE.

ANNOUNCER. "The Boy Patriot," presented to you by _____
_____. The year is 1776.
The Declaration of Independence has just been signed. The
thirteen colonies are now free and independent states, though
they are finding it difficult to convince themselves of this, to
say nothing of the rest of the world. The new country has an
army, composed mostly of hardy farmers. It has an able
Commander-in-Chief, too. But it lacks, most of all, knowledge
of the enemy's strength and condition; for an army can-

not fight intelligently if it knows nothing of its opponents.

BIZ.[1] *Hubbub. Fades as gavel knocks three times.*

WASHINGTON. Gentlemen, we are at war with the British Empire. Of its army we know nothing. As soon as possible we must find out how many troops they have on hand and what war materials are available. We can get this information only through undercover workers . . . an espionage system, as it were. Gentlemen, we must have spies if we are to win this war.

BIZ. *Hubbub.*

HALE (*his voice gradually drowning out the others*). General Washington, I would like to volunteer for such service.

BIZ. *Applause.*

WASHINGTON. Captain Hale, your country and its army, to say nothing of myself, are deeply indebted to you. Your display of courage and loyalty, I trust, will be of great inspiration to others.

MUSIC. *Up and fade.*

BIZ. *Horse and wagon moving slowly.*

GUARD. Halt! Who goes there?

HALE (*off mike*). Whoa! . . . A friend.

BIZ. *Horse snorts as horse and wagon stop.*

GUARD. Come down off that wagon till we search you.

BIZ. *Squeak of wheel as man descends.*

GUARD. What's your name?

HALE (*on mike*). Farmer Harrington, sir. I have some produce I'd like to sell.

GUARD. All right. Everything's in order. You may proceed.

HALE. Thank you.

BIZ. *Squeak of wheel as he climbs back into wagon.*

HALE. Giddap.

BIZ. *Horse and wagon up and under.*

HALE (*to himself·over sound*). Let's see now. . . . Over there are five mounted cannon . . . a storehouse for grain . . .

---

[1] BIZ—Stage business—sounds, noise, etc.

a corral with—let's see—two, four, six, eight, ten, eleven, four-teen horses . . . probably for the officers.

BIZ. *Troops marching in the distance. Cut horse and wagon.*

SERGEANT (*off mike*). Company halt! . . . Left face! . . . (*Angrily.*) What's the matter with *you*, Martin? Don't you know your left hand from your right yet? (*Fades out until barely audible but continues to shout.*) You're fighting a war. If you can't follow orders, those blithering Yankees will have an easy time of it, take it from me.

HALE (*to himself*). Four, eight, twelve, sixteen men in that squad. . . . That makes 250. . . . Guess I'd better get over to those tents . . . (*Fade*) . . . and see how many men are quartered there.

BIZ. *Horse and wagon up and under.*

STEPHEN JONES. Well, what do you know about that? Why that's Cousin Nathan Hale over there on that farm wagon. What's he doing in a British camp? I thought he was a rebel. . . . Well, maybe he's changed his mind. (*Shouts.*) Nathan! . . . Nathan Hale! . . . Hey, Nathan! Wait a minute. . . . (*Quietly.*) That's funny. He kept on as if he didn't hear me. . . . But I'm sure he did. . . . (*Fade.*) I'd better go see the General at once.

MUSIC. *Atmospheric. Up and fade.*

BIZ. *Door opens and shuts immediately. Footsteps cross room and stop.*

CAPTAIN. Well? What do you want? Out with it. Can't you see I'm busy?

JONES. Yes, sir. . . . You see, sir, I'm Stephen Jones, and I have a cousin named Nathan Hale, who is a captain in the Colonial army.

CAPTAIN. What about your cousin? We'll have the whole crew of your Yankees wiped out in a few days anyhow. . . . I'm sorry, Mr. Jones, but there's nothing I can do about your cousin. He'll have to suffer along with the others.

JONES. But you don't understand, sir. He's here . . . in this camp.

CAPTAIN (*laughing*). Ho-Ho! In *this* camp? Why, the whole Yankee army couldn't get through our lines, let alone one American captain.

JONES. But that's just it, sir. He isn't in uniform.

CAPTAIN (*excited*). What? You mean he's disguised? He's a spy then. By Godfrey, these Yankees have more nerve than a pack of wolves!

JONES (*fade*). Yes, sir. That's what I've been trying to tell you, sir, for the last five minutes.

MUSIC. *Atmospheric. Up and fade.*

CAPTAIN. All right, Captain Hale. We caught you with these papers in your possession. They condemn you as a spy. What have you to say for yourself?

HALE. Well, sir, I am an officer in the American Army. It is true that I've been visiting your camp in search of information.

CAPTAIN (*angrily*). Then you'll hang, Hale. You'll hang. We'll show you young rebel whippersnappers what it means to spy on a British camp. Nobody can get away with that out here. . . . (*Fade.*) Take him away.

ANNOUNCER. The fate of a spy—conviction without trial. The penalty—death. Hale, his doom sealed, was again locked in the jail. As he awaited the dawn of his last day on earth, a friendly guard who liked the courageous youth despite his being an enemy . . . (*Fade*) . . . gave him a few sheets of paper and a pencil.

BIZ. *Scratching of pen up and under.*

HALE (*low to himself*). Dear Mother: Don't cry when you read this, Mother. I'm dying the way I've always wanted to, you know, for my country. They have probably told you why. I was captured by the British while getting military information for General Washington. I came here of my own accord. . . .

MUSIC. *Atmospheric. Up and under.*

HALE. Dear Sister: You too would do the same thing . . . give your life for your country . . . if your country needed you. Please take good care of Mother, and don't worry. It won't be long; and I shall face it bravely knowing that you will pray for me.

MUSIC. *Up and under.*

HALE. Dearest: We planned so much . . . you and I— where we would live, what we were going to do—that this letter is indeed difficult to write. I won't see you ever again . . . but I shall carry a picture of you in my heart as I give my life for my country.

MUSIC. *Up and fade.* BIZ. *Pounding on door.*

HALE. Guard! . . . Guard!

GUARD (*off mike*). Quiet in there! Quiet! (*On mike.*) What's the matter with you?

HALE. I have some letters that the other guard said you would deliver for me.

GUARD (*angrily*). All right. Let's have them. . . . Hmmm. . . . Dear Mother: don't——

HALE. But you aren't supposed to read them. The other guard said——

GUARD (*interrupting*). Oh, I'm not supposed to read them, eh? Well, here!

BIZ. *Tearing of paper.*

GUARD. Maybe you'd like the pieces. Only a fool would let a spy write letters. . . . (*Fade.*) . . . How do we know whether they're in code or not? . . .

BIZ. *Single drum beaten slowly. Marching men.*

OFFICER. Halt.

BIZ. *Marchers stop on second beat.*

OFFICER. Are you ready, driver? You know what to do, of course?

DRIVER. All ready. Just put the mask on his head, and I'll whip up the horses.

HALE.　The mask isn't necessary.　I'm not afraid to die.

OFFICER.　All right, Captain Hale.　Climb up on the tail-board of the wagon, please.　Have you anything to say before you are hanged as a spy?

HALE.　Yes. . . .　I only regret that I have but one life to lose for my country.

OFFICER.　Are you ready, Captain Hale?

HALE.　I am ready.

OFFICER.　May God have mercy on your soul.

BIZ.　*Roll of drums increasing to maximum.*

BIZ.　*Sound of whip striking horse.　Horse and wagon start up quickly and fade out.*

BIZ.　*Drums break off sharply.*

ANNOUNCER.　Thus, Nathan Hale was hanged as a spy.　He was heartlessly denied the services of a minister, and even a copy of the Bible was refused him.　That is the fate of a captured spy—death without mercy.　But Nathan Hale died willingly—just as willingly as he accepted his country's order to spy on the British.　He died like a gentleman and a soldier, his bravery making even his executioners bow their heads in respect.

MUSIC.　*Taps up to finish.*

READER.　　　"To every man upon this earth
　　　　　Death cometh soon or late.
　　　And how can man die better
　　　　　Than facing fearful odds
　　　For the ashes of his fathers
　　　　　And the temples of his Gods?"

MUSIC.　*Theme up and under.*

ANNOUNCER.　Today's radio play was entitled *The Boy Patriot*.　It was produced by ——————————.　The characters included ———————————.　Your announcer is ——————————.

MUSIC.　*Up to end.*

THE OREGON TRAIL

ARTHUR GUITERMAN

Two hundred wagons, rolling out to Oregon,
  Breaking through the gopher holes, lurching wide and free,
Crawling up the mountain pass, jolting, grumbling, rumbling on,
  Two hundred wagons, rolling to the sea.

5 From East and South and North they flock, to muster, row on row,
A fleet of tenscore prairie ships beside Missouri's flow.
The bullwhips crack, the oxen strain, the canvas-hooded files
Are off upon the long, long trail of sixteen hundred miles.

The women hold the guiding lines; beside the rocking steers
10 With goad and ready rifle walk the bearded pioneers
Through clouds of dust beneath the sun, through floods of sweeping rain
Across the Kansas prairie land, across Nebraska's plain.

Two hundred wagons, rolling out to Oregon,
  Curved round the campfire flame at halt when day is done,
15 Rest awhile beneath the stars, yoke again and lumber on,
  Two hundred wagons, rolling with the sun.

Among the barren buttes they wind beneath the jealous view
Of Blackfoot, Pawnee, Omaha, Arapahoe, and Sioux.
No savage threat may check their course, no river deep and wide;
20 They swim the Platte, they ford the Snake, they cross the Great Divide.

They march as once from India's vales through Asia's mountain door

77

With shield and spear on Europe's plain their fathers marched
     before.
They march where leap the antelope and storm the buffalo
Still westward as their fathers marched ten thousand years ago.

25 Two hundred wagons, rolling out to Oregon,
    Creeping down the dark defile below the mountain crest,
Surging through the brawling stream, lunging, plunging,
     forging on,
    Two hundred wagons, rolling toward the West.

Now toils the dusty caravan with swinging wagon-poles
30 Where Walla Walla pours along, where broad Columbia rolls.
The long-haired trapper's face grows dark and scowls the
     painted brave;
Where now the beaver builds his dam the wheat and rye shall
    wave.

The British trader shakes his head and weighs his nation's loss,
For where those hardy settlers come the Stars and Stripes will
    toss.
35 Then block the wheels, unyoke the steers; the prize is his who
    dares;
The cabins rise, the fields are sown, and Oregon is theirs!

        They will take, they will hold,
        By the spade in the mold,
        By the seed in the soil,
40   By the sweat and the toil,
        By the plow in the loam,
        By the school and the home!

Two hundred wagons, rolling out to Oregon,
    Two hundred wagons, ranging free and far,
45 Two hundred wagons, rumbling, grumbling, rolling on,
    Two hundred wagons, following a star!

JOURNEYS

AROUND THE WORLD

H

Exploring faraway places.

THE PYGMIES

ELLEN AND ATTILIO GATTI

Toward the northwest, from Rwanda,[1] lies the Ituri. It is the beginning of the evergreen equatorial jungle, of the infinite ocean of vegetation whose waves, rolling past the few islands of civilization scattered here and there, cross all Central Africa to reach the shores of the Atlantic Ocean.

It is the kingdom of darkness, silence, mystery. Entering it, one feels suddenly cut off from all the rest of the world. In time as well as in space. For at once one has the impression of intruding upon a region belonging to the immemorial epochs of prehistoric monsters—a region which has lain there, unchanged, intact, since the beginning of days.

Nor is this merely an illusion of the imagination. The greater part of the jungle has never been explored by white men. Much of it has not even been penetrated by the natives, who are held back by their deadly fear of the mighty and terrible monsters which they believe still live in these tabu [2] zones.

The deeper one tries to penetrate into this ocean of vegetation, the harder Nature fights back. Climate, flora and fauna [3] increasingly become more excessive, monstrous, exaggerated. Trees attain unbelievable proportions. Trunks grow one across or over the other. Every slightest space between them is filled by a mad scramble of lianas,[4] creepers, mosses, thorns, caustic reeds, deadly mushrooms, poisonous knife-like leaves.

Biting ants are as long as a toe. Stinging beetles are as big

[1] RWANDA . . . ITURI—Pronounced ĕr-wän′dà . . . ĭ-tū′rĭ.
[2] TABU (tà-bōo′)—Sacred.
[3] FLORA AND FAUNA—Plant and animal life.
[4] LIANA (lê-ä′nà)—A large climbing plant.

81

as a fist.   Venomous spiders grow to be as large as half of this page.   Common are hogs five feet at the shoulder, crocs twenty-six feet in length, baboons weighing hundreds of pounds, leopards nine to ten feet from nose to tail tip.

Worst of all, here lives the Giant Gorilla, the most cruel, fierce and belligerent of all apes.   It is a colossus of formidable might and almost human cunning.   It commonly attains a weight in the neighborhood of 600 pounds and tops six feet in stature.   It can lift up to eight-foot-nine its appalling hands, which effortlessly will snap an ironwood branch as big as a human thigh, or grab two hunters by the neck and smash their heads one against the other like two egg shells.

And what is the race of supermen who can withstand the strain and dangers of such a world?   What extraordinary weapons do they possess to fight off and vanquish the stupendous monsters roaming and prowling through their somber kingdom?

Those "supermen" are the pure pygmies who variously call themselves Mambuti,[5] Tikky-Tikky, Akka, Batwa, Bamoko, or Gulebako.   Regardless of the difference in names, they are the same four-foot-six mites of humanity at its most primitive stage.   And, at the same time, they are the most robust, kind, brave, childishly carefree, and happy beings in existence.

Except for the iron spearpoints which they obtain by barter with other, more advanced natives, their weapons are still those of the primeval epochs.   Their diminutive bow has a creeper for cord.   Their miniature arrow is a reed with a feather inserted as a stabilizer at one end, the other sharpened to a point by a cutting stone, hardened in red embers, made lethal with a thick coat of vegetable poison.

Their resourcefulness does the rest.

Poorly armed as they are, the leopard would simply devour them, whenever it chose.   Instead, they plant cleverly disguised nooses and traps all around the clearing where they are

---

[5] MAMBUTI—Pronounced măm-bū′tī.

living. All night long they keep a great fire going in the middle
of it. And the leopard, its luminous eyes suffering from the
flames, prowls around and around—until one of its paws get
caught. Then a dozen spears finish the great cat. And its
skin, well cleaned with rocks chipped to a knife's shape, becomes the warm garment of a dwarf belle.

The elephant, the buffalo, the okapi,[6] the hippopotamus, the
giant hog, would smash and crush the Pygmy hunter who dares
to approach them. But to survive the Pygmy needs plenty of
meat. And each of these great animals can be easily killed,
once it is imprisoned in the bottom of a deep hole. So the
dwarf sees to it that many hundreds of such pits are always in
readiness. Many of them have been excavated by his ancestors. Many more are untiringly added the whole time. Light
sticks are poised over the pit's mouth. Big *magongo* leaves are
spread over this trellis. Then over them are strewn dead leaves
and branches, even manure, small ant-heaps, clods of moss—
until not even the most suspicious eyes can detect a difference
from the surrounding ground.

If their hunting compels the dwarfs to cross a stream in
which crocodiles abound, they don't even try their precious
spears on the saurian's [7] metal-like cuirass.[8] Instead, they get
themselves some long lianas. All together they soften those
natural ropes by twisting them over and over, tie them one to
the other until the proper length is attained, climb up a convenient tree and fasten the liana to a solid branch. At the
hanging end, they make a rough seat and one of the youngest
hunters slips into it.

The rest of the tribe, by means of a vegetable cable thrust
over the top branches of another tree, pull the hunter up.
High, high up. Then they cut the rope and let him go. At
dizzy speed the flying dwarf swings down toward the water,
soars up toward the treetops on the opposite shore. Quick as

[6] OKAPI (ō-kä′pē)—An animal somewhat like a giraffe.
[7] SAURIAN (sô′rĭ-ăn)—Lizard-like reptile.
[8] CUIRASS (kwê-răs′)—Armor.

83

a monkey he grasps a branch. Helping himself with legs and hands, he climbs out of his seat, ties it to the branch while he finds a heavy piece of wood. Once this is secured, he attaches it to the seat and lets the whole contraption swing back for another passenger.

The crocs snap their horrible jaws. With blind rage they beat the water with their tails. The impact of one such blow could smash to death ten pygmies at a time. But swift as crocs are, the flying little men are swifter.

If the whole tribe must cross the river, the hunters swing back and forth until several lianas are strung between the top of a tree on one shore and the top of a tree on the other. Time being of no consequence in the jungle, slowly those main lianas are tied together with hundreds and hundreds of smaller ones. Rough stairs of sticks are fastened to the trunks of both trees. By the end all that women, children and old men have to do is to climb up, to cross the swaying but perfectly safe, quite durable suspension bridge, and to climb down the other side.

Thus, in the same manner as their forefathers did tens of thousands of years ago, the pygmies joyfully face and cleverly overcome any of the infinite difficulties, hardships and dangers of their forbidding world of wet gloom.

In the Belgian Congo alone their kingdom extends over a quarter of a million square miles. This kingdom which the Bantu [9] fears and carefully avoids, which the white man has slightly indented here and there with a road or a mine and can penetrate only at the will of the pygmies and at the cost of his own health and vitality, is divided into hunting territories, each exclusively reserved to a clan.

The boundaries, majestic rivers and high mountains, are actually natural frontiers impassable to the dwarfs. But the pygmies believe that each of them was intentionally put there for no other purpose by Muungu [10] himself, the greatest of their

[9] BANTU (băn'-tōo)—A member of an African tribe living in equatorial and southern Africa.
[10] MUUNGU—Pronounced mōō-ŭn'gōō.

84

gods. Of him they have a hazy, touchingly poetic conception. "It is he," they say, "who is the maker and the owner of the world. It is he who sometimes comes on earth, when his steps shake the ground with earthquakes. But usually he lives in the skies. There, the sun is his fire by day, the moon his torch by night. The winds are his breath, the clouds the smoke of his pipe. The thunder is his voice, the hurricane his wrath."

There are only five of these clans, which means that they have an average of fifty thousand square miles each. These enormous expanses are divided between the various tribes that compose each clan, according with a delimitation established by distant ancestors.

These tribe-families to which a man belongs from birth to death and into which womenfolk of other tribes of the same clan are merged from the moment of their marriage, are self-contained, self-sufficient, rabidly independent, thoroughly democratic little communities of forty to sixty individuals. One which we know intimately for having shared with it several years of jungle life, and which can be taken as typical of the one thousand odd such tribes estimated to compose the total of the five clans, is that of sultani Makulu-Kulu.[11]

The name of this four-foot-five chief literally means "Little Butterfly." In his close-knit community there is no place or reason for jealousy, envy or hatred. Its fifty-six members can depend on no mercy from nature, on no outside assistance to help them overcome the fearful odds presented by every day. Each of them freely gives something to all. From all the others each individual freely gets what they best can give him.

There are three old men who cannot hunt any longer. One is Makulu-Kulu's father, the tribe's former chief, and his two brothers. They give their counsel, the fruits of their wisdom, experience and knowledge. And highly honored are they. Respectfully they are listened to. All their needs are tenderly cared for.

[11] SULTANI (sŭl-tăn'ĭ) MAKULU-KULU (má-kū'lŭ kū'lŭ)—Sultani means ruler or sovereign.

Makulu-Kulu became his tribe's chief when his father grew too old. Not because he was the oldest son. But because he was the ablest and the bravest of men.

As the tribe's sultan, he guides his hunters on the trail and directs them in the attack. He is the first in moments of great danger, the last in a perilous retreat. The welfare of the whole tribe is his burden, and he must see that fifty-five other stomachs are kept well filled. He decides what should be set aside for bartering with the Bantus living at the edge of the jungle, leads the many day-long journeys to their villages and, once there, it is he who dramatically does all the bargaining.

He approves of marriages and decides the name of the newborn. He supervises the burying of the dead. Over each grave, a simple hole in the ground at half a day of march from where the tribe is at the time, he builds the altar of Muungu— some arched sticks covered with *magongo* leaves—in which he places offerings of meat and wild *tumbako* so that Muungu will be sure to come and take the dead's spirit into the great hunting territories of the above.

And as he, Makulu-Kulu, does more and better than anybody else, so he gets twice whatever anyone else receives or conquers. Which accounts for his being the only one in the tribe who has three wives. That represents a triple ration of worry. But it means also a triple source of service and comfort and children.

The tribe's little ones, eight plump babies still carried on their mothers' backs or sometimes on the top of their heavy loads, give joy and pride to their parents. The eleven other children of ages running up to fifteen, help with numberless little tasks such as gathering dry wood and eatable roots, repairing hunting nets, and so on. And they are all abundantly nourished, carefully tended, patiently taught.

The hunters, seven not yet married, six with a wife each and two older ones doubly wed, are Makulu-Kulu's younger brothers, his sons, cousins or nephews. They, as well as he, make bows and arrows, machetes,[12] and spear handles, clay pots for cooking. They collect, dry and prepare calabashes [13] for carrying water and for the water pipes which women and children share with alike zest. They gather wild tobacco, rare fruits and mushrooms. They extract poison from the roots of the *kilabo* to smear with death the points of their arrows and spears. And they are responsible for most of the preparation of clothing from the bark of trees. This bark they cut in the proper size. The womenfolk repeatedly boil it. The men beat it with an ivory hammer, until the material is thin and soft. Then the women dye it by boiling it with the dark yellow, brown or purple wooden splinters which the hunters chip off certain jungle trees.

Most of the men's time, however, is devoted to tracking and trapping and hunting. And when they return from their hunting expeditions, the meat they bring is for everybody, in equal parts. And so are the surplus meat to be smoked and the elephant ivory which later will be swapped with the Bantus for iron spear points, stems of bananas, baskets of manioca,[14] beans and sweet potatoes.

And, back to their village, they receive a joyous welcome, find their huts warm and dry, the fire burning, the meal ready.

The womenfolk, thirteen wives and five girls of marrying age, take care of the children, fetch water, keep the huts in good repair. They crush seeds, cook meals, weave for the men rakish little straw hats, brilliantly crowned with tufts of feathers. And once in a while they find time also to prepare antelope hide skirts or child-carrying bandoliers for themselves.

When the whole tribe goes hunting far away, the whole household is moved on the backs of the women. Furniture, furnishings, provisions are piled up on each woman's bent back. The load, often bigger than herself, is held by a fiber rope pass-

[12] MACHETE (mä-chä′tä)—A large, heavy knife.
[13] CALABASH (kăl′á-băsh)—A utensil made from the dry shell of a calabash or gourd.
[14] MANIOCA (măn-ĭ-ŏk′á)—A starchy food from the plant of the same name.

ing around her forehead. Somehow, she finds the way of carrying her baby, too, and of keeping an eye on the other children.

The hunters scurry ahead and around entirely unburdened. They have more important things to do. They must carve a path where there is no animal trail. They must protect the procession from the attack of wild beasts. They must fall a tree to bridge an unfordable stream or weave a liana bridge above a dangerous river.

Of course, many a time the unexpected leaps into the life of the tribe and threatens to mar its regular rhythm with stark tragedy.

For instance, spine-chilling roars of fury may suddenly be awakening all the echoes of the pygmy's dark jungle. A hunter looking for honey, has gone too far from his companions. Absorbed in his search, he has relaxed for a second from his usual caution. A giant gorilla has discovered him. The dwarf springs, runs for life. The ape, a male of nightmarish proportions, lunges ahead, crashes through every obstacle.

Now the gorilla's fists begin to beat a wild tattoo on the expanse of his silverish chest. It means that the great ape is sure that his fury is going to be soon satisfied. The distance diminishes. The cavernous mouth of the gorilla lets out another blood-curdling yell.

What chance does the poor little dwarf stand? His end is near, and it will be horrible. He hesitates a second. He seems to stumble. Is he going to fall? No. Swiftly he has planted his spear, handle in the ground, sharp point at an angle, toward the rapidly approaching gorilla. It's hidden in the vegetation.

The dwarf is running again, but slower now. And he is shouting. Is he crazy to waste his last energies when he knows that no help could reach him in time? He isn't. He is trying to madden even more his pursuer, instead.

In this he certainly succeeds. Blind with rage, the ape forgets all prudence. His burning eyes on the little, helpless figure ahead, he rushes forward as fast as he can. He stretches his long, hairy arms quicker to reach the sure prey—and he lets out a scream of agony. His huge belly has come in contact with the unnoticed spear. His momentum has impaled him. The poison spread on the stone point works instantly.

The dwarf, panting, halts. In a few minutes many shadows will materialize out of the shadows which surround him. He knows that all his tribe is already running toward him. Together they will share with him the meat of the gorilla, to the pygmies the most coveted of all foods.

Meanwhile the dwarf feels a vague need to celebrate his escape, his victory. He picks two red flowers of the mukho tree. And, in the absence of a lapel, rakishly he sticks them one on each side, through the hole across the cartilage of his nose!

VOLCANO IN HIS CORNFIELD!

CLYDE FISHER

You can imagine Dionisio Pulido's [1] amazement. A simple Indian farmer, he was plowing his cornfield, down there in Mexico, as he had done every year for most of a lifetime. And suddenly, out in the middle of the field, a column of smoke began to rise right out of the earth.

Dionisio ran over, and saw that the smoke was coming out of a little hole. He dropped a stone on the hole, but the smoke pushed right out around it. He hurried in alarm to his wife, and together they legged it to the village to get the priest. By the time they got back with the wondering padre, the hole was thirty feet deep, and smoke was pouring out in dense clouds.

A volcano had been born—the first volcano in our lifetime known to have started from scratch. In a week it had built a cone 550 feet high; in ten weeks it was 1,100 feet high. A few months later, when I got there, it was more than 1,300 feet high. And it is still growing.

[1] DIONISIO PULIDO—Pronounced dē-ō-nē′sĭ-ō poŏ-lē′dō.

89

It was just about a year ago that the volcano, a-borning, drove Dionisio out of what used to be his cornfield. Since then scientists have had, for the first time, a chance to observe a volcano from its earliest stages on. Only a few from this country, however, have been able so far to make the pilgrimage. I traveled, with my brother, by plane, automobile and on horseback to find out what happens when a volcano pops up in somebody's back yard.

The volcano, called Parícutin,[2] is named after a near-by Indian village of the same name in the State of Michoacán,[3] about two hundred miles, as the crow flies, west of Mexico City. It is well over three hundred miles, however, by the winding automobile road, the last twenty miles of which are thickly covered with volcanic ash. If there ever was any road over the last three or four miles from San Juan de las Colchas [4] (Saint John of the Bedspreads), it has been completely obliterated. You go on by horseback, through ash more than foot deep.

[2] PARÍCUTIN—Pronounced pà-rē′kū-tīn.   [3] MICHOACÁN—Mē-chō-ä-kän′.
[4] SAN JUAN DE LAS COLCHAS—Pronounced săn hwän′ dê lä kôl′käs.

By the time you get to San Juan, you are acutely and depressingly aware of what an unpleasant neighbor a volcano is. Instead of the carefully-tilled fields of maize and the masses of wild flowers that you have been seeing along the way, the countryside has become increasingly a dead mass of gray ash. It covers everything, sifts in everywhere. In San Juan the schoolhouse and several other buildings have been crushed by the weight of the ash on their roofs. However, most of the dwelling houses still stand, thanks to unusually steep roofs. *The only livelihood left for the Indians is serving as guides or renting horses to sight-seers. The cornfields are ruined for hundreds of years, and even the trees are dead or dying.*

It isn't only the ever-sifting ash which gives you notice, miles away, that you are approaching the volcano; there is also the noise. I never realized what a noisy thing a volcano can be: it explodes violently every few seconds, as if a whole battery of artillery were confined in it. This, of course, is not true of all volcanoes. Some types just flow steadily and in comparative quiet, but Parícutin does its erupting in booming salvos.[5]

With every noisy explosion, large "bombs," or fragments of rock are thrown hundreds of feet into the air. Our first close view of the volcano was at night, when it is most spectacular; and these bombs glow with incandescence. The whole effect is like a gigantic fireworks display, with the light shining for hundreds of feet above the crater, and the heavy, incandescent material glowing eerily as it falls and rolls toward the base.

The only lava that we saw flowing during our visit was from a new baby crater that had broken out at the base of the main cone a month or so before. This flow was a mile long and some 1,200 feet wide. When we went close enough to take pictures of the lava flow, it was so hot that we had to keep the camera lens covered to prevent it from being damaged; then we would uncover it, snap a picture, and dash quickly away to avoid being broiled.

[5] SALVO (săl′vō)—A volley, or discharge as of a cannon.

Yet, contrary to popular belief, there is no actual fire in a volcano, and what looks like smoke is really a combination of cinders and dust. In the daytime, about all that you can see is the immense cloud of this smoke-that-isn't-smoke. The coarser cinders fall back on the cone, and the finer ash blows away to plague the countryside. Some of it has even been collected in Mexico City, two hundred miles away. In the vicinity of the volcano you breathe it continually; it gets into your hair; you feel it between your teeth. It so fills the sky that some of the brighter stars look distinctly green! And lightning frequently flashes in the column of volcanic ash, followed by short claps of thunder, when there isn't a cloud in the heavens.

An amazing and boisterous phenomenon, the volcano! I certainly hope one doesn't ever come to life in my back yard.

TRAVEL

ROBERT LOUIS STEVENSON

I SHOULD like to rise and go
Where the golden apples grow;—
Where below another sky
Parrot islands anchored lie,
5   And, watched by cockatoos and goats,
Lonely Crusoes building boats;—
Where in sunshine reaching out
Eastern cities, miles about,
Are with mosque and minaret
10   Among sandy gardens set,
And the rich goods from near and far
Hang for sale in the bazaar;—
Where the Great Wall round China goes,
And on one side the desert blows,

9. MOSQUE (mŏsk) AND MINARET (mĭn'a̐-rĕt)—A mosque is a Mohammedan place of worship. A minaret is a slender tower attached to a mosque.

15   And with bell and voice and drum,
Cities on the other hum;—
Where are forests, hot as fire,
Wide as England, tall as a spire,
Full of apes and cocoanuts
20   And the Negro hunters' huts;—
Where the knotty crocodile
Lies and blinks in the Nile,
And the red flamingo flies
Hunting fish before his eyes;—
25   Where in jungles, near and far,
Man-devouring tigers are,
Lying close and giving ear
Lest the hunt be drawing near
Or a comer-by be seen
30   Swinging in a palanquin;—
Where among the desert sands
Some deserted city stands,

30. PALANQUIN (păl-ȧn-kēn')—A conveyance borne on the shoulders of men by means of projecting poles.

All its children, sweep and prince
Grown to manhood ages since,
35 Not a foot in street or house,
Not a stir of child or mouse,
And when kindly falls the night
In all the town no spark of light.
There I'll come when I'm a man
40 With a camel caravan;
Light a fire in the gloom
Of some dusty dining-room;
See the pictures on the walls,
Heroes, fights and festivals;
45 And in a corner find the toys
Of the old Egyptian boys.

EDUCATION OF GAY-NECK

DHAN GOPAL MUKERJI

Calcutta, famed capital of India, boasts of more than a million people and of more than two million pigeons. One out of every three Hindu boys has at least a dozen pet pigeons, and Dhan Gopal Mukerji[1] was no exception. One of his favorite pets was the tumbler-carrier pigeon, Gay-Neck, so called because of the brilliant plumage of his throat.

THERE are two sweet sights in the bird world. One when the mother breaks open her egg in order to bring to light her child, and the other when she broods and feeds him. Gay-Neck was brooded most affectionately by both his parents. This brooding did for him what cuddling does for human children. It gives the helpless ones warmth and happiness. It is as necessary to them as food. This is the time when a pigeon hole should not be stuffed with too much cotton or flannel;

[1] DHAN GOPAL MUKERJI—Pronounced dän gō'pàl mōō-kēr'jĭ.

which should be put there more and more sparingly so that the temperature of the nest does not get too hot. Ignorant pigeon fanciers do not realize that as the baby grows larger he puts forth more and more heat from his own body. And I think it is wise not to clean the nest frequently during this time. Everything that the parents allow to remain in the nest contributes to making their baby comfortable and happy.

I remember distinctly how, from the second day of his birth, little Gay-Neck automatically opened his beak and expanded his carnation-colored body like a bellows every time one of his parents flew back to their nest. The father or the mother put their beaks into his wide-open maw and poured into it the milk made in their own organs from millet seeds that they had eaten. I noticed this; the food that was poured into his mouth was very soft. No pigeon ever gives any seeds to its baby even when it is nearly a month old without first keeping them in its throat for some time, which softens the food before it enters the delicate stomach of the baby.

Our Gay-Neck was a tremendous eater. He kept one of his parents busy getting food while the other brooded or stayed with him. I think the father bird brooded and worked for him no less hard than the mother. No wonder his body grew very fat. His carnation color changed into a yellowish white—the first sign of feathers coming on. Then that gave way to pricky white feathers, round and somewhat stiff like a porcupine needle. The yellow things that hung about his mouth and eyes fell away. Slowly the beak emerged, firm, sharp and long. What a powerful jaw! When he was about three weeks old an ant was crawling past him into the pigeon hole at whose entrance he was sitting. Without any instruction from anybody he struck it with his beak. Where there had been a whole ant, now lay its two halves. He brought his nose down to the dead ant and examined what he had done. There was no doubt that he had taken that black ant for a seed and killed an innocent passer-by who was friendly to his race. Let us hope he was

ashamed of it.   Anyway, he never killed another ant the rest
of his life.

By the time he was five weeks old he could hop out of his
birth-nest and take a drink from the pan of water left near the
pigeon holes.   Even now he had to be fed by his parents,
though every day he tried to get food on his own account.   He
would sit on my wrist and dig up a seed at a time from the palm
of my hand.   He juggled it two or three times in his throat like
a juggler throwing up balls in the air, and swallowed it.   Every
time Gay-Neck did that, he turned his head and looked into my
eyes as much as to say: "Am I not doing it well?   You must
tell my parents how clever I am when they come down from
sunning themselves on the roof."   All the same, he was the
slowest of my pigeons in developing his powers.

Just at this time I made a discovery.   I never knew before
how pigeons could fly in a dust storm without going blind.   But
as I watched the ever growing Gay-Neck I noticed one day that
a film was drawn over his eyes.   I thought he was losing his
sight.   In my consternation I put forth my hand to draw him
nearer to my face in order to examine him closely.   No sooner
had I made the gesture than he opened his golden eyes and receded into the rear of the hole.   But just the same I caught and
took him up on the roof, and in the burning sunlight of May I
scrutinized his eyelids.   Yes, there it was: he had, attached to
his eyelid, another thin lid delicate as tissue paper, and every
time I put his face toward the sun he drew that film over the
two orbits of gold.   And so I learned that it was a protective
film for the eye which enabled the bird to fly in a dust storm
or straight toward the sun.

In another fortnight Gay-Neck was taught how to fly.   It
was not at all easy, bird though he was by birth.   A human
child may love the water, yet he has to make mistakes and
swallow water while learning the art of swimming.   Similarly
with my pigeon.   He had a mild distrust of opening his wings,
and for hours he sat on our roof, where the winds of the sky

blew without quickening him to flight. In order to make the situation clear, let me describe our roof to you. It was railed with a solid concrete wall as high as a boy of fourteen. That prevented even a sleepwalker from slipping off the height of four stories on the summer nights, when most of us slept on the roof.

Gay-Neck I put on that concrete wall every day. There he sat for hours at a time facing the wind, but that was all. One day I put some peanuts on the roof and called him to hop down and get them. He looked at me with an inquiring eye for a few moments. Turning from me he looked down again at the peanuts. He repeated this process several times. When at last he was convinced that I was not going to bring these delicious morsels up for him to eat, he began to walk up and down the railing craning his neck occasionally towards the peanuts about three feet below. At last after fifteen minutes of heartbreaking hesitancy he hopped down. Just as his feet struck the floor his wings, hitherto unopened, suddenly spread themselves out full sail as he balanced himself over the nuts. What a triumph!

About this time I noticed the change of colors on his feathers. Instead of a nondescript gray-blue, a glossy aquamarine glowed all over him. And suddenly one morning in the sunlight his throat glistened like iridescent beads.

Now came the supreme question of flight. I waited for his parents to teach him the first lessons, though I helped the only way I could. Every day for a few minutes I made him perch on my wrist, then I would swing my arm up and down many times, and in order to balance himself on such a difficult perch he had to shut and open his wings frequently. That was good for him, but there ended my part of the teaching. You may ask me the reason of my hurrying matters so. He was already behind in his flying lessons, and in June, the rains begin to fall in India; and with the approach of the rainy season any long flight becomes impossible. I wished to train him in learning his directions as soon as I could.

However, one day long before the end of May, his father undertook the task. This particular day a brisk north wind, that had been sweeping about and cooling the atmosphere of the city, had just died down. The sky was clear as a limpid sapphire. The spaces were so clear that you could see the housetops of our town, then the fields and arbors of the country in the farthest distance. About three o'clock in the afternoon Gay-Neck was sunning himself on the concrete wall of the roof.

His father, who had been flying about in the air, came down and perched next to him. He looked at his son with a queer glance, as much as to say: "Here, lazybones, you are nearly three months old, yet you do not dare to fly. Are you a pigeon or an earthworm?" But Gay-Neck, the soul of dignity, made no answer. That exasperated his father who began to coo and boom at him in pigeon language. In order to get away from that volubility Gay-Neck moved, but his father followed cooing, booming, and banging his wings. Gay-Neck went on re-moving himself farther and farther, and the old fellow, instead of relenting, redoubled his talk and pursued. At last the father pushed him so close to the edge that Gay-Neck had only one alternative, that is, to slip off the roof. Suddenly his father thrust upon his young body all the weight of his old frame. Gay-Neck slipped. Hardly had he fallen half a foot when he opened his wings and flew. Oh, what an exhilarating moment for all concerned! His mother, who was downstairs dipping herself in the water and performing her afternoon toilet, came up through the staircase and flew to keep her son company. They circled above the roof for at least ten minutes before they came down to perch. When they reached the roof the mother folded her wings as a matter of course and sat still. Not so the son: he was in a panic, like a boy walking into cold and deep water. His whole body shook, and his feet trod the roof gingerly as he alighted, skating over it furiously and flapping his wings in order to balance himself. At last he stopped, as his chest struck the side of the wall, and he folded his wings as swiftly as we shut a fan. Gay-Neck was panting with ex-citement, while his mother rubbed him and placed her chest against him as if he were a mere baby who badly needed brood-ing. Seeing that his task had been done successfully, Gay-Neck's father went down to take his bath.

Now that, like a newly trained diver, he had overcome his fear of plunging into the air, Gay-Neck ventured on longer and higher flights. In a week's time he was able to fly steadily for half an hour, and when he came home to the roof, he swooped down as gracefully as his parents. There was no more of that panicky beating of wings in order to balance himself as his feet touched the roof.

His parents, who had accompanied Gay-Neck in his prelimi-nary flights, now began to leave him behind, and to fly much higher above him. For a while I thought that they were trying to make him fly still higher; for the son always made an effort to reach the level of his parents. Perhaps his elders were setting the little fellow a superb example. But at last one day early in June, that explanation of mine was shaken by the following fateful incident. Gay-Neck was flying high: he looked half his usual size. Above him flew his parents almost as small as a man's fist. They were circling above him with the regularity of a merry-go-round. It looked monotonous and meaningless. I removed my gaze from them; after all it is not comfortable to look upward steadily for long. As I lowered my eyes toward the horizon they were held by a black spot moving swiftly and growing larger every second. I wondered what sort of a bird he was coming at such a speed in a straight line, for in India birds are named in the Sanskrit,[1] Turyak, or "curvetracers."

But this one was coming straight, like an arrow. In another two minutes my doubts were dispelled. It was a hawk making for little Gay-Neck. I looked up and beheld a miraculous sight. His father was tumbling steadily down in order to reach his level, while his mother, bent on the same purpose, was making swift downward curves. Ere the terrible hawk had come within ten yards of the innocent little fellow, both his flanks were covered. Now the three flew downwards at a right angle from the path of their enemy. Undeterred by such a move, the hawk charged. At once the three pigeons made a dip which frustrated him, but the force with which he had made the attack was so great that it carried him a long distance beyond them. The pigeons kept on circling in the air with an ever-increasing downward trend. In another minute they were halfway to our roof. Now the hawk changed his mind. He went higher and higher into the sky: in fact he flew so high that the pigeons could not hear the wind whistling in the feathers of his wings; and as he was above them they could not see their foe. Feeling that they were safe, they relaxed. It was evident that

---

[1] SANSKRIT—The ancient language of India.

they were not flying as fast as before. Just then I saw that above them, way up, the hawk was folding his wings: he was about to drop and in an instant he fell upon them like a stone. In desperation I put my fingers in my mouth and made a shrill whistle, a cry of warning. The pigeons dived like a falling sword, yet the hawk followed. Inch by inch, moment by moment he was gaining on them. Faster and faster he fell: now there was scarcely twenty feet between him and his prey. There was no doubt that he was aiming at Gay-Neck. I could see his sinister claws. "Won't those stupid pigeons do anything to save themselves?" I thought in an agony. He was so near him now—if they would only keep their heads and—just then they made a vast upward circle. The hawk followed. Then they flew on an even but large elliptical path. If a bird flies in a circle he either tends to swing to the center of that circle or away from it. Now the hawk missed their intention and tended toward the center, making a small circle inside their big one. No sooner was his back turned to them than the three pigeons made another dive, almost to our roof, but the sinister one was not to be deterred. He followed like a tongue of black lightning. His prey made a curving dive on to the roof, where they were safe at last under my widespread arms! That instant I heard the shriek of the wind in the air; about a foot above my head flew by the hawk, his eyes blazing with yellow fire and his claws quivering like the tongue of a viper. As he passed I could hear the wind still whistling in his feathers.

After that narrow escape of my pet birds, I began to train Gay-Neck to a sense of direction. One day I took all three birds in a cage towards the east of our town. Exactly at nine in the morning I set them free. They came home safely. The next day I took them an equal distance to the west. Inside of a week they knew the way to our house from within a radius of at least fifteen miles in any direction.

Since nothing ends smoothly in this world, the training of Gay-Neck finally met with a check. I had taken him and his parents down the Ganges in a boat. When we started it was about six in the morning. The sky was littered with stray clouds, and a moderate wind was blowing from the south. Our boat was piled high with rice white as snow on whose top were heaped mangoes red and golden in color, like a white peak afire with the sunset.

I should have foreseen that such auspicious weather might turn suddenly into a terrible storm, for after all, boy though I was, I knew something about the freaks of the monsoon [2] in June.

Hardly had we gone twenty miles before the first rain-clouds of the season raced across the sky. The velocity of the wind was so great that it ripped off one of the sails of our boat. Seeing that there was no time to be lost, I opened the cage and released the three pigeons. As they struck the wind they vaulted right over and flew very low, almost falling into the water. They flew thus close to the surface of the river for a quarter of an hour, making very little headway against the hard wind. But they persisted and another ten minutes saw them safely tacking and flying landward. Just about the time they had reached the string of villages on our left, the sky grew pitch black, a torrential cloudburst blotted everything out, and we saw nothing but inky sheets of water through which the lightning zig-zagged and danced the dance of death. I gave up all hope of finding my pigeons again. We were almost ship-wrecked ourselves, but fortunately our boat was beached on the shore of a village. Next morning when I came home by train I found two wet pigeons instead of three. Gay-Neck's father had perished in the storm. No doubt it was all my fault, and for the few days that followed our house was given up to mourning. The two pigeons and I used to go up on the roof whenever the rain left off a bit in order to scan the sky for a glimpse of the father. Alas, he never returned.

[2] MONSOON—A wind from the Indian Ocean.

GRAINS OF WHEAT

Dale Nichols

DALE NICHOLS

American School

Born in 1904 on a farm five miles west of David City, Nebraska, Dale Nichols found inspiration for his paintings within hand's reach. He is especially fond of winter landscapes and painted his first canvas, "The Sanley Farm" in the winter of 1933. Setting up his easel in an abandoned cornfield, he painted even when the temperature went down to six degrees below zero.

Many of Nichols' pictures are also of summer scenes, like "Grains of Wheat." His landscapes are strong in line and form and give one a feeling of serenity and contentment. He says, "I paint barns and rural life, not because it may have been or is the vogue, but because my twenty years as a farmer provide me with an essential and intimate knowledge of my subject matter. . . . I strive to make others feel the ever constant urge within man to lift himself higher and onward."

On a recent visit to Alaska, Nichols was struck by the utterly different beauty of Alaskan landscapes with their mighty snow-capped mountains, glaciers, and forests. He called Alaska "a land like paradise, a country magnificently beautiful." Many of his paintings, the Alaskan scenes in particular, are characterized by the use of a brilliant light blue color.

"Grains of Wheat" is in a collection of contemporary art of the Western Hemisphere, owned by the International Business Machines Corporation of New York City.

FREEDOM AGAIN AT LAST

ERIC KNIGHT

It was said that Sam Carraclough [1] owned the finest dog in Greenall Bridge, a pleasant Yorkshire village in northern England. There were many splendid dogs in that village, but none possessed the intelligence, beauty, or aristocratic bearing of Sam's Lassie. Sam had sworn that he would never sell her—but the day came when Sam, like so many of the colliers in the village, was forced to "eat his pride that his family might eat bread." He sold Lassie to the Duke of Rudling who had long wished to buy her. No longer did Sam's young son, Joe, find her waiting every afternoon at the school-yard gate. Then one day she was there again. Three times she escaped from the Duke's trainer, Hynes, and made her way back to the boy. Each time Sam returned her to her new owner, and in desperation the Duke ordered her taken to his estate in the Scottish Highlands, a "long, long road" from the village of Greenall Bridge.

IT WAS Lassie's time sense that did it—that curious sense in an animal which tells it exactly what time of the day it is.

For had it been any other part of the day, Lassie might have followed her lifetime training to obey a spoken order and returned to Hynes as he bid her. But she did not.

It had been while on one of the newly ordered walks, with Lassie going along obediently at Hynes's heel. The leash was about Lassie's neck, but she neither tugged ahead on it nor lingered behind so that it tugged at her. She was going as a well-trained dog should go, close at the left heel so that her head almost touched Hynes's knee.

Everything was orderly as could be wished—only that Hynes had not forgotten his resentment about being forced to take exercise himself so that Lassie could be kept in good fettle. He wanted to get back to his tea—and he still wanted to show Lassie "who was boss."

And so, quite needlessly, he suddenly tugged on the leash. "Come along wiv yer, will yer?" he snapped.

[1] CARRACLOUGH—Pronounced kăr'á-klŭf.

Lassie felt the sudden tug on her neck and hesitated. She was only slightly puzzled. She knew from long training that she was doing exactly what was expected of her. Obviously, though, this man expected something else. She wasn't sure what it was.

So in that moment of indecision, she slackened her pace. Almost gladly Hynes noted this. He turned and yanked at the leash.

"Come on, now. Come on when I tell yer," he shouted.

Lassie backed away from the threatening tone. Hynes yanked again. Lassie did what any dog will do: she braced herself for the tug and lowered her head.

Hynes tugged harder. The leash slipped up over Lassie's head.

She was free!

In the split second that Hynes saw that, he acted according to his nature—but not according to his own knowledge as a dog-man. He jumped to grab Lassie. It was exactly the wrong thing to do. For instinctively she jumped away to elude him.

Hynes's action had done only one thing. It had shown Lassie clearly that she wanted to keep away from him. Had he spoken to her in an ordinary manner, she might have come to him. In fact, if he had just ordered her to heel, she might have followed him back to the kennel held by nothing more than her trained habits of obedience to man.

Hynes was enough of a dog-man, however, to understand this—to see that he had made a bad mistake, that if he moved menacingly again, he might frighten the dog even more. So he began to do what he should have done in the first place.

"Here, Lassie. Come here," he said.

Lassie stood in indecision. One instinct told her to obey. But the memory of the sudden leap at her was too fresh.

Hynes saw that. He lifted his voice in a high, wheedling tone which he thought might be alluring.

"Nice Lassie. Nice dog," he chanted. "Nice dog—now stay there. Don't you move, now. Stay there."

He half knelt, and snapped his fingers to hold the dog's attention. Imperceptibly, inch by inch, he crept nearer.

"Stand still, now," Hynes ordered.

The lifetime of training that Sam Carraclough had given Lassie seemed to have its effect now. For even though Lassie disliked Hynes, she had been schooled that she must obey human beings who spoke the words of command to her.

But there was another lifetime impulse that stirred her— although only faintly. It was the time sense.

Dimly, mistily, it began to waken in her. She did not know it or reason it or think it clearly as a man would. It began to grow in her faintly. It was only a weak stirring.

It was time—time to—time to . . .

She watched Hynes creeping nearer. Her head lifted a trifle.

It was time—time to—time to go . . .

Hynes edged himself nearer. In another second he would be near enough to grab the dog—to sink his fingers into the wealth of heavy mane and hang on until he could slip the guardian leash over her head again.

Lassie watched him. The stirring was becoming plainer.

It was time—time to go for . . .

Hynes gathered himself. As if sensing it, Lassie moved. Quickly she backed away two paces from the crawling man. She wanted to be free.

"Drat you," Hynes exploded.

As if he realized this mistake, he began all over again.

"Nice Lassie, now. Stand still, there. Stand still. Stay there."

Lassie was not listening to him now, however. With only a small part of her senses she was watching the man edging nearer. All the rest of her was increasingly intent upon the stirring that was becoming clearer and clearer. She wanted time. She felt somehow that if this man reached her, she would be disappointed once more.

She stepped back again. And just at that moment Hynes leaped. Lassie dodged aside.

Angrily Hynes stood erect. He walked toward her, speaking soothing words. Lassie backed away. Always she kept the same distance between Hynes and herself—the distance an animal knows so well—the distance which places it beyond the sudden reach of an enemy.

Her instinct was saying:

"Keep away from him. Do not let him reach you. For there is something—something else. It is time—time to go— time to go for the . . ."

And then, suddenly, in that second, Lassie knew. She knew as surely and irrevocably as the hands of a clock that point to five minutes to four.

It was time to go for the boy!

She wheeled and began trotting away—trotting as if she had but to go a few hundred yards. There was nothing to tell her that the rendezvous she would keep was hundreds of miles and scores of days away. There was only the plain, unadorned knowledge of a duty to be done. And she was going to do it as best she could.

But now, behind her, she heard Hynes. He was running, shouting. She broke from her trot into a gentle lope. She was not afraid. It was as if she knew surely that this two-footed creature could never catch up with her. She didn't even need to put on speed. Her thrown-back ears told her how near Hynes was. Then, too, dogs, like most other animals, have their eyes set much more at the side of their heads than do human beings, and thus are able to see behind them with only the slightest turn of the head.

Lassie did not seem to worry about Hynes. She just kept on going in her steady lope, down the path, over the lawn.

For a second, Hynes's heart leaped with hope. Perhaps, he thought, Lassie would head back to the kennels.

But the kennels, where she had been chained and penned, were not a home for Lassie. They were a hated place. And Hynes's hope died as he saw the collie turn down the gravel path toward the front gate.

Hynes's heart gave a leap again. The gate was always closed, and the walls about the "home" part of the estate were tall, frowning granite ones. Perhaps he could corner her yet.

Priscilla and her grandfather rode up the road from the fishing village and halted by the iron gate to the estate.

"I'll open it, Grandfather," the girl said.

She slipped lightly from her saddle as the Duke began mumbling in protest. But Priscilla knew she could dismount and mount again much more easily than her grandfather. For despite all the protests, he was an old man, and climbing up into the saddle of even the quietest horse was a task accompanied by much fuming and puffing and groaning.

Linking the reins over her crooked arm, the girl drew back the bolt and, putting her weight against the wrought-iron structure, she swung it slowly back on its hinges.

It was only then that she heard the noise. Looking up the path, she saw Hynes. He was racing toward her. Before him was the beautiful collie. And Hynes was shouting:

"Close that gate, Miss Priscilla! Close that gate! That collie's loose. Don't let 'er get hout! Close the gate!"

Priscilla looked about her. Before her was the great gate. All she needed to do was swing it shut, and Lassie was trapped inside the home grounds.

She looked up at her grandfather. He was unaware of all the stir. His deaf ears had not caught the high shoutings of Hynes.

Priscilla began to pull the gate. For a second she swung her weight back on it. She half heard her grandfather beginning to roar in puzzled protest. But then she forgot that, and she saw only one picture in her mind.

It was the picture of a village boy just a little taller than herself, standing beside the meshed wire of a run, saying to his dog: "Bide here forever and leave us be—and don't never come home no more." And she knew then that while the boy was saying it, every sense and part of him was crying out to say just the opposite.

So she stood, seeing the picture in her mind, listening to the words again as if they were spoken plainly. And still she had not closed the gate.

Her grandfather was still fuming, knowing something was happening that his aged senses could not grasp. Hynes was still screaming:

"Close that gate, Miss Priscilla. Close it!"

Priscilla stood in the moment of indecision, and then quickly she began swinging the gate wide open. There was a blur that flashed past her knees and then Priscilla stood, looking down the road, watching the dog go steadily at a lope as if it knew it had a long, long way to go. So she lifted her hand.

"Good-by, Lassie," she said, softly. "Good-by and—good luck!"

On his horse sat the Duke, not looking down the road at the collie, but staring at his granddaughter.

"Well, drat my buttons," he breathed. "Drat my buttons."

THE WILD GOAT'S KID

LIAM O'FLAHERTY

HER nimble hoofs made music on the crags all winter, as she roamed along the cliff tops over the sea.

During the previous autumn, when goats were mating, she had wandered away, one of a small herd that trotted gaily after a handsome fellow, with a splendid gray-black hide and winding horns. It was her first mating. Then, with the end of au-

tumn, peasant boys came looking for their goats. The herd
was broken up. The gallant buck was captured and slain by
two hungry dogs from the village of Drumranny. The white
goat alone remained. She had wandered too far away from her
master's village. He couldn't find her. She was given up as
lost.

So she became a wild one of the cliffs, where the sea-
gulls and the cormorants [1] were lords, and the great eagle of
Moher [2] soared high over the thundering sea. Her big, soft,
yellow eyes became wild from looking down often at the sea,
with her long chin whiskers swaying gracefully in the wind.
She was a long, slender thing, with short, straight horns and
ringlets of matted hair trailing far down on either haunch.

With her tail in the air, snorting, tossing her horns, she fled
away when anybody approached her. Her hoofs would patter
over the crags until she was far away. Then she would stand
on some eminence [3] and turn about to survey the person who had
disturbed her, calmly, confident in the power of her slender
legs to carry her beyond pursuit.

She roamed at will. No stone fence however high could re-
sist her long leap, as she sprang on muscular thighs that bent
like silk. She was so supple that she could trot on the top of a
thin fence, carelessly, without a sound except the gentle tapping of her delicate hoofs. She hardly ever left the cliff tops.
There was plenty of food there, for the winter was mild, and
the leaves and grasses that grew between the crevices of the
crags were flavored by the strong, salt taste of the brine carried up on the wind. She grew sleek and comely.

Toward the end of winter a subtle change came over her.
Her hearing became more acute. She took fright at the least
sound. She began to shun the sea except on very calm days,
when it did not roar. She ate less. She grew very particular
about what she ate. She hunted around a long time before she

[1] CORMORANT (kôr′mô-rănt)—A greedy sea bird.
[2] MOHER—The cliffs of Moher on the coast of western Ireland.
[3] EMINENCE—High hill.

chose a morsel. She often went on her knees, reaching down to the bottom of a crevice to nibble at a briar that was inferior to the more accessible ones.

Winter passed. Green leaves began to sprout. Larks sang in the morning. There was sweetness in the air and a great urge of life. The white goat, one morning a little after dawn, gave birth to a gray-black kid.

The kid was born in a tiny, green glen under an overhanging ledge of low rock that sheltered it from the wind. It was a male kid, an exquisite, fragile thing, tinted delicately with many colors.

The white goat bleated over him, with soft eyes and shivering flanks, gloating over the exquisite thing that had been created. And she had this delicate creature all to herself, in the wild solitude of the beautiful little glen, within earshot of the murmuring sea, with the little birds whistling their spring songs around about her, and the winds coming with their slow whispers over the crags. The first tender hours of her first motherhood were undisturbed by any restraint, not even the restraint of a mate's presence. In absolute freedom and quiet, she watched with her young.

How she maneuvered to make him stand! She breathed on him to warm him. She raised him gently with her forehead, uttering strange, soft sounds to encourage him. Then he stood up, trembling, staggering, swaying on his curiously long legs. She became very excited, rushing around him, bleating nervously, afraid that he should fall again. He fell. She was in agony. Bitter wails came from her distended jaws and she crunched her teeth. But she renewed her efforts, urging the kid to rise, to rise and live . . . to live, live, live.

He rose again. Now he was steadier. He shook his head. He wagged his long ears as his mother breathed into them. He took a few staggering steps, came to his padded knees, and rose again immediately.

She stayed with him all day in the tiny glen, just nibbling a few mouthfuls of the short grass that grew around.   Most of the time she spent exercising her kid.   With a great show of anxiety and importance, she brought him on little expeditions across the glen to the opposite rock, three yards away and back again.   At first he staggered clumsily against her side, and his tiny hoofs often lost their balance on tufts of grass, such was his weakness.   But he gained strength with amazing speed, and the goat's joy and pride increased.   She suckled and caressed him after each tiny journey.

When the sun had set he was able to walk steadily, to take little short runs, to toss his head.   They lay all night beneath the shelter of the ledge, with the kid between his mother's legs, against her warm body.

Next morning she hid him securely in a crevice of the neighboring crag, in a small groove between two flags [4] that were covered with a withered growth of wild grass and ferns.   The kid crawled instinctively into the warm hole without any resistance to the gentle push of his mother's horns.   He lay down with his head toward his doubled hind legs, and closed his eyes.   Then the goat scraped the grass and fern stalks over the entrance hole with her forefeet, and she hurried away to graze, as carelessly as if she had no kid hidden.

All the morning, as she grazed hurriedly and fiercely around the crag, she took great pains to pretend that she was not aware of her kid's nearness.   Even when she grazed almost beside the hiding-place, she never noticed him, by look or by cry.   But still, she pricked her little ears at every distant sound.

At noon she took him out and gave him suck.   She played with him on a grassy knoll and watched him prance about.   She taught him how to rear on his hind legs and fight the air with his forehead.   Then she put him back into his hiding place and returned to graze.   She continued to graze until nightfall.

Just when she was about to fetch him from his hole and take him to the overhanging ledge to rest for the night, a startling

[4] FLAGS—Large flat stones.

sound reached her ears. It came from afar, from the south, from beyond a low fence that ran across the crag on the skyline. It was indistinct, barely audible, a deep, purring sound. But to the ears of the mother-goat, it was loud and ominous as a thunderclap. It was the heavy breathing of a dog sniffing the wind.

She listened stock-still, with her head in the air and her short tail lying stiff along her back, twitching one ear. The sound came again. It was nearer. Then there was a patter of feet. Then a clumsy, black figure hurtled over the fence and dropped on to the crag, with awkward secrecy. The goat saw a black dog, a large, curly fellow, standing by the fence in the dim twilight, with his forepaw raised and his long, red tongue hanging. Then he shut his mouth suddenly, and raising his snout upward sniffed several times, contracting his nostrils as he did so, as if in pain. Then he whined savagely, and trotted toward the goat sideways.

She snorted. It was a sharp, dull thud, like a blow from a rubber sledge. Then she rapped the crag three times with her left forefoot, loudly and sharply. The dog stood still and raised his forepaw again. He bent down his head and looked at her with narrowed eyes. Then he licked his breast and began to run swiftly to the left. He was running toward the kid's hiding place, with his tail stretched out straight and his snout to the wind.

With another fierce snort the goat charged him at full speed, in order to cut him off from his advance on the kid's hiding place. He stopped immediately when she charged. The goat halted, too, five yards from the hiding place, between the dog and the hiding place, facing the dog.

The dog stood still. His eyes wandered around in all directions, with the bashfulness of a sly brute, caught suddenly in an awkward position. Then slowly he raised his bloodshot eyes to the goat. He bared his fangs. His mane rose like a fan. His tail shot out. Picking his steps like a lazy cat, he approached her without a sound. The goat shivered along her left flank, and she snorted twice in rapid succession.

When he was within six yards of her he uttered a ferocious roar—a deep, rumbling sound in his throat. He raced toward her, and leaped clean into the air, as if she were a fence that he was trying to vault. She parried him subtly with her horns, like a swordthrust, without moving her forefeet. Her sharp horns just grazed him as he whizzed past her head. But the slight blow deflected his course. Instead of falling on his feet, as he had intended cunningly to do, between the goat and the kid, he was thrown to the left and fell on his side, with a thud. The goat whirled about and charged him.

But he had arisen immediately and jerked himself away, with his haunches low down, making a devilish scraping and yelping and growling noise. He wanted to terrify the kid out of his hiding place. Then it would be easy to overpower the goat, hampered by the task of hiding the kid between her legs.

The kid uttered a faint, querulous cry, but the goat immediately replied with a sharp, low cry. The kid mumbled something indistinct, and then remained silent. There was a brushing sound among the ferns that covered him. He was settling himself down farther. The goat trotted rigidly to the opposite side of the hiding place to face the dog again.

The dog had run away some distance, and lay licking his paws. Now he meant to settle himself down properly to the prolonged attack, after the failure of his first onslaught. He yawned lazily and made peculiar, mournful noises, thrusting his head into the air and twitching his snout. The goat watched every single movement and sound, with her ears thrust forward past her horns. Her great, soft eyes were very wild and timorous in spite of the valiant posture of her body, and the terrific force of the blows she delivered occasionally on the hard crag with her little hoofs.

The dog remained lying for half an hour or so, continuing his weird pantomime. The night fell completely. Everything became unreal and ghostly under the light of the distant myriads of stars. An infant moon had arisen. The sharp rushing wind and the thunder of the sea only made the silent loneliness of the night more menacing to the white goat, as she stood bravely on the limestone crag defending her newborn young. On all sides the horizon was a tumultuous line of barren crag, dented with shallow glens and seamed with low, stone fences that hung like tattered curtains against the rim of the sky.

Then the dog attacked again. Rising suddenly, he set off at a long, swinging gallop, with his head turned sideways toward the goat, whining as he ran. He ran around the goat in a wide circle, gradually increasing his speed. A white spot on his breast flashed and vanished as he rose and fell in the undulating stretches of his flight. The goat watched him, fiercely rigid from tail to snout. She pawed the crag methodically, turning around on her own ground slowly to face him.

When he passed his starting point, he was flying at full speed, a black ball shooting along the gloomy surface of the crag, with a sharp rattle of claws. The rattle of his claws, his whining and the sharp tapping of the goat's forefeet as she turned about, were the only sounds that rose into the night from this sinister engagement.

He sped round and round the goat, approaching her imperceptibly each round, until he was so close that she could see his glittering eyes and the white lather of rage on his half-open jaws. She became slightly dizzy and confused, turning about so methodically in a confined space, confused and amazed by the subtle strategy of the horrid beast. His whining grew louder and more savage. The rattle of his claws was like the clamor of hailstones driven by a wind. He was upon her.

He came in a whirl on her flank. He came with a savage roar that deafened her. She shivered and then stiffened in rigid silence to receive him. The kid uttered a shrill cry. Then the black bulk hurtled through the air, close up, with hot breathing, snarling, with reddened fangs and . . . smash.

117

He had dived for her left flank. But as he went past her head she turned like lightning and met him again with her horns. This time she grazed his side, to the rear of the shoulder. He yelped and tumbled sideways, rolling over twice. With a savage snort she was upon him. He was on his haunches, rising, when her horns thudded into his head. He went down again with another yelp. He rolled over and then suddenly, with amazing speed, swept to his feet, whirled about on swinging tail and dived for her flank once more. The goat uttered a shriek of terror. He had passed her horns. His fangs had embedded themselves in the matted ringlet that trailed along her right flank. The dog's flying weight, swinging on to the ringlet as he fell, brought her to her haunches.

But she was ferocious now. As she wriggled to her feet beside the rolling dog that gripped her flank, she wrenched herself around and gored him savagely. He yelled and loosed his hold. She rose on her hind legs in a flash, and with a snort she gored him again. Her sharp, pointed horns penetrated his side between the ribs. He gasped and shook his four feet in the air.

Then she pounded him with her forefeet, beating his prostrate body furiously. Her little hoofs pattered with tremendous speed for almost a minute, She beat him blindly, without looking at him.

Then she suddenly stopped. She snorted. The dog was still. He was dead. Her terror was passed. She lifted her right forefoot and shook it with a curious movement. Then she uttered a wild, joyous cry and ran toward her kid's hiding place.

Night passed with a glorious dawn that came over a rippling sea from the east. A wild, sweet dawn, scented with dew and the many perfumes of the germinating earth. The sleepy sun rose brooding from the sea, golden and soft, searching far horizons with its concave shafts of light. The dawn was still. Still and soft and pure.

The white goat and her kid were traveling eastward along the cliff tops over the sea. They had traveled all night, flying from the horrid carcass of the beast that lay stretched on the crag beside the little glen. Now they were far away, on the summit of the giant white Precipice of Cahir. The white goat rested to give suck to her kid, and to look out over the cliff top at the rising sun.

Then she continued her flight eastward, pushing her tired kid before her gently with her horns.

THE DOG OF MONTARGIS

ANDREW LANG

FOR three days, Aubrey de Montdidier [1] had not been seen by his friends and comrades in arms. On Sunday morning, he had attended mass in the Church of Our Lady, but it was noticed that in the afternoon he was absent from the great tournament which was held at Saint Katherine's.

[1] AUBREY DE MONTDIDIER—Pronounced ô-brā' dĕ môn-dēd'yĕ.

119

This astonished his friend, the young Sieur de Narsac,[2] who had appointed to meet him there, that they might watch together the encounter between a Burgundian [3] knight and a gentleman from Provence,[4] both renowned in tilting, who were to meet together for the first time that day in Paris.

It was unlike Aubrey to fail to be present on such an occasion; and when, for three successive days, he did not appear at his accustomed haunts, his friends grew anxious, and began to question among themselves whether some accident might not have befallen him.

Early on the morning of the fourth day, De Narsac was awakened by a continuous sound, as of something scratching against his door. Starting up to listen, he heard, in the intervals of the scratching, a low whine, as of a dog in pain. Thoroughly aroused, he got up and opened the door. Stretched before it, apparently too weak to stand, was a great gaunt greyhound, spent with exhaustion and hunger. His ribs stood out like the bars of a gridiron beneath his smooth coat; his tongue hung down between his jaws, parched and stiff; his eyes were bloodshot, and he trembled in every limb.

On seeing De Narsac, the poor creature struggled to his feet, feebly wagged his tail, and thrust his nose into the young man's hands. Then only did De Narsac recognize in the half-starved skeleton before him the favorite dog and constant companion of his friend, Aubrey de Montdidier.

It was clear from the poor animal's emaciated appearance that it was in the last stage of exhaustion. Summoning his servant, De Narsac ordered food and water to be brought at once; and the dog devoured the huge meal set before it.

From his starved appearance, and from the voracity with which he devoured the food set before him, it was evident that he had had nothing to eat for some days.

---

[2] SIEUR DE NARSAC (syûr dĕ när′säk)—Sieur is a shortened form of monsieur, meaning *Sir*.
[3] BURGUNDIAN—From the province of Burgundy, in southern France.
[4] PROVENCE (prŏ-väns′)—An old province in southeastern France.

No sooner was his hunger appeased, than he began to move uneasily about the room. Uttering low howls of distress from time to time, he approached the door; then, returning to De Narsac's side, he looked up in his face and gently tugged at his mantle, as if to attract attention. There was something at once so appealing and peculiar in the dog's behavior that De Narsac's curiosity was aroused, and he became convinced that there was some connection between the dog's starved appearance and strange manner and the unaccountable disappearance of his master. Perhaps the dog might supply the clue to Aubrey's place of concealment.

Watching the dog's behavior closely, De Narsac became aware that the dumb beast was inviting him to accompany him. Accordingly, he yielded to the dog's apparent wish, and, leaving the house, followed him out into the streets of Paris.

Looking round from time to time to see that De Narsac was coming after him, the greyhound pursued its way through the narrow, tortuous streets of the ancient city, over the Bridge, and out by the Porte St. Martin, into the open country outside the gates of the town. Then, continuing on its track, the dog headed for the Forest of Bondy, a place of evil fame in those far-off days, as its solitudes were known to be infested by bands of robbers.

Stopping suddenly in a deep and densely wooded glade of the wood, the dog uttered a succession of low, angry growls; then, tugging at De Narsac's mantle, it led him to some freshly turned-up earth, beneath a widespreading oak tree. With a piteous whine, the dog stretched himself on the spot, and could not be induced by De Narsac to follow him back to Paris, where he straightway betook himself, as he at once suspected foul play.

A few hours later, a party of men, guided to the spot by the young Sieur de Narsac, removed the earth and dead leaves and ferns from the hole into which they had been hastily flung, and discovered the murdered body of Aubrey de Montdidier. Hur-

riedly a litter was constructed of boughs of trees, and, followed
by the dog, the body was borne into Paris, where it was soon
afterwards buried.

From that hour, the greyhound attached himself to the Sieur
de Narsac. It slept in his room, ate from his table, and followed close at his heels when he went out of doors.

One morning, as the two were threading their way through
the crowded Rue St. Martin, De Narsac was startled by hearing a low, fierce growl from the greyhound. Looking down, he
saw that the creature was shaking in every limb; his smooth
coat was bristling, his tail was straight and stiff, and he was
showing his teeth. In another moment, he had made a dart

from De Narsac's side, and had sprung on a young gentleman
named Macaire,[5] in the uniform of the king's bodyguard, who,
with several comrades in arms was sauntering along the opposite side of the street. There was something so sudden in the
attack that the Chevalier [6] Macaire was almost thrown on the

[5] MACAIRE—Pronounced mȧ-kär′.
[6] CHEVALIER (shĕv-à-lēr′)—Knight, cavalier.

ground. With their walking-canes, he and his friends beat off the dog; and on De Narsac coming up, it was called away, and, still trembling and growling, followed its master down the street.

A few days later, the same thing occurred. De Narsac and the Chevalier Macaire chanced to encounter each other walking in the royal park. In a moment the dog had rushed at Macaire, and, with a fierce spring at his throat had tried to pull him to the ground. De Narsac and some officers of the king's bodyguard came to Macaire's assistance, and the dog was called off.

The rumor of the attack reached the ears of the king, and mixed with the rumor were whisperings of a long-standing quarrel between Macaire and Aubrey de Montdidier. Might not the dog's strange and unaccountable hatred for the young officer be a clue to the mysterious murder of his late master?

Determined to sift the matter to the bottom, the king summoned De Narsac and the dog to his presence at the Hotel St. Pol. Following close on his master's heels, the greyhound entered the audience-room, where the king was seated, surrounded by his courtiers. As De Narsac bowed low before his sovereign, a short fierce bark was heard from the dog; and, before he could be held back, he had darted in among the startled courtiers, and had sprung at the throat of the Chevalier Macaire, who, with several other knights, formed a little group behind the king's chair.

It was impossible longer to doubt that there was some ground for the surmises that had rapidly grown to suspicion, and that had received sudden confirmation from the fresh evidence of the dog's hatred.

The king decided that there should be trial by the judgment of God, and that a combat should take place between man, the accused, and dog, the accuser. The place chosen for the combat was a waste, uninhabited plot of ground, frequently selected as a duelling-ground by the young gallants of Paris.

In the presence of the king and his courtiers, the strange unnatural combat took place that afternoon. The knight was armed with a short thick stick; the dog was provided with an empty barrel, as a retreating ground from the attacks of his adversary.

At a given signal, the combatants entered the lists. The dog seemed quite to understand the strange duel on which it was engaged. Barking savagely, and darting round his opponent, he made attempts to leap at his throat; now on this side, now on that he sprang, jumping into the air, and then bounding back out of reach of the stick. There was such swiftness and determination about his movements, and something so unnatural in the combat, that Macaire's nerve failed him. His blows beat the air, without hitting the dog; his breath came in quick short gasps; there was a look of terror on his face; and for a moment, overcome by the horror of the situation, his eye quailed and sought the ground.

At that instant, the dog sprang at his throat, and pinned him to the earth. In his terror, he called out, and acknowledged his crime, and implored the king's mercy. But the judgment of God had decided. The dog was called off before it had strangled its victim, but the man was hurried away to the place of execution, and atoned that evening for the murder of the faithful greyhound's master.

The dog has been known to posterity as the Dog of Montargis [7] as in the Castle of Montargis there stood for many centuries a sculptured stone mantelpiece, on which the combat was carved.

[7] MONTARGIS—Pronounced môn-tàr-zhē'.

THE GOOD JOAN

LIZETTE WOODWORTH REESE

U   Along the thousand roads of France,
Now there, now here, swift as a glance,
A cloud, a mist blown down the sky,
Good Joan of Arc goes riding by.

1G 5 In Domremy at candlelight,
The orchards blowing rose and white
About the shadowy houses lie;
U   *And Joan of Arc goes riding by.*

1B   On Avignon there falls a hush,
  10 Brief as the singing of a thrush
Across old gardens April-high;
U   *And Joan of Arc goes riding by.*

G   The women bring the apples in,
Round Arles when the long gusts begin,
  15 Then sit them down to sob and cry;
U   *And Joan of Arc goes riding by.*

B   Who saith that ancient France shall fail,
A rotting leaf driv'n down the gale?
Then her sons know not how to die;
  20 Then good God dwells no more on high!

5. DOMREMY (dôn-rĕ-mē′)—The birthplace of Joan of Arc.
9. AVIGNON (ä-vē-nyôn′)—A city in France, once the home of the popes.
14. ARLES (ärl)—Another city in France of significance in the life of Joan of Arc.

U   Tours, Arles, and Domremy reply!
For Joan of Arc goes riding by.

SPANISH JOHNNY

WILLA CATHER

The old West, the old time,
   The old wind singing through
The red, red grass a thousand miles—
   And, Spanish Johnny, you!
5 He'd sit beside the water ditch
   When all his herd was in,
And never mind a child, but sing
   To his mandolin.

The big stars, the blue night,
10   The moon-enchanted lane;
The olive man who never spoke,
   But sang the songs of Spain.
His speech with men was wicked talk—
   To hear it was a sin;
15 But those were golden things he said
   To his mandolin.

The gold songs, the gold stars,
   The world so golden then;
And the hand so tender to a child—
20   Had killed so many men.
He died a hard death long ago
   Before the Road came in—
The night before he swung, he sang
   To his mandolin.

126

THE FUNERAL

Antonio Bellolio

ANTONIO BELLOLIO

South American School

One of the foremost Latin-American painters today is Antonio Bellolio, a native of Guayaquil, Ecuador. While still a child in primary school he was sent by the municipality of Guayaquil to the Quito School of Fine Arts and showed such promise that the government of Ecuador sent him to France and Italy to develop his powers. After ten years of intense study he returned to Ecuador and became a professor of painting at the School of Fine Arts, Guayaquil. Many of the pictures painted during his years in Europe have been purchased by the Ecuadorian Government for the National Museum.

Bellolio's paintings of Ecuadorian Indian customs have won great praise in Venezuela, Chile, and Argentina. The Caracas newspapers in particular commended his work. Besides his artistic talent, Bellolio has a flair for writing and for several years was the art editor of the Elite *magazine and an honorary member of the Club Caracas.*

Bellolio's work has a remarkably individual quality which is chiefly due to the unique coloring of his scenes. His portraits also have been highly acclaimed.

"The Funeral," which is typical of his work, is in a collection of contemporary art of the Western Hemisphere owned by the International Business Machines Corporation, New York City.

NUVAT THE BRAVE

RADKO DOONE

It is said that an Eskimo, though he may be frightened by spirits or things invisible, never fears what he can see and fight. It was not so with Nuvat, for Nuvat had once been frightened by a polar bear. In the eyes of the villagers Nuvat was a coward—he who was the son of Yekut, the greatest bear-hunter of the tribe. In all the village he had only two friends—Wanga, the small quiet child whom Yekut had rescued when her family had been attacked by wolves, and Kakk, his great black dog. Because of Wanga's belief in him a great resolve slowly took hold of Nuvat. He would prove himself worthy of her confidence. And suddenly the opportunity came. Towards the close of winter, Arctic storms swept the land. Food supplies were low, but men and dogs could not venture forth to hunt. For ten days the storms raged. Then, in a lull between storms and while the men were debating on the safety of the hunting trip, Nuvat set out alone to secure food for his family and friends.

Nuvat [1] found the going to the sealing grounds even more difficult than he had expected. It was the beginning of March. The continuous polar night was over and short days had begun; but it was still intensely cold. The ice was almost impassable in places; hard as steel, it still had been carved and cut by the wind-driven snow of the last few days into saw-like edges. The hungry dogs were almost exhausted by the time they reached the smooth floes.

Nuvat stopped them in a slightly sheltered spot behind some broken ice, turned the light sled on runners of whalebone upside down, and anchored it by driving the deerhorns strapped to the back, deep into the hard snow. The dogs rubbed their muzzles this way and that on the snow to brush off the frost which had collected about their mouths from their breathing; then lay down with their backs to the wind, and curled their noses into their bushy tails for warmth. If they had not rubbed off the frost from their faces, it would have melted

---

[1] NUVAT—Pronounced noo'vät.

while they rested, and later have frozen to ice about their muzzles, clamping their jaws shut and even stopping their breathing.

Kakk did not lie down with the rest. As if he knew just what his master was about, he began to run ahead over the ice, with a whine of excitement, sniffing long and carefully at every rounded hump of snow. Nuvat realized he had been well-trained as a seal dog by his first master, whoever he might have been. Walking along behind him, Nuvat searched, too, seeking the little rounded saucer-like depression in the snow mound which would mean a seal's breathing hole was beneath.

A seal is a warm-blooded animal which cannot breathe under water; every little while he has to come up for air. That is all very well during the summer when the sea is free, or even during the autumn and early winter when the ice is freezing—for until it is more than four inches thick the seal can butt his head up through the soft "mush ice" anywhere. But when the sea really begins to freeze over, and the ice thickens to one—two— five—and even seven feet or more, it is a different matter: The seal, locked under those endless miles of ice, would smother if he did not keep breathing holes open to which he can come every so often for long, deep breaths of air.

It takes unending vigilance on the part of the seal to keep his holes open. He must come every day while the ice is freezing, and gnaw away the new ice, as a rat would gnaw up through a broad, flat board. By the middle of winter he has made a long, cigar-shaped tunnel large enough for his body to come up through the ice to each breathing hole. This is not so difficult after the snow covers it over, for under the blanket of snow the ice does not skim over quite so fast—and besides, snow covers the hole from sight of the seal's enemies, the polar bear, the polar fox, and men. And the air filters down through the coarse snow quite freely, so the seal has no difficulty in breathing beneath it.

Nuvat had not gone more than two hundred yards, when Kakk began to whine, and dig at a little mound of snow.

Nuvat hurried to him, and with a few low words sent him back to join the other dogs. He went unwillingly, stopping now and then to turn around and look back; but Nuvat knew he would obey, and paid no more attention to him.

With his foot, Nuvat pressed the snow down in the center of the mound. Then he drew out of his fur shirt a long sliver of walrus ivory like a very slender knitting needle, with a flat circle of ivory on one end. With the help of his spear he pushed this all the way down through the snow so that the flat ivory circle was a little way under the water in the air hole. Then, gripping his big sealing spear, he lay down beside the hole and waited, not moving. How long he might have to wait, he did not know. A seal always has several breathing holes and sometimes it is hours before it comes back to each one.

Nuvat felt very confident as he waited. He was sure he would not miss this time. It seemed so easy out here by himself, with no one to laugh at him if he failed. He did not believe he would ever fail again.

Out over the sea the mists were high and the air clear and gray. Nuvat saw that the horizon far to the north had a black tint.

"The sea is already clear of ice up there," he thought to himself. "The wind is setting in from the south, and if the storm breaks loose any of those great ice pans along the shore, it will drive them out into open water and make hunting dangerous for days to come."

He knew that a dark stripe on the horizon always means uncovered water in the Arctic winter. The leaden sky, without any light of its own, reflects slightly the whiteness of the endless snowy pall stretching over the frozen sea; and therefore, though it is still dark, it gives forth a sort of pale, weak glimmer. But if strong winds break the ice anywhere, or the tide of the ocean currents pushes it apart, then above this dark surface of uncovered water the sky darkens and is seen at a distance as a black stripe on the horizon.

Nuvat lay motionless for a long time by the seal hole. He began to feel drowsy from the cold, but he knew that he must not sleep. He thought of crawling back to the sled for the heavy sealskin strap to bind about his legs, as hunters do when they have to wait so long, to keep their freezing limbs from shivering and making little scratching sounds on the ice which would frighten away the seal.

Suddenly the slender needle of ivory in the hole began to quiver. The seal was coming into the ice-hole, disturbing the water ahead of him. Nuvat instantly raised himself on one elbow and then to his knees, lifted his spear and watched the indicator intently.   After a moment the ivory needle slowly tilted to one side and sank down, as the seal's nose touched the circle in the water and pushed it aside—which meant that his nose was right at the breathing hole. Nuvat drew back his arm and hurled the spear with all his strength straight down through the snow beside the indicator, into the creature's neck. The seal dived; but the double-barbed spear point of walrus ivory was arranged to slip loose from the wooden shaft, and the long sealskin strap attached to it did not let the wounded animal escape.

Holding the strap firmly in one hand, Nuvat instantly reversed the spear shaft with the other and began to break away the skimming of new ice with the ivory-tipped butt, enlarging the hole so he could drag the seal out. Drawing in the strap foot by foot, he at last pulled the seal up on the ice and despatched it with a heavy blow. Then he brought the sled over, loaded on the seal, and walking beside it, started the long, painful journey back to the village.

There was no time to try to kill a second seal before the storm returned. Already the wind was whistling among the ice hummocks—the Storm Spirits shrieking at him. The *angokoks* had said it would not wait long, and Nuvat knew that when it struck, everything would be blotted out, and he would have to trust the dogs to find the village. Of course the one seal was not enough for any great feast; but at least no one would be hungry in the village tonight.

Nuvat was so excited over his success, he shouted aloud and laughed as he urged the dogs along. How Wanga's eyes would sparkle when she saw him coming! All the women of the village would run out to meet his sled and help to pull it in. And father Yekut would hold up his head now, when his son's name was spoken.

Nuvat pushed at the sled and pulled with the dogs in his hurry, struggling over the highest ice ridge which lay between them and the mainland. At the top he stopped a moment to rest, looked out toward the village—and gave a gasp of horror! Between himself and the mainland a long crack had opened and was widening every moment. What he feared for the hunters had come to pass already—the ice pan on which he stood had been broken loose by the storm!

With a wild shout Nuvat brought the dogs to their feet and started racing along the edge of the ice toward the north. It seemed to him the crack looked narrower up there where it disappeared—perhaps the pan was not broken completely loose from the shore ice yet. Perhaps he still had a chance to escape!

He wrenched at the sled with the dogs, dragging it this way and that, sometimes tilted half over on the rough ice. His thoughts were full of terrible tales of hunters lost on the ice and never seen again. The dogs did not understand what was wrong, but they felt Nuvat's terror and threw themselves against the traces, pulling with all their strength.

When he was so exhausted he could hardly stagger, Nuvat left the sled a moment and clambered up to the top of an ice-hill. He looked out eagerly—then flung out his arms and gave a despairing cry. All about him, north and south, he could see the dark frost-smoke of open water. The channel between him and the mainland had widened till the huts of the village looked like small snow hummocks.

He was lost!

For a moment Nuvat stood silent in the face of this terrifying situation, watching the black channel widen between himself and the shore. Then, as he realized he was drifting farther from home every minute, he began to shout at the evil spirits who he thought had done him this harm.

"I am not Nuvat!" he cried at them. "I am not a man—your eyes have deceived you, O Evil Ones! I am only a worthless brown stone lying on the snow. I am only a piece of driftwood. Sedna [2] does not want me in her igloo under the sea. She could not make of me even the handle of a knife! Nuvat is not here on the ice pan—do you hear me, O Evil Ones? I am far away on the land, beyond the ice hills!" This he shouted to deceive them, so that those who wanted to destroy him would look for him somewhere else, and he could escape. He beat upon his chest in his terror—and his hand felt the amulet [3] Wanga had given him.

And then suddenly Nuvat was terribly ashamed of being

[2] SEDNA—An Eskimo deity, or spirit.   [3] AMULET—Charm.

afraid. He stood still for a moment remembering how little Wanga had thought he was braver than all the rest! He threw back his head and looked out at the sea: "I have lied to you!" he shouted loudly. "It is I, Nuvat, who stands here on the ice pan. But I am not afraid of you, O Evil Ones! My *tongak* will show me the way out of this danger!"

The Eskimos are a very primitive people and have no religion such as we have, with one great and good God who rules all. They believe in many spirits or Unseen Ones, everywhere —some good, and some bad. Thus every Eskimo has a *tongak,* or spirit-protector, who takes charge of him when he is born and helps him in all the dangers and difficult places of his life, if the man acts rightly and deserves his help. Holding the amulet in his hand, Nuvat sang a prayer to his *tongak* ". . . It is to do good that I have come out on the ice . . . to find meat . . . the meat is needed in the village. O show me the way back over the wide path of waters," he begged.

While he sang, the ice pan drifted farther and farther away; the mainland was growing faint and distant. As the ice met the force of the ocean waves, great pieces began to break off its edges and drift away by themselves. Nuvat realized that it was dangerous near the edge, and hastily urged his dogs back toward the center of the ice pan. With a long sealskin thong he harnessed Kakk in front of the spotted leader of his father's team so that he could help pull, and adding his own strength to help lift the heavy sled over rough ice blocks, he managed to reach an ice hill a half-mile or so back from the edge.

The wind had risen to a gale that held him up when he leaned against it, and it was growing stronger every minute. But near the top of the ice hill, Nuvat found a sort of cave sheltered on three sides by piled-up ice blocks. There, protected from the storm, he unharnessed the dogs and tried to make himself as comfortable as he could.

He cut strips of meat from the seal and fed the dogs, and took a strip himself, eating it raw as they did. This did not interfere with his appetite. Often at home when he had a fire, he ate some of his meat raw. As a matter of fact, Eskimos prefer uncooked meat when there is heavy work ahead, because a small amount of raw meat gives more strength and nourishment than the same amount cooked. That, too, is why Eskimos never suffer from scurvy, that scourge of the early explorers. Cooked food they usually eat only at the end of the day, when they have a long night of rest ahead of them.

By the time the meal was finished, the short day had ended and the pale grayness had merged into black night, filled with the shrieking of the Storm Spirits. The ice island drifted faster and faster; the coast of the land was out of sight long ago. The dogs, satisfied with their bite of food, curled their noses into their tails and went to sleep. All but Kakk, who came and lay down between Nuvat's feet, watching him with wide, anxious eyes. Kakk knew something was wrong. It was not because they were out on the ice—he had often camped out with the hunters at night,—but he felt the trouble of his master.

At last Nuvat decided that he could do nothing by thinking and worrying. He must wait and see what would happen. So he unlashed the fur sleeping bag from the sled and crawled into it, with Kakk curled up close against his side. He was so tired that he was asleep almost before he had pulled the flap over his head. Hours later he woke, and heard the storm still raging. He could feel the tremor of the ice pan as it drove through the sea before the wind. It seemed to him the shrieking of the wind was not quite so violent as before; the storm was blowing itself out. Nuvat covered up his head and slept again.

This time, sleeping, he dreamed that he was at home in the warm igloo with his seal. It had been divided and everybody had eaten; rich broth bubbled in the stone cooking-pot hung above the lamp, and the faces of the little children were all glistening with the blubber they had been chewing. Father Yekut's igloo was full of hunters who had come to hear the story of Nuvat's hunt. He stood in the middle of the floor and acted it out for them, every move that he had made, as the hunters always did at the end of the day. The men nodded and grunted, "Ahey!" in admiration, as they listened.

Nuvat had just reached the place in the story where he was spearing the seal, when he was awakened by a terrific crash and a jarring and grinding as if whole worlds were smashing together. He pulled his head out of the sleeping-bag and looked about wildly, still half in his dream, but the people and the gleaming walls of the igloo were gone! Even the storm was gone, and a broad, rainbow-colored ribbon of the Aurora Borealis [4] overhead poured down multi-colored light like raining fire over the snow, illumining the whole world with trembling, unreal brilliance. Everywhere, as far as he could see, stretched gleaming snowfields, sparkling with purple and red and diamond fire. Far to the south a low bank of cloud along the horizon showed where the storm was creeping away over the edge of the world.

Nuvat came back from his dream, realized where he was, and began to shout with joy. The wind had driven the ice island to the coast while he slept, he decided, and the jarring crash must have come when it smashed into the shore-ice and locked there. He routed out his dogs and started to harness them, hurrying for fear the ice pan would drift away again before he could escape from it.

"*Huk! huk!*—go forward!" he shouted. "It may be we shall see the village again before the next day ends."

They had hardly started before the Aurora Borealis went out, instantly, like a candle blown out in the dark, leaving them in pitch blackness. Nuvat struggled on as far as he could by the pale gleam of the snow. As soon as he thought he was off the ice pan onto solid shore-ice, he unharnessed the dogs again and crawled into his sleeping-bag to wait for daylight.

When he woke at dawn, there was not a sign of his dogs anywhere about. But Nuvat was not worried. By stooping down

---

[4] AURORA BOREALIS (ô-rō′ra̤ bō-rē-ā′lĭs)—The Northern Lights.

and looking closely he could see what appeared to be a little feather of steam floating above a mound of snow; it was the frozen breath of a dog above his sleeping-hole. Nuvat wasted no time trying to hunt them up. He cut a small chunk of meat from the seal, held it between his hands to thaw it so it would smell stronger, and threw it on the snow. In an instant black noses began to pop up through the drifts here and there, and out came one dog after another in a flurry of snow, and made a rush for the meat. It was the black and white leader, Unapeek —which means the Little Hunting Spear—who got it.

When Nuvat harnessed the other dogs he called Kakk to take his place in the team; but to his surprise, Kakk would not come. He ran away and sat on the snow, whining. Nuvat took his whip and started after him, but Kakk only ran farther and stood looking at him, pricking and flattening his ears and whining as if he wanted to tell him something. Nuvat was puzzled; never before had Kakk disobeyed him. At any other time he would have spent all day, if necessary, making him obey—for a dog must never be allowed to get the better of his master. But now he was in too great a hurry to waste the time. Very much upset, he came back to the sled and started off with the other dogs, letting Kakk go his way.

Then he had a greater surprise. For instead of running away, Kakk circled around and fell in ahead of the team, about a dozen yards in front of the spotted leader, and began to pick the best way through the rough ice, looking back to see that they were following.

It dawned upon Nuvat that Kakk really had been trying to tell him something: he had been trained to be what is called a "loose leader." Nuvat remembered hearing the old hunters say that some faraway tribes trained their best dogs that way, to pick the trail, and this was what Kakk had been trying to make him understand. He looked after the black dog with pride in his eyes. He would show the other hunters how clever his dog was, as soon as they got back to the village.

THE VIOLIN-MAKER OF CREMONA

FRANÇOIS COPPÉE

In this play by the famous French author, François Coppée,[1] we find ourselves among the Italian musicians and artisans of the eighteenth century. The family of Amati [2] had worked for two centuries in an unbroken line of father to son, as the violin-masters of Cremona. Then Nicolo had been born—Nicolo Amati (1596–1684) in whom two hundred years of skill reached a new perfection.

This great master taught the art to Antonio Stradivari,[3] then a Cremona lad. He, in turn, perfected the work of Amati, and became himself the greatest master of all time. No one has ever equalled his artistry. Today, a Stradivarius violin is a priceless treasure. Stradivari achieved the perfect pattern for assembling the carefully wrought and complex pieces of mellow wood into precise delicacy of form—using just the right kind and amount of glue, and finishing with a secret varnish which added fullness of tone and a rich amber glow to his beautiful violin. This was in 1700.

When our play opens half a century later, Cremona is still proudly carrying on in the glory of his name. Although Stradivari himself has died, taking with him the secret of the famous varnish, his pupil,

[1] FRANÇOIS COPPÉE—Pronounced frän-swä′ kô-pā′.
[2] AMATI—Pronounced ä-mä′tē.   [3] STRADIVARI—Pronounced strä-dē-vä′rē.

Taddeo Ferrari,[4] upholds the master's traditions in his own careful workshop. Imbued with the teaching and standards of the greatest violin-maker the world has ever known, Ferrari knows nothing more important than his musical trade of violin-making.

CHARACTERS

TADDEO FERRARI, *master violin-maker*
GIANNINA, *his daughter*
SANDRO, *his pupil*
FILIPPO, *another of his pupils*
GUILD OF VIOLIN-MAKERS *and attendants*

SCENE. *Cremona about the year 1750. A violin workshop of the eighteenth century. At the rear, a workbench and a door, which opens upon the street. Violins, cellos, bass-viols, and other musical instruments are scattered around the workshop. At left, there is a counter in full view and a door. At right, a large armchair is placed near a table. As the scene opens,* GIANNINA *stands by* MASTER FERRARI, *seated in the armchair.*

Ferrari. No, Giannina.[5] I have made a vow and I am going to keep it. As surely as my name is Taddeo Ferrari, master violin-maker, patron, and trustee of the people of my trade, whose banner I carry in the processions,[6] you shall be married, and in this way.

Giannina. But Father——

Ferrari. I am proceeding as a reasonable man. Our old mayor, recently dead (may he rest in peace!), wishing that the fame of stringed instruments coming from our old and famous city should continue to be more and more deserved, has just bequeathed his gold chain to the skilled workman that shall make the best violin in the city. The competition is free, and

---

[4] TADDEO FERRARI—Pronounced tä-dā′ō fĕr-rä′rē.
[5] GIANNINA—Pronounced jän-nē′nà.
[6] WHOSE BANNER I CARRY IN THE PROCESSIONS—It was the custom for members of a trade to form a kind of association called a guild. These guilds had festival days and processions, and in the procession the banner was carried by ⁺he master, or most skilled workmen of the group.

will be judged today. I, a simple artisan, inspired by him, have promised to give my house and my daughter to the one, who by his talent will receive the mayor's golden chain. And, by the saints, it shall be done! It's agreed, concluded, arranged! There's nothing to be excited about!

Giannina. I told you there is someone I prefer.

Ferrari. O, Sandro! [7] You'll forget him.

Giannina. But if this unknown artist should be an evil fellow, not worthy of your house at all?

Ferrari. A skilled workman is always a good man.

Giannina. . . . A lazybones, without a care for the future?

Ferrari. When he is better paid, he can work less.

Giannina. . . . A brute who would beat his wife? There are such men.

Ferrari. If he had not peace at home, I should not blame him.

Giannina. But if he should be so perverse as to refuse my hand? Then——

Ferrari. Such a funny one would certainly be hard to please! No, no, a good match like you, Giannina, is not to be found every day. Your dowry of two thousand crowns is not a trifle —and with my business, favored pupil as I am of the famous Stradivari— Nay, nay! Besides, I have given my word! So let's say no more about it.

Giannina. But, my father——

Ferrari. That will do!

Giannina. If the victor—I laugh to even think of it—if he should be your small pupil Filippo? [8]

Ferrari. Filippo?

Giannina. Suppose he gets the prize?

Ferrari. Well, I shouldn't be very much surprised, and if he should bring me the mayor's chain, you would marry him the following week.

Giannina. Marry Filippo?

---

[7] SANDRO—Pronounced sän'drō.   [8] FILIPPO—Pronounced fê-lēp'pō.

Ferrari. Why not?

Giannina. A hunchback!

Ferrari. If he had two humps like a camel, he should be your husband.

Giannina. May heaven protect me!

Ferrari. Isn't Filippo one of the best of fellows—good, useful, honest? He looks a little sad, he is hunchbacked—that's true—but he is a great artist. In the little concert that he gave one day, as I listened he drew from the strings such grief and charm that two great tears dropped from my eyes. And you know, my daughter, that I am a severe judge of music.

Giannina. I esteem Filippo, just as you do, Father. I pity him, and I have done my best, I hope, to make him forget his misery and his deformity which the poor creature endures with such sweetness. He has been as my brother since the day the poor lad stopped at our door to beg for bread. But could I love him—Filippo, the hunchback? Think, Father!

Ferrari. Ta-ra-ta-ta! If you can't offer any more serious objection than that, just leave it there. I am going down cellar to choose our choicest wine for this great day of celebration.

[FERRARI *exits at left.* GIANNINA *drops into the chair with a sigh.* SANDRO *enters from the rear, carrying a black violin case which he places on the counter at the left. When she sees him,* GIANNINA *rises in greeting.*]

Sandro. Well, Giannina?

Giannina (*holding out her hands to him*). Sandro!

Sandro. What's the news? Does the Master still hold to his vow to give you to the best workman in the city?

Giannina. Yes, more firmly than ever.

Sandro. What madness! But does he know how much I love you, and if I cannot wed you, I shall surely die?

Giannina. He said I would forget you.

Sandro. He is cruel!

Giannina (*pointing to the violin case*). Have you finished your masterpiece?

Sandro. If I were as lazy as a snake, I would still be ready; for alas! it is my last hope. Today the experts will decide my lifelong happiness.

Giannina. And are you satisfied with it?

Sandro. Yes and no. I understand my trade, and have made the violin according to the best rules of the art. Its high tones are pure; its low tones, deep. All my time I have devoted to it, with infinite care. I have carefully chosen my wood, my strings, and my varnish. It is an instrument worthy of a master, I am sure.

Giannina (joyfully). The prize will be yours, Sandro!

Sandro. Perhaps.

Giannina. But of course you will win the prize! Why do you doubt it? There is no rival you need fear. Is not my father the first artist of Cremona—he from whom you learned your art? Oh, I wish above all that you win the prize!

Sandro. No rival from another workshop makes me fear.

Giannina. Well?

Sandro. But I have one in our own.

Giannina. What! In our workshop?

Sandro. Yes, the hunchback! It was an evil day for me when you took him into your house.

Giannina. I did not know Filippo would compete!

Sandro. Yesterday he told me so, the little snake-in-the-grass—before your father.

Giannina (thoughtfully). My father, who but now was saying that if he received the prize, I would nevertheless be forced to have him for a husband . . .

Sandro. Didn't I tell you?

Giannina (laughing to throw off the thought). We shall need the protection of my guardian angel!

Sandro (still doubtful). He thinks you are free—he may hope.

Giannina. Such a suspicion of the poor fellow does not occur to me. He wants the gold chain and the title of master, and surely we would expect him to be ambitious. But he knows himself too well to claim my hand.

Sandro. I cannot believe that—and I am sure he will win. In all my life, I have never been so wretched and unhappy, nor so envious.

Giannina. You envious, Sandro? Oh, no!

Sandro. Yes, I am, for I know his work; and soon everyone will know it as I do. Listen! The other night I was at my window, enjoying the quiet evening and thinking of you. In the darkness, I heard a nightingale singing, and it seemed his pearly notes mingled with the stars. Suddenly, I heard another song, just as sublime, as touching, as that of the bird. I leaned out and saw the hunchback alone in his attic, seated at his desk, bow in hand. His violin with an accent almost human was pouring out tones of love and sorrow intermingled, equalling in sweetness the voice of the nightingale. For a while I listened entranced, and then so pure was the beauty of his music throbbing out into the evening breeze, twining its melody into the bird's ecstatic song, that I could no longer tell which was the hunchback's magic tone, and which the song of the nightingale.

Giannina. Can the success of a rival make you so sad?

Sandro. It is a feeling unworthy of an artist, I know. But if your father favors him, and he should come out victor . . .

Giannina. It is you whom I love. I will be yours, come what may.

Sandro. You are sure?

Giannina. Yes, I am sure.

Sandro. You are the most precious girl in the world.

Giannina. Here is my hand—to pledge our vow.

Sandro (kissing her hand). So be it. I am more content.

[*Loud noises are heard outside.*]

Giannina. What is that racket?

[FILIPPO *rushes in, and quickly slams the door behind him. He is out of breath, and much disturbed.*]

Filippo. Oh, I am here at last. The little ragamuffins! They almost got me.

Giannina. What is it, Filippo? Who was following you?

Filippo. Some little rogues, who tried to knock me down with stones and broken glass. (*He slips into the chair, resting his forehead on his hands. When he takes away his hands, there is blood on his forehead.*)

Sandro. You are bleeding!

Giannina. Water—quick! (*She goes to the sideboard to get a basin, returns and kneels to bathe* FILIPPO's *head.*)

Sandro. Tell us what happened.

Filippo. It is really not very important. Fifteen or twenty rascally schoolboys were throwing stones at a poor sick dog, who was dragging himself along with a broken paw. The miserable creature, backed against the wall, was trying to defend himself with a show of teeth. I who have often been tormented turned sick with sorrow at the sight, and begged them to have pity. They forgot about the dog; grew angry at the hunchback. It was much more fun to chase a running prey. Up and down the alleys I dodged—had they caught me, there would have been no more poor Filippo. But I saved the life of that defenseless dog! (*He falls exhausted back into the armchair.* GIANNINA *bathes his head with her kerchief, dipped from the basin.*)

Giannina (*with spirit*). Those blackguards! Was there ever such malice? (*To* FILIPPO.) Poor fellow!

Filippo (*aside*). Her hand on my forehead— Oh, delight!

Giannina. Do you feel better, now?

Filippo (*getting up, and speaking with tremulous voice*). Yes, you are most kind.

Sandro (*aside*). Indeed, that voice speaks more than gratitude. I was not mistaken. He loves her!

[FERRARI *enters, carrying a basket of wine bottles.*]

Giannina. Father . . .

Ferrari. Is it you, my Giannina? I was looking for you.

Soon, when they have tested the violins, and we know the lucky one you are to marry, I shall entertain the brotherhood at dinner. Come! Help me to get ready, that I may look fine in my best wig and blue festal coat. Come! (*He leaves at right, followed by* GIANNINA.)

Sandro. The eventual moment is fast approaching, Filippo.
Filippo. Yes, comrade.
Sandro. Your violin—it is ready?
Filippo. Yes.
Sandro. You are satisfied with it?
Filippo. Yes, indeed. And you?
Sandro. No, I— No, not quite.
Filippo. I am sorry. In this courteous and friendly competition, my one consolation for failing would be to see you succeed, my comrade in work. Here, give me your hand in friendship before we go forth to the contest.

146

Sandro (after a silence). No! (*He leaves hastily, at left.*)

Filippo. It is jealousy which torments him—him, with his strength and beauty! Would that a man might rejoice at the bit of merit he finds in a poor friend, who never begrudged him his comeliness. But there—he suffers and I must not blame him. Still it would be good to be friends, as well as rivals. Little does he know your worth, O friendly heart, that yearns for his comradeship. Yet, there is my masterpiece, a solace for all sorrow. Poor, dear violin! how like unto me you are—an exquisite soul in an unshapely case. (*He goes to the cupboard, and gets his violin, which is in a red case, and puts it on the table on his right. As he speaks, he lifts it from the case.*)

Come, I wish to see you once again, O my work, dear creation upon which I, the feeble workman, had the strength to spend so many days and nights of effort and of toil. Come, soon there will issue from your deep bosom the chattering scherzo [9] and the weeping lento [10]—the concert of beauty you can give to the world. I may not again wake the song that sleeps in your heart—only once again would I see myself mirrored in your shining wood—to know that I, the hunchback, am he who have given you your golden voice. Farewell, oh dear and noble instrument. I beg that you remember him whose heart speaks to you now, the outcast artist who has breathed into your form the flame of music. (*Puts violin back in red case.*)

How much a child I am! Poor fool, to thus deceive myself! It is not for glory that I bent my fullest effort to this task! It is for her—the sweet, the beautiful Giannina. Of all the world, 'tis she alone whose kindness has reached out to me—cruelly misshapen wretch. When first I wandered to her father's door, a homeless child, she took me in—nor did she laugh at me. Surely so kind, so beautiful a one cannot look upon this cherished love as an offense.

[9] SCHERZO (skĕr'tsō)—A playful, humorous movement.
[10] LENTO—A slow movement.

Still, if I win the prize, I shall not ask fulfillment of her father's vow. Only can I hope that when I offer her the golden chain, when she will know that all my genius has been inspired by her, perhaps this daughter of an artist will forget the rest, and think only of my talent. Perhaps—who can tell?—if her heart is still free—for so many reasons, she might indeed . . . Oh, this impossible dream is killing me!

Giannina (*entering*). He is alone. Now I shall find out if Sandro still can hope to win. (*Aloud*.) Filippo!

Filippo (*startled out of his reverie*). It is she!

Giannina. I am disappointed, Filippo, that I alone have not been told what everyone else knows—that you have kept it secret from me, who would have rejoiced to know.

Filippo. What is it that I have kept from you?

Giannina. That you are competing for the prize.

Filippo. It is true, and you above all would have been the first to hear about it. But when I knew about the vow of the master—forgive me, Giannina, then I dared not tell you.

Giannina. I understand—but let's leave that. My old father really loves me too well to thus leave in chance the care of my happiness. But as for the chain of gold, and the master's title—that is different. Each craftsman in the city has the right to aspire to that, and you especially from what I have just learned.

Filippo. What is it you have heard?

Giannina. That you have fashioned an exquisite instrument, a masterpiece . . .

Filippo. Truly I have done my best, but to whom will it matter whether I succeed or fail?

Giannina. To whom? Will we not all be interested? Are we not your friends?

Filippo. Forgive me, Giannina. I am stupid. One seems distrustful when one is simply timid, and I owe you half of all my secrets. When I was wretched, you pitied me, and I know you will be glad if any honor comes to me. I am indeed sorry.

I want to tell you everything, for I was ungrateful and offended you. Know then that I am almost sure to succeed. Whether by talent or only good luck, I do not know, but I have succeeded completely. (*He shows his violin.*) With all possible care, I built the box of old fir and the handle of maple—from the start, I wrought with finest art. But that is nothing—the other violins may be just as good. The master stroke is that I discovered again, during a sleepless night, the secret of the amber varnish of former times—the lost secret of the old masters.

Giannina. What? The famous lustrous varnish of Stradivari and Amati?

Filippo (*enthusiastically*). I have it! Tomorrow, all shall know the formula! I have compared my work with their violins—it has the same sound. Exactly the same sound, I tell you. I am sure of it!

Giannina (*aside*). Alas! poor Sandro!

Filippo. Since that happy day, I have hidden my secret like a lover. Whether I get the prize or not, what does it matter to me, now? My life is a festival.

Giannina (*aside*). Poor, poor Sandro. (*Aloud.*) Is it as fine as that?

Filippo. Listen only to its sound of *la*.

Giannina. Oh, play some song. I would like so much to hear it.

Filippo (*aside*). Her voice—her plea is almost tender. Does she wish me to succeed? (*Aloud.*) Do you really want me to?

Giannina. I truly do. (*Aside.*) It is the only way to know whether he flatters himself or speaks the truth.

Filippo. I will play, if you please, the Corelli sonata in *sol*.

Giannina. Anything you wish.

Filippo (*behind the counter*). Listen to this. (*Silent scene.* FILIPPO *plays the first measures of a majestic theme on his violin, which has a wonderful richness of tone. The face of* GIANNINA *who is listening attentively is not slow to express a sorrowful admiration. Her head drops into her hands, and she*

bursts into tears. FILIPPO *at last sees this, and cries out.*)
What do I see? Giannina, weeping? Is it not consoling and
beautiful that this hunchback who has made so many laugh,
should with music bring tears to your eyes? I have made you
weep—now do I need no other glory—no prize more precious
than the dear diamonds that fall from your eyes. Now can I
hold up my head in pride, now——

Giannina. Stop! I cannot longer keep my purpose from
you. I understand your pride as an artist, and share it as I
have shared your grief. But it is not that which makes my
tears flow.

Filippo. What is it, then?

Giannina. What I must say will hurt you, but you will pity
me, I am sure, when I tell you that among the competitors is
one for whom I wished success, one whom I love . . . and all
my happiness is now destroyed by what I hear.

Filippo. Ah!

Giannina. Do not be angry with me, Filippo. I did not
know of your great talent. In my father's shop, I thought of
you still as an unskilled workman. And it was so natural that
I should wish success for the man I love. If I had but understood—believe me when I say that it would have been hard for
me to have decided between you. How easily I could have
accepted the idea of your genius! Then I would not have
wept as I did today.

Filippo (*pointing to the door from which* SANDRO *left*). You
love him?

Giannina (*in a low voice*). Yes.

Filippo. Sandro?

Giannina. I entrust to you freely the secret of my love. He
cherished also the hope of winning, and it was, I admit, my
most ardent wish. But now after what I have just heard, I see
that he cannot claim the prize, which would make our dream
come true. To lose such a dear hope is cruel, is it not? Yet
my sorrow has no bitterness in it—no, because it is my child-

hood friend, my brother, who deserves this great reward. Still it overwhelms me— Forgive my helpless tears. (*She weeps freely.*)

Filippo. In truth, I suffer as much as you, and I beg of you . . .

Giannina. I am sorry—this is most unfair. I forget your misfortune, in thinking of my own. I do not remember that you, my poor friend, have only your art to console you. It shall be so—I will weep no more— Love to my dearest Sandro, and glory to you. You are the great artist whom I admire. Indeed, I wish to see you happy. (*She takes both of his hands.*) And I shall weep no more. It must be this way—it must! See, I am smiling. (*She bursts out sobbing.*) But it is more than I can bear. (*She goes out.*)

Filippo (*after a moment of sorrowful thought*). What, now, is there left? All is said. She loves another. Another! Yes, that handsome one—my fellow craftsman. And indeed, 'tis right that she should love him! Would it help to protest that she is unjust, and be angry with her? Whom would she naturally choose—she the young maid and fair—between one such dream lover and you—misshapen fellow who makes all to laugh who look upon you!

Miserable cripple, go look at yourself in the mirror! How could she love such as you? Blind! Blind and foolish! To think that I could see nothing of this, nor of her love for this Sandro! You, hunchback, what good will it do you now to win the reward and the prize? I wished to make her happy, and I have only made her sad.

I will not compete! Next in skill after me, in the city, is Sandro. He shall win the prize, and she will be happy again. Come (*Taking his violin.*)—you shall give your life for her happiness—your beautiful song shall be broken, too. (*About to crush violin over his knee, he stops suddenly.*) What an unhappy idea! How fiercely my heart throbs! What if some other workman should win the prize? She would be forced to marry that strange one! (*Looking at the two violin cases on the table.*) I could change— (*His voice full of doubt.*) Ah, no! It is too much. This dear work of my hands I cannot give to him who took my sweeter dream. But, come, it must be done. It was for her this masterpiece was made, and it shall be given for her happiness. A change of cases, and all will be well. Sandro is not so great an artist that he will see the difference between his work and mine when the experts judge them. Courage—let it be done. (*Changes the violins, putting his own in* SANDRO's *case.*) All is finished.

[FERRARI *enters from rear.*]

Ferrari. Come, Sandro, Filippo. 'Tis time to go. Are you not ready yet?

[*Enter* SANDRO *from right.*]

Sandro. I am coming, master.

Filippo. And here are our violins.

Ferrari. My children, I trust that one of you will win and do credit to your master and your workshop. Others may scrape their bows until they burst with music, but the skill which I have taught you should claim the prize. Now from all the town, people are gathering with kerchief and colored dress to see the judges take their places; the choir master is seated in his armchair; and through the air there breathes a strain of melody. Cremona is pulsing with rhythm, like a quiet hall before a symphony.

Sandro. So, master, it is time to leave?

Ferrari. Yes, let us go.

Sandro. Are you coming with me, Filippo?

Filippo. No, comrade. On so beautiful and musical a day, let the hunchback stay indoors and leave unmarred the gala scene. Would you but do me the kindness to take my violin with yours? 'Tis but a step from here.

Sandro (*taking the hand* FILIPPO *holds out to him*). I will do it. (SANDRO *exits with the two violin cases, at the right.*)

Filippo (*aside*). The sacrifice is made. Even in love, what courage it takes! (*Aloud to* FERRARI.) Are you not going to see his work crowned?

Ferrari. To be sure, to be sure! But the prize is not his, as yet, and you yourself may win the golden chain. Have you less talent, less intelligence than he?

Filippo. You know I have no chance.

Ferrari. 'Tis confidence you're lacking. As straight as a steeple you may not be, but you are a good violin-maker. And if the prize is for you, I tell you you shall be my son-in-law and my successor.

Filippo. But master . . .

Ferrari. Enough! Enough! I must be off. (*Exits.*)

Filippo. Truly, I need all my courage. (*Enter* GIANNINA.) What? Does she come again?

Giannina. Filippo, I have just come from the church. I went—forgive me, I was so sad at heart—to pray that Sandro might still be the winner, in spite of everything. But kneeling before our Saint Cecilia, I felt how wrong it was to ask God to do anything unjust. So whatever happens, I have vowed to always be the same toward you. Good-by . . . (*She crosses the stage, and goes out right.*)

Filippo. Alas! How much she loves him. Had I but been strong and beautiful, how much she would have loved me!

[SANDRO *enters hastily from the right, in great distress.*]

Sandro. Filippo! Filippo!

Filippo. What is this? Tears in your eyes, and your face so pale! What dreadful thing has happened?

Sandro. I have done a shameful deed. I am a wicked scoundrel. Oh, forgive! forgive! forgive!

Filippo. Who? Me pardon you, my friend? For what?

Sandro. You see, I loved her so much. It was too great an anguish that a rival should surpass me in her eyes . . . I am so envious a wretch. The temptation came to me when I held your masterpiece in my hands. Crazy with rage and grief, I yielded. Near here, trembling as a thief in the shadow of a doorway . . . Filippo . . . I changed our violins in their cases!

Filippo (*a little staggered*).   You?

Sandro.   Then I took them before the judges.   The moment the expert opened our two cases, I could not bear the sight.   I ran away.   Avenge yourself!   Before everyone denounce my deed!   But for the sake of pity, do not compel me to bear this shame before her.   I will write you a confession, then go away and die, for shame is deadly, deadly.   (*He falls to his knees.*)

Filippo.   No, Sandro.   I do not need vengeance.   You have brought upon yourself your own punishment.

Sandro.   What is it you say?

Filippo.   The glory of my masterpiece, I had given to you . . . and you have given it back to me.

Sandro (*perplexed*).   I do not understand.

Filippo.   Those instruments you changed.   I myself had already changed them in their cases.

Sandro.   What do I hear?   My remorse allows me not to understand.   Why did you do it?

Filippo.   Because I adore her.   And because it is you whom she prefers.   If my heart is touched with regret at your deed, it is because your action has taken away what I would have done for her.

Sandro (*rising*).   Still is my crime as great, and I must bear punishment.   Say but the word, and I will go away.   She will forget me—you are more worthy of her.   I must go!

[*Confused noises outside.*]

Filippo.   No, stay!   Obey me!

[FERRARI *enters from rear door, and raises his hand on seeing* FILIPPO.   *He is followed by the whole guild of violin-makers, and two pages, decked out in the colors of the city, one carrying the mayor's gold chain on a cushion, and the other* FILIPPO'S *violin, decorated with ribbons and flowers.* GIANNINA *appears on the threshold of the door at the right.*]

Ferrari (*to* FILIPPO).   Come to my arms, my son!   I proclaim you king of the trade, winner of the prize, and Master of the Violin-Makers of Cremona. Here, before the entire brotherhood of our craft, I first keep my promise to the winner, my associate, my son-in-law. Now . . . the gold chain. . . .

Filippo (*taking it from his hands and placing it 'round the neck of* GIANNINA). Gladly I offer it to Giannina, the beautiful, begging her to make it her favorite jewel, when she is the wife of my comrade, Sandro.

Giannina. Dear Filippo!

Sandro (*in a low voice to* FILIPPO). My noble friend! My brother!

Ferrari. Stop! Is it a vow you have taken not to marry that makes you give up your prize like this?

Filippo. No, my good master, no. Tomorrow I shall start out on a journey through the whole of Italy, carrying your fame to every corner of the land. I have had a dream—a mad and foolish dream—from which I am but now awake. All I can wish is that farewell regrets will follow me, as the eye seeks the departing flight of a lone swallow. I ask no faithful memories—only a regret. It is all that my poor life is worth. (*He draws* SANDRO *and* GIANNINA *close to him.*)

And when in the workshop you again take up our labors— you, my comrade at your old place, with her beside you—if perchance a string you stretch upon the wood breaks with a plaintive sound, remember Filippo who felt his poor heart break at this, our last farewell. Nothing you could do would change it—that is true. Still I would like to know that you will not forget that I have loved you dearly.

Ferrari. Ungrateful one! Do you want my house to fall to ruin?

Filippo. You still have Sandro.

Ferrari. Happiness and fortune you throw away! Is there nothing you are keeping?

Filippo (*taking his violin*). This only. (*Aside.*) It will be my comrade and my consolation.

GIVE A MAN A HORSE

CHARLES J. FINGER

Eighteen-year-old Bob Honore loved only two things—horses and the sea. His uncles, however, wishing to launch him on a business career, had found him a place in the office of Mitchell's Iron and Steel Company. To Bob the stuffy office soon became a house of bondage. There seemed no escape. Then suddenly, commissioned by his firm to supervise the loading of a schooner with supplies and stock for a South American ranch, Bob found himself set upon a series of adventures more exciting than his wildest dreams. We find him, at the moment, sharing the experiences of shipwreck and storm off the islands of the Magellan Strait with an Indian companion named Dara.

Bob awoke with a confused notion, which at first he thought was a dream, that some monstrous thing was bearing down on the boat. The swift thought came that they were headed for a black precipice, but soon the idea gave way to the truth. The sharp-edged black tower resolved itself into the bow of a steamer and a hill of white water on which the boat was rising. Against that white wave he saw his Indian companion standing with arms upraised. For a split instant Dara stood on the thwart, then he disappeared. With a click, many things rushed together—the knowledge that those on board the vessel could hear nothing even though a watch on deck might have been attentive. The fact that the little motorboat was a wreck, the thought that even if he and Dara had not slept, the accident would have been unavoidable in that black night. Those thoughts came in a flash as he dived overboard and struck out, swimming strongly away from the steamer.

When he came up, for he kept under water until his lungs seemed likely to burst, he turned a little to see the black hull, high towering, and found himself being swept away from the vessel. He had a vision of bright spots of light, of a ruddy glare that came from the steamer's funnel, then of the tossing water that was the vessel's wake. Obeying an impulse, although he knew it to be useless, he summoned strength enough to call, "Help!" then to utter a series of "Oh's!" But his voice was only a faint sigh in that tumultuous night world. As he swam, he was aware of the calmness of the star-sprinkled sky, of the white wake, and the diminishing glare of fire on smoke. He kept his eyes on that for a long time, half fascinated by the sight. One moment he looked away and when he sought it again, it had gone. Once something soft and clinging folded itself about his chest, and he had a moment of fear until he discovered it was one of the blankets. For a while he had difficulty in disengaging himself from it.

After that the world was all effort and struggle and loneliness, and he found himself doing some complicated thinking in a fragmentary way. He had to bring himself to the idea of swimming with, not against or across, the current, which ran swift in these straits. That resolution came when he realized that he had been attempting to swim after the steamer. Also he had to rest occasionally, which was not easy in those cold,

Antarctic waters, but it served him well when he turned on his back and swam, although, looking at the stars, he seemed to be making no progress. Once, turning thus, he saw a dark cloud, and the fear of a sudden storm made his heart skip a beat. It took a deliberate effort to bring himself to logical thinking, but when he had himself again under control and looked once more at the cloud, he saw that the edge where the sky cut across the world was too high to be horizon; so the black patch stood for land. Not until then did the immediate past present itself in orderly array: the storm, sleeping in the drifting boat, awakening to see Dara about to dive. Until then he had forgotten Dara.

He raised his voice in a "Ho! Dara!" and the sound, so thin and feeble, startled him and made him realize the noise of waters to which he had grown accustomed. Also the hearing of his own voice almost frightened him, as if it might awaken strange creatures. A long time passed before Bob could bring himself to call again. When he did, it was with an effort, and it puzzled him to hear another voice quite near.

"Me no shout, me swim," it called.

"Dara," gasped Bob, and the world seemed much lighter and life more hopeful for the companionship.

"Plenty much water long way," said Dara.

Bob had nothing to say to that, for a swift vision came to him of the old farmhouse and the barn, and he found himself wondering whether he had been a fool to leave it, bent on success. But it was only a flash, and there were others, as when he remembered a passage read long ago in a book. He had an impression of a hand touching his shoulder, but the impression meant nothing until he felt the slap a second time and knew it to be Dara who had touched him.

"Good," he said.

"Good," echoed Dara, and added an instruction, bidding Bob swim in a certain direction. So steadily, sturdily they kept on and came to a place where the current flowed more evenly, although they were in a place of deeper blackness because of the overshadowing cliff. Bob remembered afterwards a moment when two purposes were struggling in his mind, one telling him that it would be good to rest and that drowning was easy, the other bidding him keep up the fight. But Dara, swimming vigorously, passed him, and the sight urged Bob to new effort. Then came another time of fierce struggle with a current that seemed to be sweeping him away from the dark mass that was land, which was succeeded by a sensation of wonder.

Many things rushed on him at once—that the gray of dawn was in the sky, that the deep, black cloud was a cliff, that a sandy beach ahead lay very near. Next, he found himself clutching at shifting sand and realized that the undertow was dragging him; but there, most surprisingly, was Dara standing with water swirling about his knees. He felt Dara's hand clasp his wrist, and he knew that he himself had firm hold on the Indian's right arm. Then he found himself on his knees, very tired indeed, very thankful, too, for the help the Indian gave. But he did not remember climbing out of the water or making his way up the beach to dry sand, although he did remember casting himself down on it and finding it warm and saying with an effort, "All out of breath, Dara."

In reply, the Indian lad seemed to say reassuring words which were comforting to hear.

There were times during those two days as castaways when Bob had moments of wonder because he forgot their plight. He discovered that they could laugh, enjoy the world, and sleep the healthy sleep of tired youth. If a picture had been drawn of anxiety and worry, it would have been false. Yet in Bob's mind the idea rested that they were marking time while waiting for rescue. He discovered, on the evening of the second day, that his idea and Dara's were poles apart.

"Maybe," he began setting forth what he had in mind with

careful precision, "we ought to start walking south and find a way to get back to the island."

His Indian companion looked up with something like pained surprise, then shook his head. When he spoke, he made it clear that he had no such intention.

"Why should I go back when I want to see the world and the place where horses are?" Bob understood him to say.

"But we have nothing," Bob answered. "No clothes, no weapons, no provisions."

That puzzled Dara, who made reply to the effect that food was everywhere, that animals could be caught, that therefore clothes could be made and that he could make bows and arrows and boledores [1] too. Furthermore he could teach Bob to make things and to use weapons that could be made.

Bob considered that a while. He had thought of adventure and of a new land but always with the aid of what he could carry with him out of civilization. Dara had, in very truth, already commenced his adventure.

"With horses, . . ." he began, and Dara interrupted.

"We shall find the place where they are and catch them."

"But how? With bare hands?" asked Bob.

"I do not know. We shall see," came the reply.

That again set Bob to wondering. It seemed absurd to believe that two youths with bare hands could catch wild horses, but on the heels of that idea came another thought. Obviously, sometime and somewhere unarmed men had caught not only horses, but yak, elephants, camels, cows, reindeer, asses, leopards, to say nothing of falcons and other birds, which they had taught to hunt in the air and dive into the water for fish.

Dara broke the silence. "If you want to go back, I go with you, but must leave again when you find your own people," he said.

"Dara, you're a good scout!" exclaimed Bob. Then with

[1] BOLEDORE (bōl′ĕ-dôr)—A missile weapon, or *bolas*, consisting of several balls of stone or metal fastened to connected cords and hurled so as to entangle cattle or game.

sudden resolution he added, "Let's go on with the game." That moment marked a change, and thereafter Bob's moments of dreariness were few and his days were full of novelty and delight. From that moment he set himself to the task of becoming fit. While Dara, in the days that followed, employed himself making a canoe, Bob practiced with the bow and arrows that Dara had made. He learned how to catch upland geese, to know edible plants, to skin animals he or Dara had shot, and to prepare the meat. He took especial delight in learning to throw the boledores, the use of which he found far easier than the lazo,[2] although it was a long time before he gained the expertness of his Indian companion.

But in those three weeks of preparation, they walked many miles and climbed many Andean peaks for the purpose of learning the lay of the land and something of the great inland sea that lay east of the Andes and which they proposed to sail. They were to discover, later, that it was rather a confusion of great fjords than a sea. It was on one of those excursions, when they were resting by a bright, brawling mountain creek, that Bob, scooping up a handful of gravel in which he saw bright particles, made an exclamation of surprise.

Dara looked up without exhibiting any show of curiosity, and calmly asked what his companion had found.

"Gold! It's gold," was the answer, as Bob showed the glittering particles to the Indian, then poured it into Dara's hand for closer examination.

"I've seen it when I was in the mission," the Indian answered calmly and spilled it into the creek.

For a brief moment Bob felt annoyed, but he dismissed the feeling, putting Dara's act down to ignorance of the value of the metal. He tried to explain and ended up by saying, "We ought to keep it. It'll come in handy some day."

Dara shrugged his shoulders and turned to pluck and eat berries from a caliphat bush. "There is plenty," he said. "It's

[2] LAZO (lā'thō)—Lasso.

no good for eating. Also gold brings white men and trouble for Indians."

"What a land!" ejaculated Bob. "Gold for the picking up. Seal and otter skins for the taking. Ostrich feathers. If we had them up north . . ."

Dara pondered. "You said up north you pay money for ice," he said in effect. "Here are glaciers." He pointed to a beryl-blue gash in the side of a distant mountain. "That, too, would mean much if you had it up north. There are icebergs. Can you take them up north?"

Bob grunted.

When the day came on which they started on their canoe voyage, both Bob and Dara were much more interested in the shapeliness of their little craft than they were in the gold. Indeed it was Dara who thought of it. They had loaded the canoe and were on the point of pushing off on the inland voyage when Dara said something, then ran up the bank to the bush where the hidden bag of nuggets lay forgotten under a bush. He pitched the bag to Bob, who caught it and laid it in the canoe, then tossed over three extra nuggets that had been found after the incident of the overturned rock. Two of them Bob caught, but the third and largest he missed, and, without a tremor Bob saw it strike the gunwale of the canoe, then bounce off into the water. An hour later he had forgotten the incident.

Indeed, a hundred things combined to make him forget it, for, during the two days in which they paddled along the coast of that inland sea, they drew in pleasure and delight with the air they breathed. There was not an hour but yielded up its pleasure. They were in a world alive with sea birds, gulls, sea mews, ducks, and other winged creatures new to Bob. Seals sunned themselves on rocks, and penguins watched them with curious eyes. The clearness of sky, the cleanness of hill, the majesty of the mountains, the slow swell of that landlocked sea, the splash of a leaping porpoise, grassy, sun-flooded valleys that came down to the sea, crags and precipices, every headland which they rounded revealed new secrets and made for their happiness. When they landed to rest at noon or to camp at night, it was beside some flashing mountain stream where birds that had never known the startling noise of a gun hardly noticed them, and Dara's swift, silent arrow took its prey without causing alarm.

On the morning of the third day they ran the canoe on to a point of land and left it, to climb a lofty hill which proved to be the end of a ridge that ran north and east, then rose to form one of the foothills of the Andes. Like a map outspread they saw the sea they had sailed, the deep fjords both to their right hand and their left. They were on a twin peninsula, the isthmus of which was a steep hill, a part of the ridge on which they stood. On the south side of the isthmus the mountain formed a cliff that dropped sheerly into the sea. On the north side a strip of sea sand lay between mountain and fjord. They were discoverers of an uncharted land. And what a land of richness it was! There were valleys of parklike beauty in which deer grazed; other valleys where tall guanaco lived unmolested; streams, flamingo-haunted lakes, trees, thickets. It was a paradise of birds, of animals, of growing things. So all that day and the next the two companions wandered about enchanted.

At one time Dara, who was a few paces ahead, threw up a warning hand, which made Bob stop in his tracks, then on another signal he went forward cautiously until he came to the edge of the ridge and could look down into the valley. He saw a well-grassed hollow and a shining lagoon and grazing there a troop of some forty horses and mares. With a shock of surprise he realized that these were probably the descendants of those purebred Arabian horses which were first loosed in the Argentine by Pedro de Mendoza [3] in the year 1535.

---

[3] PEDRO DE MENDOZA (pā′drō dĕ mĕn-dō′sä)—A Spanish explorer who founded Buenos Aires.

Dara's delight was no less unbounded than Bob's. He stepped back from the edge of the ridge to caper with joy, snapping his fingers and thumb, laughing, his eyes sparkling. Less demonstrative, but no less excited, Bob stood looking. In that clear air he could see enough to assure himself of the beauty and hardihood of the wild creatures, which, having stood the

rigors of climate for generations, also the attacks of wild animals and hardships of many kinds, had become the kings of their kind. But knowing their sensitiveness, their keen sense of smell which made them aware of an enemy, he feared that at the least sign of danger they would flee into inaccessible places and perhaps desert the peninsula.

It became important, both lads knew, that the animals should be kept within that eight square miles of land for a time. So the companions hit upon an idea of making their camp on the narrow neck of land forming the isthmus. If the wild creatures stampeded and took to the heights, the camp fire would turn them. Southward the cliff ran sheer into the sea, so they could not pass there. Northward a strip of sea sand, twenty feet wide, lay between the foot of the hill and water. Thus the wild horses were inclosed in a magnificent pasture of eight square miles, within which were both narrow and wide canyons, and many a box canyon that formed a three-sided corral.

After that came many days of watchfulness during which the two hunters managed, on many occasions, to get close to the horses if they kept to leeward of them. Often the least movement that resulted in the snapping of a twig or the falling of a stone, was enough to arouse suspicion in the wild animals; whereupon the leader, or some wise mare, would raise a head, prick vigilant ears, look with startled eyes, and give a warning neigh, at which the others would take alarm. In spite of frail barricades they would have found the wide pampas and been seen no more. But Dara's silent arrow when they hunted for meat took its toll and never missed; and they exercised care that their hunting was done far away from the horses. To leave the beautiful creatures undisturbed in the valley where the grass was belly deep became the boys' chief care.

Taking advantage of cover and of wind, there were times when they drew close enough to recognize individual animals. They saw that their color was mostly bay, sometimes approaching chestnut color and sometimes brown, although here and there were piebalds, cream color or gray. Upon one, a black horse with two white feet, Dara set his heart. Another, a mare, chestnut in color, bore marks which told of a former captivity. A white ring of hair midway between her back and belly indicated the use of a cinch ring, and her mane told of clipping and trimming, although not recently. With her ran a year-old colt, fawn color, with black tail and mane; and it was plain that before very long she would bear a foal. Bob marked her for his own. But he also marked another, a handsome black with the build of a race horse, a glorified creature.

That was the beginning of two weeks of careful work for Bob

and Dara. At the end of that time the mare not only submitted to their handling, but her colt, too, had accepted their friendship.

Victory came on the heels of victory when Dara, having fashioned a set of boledores, caught his chosen horse. The wooden balls were not so likely to do damage as stone balls, for many a horse brought to a stand when the boledores tangle has had a leg broken when the whirling arms whipped around faster and faster as the circle narrowed, until the balls did their irreparable damage.

Dara concealed himself, and the mare with her foal and colt were tethered in the vega.[4] At that lucky moment when six horses, separated from the main body, were headed in the direction of the decoys, Bob stepped into sight. The six swift creatures, taking sudden alarm, broke into a thundering gallop toward the mare. Out stepped Dara, swinging his boledores high above his head. He let them fly at the right moment. They circled, flying straight, and caught the horse about the forelegs, bringing the gallant creature down on his knees, while the other horses, turning as by a single movement, thundered away, leaving their luckless fellow kicking and squealing and endeavoring to free himself from the strange entanglement. After that Bob and Dara worked fast, the former running forward to hold down the animal's head by pressure of his left knee on his neck but keeping out of reach of the thrashing hoofs; the latter preparing as he ran, the long hidestrip which was to serve as both bit and rein. Deftly he knotted it about the lower jaw of the captured creature. A moment later Bob was standing astride the fallen horse, and when it rose after Dara had loosed the boledores, Bob rose with it.

Some horses, when first mounted, stand sullen in spite of fright, whip, or spur; some pitch and buck. Some, as if determined to kill their rider, rear on their hind legs and throw themselves over backward. Others start off at a furious gallop

[4] VEGA (vä′gä)—A moist and fertile meadow.

and try to rid themselves of the man by plunging into the brush or under low-branched trees. The horse caught by Dara's boledores was one of the latter, but, happily for the adventurers, the steep-sided vega in which they made their catch was treeless, although sprinkled with low bushes. The animal, feeling the strange burden bestride it, shook its head in an attempt to free itself from the hide strip that bound his jaw, gave an angry whinny that ended in a sort of scream, stretched forth its head with a jerk that made Bob fear the hide might

break, then dashed forward. The mare gave a whinny of surprise: the foal rushed to her side. The colt ran in a circle, stepping high; and the frightened beast tore up the two-mile-long valley, Bob sitting easily enough. His moment of anxiety having passed, he felt a great joy at the thundering noise of hoofs, the wind that pressed him, the speed, the easy motion that made his seat easy though he kept his right hand firm on the mane.

On went the terrified, wild creature, making nothing of low bushes, taking higher ones at an easy leap, often shaking its head and often straining because of the strange binding at its jaw. Over a three-foot mountain stream, then up a gentle rise and down the slope, through knee-deep grass without slackening of pace and up a steeper slope! Timid, wild creatures scurried away, startled lapwings took to flight, and a flock of ducks rose in the air with a great noise of clapping wings as if applauding the performance. A couple of herons, much alarmed, mounted suddenly and, in wild, hurried, zigzag course kept ahead of the horse as if challenging it to further trial; then with tails spread fanwise bore away to the right.

All Bob could do was to let the wild creature tire; then the time would come to begin the lesson of guidance. Ahead he saw the swampy arm of the lake, a place he had not observed closely before, and he wondered for a swift moment whether danger lay that way and if it could be true that animals knew, by some instinct, unsure ground. He made an effort to swerve the horse but without avail, and it plunged into the soft ground, going fetlock deep. As he slackened pace, Bob could see, looking a little to the right, the staring, frightened eyes and the crimson nostril and the foam-flecked shoulders. But hardly had he seen, when the horse was headed for firm ground. The rider, believing that the first fierce fight for freedom had come to an end, relaxed his vigilance. In some inexplicable way the horse became aware of that relaxation. It plunged, gave a series of side leaps, jumped high, and came down with stiff legs that jolted its rider, then reared on hind legs, pawing the air, reared again, and came down to lash out with its hind legs. It tried all the tricks possible to unseat its rider, but Bob stuck fast, not pulling, not whipping, but balancing as if he and the horse were one. It was a definite fight for victory, and the rider won. After that, in the way of wild horses, there would be no further struggle, no opposition—only obedience. After that Bob could have led the splendid creature with a silken thread.

"FREEDOM FOR OUR MINDS"

ELIZABETH FOREMAN LEWIS

THE cloud of oppression and misery that hung over all China, from the Gobi Desert [1] to the Yangtze River,[2] from the Eastern Sea to the Western Mountains, grew larger every day. There was no end to conscription of workers on the Great Wall, and from each city, town, and hamlet, men continued to march on the long, hopeless road that led to labor made doubly bitter by exile.

At first, convicts had supplied the necessary numbers; but under the combined rigors of winter, insufficient food, and arduous toil, these had disappeared as rapidly as did locusts before the first black frost. Merchants, artisans, farmers—men from every useful walk of life—all were now seized to fill the emptying ranks of workers. Terror, accompanied always by smouldering rebellion, became a malignant growth eating at the hearts of the people.

[1] GOBI (gŏ'bē) Desert—A large desert in northern China.
[2] YANGTZE (yäng'tsĕ) River—A river in southern China.

169

"Have you a son?" they muttered among themselves; "then knot a strangling cord about his neck! Better for him to die at home, than far away on the accursed Wall. Have you a daughter? Then prepare her a cup of poison! Easier death for her now than life without father, brother or husband to protect her. Dead are our leaders; doomed are our scholars! Bitter, bitter, is the fate of the Black-haired People under Ch'in!" [3]

More than twenty years had passed since the young Prince Cheng of Ch'in had made himself ruler of all China. For several centuries previous to his conquest, the various Chinese states had waged a spasmodic but unceasing civil war. In the northwest, the rough frontier state of Ch'in had shrewdly watched its neighbors' difficulties and prepared to take advantage of them. Its well-trained army was rapidly increased and little by little seized territory was added to Ch'in's boundaries.

When Prince Cheng, still a youth, succeeded his father as head of Ch'in, the time was ripe for further successes. By nature even more ambitious than his ancestors, he was spurred on by a fortune teller's prophecy: "Your achievements will be unlimited, O Prince, but your years few in number!" From that moment Cheng was obsessed by desire for power and by fear of the shortness of time in which to win it. Reaching maturity, he promptly went into action and with amazing speed subjugated all the other states.

His victories had cost more than a million Chinese lives but now with the whole land under his control, Cheng began reconstruction in his kingdom. The first move was to permit farmers to reclaim their blood-soaked fields for planting. Next, to encourage trade, new highways were laid from one end of the country to the other. Engrossed in these peaceful pursuits, the people felt their resentment change to gratitude. This feeling, however, did not last long. Cheng, who now called himself Ch'in Hsih Huang-tih [4] (First Emperor of the Ch'in

[3] CH'IN (chǐn)—A dynasty in Chinese history from 255 to 206 B.C.
[4] CH'IN HSIH HUANG-TIH—Pronounced chǐn sē hwǎng'-tī.

Dynasty), was fully aware of strong enemy tribes to the north who were as anxious to capture all China as he had previously been. To keep them out he ordered the building of the Great Wall. This broad, heavily fortified barrier when completed would stretch across North China's hills and plains for fifteen hundred miles.

When several thousand men had already perished in the work, the Chinese, sick of everything to do with war and armament, began to murmur. Hsih Huang-tih himself came from a tribe that they had always considered barbarian. Since they were no longer citizens of a group of free states, whether one barbarian or another governed them made little difference.

The new emperor shrugged his shoulders at this opposition. The wall had to be built, and if men died at the task that was not his affair. Much more to blame, in his opinion, were those communities past which the new wall ran. If they provided satisfactory food and shelter for the labor forces billeted [5] in their homes, fewer workers would die.

Such thinking by their ruler did nothing to help the growing discontent with all that he did. As the months, then years passed, Hsih Huang-tih found little happiness on China's throne. Conquering these people had been easy in comparison with the difficulty of governing them.

Night after night, in the palace at Hsien-yang, he tossed on the imperial bed of black wood inlaid with mother-of-pearl and longed for sleep to release him temporarily from the fears and problems common to his days. Often, throwing aside the silk-filled comforts he would rise, cross the room, and opening a window panel gaze out upon his sleeping capital. Sometimes moonlight lay like snow upon the roofs, touching the city with an air of peace. At such moments the Emperor's lips would twist. No one knew better than he the unreality of such a fancy, for within those darkened houses all too many citizens plotted, even at this silent hour, against him.

[5] BILLETED—Assigned for lodging.

And what the people, or petty officials, thought and did was as nothing to the opposition that the scholars offered to his plans. With the tormenting persistency of a swarm of gadflies, they dared to protest each move he made by recalling the habits of former rulers. "Even Yao and Shun," they would remind him, "did not call themselves, 'Emperor.' Even they, the noblest of China's rulers, considered the title, 'Huang-tih,' sacred to him who originally shaped China's civilization." "Even Yu, changing the disastrous course of the Yellow River —a much greater task than building a wall—used voluntary labor and not conscription!" "Even . . ."—ay, he was sick unto death of their endless examples and complaints! Imprisonment, exile to the Wall, death—none of these punishments had silenced them. The Book of History said this; the Book of Poetry mentioned that; and the Court of Records settled the matter of precedence once and for all time!

Enraged, he had finally acted upon the advice of Li Su, his premier [6] and favorite, and issued an imperial edict to close the scholars' lips forever. "Hear these words!" it had proclaimed. "Within thirty days, every subject in this Kingdom having books of poetry, philosophy, or history by the one hundred classical writers shall carry these volumes to the prefects' offices and give them to be burned!

"Hear these words! Any man withholding books in his possession shall have the symbol of guilt branded on his face and shall then be sent to labor on the Wall!

"Hear these words! Any scholar or student heard repeating even a phrase from the destroyed books shall be seized and slain in the market place."

For days the smoke from burning pyres [7] had touched his nostrils with satisfaction. In the future with their books gone, the scholars would be like bowmen lacking arrows and he, the Emperor, would at last know peace.

[6] PREMIER (prē'mĭ-ẽr)—The first minister of state, prime minister.
[7] PYRE (pīr)—Funeral pile.

No, Experience contradicted in the lonely nights, peace was not for him. Never had his mind been at rest since that fortune teller had predicted great achievements but short life for him. Even in his moments of greatest success, happiness, flicked by that ancient fear, turned to bitterness. Already the first half of the seer's prophecy had become fact and that made the second seem inevitable. By crowding the past years with undertakings that would have killed a man less strong, he had kept his sense of personal doom prisoner to the unrelenting schedule of each day. Now with the chief roots of the people's opposition being destroyed, what would remain to occupy his brain but the terror of approaching death? he asked himself.

Shivering with panic, he plunged into plans for the future. Recently an adviser had mentioned an old astrologer [8] in Kuah-chi,[9] near the Eastern Sea, who was said to have found a way of prolonging life. Perhaps this man had succeeded where so many others had failed. If not, then an expedition must be sent to those distant islands, where it was claimed that the elixir of life [10] definitely existed. No stone should be left unturned in accomplishing his determination to live for many years. Had not he, alone, conquered this great Kingdom while still little more than a youth? Now at the height of manhood, he saw no limit to what might still be accomplished. Was he then to lie down and let the fear of Death defeat him?

One night while the Emperor brooded restlessly in his palace, miles away in Tsinan [11] City the scholar and philosopher, Fu Tze Chien, and his only daughter, Hsi-wo,[12] also lay awake through the long hours. The young girl, mistress of the household since her mother's death, lay in her room and felt her

---

[8] ASTROLOGER (ăs-trŏl'ô-jer)—One who professes to foretell events by the aspects and situation of the stars.
[9] KUAH-CHI—Pronounced kwä-chǐ'.
[10] ELIXIR (ê-lǐk'sêr) of life—A substance thought to be capable of prolonging life indefinitely.
[11] TSINAN—Pronounced tsǐ-nän'.
[12] FU TZE CHIEN . . . HSI-WO—Pronounced fōō tsĕ chyĕn . . . sǐ-wō.

heartbeats thud to the rhythm of muffled activity occurring in an adjoining corridor. There in the secrecy of night the chief house servant, aided by three others faithful and dependable beyond risk, built a false wall to an alcove and sealed away the remaining fifteen books that Fu Scholar had selected to save for posterity.

Ten days earlier when the Tsinan Yamen runner (police deputy) bearing the Imperial Edict had been ushered up the garden path into the great reception hall, Fu Tze Chien had read and acknowledged the decree with habitual dignity and calm. Only when the philosopher was once more alone with his daughter in the secluded study, where an occasional piece of satin bronze or carved jade testified to the cultural development of the preceding Chou and Shang Dynasties, had despair found natural expression.

"Years have passed since scholars first learned to expect death from the Court," he told her slowly. "At that time the threat seemed of small importance, since it was thought that younger men, taught to cherish the Great Learning, would fill our places in the kingdom. These might succeed where we, their elders, had failed, and the Son of Heaven at last be influenced to copy the ways of good and just kings. But to destroy the written word—that of all fates is worst! Without learning, our people will again become like the wild tribes they were before the first Huang-tih taught men how to live."

Silence settled on the room for several minutes, then Hsi-wo had ventured, "Perhaps, Honorable Father, we might save the most treasured books. Only your closest friends know how many volumes are under this roof."

"True! But by disobeying the Highest One's decree, I destroy the first 'Great Relationship' of ruler to subject. Moreover, who has wisdom to say which books should be saved and which ones burned?"

"Some are safely written on your memory, Respected One —why not . . ."

"My memory ends with me, and that may be soon. Certainly if they discover we hide books, death will follow."

"Even this ignorant maid knows that the books are more important than life," his daughter had protested, her dark eyes fired by youthful fervor. "If we hide them well, they may never be discovered by the Court. I, myself, have thought of one place."

For a long moment Fu Scholar had studied the eager, slender figure before him and thought sadly that her sixteen years of life had been overweighted with seriousness and responsibility. In less troubled times, that pretty head would have concerned itself with bright apparel and maidenly dreams. Instead, she was sharing burdens under which even his own shoulders grew weary.

"Brave and intelligent you are," he said with warm affection, "a maid worthy of bearing the name of that great and ancient king, Fu Hsi. But think a little! To hide the books might bring punishment on you as well as me. What then of your betrothal next moon to Ming's son? Can we ask another family to share our danger?"

"Is one unimportant girl's future to be weighed in the same scales with the Great Learning? No, Honored Father, let this roof be mine for as long as I shall live," she had answered with finality—and while speaking had seen the normal paths of woman's life close before her eyes.

Torn between allegiance to his king and duty to the people, Fu Scholar had decided to sacrifice the first for the second and had selected twenty-nine books for preservation. Space in which to hide these bulky volumes, the leaves of which were sheets of bamboo fourteen inches long, was a tremendous problem particularly in this day when a man's own brother might prove to be a court spy. Chimneys and house floors, hiding-places familiar to desperate people through the centuries, were at once eliminated. Such locations would be searched first. Eventually three spots had been decided upon: behind stones

lining the well; under the broad coping of the garden pool where carp swam lazily in the sunlight; and, last, the corridor alcove being closed this night.

While the servants worked, Hsi-wo found it difficult to remain quietly in her room. With her own eyes she was anxious to see how well they had succeeded in making the new stretch of wall seem a part of the old. Fear and excitement kept her mind in turmoil. Shivering, she repeated the words of the edict: "Any man withholding books in his possession shall have the symbol of guilt branded on his face and shall then be sent to labor on the Wall."

"Any man . . . any man . . ." this said nothing about women. Indeed, women and maids were supposed to know little about books. She herself was an exception, for her father had taught his daughter as he would have taught the son he lacked. Perhaps if danger came too close, she might still find some way in which to save their household. With this thought she fell asleep.

The burning of the books was followed by a period of terror for individual citizens, unusual even in centuries fraught with warfare. Scholar after scholar, refusing to yield his books or hiding them unsuccessfully, was slain in the market place or condemned to work on the Wall. Families, friends, servants— all came under the suspicion now of conspiring with teachers to evade the Emperor's edict and few men in the kingdom escaped the fear that each day's dawn might be their last.

Fu Tze Chien's house, searched on three occasions, revealed no books other than those delivered on the prescribed day at the prefect's office. Hsi-wo went about her tasks fearfully, her ears strained to catch the sound of every unexpected visitor in the gatehouse. After a few weeks the tension seemed to ease a little and she forgot everything else in watching her father. For Fu Scholar, worn by the strain of years of fruitless effort in the fight for good government, had succumbed under this last crushing blow to men's freedom of mind.

Unable to endure a study without the sight of books, he wandered restlessly about the house or sat for long, empty hours folding and unfolding the hands that had once so skillfully graven characters into bamboo sheets. He ate little, and often at night Hsi-wo heard him pacing the corridor where some of the books lay safely hidden behind the false wall. Worry and concern added years to his daughter's age; and it was as a mature woman that she weighed the Emperor's surprising invitation to all the remaining scholars in the kingdom to attend a feast at the capital and discuss the country's problems.

Reading the document, Fu Hseng's [13] emaciated face lighted with hope for the first time in weeks. "It is a gracious note. Perhaps the Son of Heaven regrets the past and wishes to make amends," he said slowly.

With compassion Hsi-wo eyed the speaker. Age and trouble only could thus have weakened the judgment of so good and wise a man. "Only yesterday, Respected One," she protested,

---

[13] FU HSENG—A title given to one of superior scholarship.

"Wu Teacher was slain here in Tsinan City; of a certainty this invitation was written before that. Knowing this, will scholars then go to the capital to be killed?"

"Like myself, all who have been taught to obey their ruler unto death will do so. Prepare things for my journey and waste no more words!"

"Yes, Honorable Father," Hsi-wo answered gently, then slipped from the room. "He must not go there to his death," she told herself fiercely, "but how am I to stop him?"

All day long laying out food, garments, and bedding for the trip she racked her brain for some plan to defeat his purpose. And then as if in answer to her prayers, Fu Hseng's body, over-taxed by too many demands, took control of the situation. During the night the old scholar became ill and next morning, torn by fever, he forgot temporarily all that had to do with worldly affairs.

Meanwhile, striving to do their duty, seven hundred scholars from all over the kingdom journeyed to Hsien-yang, the capital. At the Court, they were received courteously and feasted. As a part of special entertainment, they were then taken to see a field of gourds which had been forced to a rare flowering in the bleak North China winter. Commenting interestedly on so unnatural a phenomenon, the serious and dignified company walked between the rows of blossoming plants to the center of the field. There suddenly a falsely constructed surface of latticed bamboo, vines, and dirt crumbled under the weight of so many people, and in a huge pit below the seven hundred scholars found their last resting place.

After this mass murder there remained in all the Kingdom only a handful of those men who had once been the intellectual leaders in every community. Like Fu Hseng, these were so ill or infirm that they were not worth persecuting and Ch'in Hsih Huang-tih, himself sick in body and mind, blotted them from his calendar.

But, in this latest act of vengeance, the Emperor had overshot his mark. Learning that the scholars had been buried alive beneath the improvised gourd field, the Chinese people felt their years of fear and resentment spark into furious flame. Now their entire heritage of history and learning had been destroyed and the average citizen felt himself treading blindly a path without an end or a beginning. No further harm could come to him from the Court, save death, and with men still dying in swarms upon the Wall and with nothing important left for which to live and work—what further threat did Death hold?

Now they would begin to feed Ch'in some of his own medicine and bitter, bitter to the taste it should be! Organizing in small secret groups, the rebels laughed wildly at the irony of the situation. "No scholars are there to tell us to obey the Son of Heaven! No books are there to say that the paths of peace and justice are the best! We shall be our own books! We shall make our own peace and justice! We, we the people, shall become the Emperor's teachers!"

While the fire of rebellion spread throughout the kingdom, Fu Tze Chien in Tsinan recovering from his illness startled Hsi-wo one afternoon by saying, "Now that my body is rested, my mind becomes busy with plans. Better it is, I think, that two people know what only one knows now. Tomorrow I begin to teach you from those books that at present remain alive only in memory."

"Honored am I among women to share learning with him who has long been called 'Fu Hseng' for scholarship greater than that of other men," she replied with a smile.

Her father studied her with narrowed eyes. "Filial thou art beyond most children. Do you never regret your choice to remain always under this roof?"

"I do not regret," Hsi-wo answered steadily.

Folding the sewing in her lap, she rose and said, "Now I go to prepare you a large bowl of gruel that you may regain strength swiftly."

While father and daughter studied through the quiet days, the ferment in the kingdom continued to work. For long it had been the Emperor's boast, "None will dare not do what the ruler likes; all will avoid what he dislikes." At this thought the people now laughed in their sleeves. They were almost ready to seize him and the throne. Give them but another year or two and they would be fully prepared to retake the kingdom. Then suddenly Ch'in Hsih Huang-tih cheated them of their main purpose. In a final struggle with the black terror that had strangled his whole manhood, he died and with him died what he had boastingly called the First Dynasty of China.

For three brief years, Li Su, the premier, managed to keep Ch'in's son on the tottering throne. Then under their leader, Kao Tsu, the people took possession of the government and established the new Dynasty of Han. When after a number of years rebellion settled gradually into peace, citizens began clamoring hungrily for learning, and from strange hiding places an occasional bamboo leaf of writing was brought forth. No place yielded treasure equal to that of Fu Hseng's and the old scholar, now very feeble, became authority on every question concerning the Ancient Wisdom. Students selected from all over the kingdom sat at his feet listening to page after page from classics of which no copy existed. When the old man wearied, his daughter, herself a rich and living book of China's ancient wisdom, took up the lessons where he had stopped.

Great in years and honors, Fu Tze Chien went finally to join his ancestors, and the Lady Hsi-wo became recognized as teacher in his stead.

If sometimes from scholarly responsibilities of age her thoughts reverted to girlhood dreams of a home and children, she considered herself well repaid for their loss. In order that wisdom might not perish from this land, she had sacrificed the natural hopes and desires of a Chinese maid, but in doing so had answered the plea of her own and her people's hearts, "Freedom for our minds, O Emperor! For without that—of what value is life?"

JOURNEYS
INTO LEGEND AND FANCY

Enjoying legends of our own land.

RIP VAN WINKLE

WASHINGTON IRVING

WHOEVER has made a voyage up the Hudson must remember the Kaatskill mountains. They are a dismembered branch of the great Appalachian family, and are seen away to the west of the river, swelling up to a noble height, and lording it over the surrounding country. Every change of season, every change of weather, indeed, every hour of the day, produces some change in the magical hues and shapes of these mountains, and they are regarded by all the good wives, far and near, as perfect barometers. When the weather is fair and settled, they are clothed in blue and purple, and print their bold outlines on the clear evening sky; but sometimes, when the rest of the landscape is cloudless, they will gather a hood of gray vapors about their summits, which, in the last rays of the setting sun, will glow and light up like a crown of glory.

At the foot of these fairy mountains, the voyager may have descried the light smoke curling up from a village, whose shingle roofs gleam among the trees, just where the blue tints of the upland melt away into the fresh green of the nearer landscape. It is a little village of great antiquity, having been founded by some of the Dutch colonists, in the early times of the province, just about the beginning of the government of the good Peter Stuyvesant [1] (may he rest in peace!), and there were some of the houses of the original settlers standing within a few years, built of small yellow bricks brought from Holland, having latticed windows and gable fronts, surmounted with weathercocks.

[1] PETER STUYVESANT (stī'vĕ-sănt)—A famous governor of New Netherland.

In that same village, and in one of these very houses (which, to tell the precise truth, was sadly time-worn and weather-beaten), there lived many years since, while the country was yet a province of Great Britain, a simple, good-natured fellow of the name of Rip Van Winkle. He was a descendant of the Van Winkles who figured so gallantly in the chivalrous days of Peter Stuyvesant, and accompanied him to the siege of Fort Christina.[2] He inherited, however, but little of the martial character of his ancestors. I have observed that he was a simple, good-natured man; he was, moreover, a kind neighbor, and an obedient henpecked husband. Indeed, to the latter circumstance might be owing that meekness of spirit which gained him such universal popularity; for those men are most apt to be obsequious and conciliating abroad, who are under the discipline of shrews at home. Their tempers, doubtless, are rendered pliant and malleable in the fiery furnace of domestic tribulation; and a curtain-lecture is worth all the sermons in the world for teaching the virtues of patience and long-suffering. A termagant[3] wife may, therefore, in some respects, be considered a tolerable blessing; and if so, Rip Van Winkle was thrice blessed.

Certain it is, that he was a great favorite among all the good wives of the village, who, as usual with the amiable sex, took his part in all family squabbles; and never failed, whenever they talked those matters over in their evening gossipings, to lay all the blame on Dame Van Winkle. The children of the village, too, would shout with joy whenever he approached. He assisted at their sports, made their playthings, taught them to fly kites and shoot marbles, and told them long stories of ghosts, witches, and Indians. Whenever he went dodging about the village, he was surrounded by a troop of them, hanging on his skirts, clambering on his back, and playing a thousand tricks

---

[2] FORT CHRISTINA—A settlement of the Swedes in New Jersey. Stuyvesant captured this settlement in 1655 and claimed the land for the Dutch.

[3] TERMAGANT (tûr'má-gănt)—Quarrelsome, scolding.

on him with impunity; and not a dog would bark at him throughout the neighborhood.

The great error in Rip's composition was an insuperable aversion to all kinds of profitable labor. It could not be from the want of assiduity [4] or perseverance, for he would sit on a wet rock, with a rod as long and heavy as a Tartar's lance,[5] and fish all day without a murmur, even though he should not be encouraged by a single nibble. He would carry a fowling-piece [6] on his shoulder for hours together, trudging through woods and swamps, and up hill and down dale, to shoot a few squirrels or wild pigeons. He would never refuse to assist a neighbor even in the roughest toil, and was a foremost man at all country frolics for husking Indian corn, or building stone fences; the women of the village, too, used to employ him to run their errands, and to do such little odd jobs as their less obliging husbands would not do for them. In a word, Rip was ready to attend to anybody's business but his own; but as to doing family duty, and keeping his farm in order, he found it impossible.

In fact, he declared it was of no use to work on his farm; it was the most pestilent little piece of ground in the whole country, everything about it went wrong, and would go wrong, in spite of him. His fences were continually falling to pieces; his cow would either go astray, or get among the cabbages; weeds were sure to grow quicker in his fields than anywhere else; the rain always made a point of setting in just as he had some out-door work to do; so that though his patrimonial estate [7] had dwindled away under his management, acre by acre, until there was little more than a mere patch of Indian corn and potatoes, yet it was the worst-conditioned farm in the neighborhood.

His children, too, were as ragged and wild as if they belonged to nobody. His son Rip, an urchin begotten in his own

[4] ASSIDUITY (ăs-ĭ-dū'ĭ-tĭ)—Diligence, application, attention.
[5] TARTAR'S LANCE—A heavy lance about sixteen feet long.
[6] FOWLING-PIECE—A light gun for bird shooting.
[7] HIS PATRIMONIAL ESTATE—Estate inherited from his ancestors.

likeness, promised to inherit the habits, with the old clothes, of his father. He was generally seen trooping like a colt at his mother's heels, equipped in a pair of his father's cast-off galli-gaskins,[8] which he had much ado to hold up with one hand, as a fine lady does her train in bad weather.

Rip Van Winkle, however, was one of those happy mortals, of foolish, well-oiled dispositions, who take the world easy, eat white bread or brown, whichever can be got with least thought or trouble, and would rather starve on a penny than work for a pound. If left to himself, he would have whistled life away in perfect contentment; but his wife kept continually dinning in his ears about his idleness, his carelessness, and the ruin he was

bringing on his family. Morning, noon, and night, her tongue was incessantly going, and everything he said or did was sure to produce a torrent of household eloquence. Rip had but one way of replying to all lectures of the kind, and that, by frequent use, had grown into a habit. He shrugged his shoulders, shook

[8] GALLIGASKINS—Loose trousers.

186

his head, cast up his eyes, but said nothing. This, however, always provoked a fresh volley from his wife; so that he was fain [9] to draw off his forces, and take to the outside of the house —the only side which, in truth, belongs to a henpecked husband.

Rip's sole domestic adherent [10] was his dog Wolf, who was as much henpecked as his master; for Dame Van Winkle regarded them as companions in idleness, and even looked upon Wolf with an evil eye, as the cause of his master's going so often astray. True it is, in all points of spirit befitting an honorable dog, he was as courageous an animal as ever scoured the woods—but what courage can withstand the ever-during and all-besetting terrors of a woman's tongue? The moment Wolf entered the house his crest fell, his tail drooped to the ground, or curled between his legs, he sneaked about with a gallows air, [11] casting many a sidelong glance at Dame Van Winkle, and at the least flourish of a broomstick or ladle he would fly to the door with yelping precipitation. [12]

Times grew worse and worse with Rip Van Winkle as years of matrimony rolled on; a tart temper never mellows with age, and a sharp tongue is the only edged tool that grows keener with constant use. For a long while he used to console himself, when driven from home, by frequenting a kind of perpetual club of the sages, philosophers, and other idle personages of the village; which held its sessions on a bench before a small inn, designated by a rubicund [13] portrait of His Majesty, George the Third. [14] Here they used to sit in the shade through a long lazy summer's day, talking listlessly over village gossip, or telling endless sleepy stories about nothing. But it would have been worth any statesman's money to have heard the profound discussions which sometimes took place, when by chance

[9] FAIN—Glad.
[10] ADHERENT—Follower.
[11] GALLOWS AIR—As though he were to be hung on the gallows.
[12] PRECIPITATION—Haste.
[13] RUBICUND—Inclining to redness, red-tinted.
[14] GEORGE THE THIRD—King of England (1760–1829) who ruled the colonies at the time.

an old newspaper fell into their hands from some passing traveler. How solemnly they would listen to the contents, as drawled out by Derrick Van Brummel, the schoolmaster, a lapper, learned little man, who was not to be daunted by the most gigantic word in the dictionary; and how sagely they would deliberate upon public events some months after they had taken place.

The opinions of this junto [15] were completely controlled by Nicholas Vedder, a patriarch of the village, and landlord of the inn, at the door of which he took his seat from morning till night, just moving sufficiently to avoid the sun, and keep in the shade of a large tree; so that the neighbors could tell the hour by his movements as accurately as by a sundial. It is true, he was rarely heard to speak, but smoked his pipe incessantly. His adherents, however (for every great man has his adherents), perfectly understood him, and knew how to gather his opinions. When anything that was read or related displeased him, he was observed to smoke his pipe vehemently, and to send forth short, frequent, and angry puffs; but when pleased, he would inhale the smoke slowly and tranquilly, and emit it in light and placid clouds; and sometimes, taking the pipe from his mouth, and letting the fragrant vapor curl about his nose, would gravely nod his head in token of perfect approbation.[16]

From even this stronghold the unlucky Rip was at length routed by his termagant wife, who would suddenly break in upon the tranquillity of the assemblage and call the members all to nought; nor was that august personage, Nicholas Vedder himself, sacred from the daring tongue of this terrible virago,[17] who charged him outright with encouraging her husband in habits of idleness.

Poor Rip was at last reduced almost to despair; and his only alternative, to escape from the labor of the farm and the clamor of his wife, was to take gun in hand and stroll away into the

[15] JUNTO—Group, gathering of men.
[16] APPROBATION—Approval.
[17] VIRAGO (vĭ-rā′gō)—Shrew, termagant, vixen.

woods. Here he would sometimes seat himself at the foot of a
tree, and share the contents of his wallet with Wolf, with whom
he sympathized as a fellow-sufferer in persecution. "Poor
Wolf," he would say, "thy mistress leads thee a dog's life of
it; but never mind, my lad, whilst I live thou shalt never want
a friend to stand by thee!" Wolf would wag his tail, look wistfully in his master's face, and if dogs can feel pity I verily believe he reciprocated the sentiment with all his heart.

II

In a long ramble of the kind on a fine autumnal day, Rip had
unconsciously scrambled to one of the highest parts of the
Kaatskill mountains. He was after his favorite sport of squir-
rel-shooting, and the still solitudes had echoed and reëchoed
with the reports of his gun. Panting and fatigued, he threw
himself, late in the afternoon, on a green knoll, covered with
mountain herbage, that crowned the brow of a precipice. From
an opening between the trees he could overlook all the lower
country for many a mile of rich woodland. He saw at a distance the lordly Hudson, far, far below him, moving on its silent
but majestic course, with the reflection of a purple cloud, or the
sail of a lagging bark,[1] here and there sleeping on its glassy
bosom, and at last losing itself in the blue highlands.

On the other side he looked down into a deep mountain
glen, wild, lonely, and shagged, the bottom filled with fragments from the impending [2] cliffs, and scarcely lighted by the
reflected rays of the setting sun. For some time Rip lay musing on this scene; evening was gradually advancing; the mountains began to throw their long blue shadows over the valleys;
he saw that it would be dark long before he could reach the village; and he heaved a heavy sigh when he thought of encoun-
tering the terrors of Dame Van Winkle.

As he was about to descend, he heard a voice from a distance hallooing, "Rip Van Winkle! Rip Van Winkle!" He

[1] BARK—Small boat.
[2] IMPENDING—Overhanging.

looked around, but could see nothing but a crow winging its
solitary flight across the mountain. He thought his fancy must
have deceived him, and turned again to descend, when he heard
the same cry ring through the still evening air: "Rip Van
Winkle! Rip Van Winkle!"—at the same time Wolf bristled
up his back, and giving a low growl, skulked to his master's
side, looking fearfully down into the glen. Rip now felt a
vague apprehension stealing over him; he looked anxiously in
the same direction, and perceived a strange figure slowly toiling

up the rocks, and bending under the weight of something he
carried on his back. He was surprised to see any human being
in this lonely and unfrequented place, but supposing it to be
some one of the neighborhood in need of his assistance he
hastened down to yield it.

On nearer approach he was still more surprised at the singu-
larity of the stranger's appearance. He was a short, square-
built old fellow, with thick bushy hair, and a grizzled beard.

His dress was of the antique Dutch fashion, a cloth jerkin [3] strapped round the waist—several pair of breeches, the outer one of ample volume, decorated with rows of buttons down the side, and bunches at the knees. He bore on his shoulder a stout keg, that seemed full of liquor, and made signs for Rip to approach and assist him with the load. Though rather shy and distrustful of this new acquaintance, Rip complied with his usual alacrity; [4] and mutually relieving one another, they clambered up a narrow gully, apparently the dry bed of a mountain torrent. As they ascended, Rip every now and then heard long rolling peals, like distant thunder, that seemed to issue out of a deep ravine, or rather cleft between lofty rocks, toward which their rugged path conducted. He paused for an instant, but supposing it to be the muttering of one of those transient thunder-showers which often take place in mountain heights, he proceeded. Passing through the ravine, they came to a hollow, like a small amphitheater, [5] surrounded by perpendicular precipices, over the brinks of which impending trees shot their branches, so that you only caught glimpses of the azure sky and the bright evening cloud. During the whole time Rip and his companion had labored on in silence; for though the former marvelled greatly what could be the object of carrying a keg of liquor up this wild mountain, yet there was something strange and incomprehensible about the unknown, that inspired awe and checked familiarity.

On entering the amphitheater, new objects of wonder presented themselves. On a level spot in the center was a company of odd-looking personages playing at ninepins. They were dressed in a quaint outlandish fashion; some wore short doublets, [6] others jerkins, with long knives in their belts, and most of them had enormous breeches, of similar style with that of the guide. Their visages, too, were peculiar; one had a

---

[3] JERKIN—Jacket, or short coat.
[4] ALACRITY (á-lăk′rĭ-tĭ)—Quickness.
[5] AMPHITHEATER (ăm-fĭ-thē′á-tĕr)—Enclosure surrounded on all sides by walls.
[6] DOUBLETS—Close-fitting body garments.

large beard, broad face, and small piggish eyes; the face of another seemed to consist entirely of nose, and was surmounted
by a white sugar-loaf hat set off with a little red cock's tail.
They all had beards, of various shapes and colors. There was
one who seemed to be the commander. He was a stout old
gentleman, with a weather-beaten countenance; he wore a laced
doublet, broad belt and hanger,[7] high-crowned hat and feather,
red stockings, and high-heeled shoes, with roses in them. The
whole group reminded Rip of the figures in an old Flemish
painting in the parlor of Dominie Van Schaick, the village par-
son, and which had been brought over from Holland at the time
of the settlement.

What seemed particularly odd to Rip was, that though these
folks were evidently amusing themselves, yet they maintained
the gravest faces, the most mysterious silence, and were, withal,
the most melancholy party of pleasure he had ever witnessed.
Nothing interrupted the stillness of the scene but the noise of
the balls, which, whenever they were rolled, echoed along the
mountains like rumbling peals of thunder.

As Rip and his companion approached them, they suddenly
desisted from their play, and stared at him with such fixed
statue-like gaze, and such strange, uncouth, lack-lustre countenances, that his heart turned within him, and his knees smote
together. His companion now emptied the contents of the keg
into large flagons, and made signs to him to wait upon the
company. He obeyed with fear and trembling; they quaffed
the liquor in profound silence, and then returned to their game.

By degrees Rip's awe and apprehension subsided. He even
ventured, when no eye was fixed upon him, to taste the beverage, which he found had much of the flavor of excellent Hollands.[8] He was naturally a thirsty soul, and was soon tempted
to repeat the draught.[9] One taste provoked another; and he
reiterated his visits to the flagon so often that at length his

[7] HANGER—Short, slightly curved sword.
[8] HOLLANDS—A brand of liquor.
[9] DRAUGHT (dråft)—Drink.

senses were overpowered, his eyes swam in his head, his head gradually declined, and he fell into a deep sleep.

III

On waking, he found himself on the green knoll whence he had first seen the old man of the glen. He rubbed his eyes— it was a bright sunny morning. The birds were hopping and twittering among the bushes, and the eagle was wheeling aloft, and breasting the pure mountain breeze. "Surely," thought Rip, "I have not slept here all night." He recalled the occurrences before he fell asleep. The strange man with a keg of liquor—the mountain ravine—the wild retreat among the rocks —the woe-begone party of ninepins—the flagon—"Oh! that flagon! that wicked flagon!" thought Rip—"what excuse shall I make to Dame Van Winkle?"

He looked round for his gun, but in place of the clean, well-oiled fowling-piece, he found an old firelock lying by him, the barrel incrusted with rust, the lock falling off, and the stock worm-eaten. He now suspected that the grave roysterers of the mountain had put a trick upon him, and, having dosed him with liquor, had robbed him of his gun. Wolf, too, had disappeared, but he might have strayed away after a squirrel or partridge. He whistled after him and shouted his name, but all in vain; the echoes repeated his whistle and shout, but no dog was to be seen.

He determined to revisit the scene of the last evening's gambol, and if he met with any of the party, to demand his dog and gun. As he rose to walk, he found himself stiff in the joints, and wanting in his usual activity. "These mountain beds do not agree with me," thought Rip, "and if this frolic should lay me up with a fit of the rheumatism, I shall have a blessed time with Dame Van Winkle." With some difficulty he got down into the glen: he found the gully up which he and his companion had ascended the preceding evening; but to his astonishment a mountain stream was now foaming down it, leaping from rock to rock, and filling the glen with babbling murmurs. He, however, made shift to scramble up its sides, working his toilsome way through thickets of birch, sassafras, and witch-hazel, and sometimes tripped up or entangled by the wild grape vines that twisted their coils or tendrils from tree to tree, and spread a kind of network in his path.

At length he reached to where the ravine had opened through the cliffs to the amphitheater; but no traces of such opening remained. The rocks presented a high impenetrable wall over which the torrent came tumbling in a sheet of feathery foam, and fell into a broad deep basin, black from the shadows of the surrounding forest. Here, then, poor Rip was brought to a stand. He again called and whistled after his dog; he was only answered by the cawing of a flock of idle crows, sporting high in air about a dry tree that overhung a sunny precipice; and who, secure in their elevation, seemed to look down and scoff at the poor man's perplexities. What was to be done? The morning was passing away, and Rip felt famished for want of his breakfast. He grieved to give up his dog and gun; he dreaded to meet his wife; but it would not do to starve among the mountains. He shook his head, shouldered the rusty fire-lock, and with a heart full of trouble and anxiety, turned his steps homeward.

As he approached the village he met a number of people, but none whom he knew, which somewhat surprised him, for he had thought himself acquainted with every one in the country round. Their dress, too, was of a different fashion from that to which he was accustomed. They all stared at him with equal marks of surprise, and whenever they cast their eyes upon him, invariably stroked their chins. The constant recurrence of this gesture induced Rip, involuntarily, to do the same, when, to his astonishment, he found his beard had grown a foot long!

He had now entered the skirts of the village. A troop of strange children ran at his heels, hooting after him, and point-ing at his gray beard. The dogs, too, not one of which he

recognized for an old acquaintance, barked at him as he passed.
The very village was altered: it was larger and more populous.
There were rows of houses which he had never seen before, and
those of which had been his familiar haunts had disappeared.
Strange names were over the doors—strange faces at the windows—everything was strange. His mind now misgave him;
he began to doubt whether both he and the world around him
were not bewitched. Surely this was his native village, which
he had left but the day before. There stood the Kaatskill
mountains—there ran the silver Hudson at a distance—there
was every hill and dale precisely as it had always been—Rip
was sorely perplexed—"That flagon last night," thought he,
"has addled my poor head sadly!"

It was with some difficulty that he found the way to his own
house, which he approached with silent awe, expecting every
moment to hear the shrill voice of Dame Van Winkle. He
found the house gone to decay—the roof fallen in, the windows
shattered, and the doors off the hinges. A half-starved dog that

looked like Wolf was skulking about it. Rip called him by name, but the cur snarled, showed his teeth, and passed on. This was an unkind cut indeed. "My very dog," sighed poor Rip, "has forgotten me!"

He entered the house, which, to tell the truth, Dame Van Winkle had always kept in neat order. It was empty, forlorn, and apparently abandoned. This desolateness overcame all his connubial fears [1]—he called loudly for his wife and children— the lonely chambers rang for a moment with his voice, and then all again was silence.

He now hurried forth, and hastened to his old resort, the village inn—but it too was gone. A large rickety wooden building stood in its place, with great gaping windows, some of them broken and mended with old hats and petticoats, and over the door was painted, "The Union Hotel, by Jonathan Doolittle." Instead of the great tree that used to shelter the quiet little Dutch inn of yore, there now was reared a tall naked pole, with something on the top that looked like a red nightcap, and from it was fluttering a flag, on which was a singular assemblage of stars and stripes—all this was strange and incomprehensible. He recognized on the sign, however, the ruby face of King George, under which he had smoked so many a peaceful pipe; but even this was singularly metamorphosed.[2] The red coat was changed for one of blue and buff, a sword was held in the hand instead of a scepter, the head was decorated with a cocked hat, and underneath was painted in large characters, GENERAL WASHINGTON.

There was, as usual, a crowd of folk about the door, but none that Rip recollected. The very character of the people seemed changed. He looked in vain for old Nicholas Vedder, with his broad face, double chin, and fair long pipe, uttering clouds of tobacco smoke instead of idle speeches; or Van Brummel, the schoolmaster, doling forth the contents of an ancient newspaper. In place of these, a lean, bilious-looking fellow, with his

[1] CONNUBIAL FEARS—Fears of his wife.
[2] METAMORPHOSED—Changed, altered.

pockets full of handbills, was haranguing vehemently about rights of citizens—elections—members of Congress—liberty—Bunker's Hill—heroes of seventy-six—and other words, which were a perfect Babylonish jargon [3] to the bewildered Rip.

IV

The appearance of Rip, with his long, grizzled beard, his rusty fowling-piece, his uncouth dress, and an army of women and children at his heels, soon attracted the attention of the tavern politicians. They crowded round him, eyeing him from head to foot with great curiosity. The orator bustled up to him, and drawing him partly aside, inquired, "on which side he voted?" Rip stared in vacant stupidity. Another short but busy little fellow pulled him by the arm, and rising on tip-toe, inquired in his ears, "whether he was Federal or Democrat?" Rip was equally at a loss to comprehend the question; when a knowing, self-important old gentleman, in a sharp cocked hat, made his way through the crowd, putting them to the right and left with his elbows as he passed, and planting himself before Van Winkle, with one arm akimbo, the other resting on his cane, his keen eyes and sharp hat penetrating, as it were, into his very soul, demanded in an austere tone, "what brought him to the election with a gun on his shoulder, and a mob at his heels, and whether he meant to breed a riot in the village?"—"Alas! gentlemen," cried Rip, somewhat dismayed, "I am a poor quiet man, a native of the place, and a loyal subject of the King, God bless him!"

Here a general shout burst from the bystanders—"a Tory! a Tory! a spy! a refugee! hustle him! away with him!" It was with great difficulty that the self-important man in the cocked hat restored order; and having assumed a tenfold austerity of brow, demanded again of the unknown culprit what he came there for, and whom he was seeking. The poor man humbly assured him that he meant no harm, but merely came there in

[3] BABYLONISH JARGON—Confused, outlandish utterances. Look up the Bible story of Babylon.

search of some of his neighbors, who used to keep about the tavern.

"Well—who are they—name them."

Rip bethought himself a moment, and inquired, "Where's Nicholas Vedder?"

There was a silence for a little while, when an old man replied, in a thin, piping voice, "Nicholas Vedder! why, he is dead and gone these eighteen years. There was a wooden tombstone in the churchyard that used to tell all about him, but that's rotten and gone too."

"Where's Brom Dutcher?"

"Oh, he went off to the army in the beginning of the war; some say he was killed at the storming of Stony Point—others say he was drowned in a squall at the foot of Anthony's Nose.[1] I don't know—he never came back again."

"Where's Van Brummel, the schoolmaster?"

"He went off to the wars, too, was a great militia general, and is now in Congress."

Rip's heart died away at hearing of these sad changes in his home and friends, and finding himself thus alone in the world. Every answer puzzled him too, by treating of such enormous lapses of time, and of matters which he could not understand: war—Congress—Stony Point;—he had no courage to ask after any more friends, but cried out in despair, "Does nobody here know Rip Van Winkle?"

"Oh, Rip Van Winkle!" exclaimed two or three.—"Oh, to be sure! that's Rip Van Winkle yonder, leaning against the tree."

Rip looked, and beheld a precise counterpart of himself as he went up the mountain; apparently as lazy, and certainly as ragged. The poor fellow was now completely confounded. He doubted his own identity, and whether he was himself or another man. In the midst of his bewilderment, the man in the cocked hat demanded who he was, and what was his name?

"God knows!" exclaimed he, at his wit's end; "I'm not my-

---

[1] ANTHONY'S NOSE—A rock or bluff on the river.

self—I'm somebody else—that's me yonder—no—that's somebody else got into my shoes—I was myself last night, but I fell
asleep on the mountain, and they've changed my gun, and
everything's changed, and I can't tell what's my name, or who
I am!"

The bystanders began now to look at each other, nod, wink
significantly, and tap their fingers against their foreheads.
There was a whisper, also, about securing the gun, and keeping the old fellow from doing mischief; at the very suggestion
of which the self-important man in the cocked hat retired with
some precipitation. At this critical moment a fresh, comely
woman pressed through the throng to get a peep at the gray-
bearded man. She had a chubby child in her arms, which,
frightened at his looks, began to cry. "Hush, Rip," cried she,
"hush, you little fool; the old man won't hurt you." The name
of the child, the air of the mother, the tone of her voice, all
awakened a train of recollections in his mind.

"What is your name, my good woman?" asked he.

"Judith Gardenier."

"And your father's name?"

"Ah, poor man, Rip Van Winkle was his name, but it's twenty
years since he went away from home with his gun, and never
has been heard of since,—his dog came home without him; but
whether he shot himself, or was carried away by the Indians,
nobody can tell. I was then but a little girl."

Rip had but one question more to ask; but he put it with a
faltering voice:—

"Where's your mother?"

"Oh, she too died but a short time since; she broke a
blood-vessel in a fit of passion at a New England peddler."

There was a drop of comfort, at least, in this intelligence.
The honest man could contain himself no longer. He caught
his daughter and her child in his arms. "I am your father!"
cried he—"Young Rip Van Winkle once—old Rip Van Winkle
now! Does nobody know poor Rip Van Winkle?"

All stood amazed, until an old woman, tottering out from among the crowd, put her hand to her brow, and peering under

it in his face for a moment, exclaimed, "Sure enough! it is Rip Van Winkle—it is himself. Welcome home again, old neighbor. Why, where have you been these twenty long years?"

Rip's story was soon told, for the whole twenty years had been to him but as one night. The neighbors stared when they heard it; some were seen to wink at each other, and put their tongues in their cheeks; and the self-important man in the cocked hat, who, when the alarm was over, had returned to the field, screwed down the corners of his mouth, and shook his head—upon which there was a general shaking of the head throughout the assemblage.

It was determined, however, to take the opinion of old Peter Vanderdonk, who was seen slowly advancing up the road. He was a descendant of the historian of that name, who wrote one of the earliest accounts of the province. Peter was the most ancient inhabitant of the village, and well versed in all the wonderful events and traditions of the neighborhood. He recollected Rip at once, and corroborated [2] his story in the most satisfactory manner. He assured the company that it was a fact, handed down from his ancestor the historian, that the Kaatskill mountains had always been haunted by strange beings. That it was affirmed that the great Hendrick Hudson, the first discoverer of the river and country, kept a kind of vigil [3] there every twenty years, with his crew of the *Half Moon;* being permitted in this way to revisit the scenes of his enterprise, and keep a guardian eye upon the river and the great city called by his name. That his father had once seen them in their old Dutch dresses playing at ninepins in a hollow of the mountains; and that he himself had heard, one summer afternoon, the sound of their ninepin balls, rolling like distant peals of thunder.

To make a long story short, the company broke up, and returned to the more important concerns of the election. Rip's daughter took him home to live with her; she had a snug, well-furnished house, and a stout cheery farmer for a husband, whom Rip recollected for one of the urchins that used to climb upon his back. As to Rip's son and heir, who was the ditto of himself, seen leaning against the tree, he was employed to work on the farm; but evinced an hereditary disposition to attend to anything else but his business.

Rip now resumed his old walks and habits; he soon found many of his former cronies, though all rather the worse for the wear and tear of time; and preferred making friends among the rising generation, with whom he soon grew into great favor.

Having nothing to do at home, and being arrived at that happy age when a man can be idle with impunity,[4] he took his place once more on the bench at the inn door, and was rev-

---

[2] CORROBORATED—Confirmed.
[3] VIGIL—Watch.
[4] IMPUNITY—Without punishment, or fear.

erenced as one of the patriarchs of the village, and a chronicle [5] of the old times "before the war." It was some time before he could get into the regular track of gossip, or could be made to comprehend the strange events that had taken place during his torpor.[6] How that there had been a revolutionary war—that the country had thrown off the yoke of old England—and that, instead of being a subject of His Majesty, George the Third, he was now a free citizen of the United States. Rip, in fact, was no politician; the changes of states and empires made but little impression on him; but there was one species of despotism under which he had long groaned, and that was—petticoat government. Happily, that was at an end: he had got his neck out of the yoke of matrimony, and could go in and out whenever he pleased, without dreading the tyranny of Dame Van Winkle. Whenever her name was mentioned, however, he shook his head, shrugged his shoulders, and cast up his eyes; which might pass either for an expression of resignation to his fate, or joy at his deliverance.

He used to tell his story to every stranger that arrived at Mr. Doolittle's hotel. He was observed, at first, to vary on some points every time he told it, which was, doubtless, owing to his having so recently awaked. It at last settled down precisely to the tale I have related, and not a man, woman, or child in the neighborhood but knew it by heart. Some always pretended to doubt the reality of it, and insisted that Rip had been out of his head, and that was one point on which he always remained flighty. The old Dutch inhabitants, however, almost universally gave it full credit. Even to this day, they never hear a thunderstorm of a summer afternoon about the Kaatskills, but they say Hendrick Hudson and his crew are at their game of ninepins; and it is a common wish of all henpecked husbands in the neighborhood, when life hangs heavy on their hands, that they might have a quieting draught out of Rip Van Winkle's flagon.

[5] CHRONICLE—A history.   [6] TORPOR—Sleep.

THE COURTSHIP OF MILES STANDISH

HENRY WADSWORTH LONGFELLOW

In the old Colony days, in Plymouth, the land of the Pil-
   grims,
To and fro in a room of his simple and primitive dwelling,
Clad in doublet and hose and boots of Cordovan leather,
Strode, with a martial air, Miles Standish, the Puritan Captain.
5 Buried in thought he seemed, with his hands behind him, and
   pausing
Ever and anon to behold his glittering weapons of warfare,
Hanging in shining array along the walls of the chamber,—
Cutlass and corselet of steel, and his trusty sword of
   Damascus,
Curved at the point and inscribed with its mystical Arabic
   sentence,
10 While underneath, in a corner, were fowling piece, musket and
   matchlock.
Short of stature he was, but strongly built and athletic,
Broad in the shoulders, deep-chested, with muscles and sinews
   of iron;
Brown as a nut was his face, but his russet beard was already
Flaked with patches of snow, as hedges sometimes in
   November.

3. DOUBLET—A close-fitting garment for men, worn in the 16th and 17th centuries.
3. CORDOVAN (kôr'-dō-văn) LEATHER—Goatskin leather was first prepared in Cordova, Spain; hence the name, Cordovan.
8. CUTLASS—A short, heavy, curved sword.
8. CORSELET—A breastplate of light armor.
8. SWORD OF DAMASCUS—The city of Damascus in Syria was famous for the production of steel blades so finely tempered that the point could be made to touch the hilt without breaking.
9. ARABIC SENTENCE—These swords were often engraved with sentences from the Koran, the Mohammedan Bible.
10. FOWLING PIECE—A light gun used in bird hunting.
10. MUSKET—A light infantry gun used in war.
10. MATCHLOCK—A heavier, old-style musket, invented toward the end of the 14th century; the lock held a match or twisted rope to retain the fire.

15 Near him was seated John Alden, his friend and household
　　companion,

　　Writing with diligent speed at a table of pine by the window;

　　Fair-haired, azure-eyed, with delicate Saxon complexion,

　　Having the dew of his youth, and the beauty thereof, as the
　　captives

　　Whom Saint Gregory saw, and exclaimed, "Not Angles but
　　Angels."

20 Youngest of all he was of the men who came in the *Mayflower*.

　　Suddenly breaking the silence, the diligent scribe inter-
　　rupting,

　　Spake, in the pride of his heart, Miles Standish the Captain
　　of Plymouth.

17. AZURE-EYED—Blue-eyed.

17. SAXON COMPLEXION—Very fair with light golden hair and rosy cheeks.

19. SAINT GREGORY—A Pope of the 6th century. While still a monk, he
noticed the white bodies and faces and golden hair of some of the youths who
stood bound at the slave-market in Rome. Upon inquiring who they were he
was told they were Angles from Britain. "Not Angles, but Angels," said he,
"and they ought to be fellow heirs of heaven."

21. SCRIBE—One who writes records; a clerk.

"Look at these arms," he said, "the warlike weapons that hang
here
Burnished and bright and clean, as if for parade or inspection!
25 This is the sword of Damascus I fought with in Flanders; this
breastplate,
Well I remember the day! once saved my life in a skirmish;
Here in the front you can see the very dint of the bullet
Fired point-blank at my heart by a Spanish arcabucero.
Had it not been of sheer steel, the forgotten bones of Miles
Standish
30 Would at this moment be mold, in their grave in the Flemish
morasses."

Thereupon answered John Alden, but looked not up from
his writing:
"Truly the breath of the Lord hath slackened the speed of the
bullet;
He in His mercy preserved you, to be our shield and our
weapon!"
Still the Captain continued, unheeding the words of the stripling:
35 "See, how bright they are burnished, as if in an arsenal
hanging;
That is because I have done it myself, and not left it to others.
Serve yourself, would you be well served, is an excellent adage;
So I take care of my arms, as you of your pens and your ink-
horn.
Then, too, there are my soldiers, my great, invincible army,
40 Twelve men, all equipped, having each his rest and his matchlock,
Eighteen shillings a month, together with diet and pillage,

25. FLANDERS—A province of Belgium.
28. ARCABUCERO (är-kä-bōo-thä′rō)—A soldier armed with a musket.
30. FLEMISH MORASSES—Swamps in the northern part of Flanders.
37. ADAGE (ăd′åj)—Proverb; a saying expressing a well-known truth.
40. REST—A support for a gun.
41. SHILLING—A British coin of silver, valued at about 24 cents.

And, like Caesar, I know the name of each of my soldiers!"
This he said with a smile, that danced in his eyes, as the sun-
beams
Dance on the waves of the sea, and vanish again in a moment.

45 Alden laughed as he wrote, and still the Captain continued:
"Look! you can see from this window my brazen howitzer
planted
High on the roof of the church, a preacher who speaks to the
purpose,
Steady, straightforward, and strong, with irresistible logic,
Orthodox, flashing conviction right into the hearts of the
heathen.
50 Now we are ready, I think, for any assault of the Indians:
Let them come, if they like, and the sooner they try it the
better,—
Let them come if they like, be it sagamore, sachem, or
powwow,
Aspinet, Samoset, Corbitant, Squanto, or Tokamahamon!"

Long at the window he stood, and wistfully gazed on the
landscape,
55 Washed with a cold gray mist, the vapory breath of the east
wind,
Forest and meadow and hill, and the steel-blue rim of the
ocean,
Lying silent and sad, in the afternoon shadows and sunshine.
Over his countenance flitted a shadow like those on the landscape,

42. CAESAR—A great Roman soldier and statesman.
46. BRAZEN HOWITZER—A short, light cannon made of brass.
49. ORTHODOX—Sound in opinion or doctrine.
52. SAGAMORE, SACHEM, OR POWWOW—Sagamore and sachem are Indian tribal chiefs, sagamore being slightly inferior to sachem. Powwow is an Indian medicine man.
53. The names in this line are Indians who visited the colony and are mentioned in the chronicles of early Puritan days. The pronunciations are ăs'pĭ-net, săm'ō-sĕt, kôr'bĭ-tänt, skwän'tō, and tŏk'ȧ-mȧ-hä'mȯn.

Gloom intermingled with light; and his voice was subdued
　　with emotion,
60 Tenderness, pity, regret, as after a pause he proceeded:
"Yonder there, on the hill by the sea, lies buried Rose Standish;
Beautiful rose of love, that bloomed for me by the wayside!
She was the first to die of all who came in the *Mayflower!*
Green above her is growing the field of wheat we have sown
　　there,
65 Better to hide from the Indian scouts the graves of our people,
Lest they should count them and see how many already have
　　perished!"
Sadly his face he averted, and strode up and down, and was
　　thoughtful.

Fixed to the opposite wall was a shelf of books, and among
　　them
Prominent three, distinguished alike for bulk and for binding;
70 Barriffe's *Artillery Guide,* and the *Commentaries* of Caesar,
Out of the Latin translated by Arthur Goldinge of London,
And, as if guarded by these, between them was standing the
　　Bible.
Musing a moment before them, Miles Standish paused, as if
　　doubtful
Which of the three he should choose for his consolation and
　　comfort,
75 Whether the wars of the Hebrews, the famous campaigns of
　　the Romans,
Or the artillery practice, designed for belligerent Christians.
Finally down from its shelf he dragged the ponderous Roman,
Seated himself at the window, and opened the book, and in
　　silence

75. WARS OF THE HEBREWS—The conquest of the heathen hosts which began
under the leadership of Joshua; these stories are in the Bible.
　75. CAMPAIGNS OF THE ROMANS—In the *Commentaries* of Caesar.
　76. BELLIGERENT (bĕ-lĭj′ĕr-ĕnt)—Warlike.
　77. PONDEROUS ROMAN—Which book did he take down?

Turned o'er the well-worn leaves, where thumb-marks thick
    on the margin,
80 Like the trample of feet, proclaimed the battle was hottest.
Nothing was heard in the room but the hurrying pen of the
    stripling,
Busily writing epistles important, to go by the *Mayflower*,
Ready to sail on the morrow, or next day at latest, God willing!
Homeward bound with the tidings of all that terrible winter,
85 Letters written by Alden, and full of the name of Priscilla,
Full of the name and the fame of the Puritan maiden Priscilla!

II

Nothing was heard in the room but the hurrying pen of the
    stripling,
Or an occasional sigh from the laboring heart of the Captain,
Reading the marvelous words and achievements of Julius
    Caesar.
90 After a while he exclaimed, as he smote with his hand, palm
    downward,
Heavily on the page: "A wonderful man was this Caesar!
You are a writer, and I am a fighter, but here is a fellow
Who could both write and fight, and in both was equally
    skillful!"
Straightway answered and spake John Alden, the comely, the
    youthful:
95 "Yes, he was equally skilled, as you say, with his pen and his
    weapons.
Somewhere have I read, but where I forget, he could dictate
Seven letters at once, at the same time writing his memoirs."
"Truly," continued the Captain, not heeding or hearing the
    other,
"Truly a wonderful man was Caius Julius Caesar!
100 Better be first, he said, in a little Iberian village,

97. MEMOIRS (mĕm'wŏrz)—Accounts of personal experiences.
100. IBERIAN—Iberia was the ancient name of Spain.

Than be second in Rome, and I think he was right when he
  said it.
Twice was he married before he was twenty, and many times
  after;
Battles five hundred he fought, and a thousand cities he conquered;
He, too, fought in Flanders, as he himself has recorded;
105 Finally he was stabbed by his friend, the orator Brutus!
Now, do you know what he did on a certain occasion in
  Flanders,
When the rear-guard of his army retreated, the front giving
  way too,
And the immortal Twelfth Legion was crowded so closely to-
  gether
There was no room for their swords?   Why, he seized a shield
  from a soldier,
110 Put himself straight at the head of his troops, and commanded
  the captains,
Calling on each by his name, to order forward the ensigns;
Then to widen the ranks, and give more room for their
  weapons;
So he won the day, the battle of something-or-other.
That's what I always say; if you wish a thing to be well done,
115 You must do it yourself, you must not leave it to others!"

All was silent again; the Captain continued his reading.
Nothing was heard in the room but the hurrying pen of the
  stripling
Writing epistles important to go next day by the *Mayflower,*
Filled with the name and the fame of the Puritan maiden
  Priscilla;

105. BRUTUS—Marcus Brutus, one of the conspirators who helped murder
Caesar, and who had been Caesar's best friend. He was persuaded to believe
that Caesar's death was for the good of Rome.
108. TWELFTH LEGION—Caesar's favorite legion, the most perfect fighting
machine of ancient times.
111. ENSIGNS—Standard bearers.

120 Every sentence began or closed with the name of Priscilla,
     Till the treacherous pen, to which he confided the secret,
     Strove to betray it by singing and shouting the name of
               Priscilla!
     Finally closing his book, with a bang of the ponderous cover,
     Sudden and loud as the sound of a soldier grounding his
               musket,
125 Thus to the young man spake Miles Standish, the Captain of
               Plymouth:
     "When you have finished your work, I have something impor-
               tant to tell you.
     Be not however in haste; I can wait; I shall not be impatient!"
     Straightway Alden replied, as he folded the last of his letters,
     Pushing his papers aside, and giving respectful attention:
130 "Speak; for whenever you speak, I am always ready to listen,
     Always ready to hear whatever pertains to Miles Standish."

         Thereupon answered the Captain, embarrassed, and culling
               his phrases:
     " 'Tis not good for a man to be alone, say the Scriptures.
     This I have said before, and again and again I repeat it;
135 Every hour in the day, I think it, and feel it, and say it.
     Since Rose Standish died, my life has been weary and dreary;
     Sick at heart have I been, beyond the healing of friendship.
     Oft in my lonely hours have I thought of the maiden Priscilla.
     She is alone in the world; her father and mother and brother
140 Died in the winter together; I saw her going and coming,
     Now to the grave of the dead, and now to the bed of the dying,
     Patient, courageous, and strong, and said to myself, that if ever
     There were angels on earth, as there are angels in heaven,
     Two have I seen and known; and the angel whose name is
               Priscilla,
145 Holds in my desolate life the place which the other abandoned.
     Long have I cherished the thought, but never have dared to
               reveal it,

Being a coward in this, though valiant enough for the most
    part.
Go to the damsel Priscilla, the loveliest maiden of Plymouth,
Say that a blunt old Captain, a man not of words but of actions,
150 Offers his hand and his heart, the hand and heart of a soldier.
Not in these words, you know, but this in short is my meaning;
I am a maker of war, and not a maker of phrases.
You, who are bred as a scholar, can say it in elegant language,
Such as you read in your books of the pleadings and wooings
    of lovers,
155 Such as you think best adapted to win the heart of a maiden."

When he had spoken, John Alden, the fair-haired, taciturn
    stripling,
All aghast at his words, surprised, embarrassed, bewildered,
Trying to mask his dismay by treating the subject with light-
    ness,
Trying to smile, and yet feeling his heart stand still in his
    bosom,
160 Just as a timepiece stops in a house that is stricken by light-
    ning,
Thus made answer and spake, or rather stammered than an-
    swered:
"Such a message as that, I am sure I should mangle and mar it;
If you would have it well done,—I am only repeating your
    maxim,—
You must do it yourself, you must not leave it to others!"

165   But with the air of a man whom nothing can turn from
    his purpose,
Gravely shaking his head, made answer the Captain of
    Plymouth:
"Truly the maxim is good, and I do not mean to gainsay it;

156. TACITURN (tăs'ĭ-tûrn)—Quiet, silent, not given to talking.
167. GAINSAY—Contradict, oppose.

But we must use it discreetly, and not waste powder for
    nothing.

Now, as I said before, I was never a maker of phrases.

170 I can march up to a fortress and summon the place to
    surrender,

But march up to a woman with such a proposal, I dare not.

I'm not afraid of bullets, nor shot from the mouth of a cannon,

But of a thundering 'No!' point-blank from the mouth of a
    woman,

That I confess I'm afraid of, nor am I ashamed to confess it!

175 So you must grant my request, for you are an elegant scholar,

Having the graces of speech, and skill in the turning of
    phrases."

Taking the hand of his friend, who still was reluctant and
    doubtful,

Holding it long in his own, and pressing it kindly, he added:

"Though I have spoken thus lightly, yet deep is the feeling
    that prompts me;

180 Surely you cannot refuse what I ask in the name of our friend-
    ship!"

Then made answer John Alden: "The name of friendship is
    sacred;

What you demand in that name, I have not the power to deny
    you!"

So the strong will prevailed, subduing and molding the gentler,

Friendship prevailed over love, and Alden went on his errand.

III

185   So the strong will prevailed, and Alden went on his errand,

Out of the street of the village, and into the paths of the forest,

Into the tranquil woods, where bluebirds and robins were
    building

Towns in the populous trees, with hanging gardens of verdure,

Peaceful, aërial cities of joy and affection and freedom.

188. VERDURE—Greenness.
189. AËRIAL (ā-ē′rĭ-ȧl)—Built in the air, high up.

190 All around him was calm, but within him commotion and con-
        flict,
     Love contending with friendship, and self with each generous
        impulse.
     To and fro in his breast his thoughts were heaving and dashing,
     As in a floundering ship, with every roll of the vessel,
     Washes the bitter sea, the merciless surge of the ocean!
195 "Must I relinquish it all," he cried with a wild lamentation,—
     "Must I relinquish it all, the joy, the hope, the illusion?
     Was it for this I have loved, and waited, and worshiped in
        silence?
     Was it for this I have followed the flying feet and the shadow
     Over the wintry sea, to the desolate shores of New England?
200 Truly the heart is deceitful, and out of its depth of corruption
     Rise, like an exhalation, the misty phantoms of passion;
     Angels of light they seem, but are only delusions of Satan.
     All is clear to me now; I feel it, I see it distinctly!
     This is the hand of the Lord: it is laid upon me in anger,
205 For I have followed too much the heart's desires and devices,
     Worshiping Astaroth blindly, and impious idols of Baal.
     This is the cross I must bear; the sin and the swift
        retribution."

     So through the Plymouth woods John Alden went on his
        errand;
     Crossing the brook at the ford, where it brawled over pebble
        and shallow,
210 Gathering still, as he went, the mayflowers blooming around
        him,
     Fragrant, filling the air with a strange and wonderful
        sweetness,

196. ILLUSION—Dream or vision.
202. DELUSIONS—Misleadings.
206. ASTAROTH (ăs'tȧ-rŏth)—The goddess of love.
206. BAAL (bā'ȧl)—The god of love.
207. RETRIBUTION—Punishment for wrong doing.

Children lost in the woods, and covered with leaves in their
    slumber.
"Puritan flowers," he said, "and the type of Puritan maidens,
Modest and simple and sweet, the very type of Priscilla!
215 So I will take them to her; to Priscilla, the mayflower of
    Plymouth,
Modest and simple and sweet, as a parting gift will I take
    them;
Breathing their silent farewells, as they fade and wither and
    perish,
Soon to be thrown away as is the heart of the giver."

So through the Plymouth woods John Alden went on his
    errand;
220 Came to an open space, and saw the disk of the ocean,
Sailless, somber and cold with the comfortless breath of the
    east wind;
Saw the new-built house, and people at work in a meadow;
Heard, as he drew near the door, the musical voice of Priscilla

212. CHILDREN LOST IN THE WOODS—A reference to the nursery tale of babes
in the wood.

Singing the hundredth Psalm, the grand old Puritan anthem,
225 Music that Luther sang to the sacred words of the Psalmist,
Full of the breath of the Lord, consoling and comforting many.
Then, as he opened the door, he beheld the form of the maiden
Seated beside her wheel, and the carded wool like a snow-drift
Piled at her knee, her white hands feeding the ravenous
    spindle,
230 While with her foot on the treadle she guided the wheel in its
    motion.
Open wide on her lap the well-worn psalm-book of Ainsworth,
Printed in Amsterdam, the words and the music together,
Rough-hewn, angular notes, like stones in the wall of a church-
    yard,
Darkened and overhung by the running vine of the verses.
235 Such was the book from whose pages she sang the Old Puritan
    anthem,
She, the Puritan girl, in the solitude of the forest,
Making the humble house and the modest apparel of homespun
Beautiful with her beauty, and rich with the wealth of her
    being!
Over him rushed, like a wind that is keen and cold and
    relentless,
240 Thoughts of what might have been, and the weight and woe
    of his errand;
All the dreams that had faded, and all the hopes that had
    vanished,
All his life henceforth a dreary and tenantless mansion,
Haunted by vain regrets, and pallid, sorrowful faces.
Still he said to himself, and almost fiercely he said it,
245 "Let not him that putteth his hand to the plow look backwards;
Though the plowshare cut through the flowers of life to its
    fountains,

225. LUTHER—Martin Luther was the German leader of the Protestant Ref-
ormation. He translated the Bible into the German language.
231. AINSWORTH—An English clergyman who translated parts of the Bible
for singing.

Though it pass o'er the graves of the dead and the hearts of
    the living,
It is the will of the Lord; and his mercy endureth forever!"

So he entered the house; and the hum of the wheel and the
    singing
250 Suddenly ceased; for Priscilla, aroused by his step on the
    threshold,
Rose as he entered and gave him her hand, in signal of
    welcome,
Saying, "I knew it was you, when I heard your step in the
    passage;
For I was thinking of you, as I sat there singing and spinning."
Awkward and dumb with delight, that a thought of him had
    been mingled
255 Thus in the sacred psalm, that came from the heart of the
    maiden,
Silent before her he stood, and gave her the flowers for an
    answer,
Finding no words for his thought. He remembered that day
    in the winter,
After the first great snow, when he broke a path from the
    village,
Reeling and plunging along through the drifts that encumbered
    the doorway,
260 Stamping the snow from his feet as he entered the house, and
    Priscilla
Laughed at his snowy locks, and gave him a seat by the fire-
    side,
Grateful and pleased to know he had thought of her in the
    snowstorm.
Had he but spoken then! perhaps not in vain had he spoken;
Now it was all too late; the golden moment had vanished!
265 So he stood there abashed, and gave her the flowers for an
    answer.

Then they sat down and talked of the birds and the beau-
    tiful spring-time;
Talked of their friends at home, and the *Mayflower* that sailed
    on the morrow.
"I have been thinking all day," said gently the Puritan maiden,
"Dreaming all night, and thinking all day, of the hedge rows
    of England,—
270 They are in blossom now, and the country is all like a garden;
Thinking of lanes and fields, and the song of the lark and the
    linnet,
Seeing the village street, and familiar faces of neighbors
Going about as of old, and stopping to gossip together,
And, at the end of the street, the village church, with the ivy
275 Climbing the old gray tower, and the quiet graves in the
    churchyard.
Kind are the people I live with, and dear to me my religion;
Still my heart is so sad, that I wish myself back in Old
    England.
You will say it is wrong, but I cannot help it: I almost
Wish myself back in Old England, I feel so lonely and
    wretched."

280   Thereupon answered the youth: "Indeed I do not con-
    demn you;
Stouter hearts than a woman's have quailed in this terrible
    winter.
Yours is tender and trusting, and needs a stronger to lean on;
So I have come to you now, with an offer and proffer of mar-
    riage
Made by a good man and true, Miles Standish, the Captain of
    Plymouth!"

285   Thus he delivered his message, the dexterous writer of
    letters,—
Did not embellish the theme, nor array it in beautiful phrases,

But came straight to the point, and blurted it out like a school-
    boy;
Even the Captain himself could hardly have said it more
    bluntly.
Mute with amazement and sorrow, Priscilla, the Puritan
    maiden,
290 Looked into Alden's face, her eyes dilated with wonder,
Feeling his words like a blow, that stunned her and rendered
    her speechless;
Till at length she exclaimed, interrupting the ominous silence:
"If the great Captain of Plymouth is so very eager to wed me,
Why does he not come himself, and take the trouble to woo me?
295 If I am not worth the wooing, I surely am not worth the
    winning!"
Then John Alden began explaining and smoothing the matter,
Making it worse as he went, by saying the Captain was busy,—
Had no time for such things;—such things! the words grating
    harshly
Fell on the ear of Priscilla; and swift as a flash she made
    answer:
300 "Has he no time for such things, as you call it, before he is
    married,
Would he be likely to find it, or make it, after the wedding?
That is the way with you men; you don't understand us, you
    cannot.
When you have made up your minds, after thinking of this one
    and that one,
Choosing, selecting, rejecting, comparing one with another,
305 Then you make known your desire, with abrupt and sudden
    avowal,
And are offended and hurt, and indignant perhaps, that a
    woman
Does not respond at once to a love that she never suspected,
Does not attain at a bound the height to which you have been
    climbing.

This is not right nor just; for surely a woman's affection
10 Is not a thing to be asked for, and had for only the asking.
When one is truly in love, one not only says it, but shows it.
Had he but waited awhile, had he only showed that he
      loved me,
Even this Captain of yours—who knows?—at last might have
      won me,
Old and rough as he is; but now it never can happen."

15   Still John Alden went on, unheeding the words of Priscilla,
Urging the suit of his friend, explaining, persuading,
      expanding;
Spoke of his courage and skill, and of all his battles in
      Flanders,
How with the people of God he had chosen to suffer affliction,
How, in return for his zeal, they had made him Captain of
      Plymouth;
20 He was a gentleman born, could trace his pedigree plainly
Back to Hugh Standish of Duxbury Hall, in Lancashire,
      England,
Who was the son of Ralph, and the grandson of Thurston de
      Standish,
Heir unto vast estates, of which he was basely defrauded,
Still bore the family arms, and had for his crest a cock argent,
25 Combed and wattled gules, and all the rest of the blazon.
He was a man of honor, of noble and generous nature;
Though he was rough, he was kindly; she knew how during
      the winter
He had attended the sick, with a hand as gentle as woman's;
Somewhat hasty and hot, he could not deny it, and headstrong,
30 Stern as a soldier might be, but hearty, and placable always,

320. PEDIGREE—Ancestry.
324. CREST—An emblem usually worn above a shield.
324. COCK ARGENT—A silver cock.
325. WATTLED GULES—The fleshy lobes which hang under the throat of the
fowl.   325. BLAZON—Coat of arms.
330. PLACABLE (plā′ká-b'l)—Capable of being pacified.

Not to be laughed at and scorned, because he was little in
    stature;
For he was great of heart, magnanimous, courtly, courageous;
Any woman in Plymouth, nay, any woman in England,
Might be happy and proud to be called the wife of Miles
    Standish!

335   But as he warmed and glowed, in his simple and eloquent
    language,
Quite forgetful of self, and full of the praise of his rival,
Archly the maiden smiled, and, with eyes overrunning with
    laughter,
Said, in a tremulous voice, "Why don't you speak for yourself,
    John?"

IV

Into the open air John Alden, perplexed and bewildered,
340 Rushed like a man insane, and wandered alone by the seaside;
Paced up and down the sands, and bared his head to the east
    wind,
Cooling his heated brow, and the fire and fever within him.
Slowly, as out of the heavens, with apocalyptical splendors,
Sank the City of God, in the vision of John the Apostle,
345 So, with its cloudy walls of chrysolite, jasper, and sapphire,
Sank the broad red sun, and over its turrets uplifted
Glimmered the golden reed of the angel who measured the city.
"Welcome, O wind of the East!" he exclaimed in his wild
    exultation,
"Welcome, O wind of the East, from the caves of the misty
    Atlantic!

332. MAGNANIMOUS—Great of mind, noble.
343. APOCALYPTICAL (à-pŏk-à-lĭp'tĭ-kăl)—Prophetic.
345. CHRYSOLITE, JASPER, AND SAPPHIRE—These gems are respectively yellow,
green, and blue in color.
347. REED—The Hebrew measure of length, about three and one-half yards
long.

350 Blowing o'er fields of dulse, and measureless meadows of sea-
grass,

Blowing o'er rocky waste, and the grottos and gardens of
ocean!

Lay thy cold, moist hand on my burning forehead, and wrap me

Close in thy garments of mist, to allay the fever within me!"

Like an awakened conscience, the sea was moaning and
tossing,

355 Beating remorseful and loud the mutable sands of the sea-
shore.

Fierce in his soul was the struggle and tumult of passions contending;

Love triumphant and crowned, and friendship wounded and
bleeding,

Passionate cries of desire, and importunate pleadings of duty!

"Is it my fault," he said, "that the maiden has chosen between us?

360 Is it my fault that he failed,—my fault that I am the victor?"

Then within him there thundered a voice, like the voice of the
Prophet:

"It hath displeased the Lord!"—and he thought of David's
transgression,

Bathsheba's beautiful face, and his friend in the front of the
battle!

Shame and confusion of guilt, and abasement and self-con-
demnation,

365 Overwhelmed him at once; and he cried in the deepest contrition:

"It hath displeased the Lord!   It is the temptation of Satan!"

350. DULSE—A sea-weed sometimes used for food.
355. MUTABLE—Susceptible to change.
358. IMPORTUNATE—Persistent, troublesome.
361–363. David, a king of Israel, caused the death of his friend Uriah by
sending him to the front line of battle, in order that he might marry Uriah's
wife, Bathsheba.
365. CONTRITION (kŏn-trĭsh'ŭn)—Sorrow for having sinned.

Then, uplifting his head, he looked at the sea, and beheld
    there
Dimly the shadowy form of the *Mayflower* riding at anchor,
Rocked on the rising tide, and ready to sail on the morrow;
370 Heard the voices of men through the mist, the rattle of cordage
Thrown on the deck, the shouts of the mate, and the sailors'
    "Aye, aye, Sir!"
Clear and distinct, but not loud, in the dripping air of the twi-
    light.
Still for a moment he stood, and listened, and stared at the
    vessel,
Then went hurriedly on, as one who, seeing a phantom,
375 Stops, then quickens his pace, and follows the beckoning
    shadow.
"Yes, it is plain to me now," he murmured; "the hand of the
    Lord is
Leading me out of the land of darkness, the bondage of error,
Through the sea that shall lift the walls of its waters around
    me,
Hiding me, cutting me off, from the cruel thoughts that
    pursue me.
380 Back will I go o'er the ocean, this dreary land will abandon,
Her whom I may not love, and him whom my heart has
    offended.
Better to be in my grave in the green old churchyard in
    England,
Close by my mother's side, and among the dust of my kindred;
Better be dead and forgotten, than living in shame and dis-
    honor!
385 Sacred and safe and unseen, in the dark of the narrow chamber
With me my secret shall lie, like a buried jewel that glimmers
Bright on the hand that is dust, in the chambers of silence and
    darkness,—
Yes, as the marriage ring of the great espousal hereafter!"

388. ESPOUSAL—Marriage, wedding.

Thus as he spake, he turned, in the strength of his strong
resolution,
390 Leaving behind him the shore, and hurried along in the twi-
light,
Through the congenial gloom of the forest silent and somber,
Till he beheld the lights in the seven houses of Plymouth,
Shining like seven stars in the dusk and mist of the evening.
Soon he entered his door, and found the redoubtable Captain
395 Sitting alone, and absorbed in the martial pages of Caesar,
Fighting some great campaign in Hainault or Brabant or
Flanders.
"Long have you been on your errand," he said with a cheery
demeanor,
Even as one who is waiting an answer, and fears not the issue.
"Not far off is the house, although the woods are between us;
400 But you have lingered so long, that while you were going and
coming
I have fought ten battles and sacked and demolished a city.
Come, sit down, and in order relate to me all that has hap-
pened."

Then John Alden spake, and related the wondrous
adventure
From beginning to end, minutely, just as it happened:
405 How he had seen Priscilla, and how he had sped in his courtship,
Only smoothing a little, and softening down her refusal.
But when he came at length to the words Priscilla had spoken,
Words so tender and cruel, "Why don't you speak for yourself, John?"
Up leaped the Captain of Plymouth, and stamped on the floor,
till his armor

394. REDOUBTABLE—Valiant, brave, feared by enemies.
396. HAINAULT (ā'nō), BRABANT (brȧ'-bäng), FLANDERS—Provinces of Belgium.

410 Clanged on the wall, where it hung, with a sound of sinister
    omen.

All his pent-up wrath burst forth in a sudden explosion,

E'en as a hand-grenade, that scatters destruction around it.

Wildly he shouted, and loud: "John Alden! you have
    betrayed me!

Me, Miles Standish, your friend! have supplanted, defrauded,
    betrayed me!

415 One of my ancestors ran his sword through the heart of Wat
    Tyler;

Who shall prevent me from running my own through the
    heart of a traitor?

Yours is the greater treason, for yours is a treason to friend-
    ship!

You, who lived under my roof, whom I cherished and loved as
    a brother;

You, who have fed at my board, and drunk at my cup, to
    whose keeping

420 I have intrusted my honor, my thoughts the most sacred and
    secret,—

You too, Brutus! ah, woe to the name of friendship hereafter!

Brutus was Caesar's friend, and you were mine, but hence-
    forward

Let there be nothing between us save war, and implacable
    hatred!"

So spake the Captain of Plymouth, and strode about in the
    chamber,

425 Chafing and choking with rage; like cords were the veins on
    his temples.

But in the midst of his anger a man appeared at the doorway,

Bringing in uttermost haste a message of urgent importance,

415. WAT TYLER—The leader of a rebellion against Richard II.
    421. YOU TOO, BRUTUS—"*Et tu, Brute*" were the words of Caesar when he
recognized his close friend, Brutus, as one of his murderers.
    423. IMPLACABLE—Unappeasable, irreconcilable, never-ending.

Rumors of danger and war and hostile incursions of Indians!
Straightway the Captain paused, and, without further question or parley,
.30 Took from the nail on the wall his sword with its scabbard of
  iron,
Buckled the felt round his waist, and, frowning fiercely, departed.
Alden was left alone.   He heard the clank of the scabbard
Growing fainter and fainter, and dying away in the distance.
Then he rose from his seat, and looked forth into the darkness,
35 Felt the cool air blow on his cheek, that was hot with the
  insult,
Lifted his eyes to the heavens, and, folding his hands as in
  childhood,
Prayed in the silence of night to the Father who seeth in secret.

Meanwhile the choleric Captain strode wrathful away to
  the council,
Found it already assembled, impatiently waiting his coming;
40 Men in the middle of life, austere and grave in deportment,
Only one of them old, the hill that was nearest to heaven,
Covered with snow, but erect, the excellent Elder of Plymouth.
God had sifted three kingdoms to find the wheat for this
  planting,
Then had sifted the wheat, as the living seed of a nation;
45 So say the chronicles old, and such is the faith of the people!
Near them was standing an Indian, in attitude stern and
  defiant,
Naked down to the waist, and grim and ferocious in aspect;
While on the table before them was lying unopened a Bible,
Ponderous, bound in leather, brass-studded, printed in Holland,

438. CHOLERIC (kŏl'ēr-ĭk)—Angry, wrathful.
442. ELDER OF PLYMOUTH—William Brewster, the pastor of the Pilgrim
Church.
443. THREE KINGDOMS—The persecuted Separatists from England, France,
and Holland had gathered at Leyden in Holland and formed one church.

450 And beside it outstretched the skin of a rattlesnake glittered,
　　Filled, like a quiver, with arrows: a signal and challenge of
　　　　warfare,
　　Brought by the Indian, and speaking with arrowy tongues of
　　　　defiance.
　　This Miles Standish beheld, as he entered, and heard them
　　　　debating
　　What were an answer befitting the hostile message and
　　　　menace,
455 Talking of this and of that, contriving, suggesting, objecting;
　　One voice only for peace, and that the voice of the Elder,
　　Judging it wise and well that some at least were converted,
　　Rather than any were slain, for this was but Christian
　　　　behavior!
　　Then out spake Miles Standish, the stalwart Captain of
　　　　Plymouth,

450. SKIN OF THE RATTLESNAKE—The token of war. This is an actual historical incident. In January, 1622, Canonicus, a Narragansett chief, sent a
rattlesnake skin filled with arrows to Governor Bradford who returned it
filled with powder.

460 Muttering deep in his throat, for his voice was husky with
   anger,
"What! do you mean to make war with milk and the water of
   roses?
Is it to shoot red squirrels you have your howitzer planted
There on the roof of the church, or is it to shoot red devils?
Truly the only tongue that is understood by a savage
465 Must be the tongue of fire that speaks from the mouth of the
   cannon!"
Thereupon answered and said the excellent Elder of Plymouth,
Somewhat amazed and alarmed at this irreverent language:
"Not so thought Saint Paul, nor yet the other Apostles;
Not from the cannon's mouth were the tongues of fire they
   spake with!"
470 But unheeded fell this mild rebuke on the Captain,
Who had advanced to the table, and thus continued
   discoursing:
"Leave this matter to me, for to me by right it pertaineth.
War is a terrible trade; but in the cause that is righteous,
Sweet is the smell of powder; and thus I answer the
   challenge!"

475 Then from the rattlesnake's skin, with a sudden, con-
   temptuous gesture,
Jerking the Indian arrows, he filled it with powder and bullets
Full to the very jaws, and handed it back to the savage,
Saying, in thundering tones: "Here, take it! this is your
   answer!"
Silently out of the room then glided the glistening savage,
480 Bearing the serpent's skin, and seeming himself like a serpent,
Winding his sinuous way in the dark to the depths of the
   forest.

         V

  Just in the gray of dawn, as the mists uprose from the
   meadows,

There was a stir and a sound in the slumbering village of
    Plymouth;
Clanging and clinking of arms, and the order imperative,
    "Forward!"
485 Given in tone suppressed, a tramp of feet, and then silence.
Figures ten, in the mist, marched slowly out of the village.
Standish the stalwart it was, with eight of his valorous army,
Led by their Indian guide, by Hobomok, friend of the white
    men,
Northward marching to quell the sudden revolt of the savage.
490 Giants they seemed in the mist, or the mighty men of King
    David;
Giants in heart they were, who believed in God and the
    Bible,—
Ay, who believed in the smiting of Midianites and Philistines.
Over them gleamed far off the crimson banners of morning,
Under them loud on the sands, the serried billows, advancing,
495 Fired along the line, and in regular order retreated.

Many a mile had they marched, when at length the village
    of Plymouth
Woke from its sleep, and arose, intent on its manifold labors.
Sweet was the air and soft; and slowly the smoke from the
    chimneys
Rose over roofs of thatch, and pointed steadily eastward;
500 Men came forth from the doors, and paused and talked of the
    weather,
Said that the wind had changed, and was blowing fair for the
    Mayflower;
Talked of their Captain's dèparture, and all the dangers that
    menaced,
He being gone, the town, and what should be done in his ab-
    sence.

488. HOBOMOK—Pronounced hŏb'ō-môk.
492. MIDIANITES AND PHILISTINES—Heathen tribes with whom the people of
Israel fought.   494. SERRIED—Crowded, pressed together.

Merrily sang the birds, and the tender voices of women
505 Consecrated with hymns the common cares of the household.
Out of the sea rose the sun, and the billows rejoiced at his
       coming;
Beautiful were his feet on the purple tops of the mountains;
Beautiful on the sails of the *Mayflower* riding at anchor,
Battered and blackened and worn by all the storms of the
       winter.
510 Loosely against her masts was hanging and flapping her
       canvas,
Rent by so many gales, and patched by the hands of the sailors.
Suddenly from her side, as the sun rose over the ocean,
Darted a puff of smoke, and floated seaward; anon rang
Loud over field and forest the cannon's roar, and the echoes
515 Heard and repeated the sound, the signal-gun of departure!
Ah! but with louder echoes replied the hearts of the people!
Meekly, in voices subdued, the chapter was read from the
       Bible,
Meekly the prayer was begun, but ended in fervent entreaty!
Then from their houses in haste came forth the Pilgrims of
       Plymouth,
520 Men and women and children, all hurrying down to the sea-
       shore,
Eager, with tearful eyes, to say farewell to the *Mayflower,*
Homeward bound o'er the sea, and leaving them here in the
       desert.

    Foremost among them was Alden. All night he had lain
       without slumber,
Turning and tossing about in the heat and unrest of his fever.
525 He had beheld Miles Standish, who came back late from the
       council,
Stalking into the room, and heard him mutter and murmur,
Sometimes it seemed a prayer, and sometimes it sounded like
       swearing.

Once he had come to the bed, and stood there a moment in
    silence;
Then he had turned away, and said: "I will not awaken him;
530 Let him sleep on, it is best; for what is the use of more
    talking!"
Then he extinguished the light, and threw himself down on
    his pallet,
Dressed as he was, and ready to start at the break of the
    morning,—
Covered himself with a cloak he had worn in his campaigns in
    Flanders,—
Slept as a soldier sleeps in his bivouac, ready for action.

535 But with the dawn he arose; in the twilight Alden beheld him
Put on his corselet of steel, and all the rest of his armor,
Buckle about his waist his trusty blade of Damascus,
Take from the corner his musket, and so stride out of the
    chamber.
Often the heart of the youth had burned and yearned to em-
    brace him,
540 Often his lips had essayed to speak, imploring for pardon;
All the old friendship came back with its tender and grateful
    emotions;
But his pride overmastered the nobler nature within him,—
Pride, and the sense of his wrong, and the burning fire of the
    insult.
So he beheld his friend departing in anger, but spake not,
545 Saw him go forth to danger, perhaps to death, and he spake not!
Then he arose from his bed, and heard what the people were
    saying,
Joined in the talk at the door, with Stephen and Richard and
    Gilbert,
Joined in the morning prayer, and in the reading of Scripture,

531. PALLET—Small, rough bed.
534. BIVOUAC—An army encampment without tents.
547. Stephen Hopkins, Richard Warren and Gilbert Winslow were members
of the colony.

WEASEL TAIL

Nickolas de Grandmaison

NICKOLAS DE GRANDMAISON

Canadian School

*Born in Russia, Nickolas de Grandmaison be-
gan his study of art in Moscow and later studied
in England. After several years in Canada, he
settled at Calgary, Alberta, and became interested in the western Indian whom he called "a
glorious colorful subject." Many of his pictures
were inspired by members of the Blackfoot tribe.
So outstanding was his work that in 1932 the
National Museum at Ottawa commissioned him
to study and paint the few remaining Indians of
the East.*

*"Weasel Tail" is characteristic of de Grand-
maison's Indian portraits. It is in a collection
of contemporary art of the Western Hemisphere
owned by the International Business Machines
Corporation, and hangs in New York City.*

And, with the others, in haste went hurrying down to the sea-
shore,
550 Down to Plymouth Rock, that had been to their feet as a doorstep
Into a world unknown,—the corner stone of a nation!

There with his boat was the Master, already a little impatient
Lest he should lose the tide, or the wind might shift to the
eastward,
Square-built, hearty and strong, with an odor of ocean about
him,
555 Speaking with this one and that, and cramming letters and
parcels
Into his pockets capacious, and messages mingled together
Into his narrow brain, till at last he was wholly bewildered.
Nearer the boat stood Alden, with one foot placed on the gunwale,
One still firm on the rock, and talking at times with the sailors,
560 Seated erect on the thwarts, all ready and eager for starting.
He too was eager to go, and thus put an end to his anguish,
Thinking to fly from despair, that swifter than keel is or
canvas,
Thinking to drown in the sea the ghost that would rise and
pursue him.
But as he gazed on the crowd, he beheld the form of Priscilla
565 Standing dejected among them, unconscious of all that was
passing.
Fixed were her eyes upon his, as if she divined his intention,
Fixed with a look so sad, so reproachful, imploring, and
patient,

552. MASTER—Captain of the ship.
552. BOAT—The small boat used for carrying passengers between the ship
and the shore.
558. GUNWALE (gŭn'ĕl)—The upper edge of a boat's side.
560. THWARTS—The seats extending across the boat.

That with a sudden revulsion his heart recoiled from its purpose,
As from the verge of a crag, where one step more is
destruction.
570 Strange is the heart of man, with its quick, mysterious in-
stincts!
Strange is the life of man, and fatal or fated are moments,
Whereupon turn, as on hinges, the gates of the wall adamantine!
"Here I remain!" he exclaimed, as he looked at the heavens
above him,
Thanking the Lord whose breath had scattered the mist and
the madness,
575 Wherein, blind and lost, to death he was staggering headlong.
"Yonder snow-white cloud, that floats in the ether above me,
Seems like a hand that is pointing and beckoning over the
ocean.
There is another hand, that is not so spectral and ghost-like,
Holding me, drawing me back, and clasping mine for
protection.
580 Float, O hand of cloud, and vanish away in the ether!
Roll thyself up like a fist, to threaten and daunt me; I heed not

572. ADAMANTINE (ăd-à-măn′tĭn)—Immovable.
576. ETHER—Air, limitless space.

Either your warning or menace, or any omen of evil!
There is no land so sacred, no air so pure and so wholesome,
As is the air she breathes, and the soil that is pressed by her
      footsteps.
585 Here for her sake will I stay, and like an invisible presence
Hover around her forever, protecting, supporting her weak-
      ness;
Yes! as my foot was the first that stepped on this rock at the
      landing,
So, with the blessing of God, shall it be the last at the leaving!"

Meanwhile the Master alert, but with dignified air and im-
      portant,
590 Scanning with watchful eye the tide and the wind and the
      weather,
Walked about on the sands, and the people crowded around him
Saying a few last words, and enforcing his careful remem-
      brance.
Then, taking each by the hand, as if he were grasping a tiller,
Into the boat he sprang, and in haste shoved off to his vessel,
595 Glad in his heart to get rid of all this worry and flurry,
Glad to be gone from a land of sand and sickness and sorrow,
Short allowance of victual, and plenty of nothing but Gospel!
Lost in the sound of the oars was the last farewell of the Pil-
      grims.
O strong hearts and true! not one went back in the *Mayflower!*
600 No, not one looked back, who had set his hand to this plowing!

Soon were heard on board the shouts and songs of the sail-
      ors
Heaving the windlass round, and hoisting the ponderous an-
      chor.
Then the yards were braced, and all sails set to the west wind,

597. VICTUAL (vĭt″l)—Food.
602. WINDLASS—The roller around which the anchor is fastened. It is
turned around to wind up the chain which lifts the anchor.
603. YARDS—The timbers on the mast used to spread the sails.

Blowing steady and strong; and the *Mayflower* sailed from the
harbor,

605 Rounded the point of the Gurnet, and leaving far to the southward

Island and cape of sand, and the Field of the First Encounter,

Took the wind on her quarter, and stood for the open Atlantic,

Borne on the send of the sea, and the swelling hearts of the
Pilgrims.

Long in silence they watched the receding sail of the vessel,

610 Much endeared to them all, as something living and human;

Then, as if filled with the spirit, and wrapt in a vision prophetic,

Baring his hoary head, the excellent Elder of Plymouth

Said, "Let us pray!" and they prayed, and thanked the Lord
and took courage.

Mournfully sobbed the waves at the base of the rock, and above
them

615 Bowed and whispered the wheat on the hill of death, and their
kindred

Seemed to awake in their graves, and to join in the prayer that
they uttered.

Sun-illumined and white, on the eastern verge of the ocean

Gleamed the departing sail, like a marble slab in a graveyard;

Buried beneath it lay forever all hope of escaping.

620 Lo! as they turned to depart, they saw the form of an Indian,

Watching them from the hill; but while they spake with each
other,

Pointing with outstretched hands, and saying, "Look!" he had
vanished.

So they returned to their homes; but Alden lingered a little,

Musing alone on the shore, and watching the wash of the billows

605. GURNET (gẽr'nĕt)—A headland or point projecting from the shore.
606. FIELD OF THE FIRST ENCOUNTER—Before the Pilgrims landed, a party
was sent ashore to explore and here they encountered a body of Indians.

525 Round the base of the rock, and the sparkle and flash of the
      sunshine,
Like the spirit of God, moving visibly over the waters.

VI

Thus for a while he stood, and mused by the shore of the
      ocean,
Thinking of many things, and most of all of Priscilla;
And as if thought had the power to draw to itself, like the
      loadstone,
530 Whatsoever it touches, by subtle laws of its nature,
Lo! as he turned to depart, Priscilla was standing beside him.
"Are you so much offended, you will not speak to me?" she
      said.
"Am I so much to blame, that yesterday, when you were plead-
      ing
Warmly the cause of another, my heart, impulsive and way-
      ward,
535 Pleaded your own, and spake out, forgetful perhaps of de-
      corum?
Certainly you can forgive me for speaking so frankly, for say-
      ing
What I ought not to have said, yet now I can never unsay it;
For there are moments in life, when the heart is so full of
      emotion,
That if by chance it be shaken, or into its depths like a pebble
540 Drops some careless word, it overflows, and its secret,
Spilt on the ground like water, can never be gathered together.
Yesterday I was shocked, when I heard you speak of Miles
      Standish,
Praising his virtues, transforming his very defects into virtues,
Praising his courage and strength, and even his fighting in
      Flanders,
545 As if by fighting alone you could win the heart of a woman,
Quite overlooking yourself and the rest, in exalting your hero.

Therefore I spake as I did, by an irresistible impulse.
You will forgive me, I hope, for the sake of the friendship
between us,
Which is too true and too sacred to be so easily broken!"

650   Thereupon answered John Alden, the scholar, the friend
of Miles Standish:
"I was not angry with you, with myself alone I was angry,
Seeing how badly I managed the matter I had in my keeping."
"No!" interrupted the maiden, with answer prompt and de-
cisive;
"No; you were angry with me, for speaking so frankly and
freely.
655 It was wrong, I acknowledge; for it is the fate of a woman
Long to be patient and silent, to wait like a ghost that is
speechless,
Till some questioning voice dissolves the spell of its silence.
Hence is the inner life of so many suffering women
Sunless and silent and deep, like subterranean rivers
660 Running through caverns of darkness, unheard, unseen, and
unfruitful,
Chafing their channels of stone, with endless and profitless
murmurs."
Thereupon answered John Alden, the young man, the lover of
women:
"Heaven forbid it, Priscilla; and truly they seem to me always
More like the beautiful rivers that watered the garden of Eden,
665 More like the river Euphrates, through the deserts of Havilah
flowing,
Filling the land with delight, and memories sweet of the
garden!"
"Ah, by these words I can see," again interrupted the maiden,
"How very little you prize me, or care for what I am saying.

659. SUBTERRANEAN RIVERS—Rivers that flow underground.
665. HAVILAH (hăv'ĭ-là)—The land rich in gold and precious stones surrounded by the river Pison.

When from the depths of my heart, in pain and with secret
    misgiving,
670 Frankly I speak to you, asking for sympathy only and kind-
    ness,
Straightway you take up my words, that are plain and direct
    and in earnest,
Turn them away from their meaning, and answer with flatter-
    ing phrases.
This is not right, is not just, is not true to the best that is in
    you;
For I know and esteem you, and feel that your nature is noble,
675 Lifting mine up to a higher, a more ethereal level.
Therefore I value your friendship, and feel it perhaps the more
    keenly
If you say aught that implies I am only as one among many,
If you make use of those common and complimentary phrases
Most men think so fine, in dealing and speaking with women,
680 But which women reject as insipid, if not insulting."

Mute and amazed was Alden; and listened and looked at
    Priscilla,
Thinking he never had seen her more fair, more divine in her
    beauty.
He who but yesterday pleaded so glibly the cause of another,
Stood there embarrassed and silent, and seeking in vain for an
    answer.
685 So the maiden went on, and little divined or imagined
What was at work in his heart that made him so awkward and
    speechless.
"Let us, then, be what we are, and speak what we think, and
    in all things
Keep ourselves loyal to truth, and the sacred professions of
    friendship.
It is no secret I tell you, nor am I ashamed to declare it:

675. ETHEREAL—Heavenly.

239

690 I have liked to be with you, to see you, to speak with you
    always.
So I was hurt at your words, and a little affronted to hear you
Urge me to marry your friend, though he were the Captain
    Miles Standish.
For I must tell you the truth: much more to me is your friend-
    ship
Than all the love he could give, were he twice the hero you
    think him."
695 Then she extended her hand, and Alden, who eagerly grasped
    it,
Felt all the wounds in his heart, that were aching and bleeding
    so sorely,
Healed by the touch of that hand, and he said, with a voice full
    of feeling:
"Yes, we must ever be friends; and of all who offer you friend-
    ship
Let me be ever first, the truest, the nearest and dearest!"

700   Casting a farewell look at the glimmering sail of the *May-*
    flower
Distant, but still in sight, and sinking below the horizon,
Homeward together they walked, with a strange, indefinite
    feeling,
That all the rest had departed and left them alone in the desert.
But, as they went through the fields in the blessing and smile
    of the sunshine,
705 Lighter grew their hearts, and Priscilla said very archly:
"Now that our terrible Captain has gone in pursuit of the In-
    dians,
Where he is happier far than he would be commanding a house-
    hold,
You may speak boldly, and tell me of all that happened be-
    tween you,

691. AFFRONTED—Offended.

When you returned last night, and said how ungrateful you
    found me."
710 Thereupon answered John Alden, and told her the whole of
    the story,—
Told her his own despair, and the direful wrath of Miles
    Standish,
Whereat, the maiden smiled, and said between laughing and
    earnest,
"He is a little chimney, and heated hot in a moment."
But as he gently rebuked her, and told her how much he had
    suffered,—
715 How he had even determined to sail that day in the *Mayflower,*
And had remained for her sake, on hearing the dangers that
    threatened,—
All her manner was changed, and she said with a faltering ac-
    cent,
"Truly I thank you for this: how good you have been to me
    always."

Thus, as a pilgrim devout, who toward Jerusalem journeys,
720 Taking three steps in advance, and one reluctantly backward,
Urged by importunate zeal, and withheld by pangs of con-
    trition,
Slowly but steadily onward, receding yet ever advancing,
Journeyed this Puritan youth to the Holy Land of his longings,
Urged by the fervor of love, and withheld by remorseful mis-
    givings.

VII

725 Meanwhile the stalwart Miles Standish was marching
    steadily northward,
Winding through forest and swamp, and along the trend of the
    seashore,
All day long, with hardly a halt, the fire of his anger
Burning and crackling within, and the sulphurous odor of pow-
    der

Seeming more sweet to his nostrils than all the scents of the forest.

730 Silent and moody he went, and much he revolved his discomfort;

He who was used to success, and to easy victories always,

Thus to be flouted, rejected, and laughed to scorn by a maiden,

Thus to be mocked and betrayed by the friend whom most he had trusted!

Ah, 'twas too much to be borne, and he fretted and chafed in his armor!

735 "I alone am to blame," he muttered, "for mine was the folly.

What has a rough, old soldier, grown grim and gray in the harness,

Used to the camp and its ways, to do with the wooing of maidens?

'Twas but a dream,—let it pass,—let it vanish like so many others!

What I thought was a flower, is only a weed, and is worthless;

740 Out of my heart will I pluck it, and throw it away, and henceforward

Be but a fighter of battles, a lover and wooer of dangers."

Thus he revolved in his mind his sorry defeat and discomfort,

While he was marching by day or lying at night in the forest,

Looking up at the trees and the constellations beyond them.

745 After a three days' march he came to an Indian encampment

Pitched on the edge of a meadow, between the sea and the forest;

Women at work by the tents, and warriors, horrid with war-paint,

Seated about a fire, and smoking and talking together;

Who, when they saw from afar the sudden approach of the white men,

750 Saw the flash of the sun on breastplate and saber and musket,

Straightway leaped to their feet, and two, from among them
    advancing,
Came to parley with Standish, and offer him furs as a present;
Friendship was in their looks, but in their hearts there was
    hatred.
Braves of the tribe were these, and brothers, gigantic in stature,
755 Huge as Goliath of Gath, or the terrible Og, king of Bashan;
One was Pecksuot named, and the other was called Watta-
    wamat.
Round their necks were suspended their knives in scabbards
    of wampum,
Two-edged, trenchant knives, with points as sharp as a needle.
Other arms had they none, for they were cunning and crafty.
760 "Welcome, English!" they said,—these words they had learned
    from the traders
Touching at times on the coast, to barter and chaffer for
    peltries.

Then in their native tongue they began to parley with
    Standish,
Through his guide and interpreter, Hobomok, friend of the
    white man,
Begging for blankets and knives, but mostly for muskets and
    powder,
765 Kept by the white man, they said, concealed, with the plague,
    in his cellars,
Ready to be let loose, and destroy his brother the red man!
But when Standish refused, and said he would give them the
    Bible,
Suddenly changing their tone, they began to boast and to
    bluster.

755. GOLIATH—A giant of the ancient times of the Hebrews.
755. OG—Another giant who was king of Bashan (bā'shăn).
756. PECKSUOT . . . WATTAWAMAT—Pronounced pĕk'sōō-ŏt, wä-tä-wä'mŏt.
758. TRENCHANT—Sharp, keen-edged.
761. BARTER AND CHAFFER FOR PELTRIES—To bargain and trade for pelts.

Then Wattawamat advanced with a stride in front of the other,
770 And, with a lofty demeanor, thus vauntingly spake to the
        Captain:
"Now Wattawamat can see, by the fiery eyes of the Captain,
Angry is he in his heart; but the heart of the brave Watta-
        wamat
Is not afraid at the sight. He was not born of a woman,
But on a mountain, at night, from an oak-tree riven by light-
        ning,
775 Forth he sprang at a bound, with all his weapons about him,
Shouting, 'Who is there here to fight with the brave Watta-
        wamat?'"
Then he unsheathed his knife, and, whetting the blade on his
        left hand,
Held it aloft and displayed a woman's face on the handle,
Saying, with bitter expression and look of sinister meaning:
780 "I have another at home, with the face of a man on the handle;
By and by they shall marry; and there will be plenty of chil-
        dren!"

        Then stood Pecksuot forth, self-vaunting, insulting Miles
            Standish;
While with his fingers he patted the knife that hung at his
        bosom,
Drawing it half from its sheath, and plunging it back, as he
        muttered,
785 "By and by it shall see; it shall eat; ah, ha! but shall speak
        not.
This is the mighty Captain the white men have sent to de-
        stroy us!
He is a little man; let him go and work with the women."

        Meanwhile Standish had noted the faces and figures of
            Indians

774. RIVEN—Rent asunder, split.

244

Peeping and creeping about from bush to tree in the forest,
790 Feigning to look for game, with arrows set on their bow strings.
Drawing about him still closer and closer the net of their ambush.
But undaunted he stood, and dissembled and treated them smoothly;

So the old chronicles say, that were writ in the days of the fathers.
But when he heard their defiance, the boast, the taunt and the insult,
795 All the hot blood of his race, of Sir Hugh and of Thurston de Standish,
Boiled and beat in his heart, and swelled in the veins of his temples.
Headlong he leaped on the boaster, and, snatching his knife from its scabbard,
Plunged it into his heart, and, reeling backward, the savage
Fell with his face to the sky, and a fiendlike fierceness upon it.

790. FEIGNING—Making believe, pretending.

800 Straight there arose from the forest the awful sound of the
warwhoop,
And, like a flurry of snow on the whistling wind of December,
Swift and sudden and keen came a flight of feathery arrows.
Then came a cloud of smoke, and out of the cloud came the
lightning,
Out of the lightning, thunder; and death unseen ran before it.
805 Frightened, the savages fled for shelter in swamp and in
thicket,
Hotly pursued and beset; but their sachem, the brave Watta-
wamat,
Fled not; he was dead. Unswerving and swift had a bullet
Passed through his brain, and he fell with both hands clutch-
ing the greensward,
Seeming in death to hold back from his foe the land of his
fathers.
810 There on the flowers of the meadow the warriors lay, and
above them,
Silent, with folded arms, stood Hobomok, friend of the white
man.
Smiling at length he exclaimed to the stalwart Captain of
Plymouth:
"Pecksuot bragged very loud, of his courage, his strength and
his stature,—
Mocked the great Captain, and called him a little man; but
I see now
815 Big enough have you been to lay him speechless before you!"

Thus the first battle was fought and won by the stalwart
Miles Standish.
When the tidings thereof were brought to the village of
Plymouth,
And as a trophy of war the head of the brave Wattawamat

816. This battle actually happened in 1623 according to the old records
handed down from that time.

246

Scowled from the roof of the fort, which at once was a church and a fortress,

820 All who beheld it rejoiced, and praised the Lord, and took courage.

Only Priscilla averted her face from this specter of terror,

Thanking God in her heart that she had not married Miles Standish;

Shrinking, fearing almost, lest, coming home from his battles,

He should lay claim to her hand, as the prize and reward of his valor.

VIII

825 Month after month passed away, and in autumn the ships of the merchants

Came with kindred and friends, with cattle and corn for the Pilgrims.

All in the village was peace; the men were intent on their labors,

Busy with hewing and building, with garden-plot and with merestead,

Busy with breaking the glebe, and mowing the grass in the meadows,

830 Searching the sea for its fish, and hunting the deer in the forest.

All in the village was peace; but at times the rumor of warfare

Filled the air with alarm, and the apprehension of danger.

Bravely the stalwart Standish was scouring the land with his forces,

Waxing valiant in fight and defeating the alien armies,

835 Till his name had become a sound of fear to the nations.

Anger was still in his heart, but at times the remorse and contrition

Which in all noble natures succeed the passionate outbreak,

Came like a rising tide, that encounters the rush of a river,

Staying its current awhile, but making it bitter and brackish.

828. MERESTEAD—A homestead near the shore.
829. GLEBE—Soil.   839. BRACKISH—Salty.

840   Meanwhile Alden at home had built him a new habitation,
Solid, substantial, of timber rough-hewn from the firs of the
    forest.
Wooden barred was the door, and the roof was covered with
    rushes;
Latticed the windows were, and the window panes were of
    paper,
Oiled to admit the light, while wind and rain were excluded.
845 There too he dug a well, and around it planted an orchard:
Still may be seen to this day some trace of the well and the
    orchard.
Close to the house was the stall, where, safe and secure from
    annoyance,
Raghorn, the snow-white bull, that had fallen to Alden's allot-
    ment
In the division of cattle, might ruminate in the night time
850 Over the pastures he cropped, made fragrant by sweet penny-
    royal.

     Oft when his labor was finished, with eager feet would the
    dreamer
Follow the pathway that ran through the woods to the house
    of Priscilla,
Led by illusions romantic and subtle deceptions of fancy,
Pleasure disguised as duty, and love in the semblance of
    friendship.
855 Ever of her he thought, when he fashioned the walls of his
    dwelling;
Ever of her he thought, when he delved in the soil of his
    garden;
Ever of her he thought, when he read in his Bible on Sunday
Praise of the virtuous woman, as she is described in the Prov-
    erbs,—
How the heart of her husband doth safely trust in her always,
860 How all the days of her life she will do him good, and not evil,

How she seeketh the wool and the flax and worketh with glad-
    ness,
How she layeth her hand to the spindle and holdeth the distaff,
How she is not afraid of the snow for herself or her household,
Knowing her household are clothed with the scarlet cloth of
    her weaving!

865   So as she sat at her wheel one afternoon in the Autumn,
    Alden, who sat opposite, and was watching her dexterous
        fingers,
    As if the thread she was spinning were that of his life and
        his fortune,
    After a pause in their talk, thus spake to the sound of the
        spindle.
    "Truly, Priscilla," he said, "when I see you spinning and spin-
        ning,
870 Never idle a moment, but thrifty and thoughtful of others,

Suddenly you are transformed, are visibly changed in a moment;

You are no longer Priscilla, but Bertha, the Beautiful Spinner."

Here the light foot on the treadle grew swifter and swifter; the spindle

Uttered an angry snarl, and the thread snapped short in her fingers;

875 While the impetuous speaker, not heeding the mischief, continued:

"You are the beautiful Bertha, the spinner, the queen of Helvetia;

She whose story I read at a stall in the streets of Southampton,

Who, as she rode on her palfrey, o'er valley and meadow and mountain,

Ever was spinning her thread from a distaff fixed to her saddle.

880 She was so thrifty and good, that her name passed into a proverb.

So shall it be with your own, when the spinning wheel shall no longer

Hum in the house of the farmer, and fill its chambers with music.

Then shall the mothers, reproving, relate how it was in their childhood,

Praising the good old times, and the days of Priscilla, the spinner."

885   Straight uprose from her wheel the beautiful Puritan maiden,

Pleased with the praise of her thrift from him whose praise was the sweetest,

Drew from the reel on the table a snowy skein of her spinning,

Thus making answer, meanwhile, to the flattering phrases of Alden:

872. BERTHA, THE BEAUTIFUL SPINNER—A queen of Burgundy noted for her deeds of piety and charity.   876. HELVETIA—Pronounced hĕl-vē'shia.
877. STALL—A bench or table where books are sold.
878. PALFREY—A small saddle horse for a lady's use.

"Come, you must not be idle; if I am a pattern for housewives,
890 Show yourself equally worthy of being the model of husbands.
Hold this skein on your hands, while I wind it, ready for knit-
ting;
Then who knows but hereafter, when fashions have changed
and the manners,
Fathers may talk to their sons of the good old times of John
Alden."
Thus, with a jest and a laugh, the skein on his hands she adjusted,
895 He sitting awkwardly there, with his arms extended before
him,
She standing graceful, erect, and winding the thread from his
fingers,
Sometimes chiding a little his clumsy manner of holding,
Sometimes touching his hands, as she disentangled expertly
Twist or knot in the yarn, unawares—for how could she help
it?—
900 Sending electrical thrills through every nerve in his body.

Lo! in the midst of this scene, a breathless messenger en-
tered,
Bringing in hurry and heat the terrible news from the village.
Yes; Miles Standish was dead!—an Indian had brought them
the tidings,—
Slain by a poisoned arrow, shot down in the front of the battle,
905 Into an ambush beguiled, cut off with the whole of his forces;
All the town would be burned and all the people be murdered!
Such were the tidings of evil that burst on the hearts of the
hearers.
Silent and statue-like stood Priscilla, her face looking backward
Still at the face of the speaker, her arms uplifted in horror;
910 But John Alden, upstarting, as if the barb of an arrow

Piercing the heart of his friend had struck his own, and had
    sundered
Once and forever the bonds that held him bound as a captive,
Wild with excess of sensation, the awful delight of his freedom,
Mingled with pain and regret, unconscious of what he was
    doing,
915 Clasped, almost with a groan, the motionless form of Priscilla,
Pressing her close to his heart, as forever his own, and ex-
    claiming:
"Those whom the Lord hath united, let no man put them
    asunder!"

Even as rivulets twain, from distant and separate sources,
Seeing each other afar, as they leap from the rocks, and pur-
    suing
920 Each one its devious path, but drawing nearer and nearer,
Rush together at last, at their trysting-place in the forest;
So these lives that had run thus far in separate channels,
Coming in sight of each other, then swerving and flowing
    asunder,
Parted by barriers strong, but drawing nearer and nearer,
925 Rushed together at last, and one was lost in the other.

IX

Forth from the curtain of clouds, from the tent of purple
    and scarlet,
Issued the sun, the great High-priest, in his garments re-
    splendent,
Holiness unto the Lord, in letters of light, on his forehead,
Round the hem of his robe the golden bells and pomegranates.
930 Blessing the world he came, and the bars of vapor beneath him
Gleamed like a grate of brass, and the sea at his feet was a
    laver!

928. HOLINESS UNTO THE LORD—Words on the band worn across the forehead of the priests of old.
929. POMEGRANATE (pŏm'grăn-àt)—A small orange-like fruit with thick rind.
931. LAVER—A vessel in which to wash, used by the Jewish priests.

This was the wedding morn of Priscilla, the Puritan
   maiden.
Friends were assembled together; the Elder and Magistrate
   also
Graced the scene with their presence, and stood like the Law
   and the Gospel,
935 One with the sanction of earth and one with the blessing of
   heaven.
Simple and brief was the wedding, as that of Ruth and Boaz.
Softly the youth and the maiden repeated the words of betrothal,
Taking each other for husband and wife in the Magistrate's
   presence,
After the Puritan way, and the laudable custom of Holland.
940 Fervently then and devoutly, the excellent Elder of Plymouth
Prayed for the hearth and the home, that were founded that
   day in affection,
Speaking of life and of death, and imploring Divine benedic-
   tions.

   Lo! when the service was ended, a form appeared on the
   threshold,
Clad in armor of steel, a somber and sorrowful figure!
945 Why does the bridegroom start and stare at the strange apparition?
Why does the bride turn pale, and hide her face on his shoulder?
Is it a phantom of air,—a bodiless, spectral illusion?
Is it a ghost from the grave, that has come to forbid the betrothal?
Long has it stood there unseen, a guest uninvited, unwelcomed.
950 Over its clouded eyes there had passed at times an expression
Softening the gloom and revealing the warm heart hidden beneath them,

936. RUTH AND BOAZ (bō'ăz)—Biblical characters whose wedding was very
short and simple.

As when across the sky the driving rack of the rain cloud

Grows for a moment thin, and betrays the sun by its brightness.

Once it had lifted its hand, and moved its lips, and was silent,

955 As if an iron will had mastered the fleeting intention.

But when were ended the troth and the prayer and the last benediction,

Into the room it strode, and the people beheld with amazement

Bodily there in his armor Miles Standish, the Captain of Plymouth!

Grasping the bridegroom's hand, he said with emotion, "Forgive me!

960 I have been angry and hurt,—too long have I cherished the feeling;

I have been cruel and hard, but now, thank God! it is ended.

Mine is the same hot blood that leaped in the veins of Hugh Standish,

Sensitive, swift to resent, but as swift in atoning for error.

Never so much as now was Miles Standish the friend of John Alden."

965   Thereupon answered the bridegroom: "Let all be forgotten between us,—

All save the dear old friendship, and that shall grow older and dearer!"

Then the Captain advanced, and, bowing, saluted Priscilla,

Gravely, and after the manner of old-fashioned gentry in England,

Something of camp and of court, of town and of country, commingled,

970 Wishing her joy of her wedding, and loudly lauding her husband.

Then he said with a smile: "I should have remembered the adage,—

MUSIC LESSON

Jan Vermeer

JAN VERMEER

Dutch School

Jan Vermeer (1632–1675), known as Vermeer of Delft because it is thought that he never left his native town in Holland, was a "poor, well-intentioned artist who had the hard luck of being a failure." Unrecognized in his own day, Vermeer has since become "a painter's painter," a master to whom artists turn for serious study on the problems of light and shade.

Vermeer was apprenticed at fifteen to a painters' guild and later became a pupil of Rembrandt. He was intensely interested in the effect of light on the objects it touched. His colors are harmonious, rich, delicate; seldom is there any absolute darkness in his paintings. "His works, small in number, are as precious as jewels," states Rockwell Kent.

"Music Lesson," now hanging in the Royal Gallery at Windsor, is an example of the dignity and quiet beauty that characterize Vermeer. One of his favorite devices is seen in this picture —the effect of light as it streams through casement windows at the side. The light is silvery in tone; the shadows are pearl-color. Interest centers in the young girl whose head and shoulders are reflected in the mirror hanging above the costly, inlaid spinet. The costume of the music-master, richly dressed in the fashion of the day, and the heavy Persian cloth which covers the table in the foreground show Vermeer's faithful portrayal of light on rich surfaces and textures. As in nature, his colors never jar.

If you would be well served, you must serve yourself; and
    moreover,
No man can gather cherries in Kent at the season of Christ-
    mas!"
Great was the people's amazement, and greater yet their re-
    joicing,
975 Thus to behold once more the sunburnt face of their Captain,
Whom they had mourned as dead; and they gathered and
    crowded about him,
Eager to see him and hear him, forgetful of bride and of
    bridegroom,
Questioning, answering, laughing, and each interrupting the
    other,
Till the good Captain declared, being quite overpowered and
    bewildered,
980 He had rather by far break into an Indian encampment,
Than come again to a wedding to which he had not been
    invited.

    Meanwhile the bridegroom went forth and stood with the
    bride at the doorway,
Breathing the perfumed air of that warm and beautiful morn-
    ing.
Touched with autumnal tints, but lonely and sad in the sun-
    shine,
985 Lay extended before them the land of toil and privation;
There were the graves of the dead; and the barren waste of
    the seashore,
There the familiar fields, the groves of pine, and the meadows;
But to their eyes transfigured, it seemed as the Garden of
    Eden,
Filled with the presence of God, whose voice was the sound of
    the ocean.

    973. This line is an old English proverb. Kent is a county in the southern
part of England. What does the proverb mean as applied to Standish?

990   Soon was their vision disturbed by the noise and stir of departure,

Friends coming forth from the house, and impatient of longer delaying,

Each with his plan for the day, and the work that was left uncompleted.

Then from a stall near at hand, amid exclamations of wonder,

Alden the thoughtful, the careful, so happy, so proud of Priscilla,

995 Brought out his snow-white bull, obeying the hand of its master,

Led by a cord that was tied to an iron ring in its nostrils,

Covered with crimson cloth, and a cushion placed for a saddle.

She should not walk, he said, through the dust and heat of the noonday;

Nay, she should ride like a queen, not plod along like a peasant.

1000 Somewhat alarmed at first, but reassured by the others,

Placing her hand on the cushion, her foot in the hand of her husband,

Gayly, with joyous laugh, Priscilla mounted her palfrey.

"Nothing is wanting now," he said with a smile, "but the distaff:

Then you would be in truth my queen, my beautiful Bertha!"

1005   Onward the bridal procession now moved to their new habitation,

Happy husband and wife, and friends conversing together.

Pleasantly murmured the brook, as they passed the ford in the forest,

Pleased with the image that passed, like a dream of love through its bosom,

Tremulous, floating in air, o'er the depths of the azure abysses.

1010 Down through the golden leaves the sun was pouring his splendors,

Gleaming on purple grapes, that, from branches above them
     suspended,
Mingled their odorous breath with the balm of the pine and
     the fir tree,
Wild and sweet as the clusters that grew in the valley of
     Eshcol!
Like a picture it seemed of the primitive, pastoral ages,
1015 Fresh with the youth of the world, and recalling Rebecca and
     Isaac,
Old and yet ever new, and simple and beautiful always,
Love immortal and young in the endless succession of lovers.
So through the Plymouth woods passed onward the bridal pro-
     cession.

1013. VALLEY OF ESHCOL (ĕsh'kôl)—Near Hebron in Palestine. From there,
the spies sent by Moses brought back clusters of grapes.
1015. REBECCA AND ISAAC—A beautiful Biblical story of how Rebecca became
the wife of Isaac.

MIKE FINK

CARL CARMER

NOBODY has ever figured it out to a standstill whether Mike Fink was a better jumper than a shooter or a better shooter than a jumper. From Pittsburgh to Cairo along the banks of the Ohio River many an evening by the fireside has been spent arguing about it. The arguers who favor Mike's shooting say he could stand on the deck of his keel-boat drifting downriver and shoot the curl out of a baby pig's tail as it rested peacefully against his baby hams in the clear Ohio air. They say he did it so often that to this day there's a breed of Ohio pigs that have straight tails from birth and that this fact is due to Mike's having shot the curls out of the tails of their parents. They also say that Mike used to shoot the topknots off wild Indians war-whooping among the sycamores on the Indiana bank. Most gracefully, too, he used his bullets to lift the combs out of the carefully done-up tresses of lovely southern ladies as they strolled along the old Kentucky shore.

But the other arguers are just as sure that Mike's real gift was for jumping. They say that when the current was swift he had been known to take off from his forward deck just as his keel-boat neared an island and come down on his after-deck near the sweep at the stern just as the boat left the island behind.

Then some who have heard this tale before shake their heads and say the teller has left out the best part of it—that while Mike was in the middle of his jump over the island a farmer down below took him for a chicken hawk and, lifting his gun, let go at him. Luckily Mike had seen the quick move below and trained his own gun, which he had forgotten to leave behind, on the farmer. Both men fired at the same moment and the two bullets were so well aimed that they met in mid-air and dropped to earth—killing on the way a large black bear that was perched in a honey tree.

Both sides of the argument use the best known of all the Mike Fink jumping stories to prove that they are right, and it is very hard to decide which side wins, for a lot depends on how the tale is told. It all began when Mike bragged that he could jump the Mississippi River at the point where the Ohio comes into it.

"You mean you could take off from Cairo, Illinois, and come down at Birds Point?" said a flat-boatman.

"That's just like a flat-boatman," said Mike, "always belittling the natural gifts of men smart enough to load their stuff into a boat with a sharp edge down the middle."

"If you can do it I'll buy me a keel-boat instead of this broad-horn," said the flat-boatman.

And so, just out of a wish to do something for a man who did not have sense enough to do something for himself, Mike said he would make the try. Saturday was the day set—in order that the school children in Illinois and Kentucky and Missouri could be there. A lot of other folks showed up, too—all the flat-boatmen on the western rivers and all the keel-boatmen and a great many people who were not boatmen at all. The time set for the jump was noon because Mike figured there would be less air stirring then. He would not want to buck a breeze or to hear a flat-boatman say he got blown across. He decided he could get enough of a start by running down Main Street in Cairo and taking off at the foot.

Promptly at noon, when the sun was overhead and the air was still, Mike started his run. He had got under way and was just passing the First National Bank lickety-split when something happened. A little girl, all dressed up in her holiday best and not knowing Mike had started, ran out into the middle of the street. "I can't tell you how I felt at that moment," said Mike later. "Should I keep right on and run her down or should I swerve and break my stride?" All who have experienced the natural courtesy of keel-boatmen know that there could be only one answer. He swerved.

So when Mike came to the foot of Main Street, Cairo, Illinois, he was not running full-tilt as he should have been but he leaped into the air anyway—aiming for Birds Point. The first part of the jump he said later was very pleasant. He could see the river below, lying still and hot, but the breeze caused by his own speed kept him cool and contented. Gradually Cairo got smaller and smaller and he could see the mid-river line where the green Ohio water joins the yellow flood of the Mississippi. Then gradually he began to lose speed. The little girl in his path had caused a bad take-off. Now he could see the houses of Birds Point getting larger and larger but he knew that he would never reach them. In a few moments he would drop into the river. With a tremendous effort he whirled about in the air and changed the direction of his jump. He was bound back towards Cairo. For a while it seemed as if he would never make it and he shut his eyes and held his nose expecting to fall into the river. When he opened them again the stores of Cairo were but a few rods away. With a last desperate effort he urged himself forward and his right foot lit on dry land. His left foot, landing behind the right, got sopping wet in Mississippi water. That is how close it was.

That famous leap made more argument than ever about Mike Fink's jumping. All the flat-boatmen said they would stick to flat-boats since Mike had failed in his try but all the keel-boatmen pointed out that three quarters of the way over and back is longer than all the way over. Nobody could come to any agreement and so Mike called to his crew and they all set out up the Ohio by catching hold of bushes along the banks and pulling the keel-boat along by them. They called this slow business "bushwhacking" and to while away the time they sang a song that every flat-boatman and keel-boatman on the Ohio used to know.

Sing the first stanza as if you were floating swiftly down stream, the second as if you were bushwhacking back.

262

SHAWNEE TOWN

HARD upon the beach oar,
She moves too slow;
All the way to Shawnee town,
Long time ago.

Now the river takes her,
We'll get there soon;
Bushwack her back home again,
Under the moon.

Dipping into folk tales of other nations.

WALTZING MATILDA

AUSTRALIAN FOLK SONG

B   ONCE a jolly swagman camped beside a billabong
         Under the shade of a koolibah tree,
G   And he sang as he watched and waited till his billy boiled,
         "You'll come a-waltzing, Matilda, with me."

Chorus

U   5   "Waltzing, Matilda, Waltzing, Matilda,
         You'll come a-waltzing, Matilda, with me."
         And he sang as he watched and waited till his billy boiled,
         "You'll come a-waltzing, Matilda, with me."

B   Down came a jumbuck to drink at the billabong,
    10   Up jumped the swagman and grabbed him with glee,
G   And he sang as he stowed that jumbuck in his tucker bag,
         "You'll come a-waltzing, Matilda, with me."

B   Up rode the squatter mounted on his thoroughbred,
         Up rode the troopers, one, two, three!
U   15   "Where's the jolly jumbuck you've stowed in your tucker
           bag?
         You'll come a-waltzing, Matilda, with me."

B   Up jumped the swagman and jumped into the billabong:
         "You'll never take me alive," says he.
G   And his ghost may be heard as you pass by the billabong,
    20   Singing, "You'll come a-waltzing, Matilda, with me."

1. SWAGMAN—An Australian bushman tramping with a swag, or bundle.
1. BILLABONG—A pool.   2. KOOLIBAH—A kind of Australian gum tree.
3. BILLY—A bushman's kettle.   9. JUMBUCK—A sheep.
11. TUCKER—Food.   13. SQUATTER—Settler.

MOTHER VOLGA AND HER CHILD

AGNES FISHER

ONCE upon a time the people who lived on the shores of the River Volga were wakened from their sleep in the dead of night by a great rumbling noise. It was like thunder except that it never paused. The frightened people jumped out of their beds, and ran outside. They looked here and there and everywhere, yet they could find neither giant nor dragon nor an old scolding woman.

Then, suddenly, a wise old man exclaimed, "I know whence it comes. It is from the Volga. For some reason she is bursting with wrath."

"You are right," said another wise man, "and if we are going to escape her anger, we must devise some means of holding her within her banks."

So a committee was formed to approach the river. Some were instructed to talk to the river, for of all rivers the Volga is the most wise and reasonable. If the spokesmen should fail to persuade her to be calm and quiet, others were instructed to build up her banks with earth and stones and trees.

Very quietly the men crept to the shores of the river in the dead of night, for they did not want the Volga either to hear or see them coming, in case she would be so enraged that, without ever giving the spokesmen a chance to speak, she would rise up and sweep them away in her blue waters. Imagine their surprise, then, when they stood on her banks, and found that the water was as calm as a little mill stream. It flowed steadily and smoothly with barely a ripple to break its even, glassy surface. Yet the noise was terrific. It was louder even than thunder.

"What can be the meaning of this?" the poor, pale, frightened people whispered to one another.

"Let us get down on our knees, and crawl to the very edge of

265

the bank," one man said, and so they crawled stealthily, and with their ears to the ground listened carefully. Soon they heard not one voice but two, and one was as loud and angry as the other. This is what they heard:

"I, the Volga, am mightier by far than you," the Volga roared. "Throughout the world, men call me Mother Volga."

"Mighty you may be," came the answer, spoken with a sneer, "but you are lazy, while I am swift as a doe and beautiful as the maiden of spring. Therefore, I, the Vazuza,[1] am more greatly respected than you."

They wrangled all that night and the next night and for many nights. They wrangled so long and so furiously that the people could get no sleep, except in the daytime when the rivers calmed down a little. However, when the sun shines is no time for an industrious Russian farmer to sleep. So the people called a council of the wisest men, who lived on the banks of the Volga and on the banks of the Vazuza, and said,

[1] VAZUZA—Pronounced vă-zōō′zȧ.

"You must silence these mad rivers, for if you don't we shall become as crazy as they are."

"I know what to do," one very wise man said. "Leave it to me, and tonight I shall surely silence them."

No one thought he would, of course, but everyone was willing to let him try.

"This argument appears to be endless," the man said to the rivers.

"I am the strongest river in all Russia," the Volga cried.

"I am the most dearly loved," the Vazuza said.

"I am the wisest, most highly respected, and mightiest in all the world," the Volga roared.

"Indeed you are not," the Vazuza began, but the man stamped his feet and shouted, "Hush! Hush! Listen to me."

"We'll listen," the rivers muttered not at all politely.

"Well then, this is my suggestion," the man said thoughtfully. "Let the two of you flow together side by side, and whichever one reaches the Caspian Sea first will be proclaimed the wisest, mightiest, most dearly loved, and most highly respected river in all Russia, if not in the whole world."

So the Volga and the Vazuza did as the man suggested, and he went back to his people, greatly rejoiced with what he had done. "They are like twins," he told everyone, "and they will love each other as twins do."

But in the night the Vazuza changed her course, and fled from the Volga, thinking that she was taking a short, straight path to the Caspian. The Volga flowed on, neither slowly nor swiftly but steadily, very steadily, and at Zubtsof [2] she met the Vazuza. This frightened the Vazuza greatly. She thought that the Volga possessed some power of magic, for how else, she asked herself, could the River Volga come to Zubtsof as quickly as she had.

"I took a straighter path than you," the Vazuza cried, "and yet here you are, laughing at me. What does it mean?"

[2] ZUBTSOF—Pronounced zo͞obt′sôf.

"Nothing except that I am wiser than you," the Volga answered.

"I moved swiftly, and yet here you are even with me," the Vazuza cried. "What does it mean?"

"Nothing except that I am steadier than you," the Volga answered.

Then the Vazuza wept tears of rage and tears of shame and tears of fear.

"Oh, dear Mother Volga," she begged, "I am just a little baby river. I have neither your strength nor wisdom."

The Volga felt sorry for the Vazuza, so she took her in her arms, and carried her to the Caspian, and to this day she still bears her tenderly to the sea. But the Vazuza has one special piece of work to do that no one but she can do. Every spring she wakens first from the winter's sleep, and rouses the Volga with these gentle words, "Dear Mother Volga, awake, awake. The spring maiden is dancing on your shore. It is time for us to flow once more."

So the Volga bursts her bonds of ice, and flows neither slowly nor swiftly but steadily to the Caspian, and from Zubtsof to the sea she carries the Vazuza in her arms.

THE PEDDLER OF BALLAGHADEREEN

RUTH SAWYER

MORE years ago than you can tell me and twice as many as I can tell you, there lived a peddler in Ballaghadereen.[1] He lived at the crossroads, by himself in a bit of a cabin with one room to it, and that so small that a man could stand in the middle of the floor and, without taking a step, he could lift the latch on the front door, he could lift the latch on the back door,

---

[1] BALLAGHADEREEN—Pronounced băl-ăg-hăd'ĕr-ēn.

and he could hang the kettle over the turf. That is how small and snug it was.

Outside the cabin the peddler had a bit of a garden. In it he planted carrots and cabbages, onions and potatoes. In the center grew a cherry tree—as brave and fine a tree as you would find anywhere in Ireland. Every spring it flowered, the white blossoms covering it like a fresh falling of snow. Every summer it bore cherries as red as heart's blood.

But every year, after the garden was planted the wee brown hares would come from the copse near by and nibble-nibble here, and nibble-nibble there, until there was not a thing left, barely, to grow into a full-sized vegetable that a man could harvest for his table. And every summer as the cherries began to ripen the blackbirds came in whirling flocks and ate the cherries as fast as they ripened.

The neighbors that lived thereabouts minded this and nodded their heads and said: "Master Peddler, you're a poor, simple man, entirely. You let the wild creatures thieve from you without lifting your hand to stop them."

And the peddler would always nod his head back at them and laugh and answer: "Nay, then, 'tis not thieving they are at all. They pay well for what they take. Look you—on yonder cherry tree the blackbirds sing sweeter nor they sing on any cherry tree in Ballaghadereen. And the brown hares make good company at dusk-hour for a lonely man."

In the country roundabout, every day when there was market, a wedding, or a fair, the peddler would be off at ring-o'-day, his pack strapped on his back, one foot ahead of the other, fetching him along the road. And when he reached the town diamond he would open his pack, spread it on the green turf, and, making a hollow of his two hands, he would call:

> "Come buy a trinket—come buy a brooch—
> Come buy a kerchief of scarlet or yellow!"

In no time at all there would be a great crowding of lads and lasses and children about him, searching his pack for what they

might be wanting. And like as not, some barefooted lad would hold up a jack-knife and ask: "How much for this, Master Peddler?"

And the peddler would answer: "Half a crown."

And the lad would put it back, shaking his head dolefully. "Faith, I haven't the half of that, nor likely ever to have it."

And the peddler would pull the lad over to him and whisper in his ear: "Take the knife—'twill rest a deal more easy in your pocket than in my pack."

Then, like as not, some lass would hold up a blue kerchief to her yellow curls and ask: "Master Peddler, what is the price of this?"

And the peddler would answer: "One shilling sixpence."

And the lass would put it back, the smile gone from her face, and she turning away.

And the peddler would catch up the kerchief again and tie it himself about her curls and laugh and say: "Faith, there it looks far prettier than ever it looks in my pack. Take it, with God's blessing."

So it would go—a brooch to this one and a top to that. There were days when the peddler took in little more than a few farthings. But after those days he would sing his way homeward; and the shrewd ones would watch him passing by and wag their fingers at him and say: "You're a poor, simple man, Master Peddler. You'll never be putting a penny by for your old age. You'll end your days like the blackbirds, whistling for crumbs at our back doors. Why, even the vagabond dogs know they can wheedle the half of the bread you are carrying in your pouch, you're that simple."

Which likewise was true. Every stray, hungry dog knew him the length and breadth of the county. Rarely did he follow a road without one tagging his heels, sure of a noon-day sharing of bread and cheese.

There were days when he went abroad without his pack, when there was no market-day, no wedding or fair. These he spent with the children, who would have followed him about like the dogs, had their mothers let them. On these days he would sit himself down on some doorstep and when a crowd of children had gathered he would tell them tales—old tales of Ireland—tales of the good folk, of the heroes, of the saints. He knew them all, and he knew how to tell them, the way the children would never be forgetting one of them, but carry them in their hearts until they were old.

And whenever he finished a tale he would say, like as not, laughing and pinching the cheek of some wee lass: "Mind well your manners, whether you are at home or abroad, for you can never be telling what good folk, or saint, or hero you may be fetching up with on the road—or who may come knocking at your doors. Aye, when Duirmuid,² or Fionn or Oisin or Saint Patrick walked the earth they were poor and simple and plain men; it took death to put a grand memory on them. And the poor and the simple and the old today may be heroes tomorrow —you never can be telling. So keep a kind word for all, and a gentling hand."

² DUIRMUID (dwēr'mwē) . . . FIONN (fĭn) . . . OISIN (ō'-shēn)—Mythical Celtic bards and heroes. Saint Patrick is the patron saint of Ireland.

Often an older would stop to listen to the scraps of words he was saying; and often as not he would go his way, wagging his finger and mumbling: "The poor, simple man. He's as foolish as the blackbirds."

Spring followed winter in Ireland, and summer followed close upon the heels of both. And winter came again and the peddler grew old. His pack grew lighter and lighter, until the neighbors could hear the trinkets jangling inside as he passed, so few things were left. They would nod their heads and say to one another: "Like as not his pockets are as empty as his pack. Time will come, with winter at hand, when he will be at our back doors begging crumbs, along with the blackbirds."

The time did come, as the neighbors had prophesied it would, smug and proper, when the peddler's pack was empty, when he had naught in his pockets and naught in his cupboard. That night he went hungry to bed.

Now it is more than likely that hungry men will dream; and the peddler of Ballaghadereen had a strange dream that night. He dreamed that there came a sound of knocking in the middle of the night. Then the latch on the front door lifted, the door opened without a creak or a cringe, and inside the cabin stepped Saint Patrick. Standing in the doorway the good man pointed a finger; and he spoke in a voice tuned as low as the wind over the bogs. "Peddler, peddler of Ballaghadereen, take the road to Dublin town. When you get to the bridge that spans the Liffey [3] you will hear what you were meant to hear."

On the morrow the peddler awoke and remembered the dream. He rubbed his stomach and found it mortal empty; he stood on his legs and found them trembling in under him; and he said to himself: "Faith, an empty stomach and weak legs are the worst traveling companions a man can have, and Dublin is a long way. I'll bide where I am."

That night the peddler went hungrier to bed, and again came the dream. There came the knocking on the door, the lifting

[3] LIFFEY (lĭf'ĭ)—A river which flows into Dublin bay.

of the latch. The door opened and Saint Patrick stood there, pointing the road: "Peddler, peddler of Ballaghadereen, take the road that leads to Dublin town. When you get to the bridge that spans the Liffey you will hear what you were meant to hear!"

The second day it was the same as the first. The peddler felt the hunger and the weakness stronger in him, and stayed where he was. But when he woke after the third night and the third coming of the dream, he rose and strapped his pack from long habit upon his back and took the road to Dublin. For three long weary days he traveled, barely staying his fast, and on the fourth day he came into the city.

Early in the day he found the bridge spanning the river and all the lee-long day he stood there, changing his weight from one foot to the other, shifting his pack to ease the drag of it, scanning the faces of all who passed by. But although a great tide of people swept this way, and a great tide swept that, no one stopped and spoke to him.

At the end of the day he said to himself: "I'll find me a blind alley, and like an old dog I'll lay me down in it and die." Slowly he moved off the bridge. As he passed by the Head Inn of Dublin, the door opened and out came the landlord.

To the peddler's astonishment he crossed the thoroughfare and hurried after him. He clapped a strong hand on his shoulder and cried: "Arra, man, hold a minute! All day I've been watching you. All day I have seen you standing on the bridge like an old rook with rent wings. And of all the people passing from the west to the east, and of all the people passing from the east to the west, not one crossing the bridge spoke aught with you. Now I am filled with a great curiosity entirely to know what fetched you here."

Seeing hunger and weariness on the peddler, he drew him toward the inn. "Come; in return for having my curiosity satisfied you shall have rest in the kitchen yonder, with bread and cheese and ale. Come."

So the peddler rested his bones by the kitchen hearth and he ate as he hadn't eaten in many days. He was satisfied at long last and the landlord repeated his question. "Peddler, what fetched you here?"

"For three nights running I had a dream—" began the peddler, but he got no further.

The landlord of the Head Inn threw back his head and laughed. How he laughed, rocking on his feet, shaking the whole length of him!

"A dream you had, by my soul, a dream!" He spoke when he could get his breath. "I could be telling you were the cut of a man to have dreams, and to listen to them, what's more. Rags on your back and hunger in your cheeks and age upon you, and I'll wager not a farthing in your pouch. Well, God's blessing on you and your dreams."

The peddler got to his feet, saddled his pack, and made for the door. He had one foot over the sill when the landlord hurried after him and again clapped a hand on his shoulder.

"Hold, Master Peddler," he said, "I too had a dream, three nights running." He burst into laughter again, remembering it. "I dreamed there came a knocking on this very door, and the latch lifted, and, standing in the doorway, as you are standing, I saw Saint Patrick. He pointed with one finger to the road running westward and he said: 'Landlord, Landlord of the Head Inn, take *that* road to Ballaghadereen. When you come to the crossroads you will find a wee cabin, and beside the cabin a wee garden, and in the center of the garden a cherry tree. Dig deep under the tree and you will find gold—much gold.'"

The landlord paused and drew his sleeve across his mouth to hush his laughter.

"Ballaghadereen! I never heard of the place. Gold under a cherry tree—whoever heard of gold under a cherry tree! There is only one dream that I hear, waking or sleeping, and it's the dream of gold, much gold, in my own pocket. Aye, listen, 'tis a good dream." And the landlord thrust a hand into his pouch and jangled the coins loudly in the peddler's ear.

Back to Ballaghadereen went the peddler, one foot ahead of the other. How he got there I cannot be telling you. He unslung his pack, took up a mattock lying near by, and dug under the cherry tree. He dug deep and felt at last the scraping of the mattock against something hard and smooth. It took him time to uncover it and he found it to be an old sea chest, of foreign pattern and workmanship, bound around with bands of brass. These he broke, and lifting the lid he found the chest full of gold, tarnished and clotted with mold; pieces-of-six and pieces-of-eight and Spanish doubloons.

I cannot begin to tell the half of the goodness that the peddler put into the spending of that gold. But this I know. He built a chapel at the crossroads—a resting-place for all weary travelers, journeying thither.

And after he had gone the neighbors had a statue made of him and placed it facing the crossroads. And there he stands to this day, a pack on his back and a dog at his heels.

THE PIED PIPER OF HAMELIN

ROBERT BROWNING

G   HAMELIN TOWN'S in Brunswick,
      By famous Hanover city;
    The River Weser, deep and wide
    Washes its walls on the southern side;
5   A pleasanter spot you never spied;
      But, when begins my ditty,
    Almost five hundred years ago,
    To see the townsfolk suffer so
      From vermin, was a pity.

1. HAMELIN (häm'ê-lǐn)—The present town of Hameln in the German state of Brunswick.
3. WESER (vā'zēr)—One of the principal rivers of north Germany.

II

B 10   Rats!
  They fought the dogs and killed the cats,
   And bit the babies in the cradles,
  And ate the cheeses out of the vats,
   And licked the soup from the cooks' own ladles,
15 Split open the kegs of salted sprats,
  Made nests inside men's Sunday hats,
  And even spoiled the women's chats,
   By drowning their speaking
   With shrieking and squeaking
20 In fifty different sharps and flats.

III

  At last the people in a body
   To the Town Hall came flocking:
1B(♯1) " 'Tis clear," cried they, "our Mayor's a noddy,
   And as for our Corporation—shocking
25 To think we buy gowns lined with ermine
  For dolts that can't or won't determine
  What's best to rid us of our vermin!
  You hope, because you're old and obese,
  To find in the furry civic robe ease?
30 Rouse up, Sirs! Give your brains a racking
  To find the remedy we're lacking,
  Or, sure as fate, we'll send you packing!"
B At this the Mayor and Corporation
  Quaked with a mighty consternation.

IV

1B(♯1) 35 An hour they sat in Council;
  At length the Mayor broke silence:

15. SPRATS—Herring.   23. NODDY—Simpleton.
24. CORPORATION—The aldermen of the city.
25. ERMINE—In the Middle Ages, official robes were often trimmed with ermine, a costly fur.
28. OBESE (ŏ-bēs')—Very fat.

"For a guilder I'd my ermine gown sell;
   I wish I were a mile hence!
It's easy to bid one rack one's brain—
40 I'm sure my poor head aches again,
I've scratched it so, and all in vain.
Oh, for a trap, a trap, a trap!"

B   Just as he said this, what should hap
At the chamber door, but a gentle tap?
B(♯1) 45 "Bless us!" cried the Mayor, "what's that?"
B   (With the Corporation as he sat,
Looking little though wondrous fat;
Nor brighter was his eye, nor moister
Than a too-long-opened oyster;
50 Save when at noon his paunch grew mutinous
For a plate of turtle green and glutinous.)
B(♯1)   "Only a scraping of shoes on the mat!
Anything like the sound of a rat
Makes my heart go pit-a-pat!"

V

55 "Come in!" the Mayor cried, looking bigger,
G   And in did come the strangest figure!
His queer long coat, from heel to head
Was half of yellow and half of red;
And he himself was tall and thin,
60 With sharp blue eyes, each like a pin,
And light loose hair, yet swarthy skin,
No tuft on cheek nor beard on chin,
But lips where smiles went out and in;
There was no guessing his kith and kin;
65 And nobody could enough admire
The tall man and his quaint attire.
Quoth one: "It's as if my great-grandsire,

37. GUILDER (gīld′ēr)—A common German coin of the Middle Ages.
51. GREEN AND GLUTINOUS—These words modify turtle (soup). Glutinous
means thick.

Starting up at the trump of Doom's tone,
Had walked this way from his painted tombstone!"

VI

70   He advanced to the council table:

1B(♯2)   And, "Please your honors," said he, "I'm able,
      By means of a secret charm, to draw
    All creatures living beneath the sun,
    That creep, or swim, or fly, or run,

75   After me so as you never saw!
    And I chiefly use my charm
    On creatures that do people harm—
    The mole, the toad, the newt, the viper;
    And people call me the Pied Piper."

G 80   (And here they noticed round his neck
      A scarf of red and yellow stripe
    To match his coat of the selfsame cheque;
      And at the scarf's end hung a pipe;

278

And his fingers, they noticed, were ever straying
85   As if impatient to be playing
Upon his pipe, as low it dangled
Over his vesture so old-fangled.)

B(#2)   "Yet," said he, "poor piper as I am,
In Tartary I freed the Cham,
90   Last June, from his huge swarm of gnats;
I eased in Asia the Nizam
    Of a monstrous brood of vampire bats:
And as for what your brain bewilders,
    If I can rid your town of rats
95   Will you give me a thousand guilders?"

B(#1)   "One! fifty thousand!" was the exclamation
Of the astonished Mayor and Corporation.

VII

G   Into the street the Piper stept,
    Smiling first a little smile,
100   As if he knew what magic slept
    In his quiet pipe the while;
Then, like a musical adept,
To blow the pipe his lips he wrinkled,
And green and blue his sharp eyes twinkled,
105   Like a candle-flame where salt is sprinkled;
And ere three shrill notes the pipe had uttered,
You heard as if an army muttered;

B   And the muttering grew to a grumbling;
And the grumbling grew to a mighty rumbling;
110   And out of the houses the rats came tumbling.
Great rats, small rats, lean rats, brawny rats,
Brown rats, black rats, gray rats, tawny rats,
Grave old plodders, gay young friskers,
    Fathers, mothers, uncles, cousins,

89. CHAM (kăm)—The reference is to the Grand Cham of Tartary, a romantic figure in the tales of travel of the Middle Ages.
    91. NIZAM (nī-zăm′)—Another half-fabulous Asiatic monarch who appealed
to the romantic imagination of the Middle Ages.

115   Cocking tails, and pricking whiskers,
  Families by the tens and dozens,
 Brothers, sisters, husbands, wives—
 Followed the Piper for their lives.
 From street to street he piped, advancing,
120 And step for step they followed dancing,
 Until they came to the River Weser,
  Wherein all plunged and perished!
 —Save one, who, stout as Julius Cæsar,
 Swam across and lived to carry
125 (As he, the manuscript he cherished)
 To Rat-land home his commentary:

1B(#3) Which was, "At the first shrill note of the pipe
 I heard a sound as of scraping tripe,
 And putting apples, wondrous ripe,
130 Into a cider press's gripe:
 And a moving away of pickle tub boards,
 And a leaving ajar of conserve cupboards,
 And a drawing the corks of train oil flasks,
 And a breaking the hoops of butter-casks:
135 And it seemed as if a voice
  (Sweeter far than by harp or by psaltery
  Is breathed) called out, 'Oh, rats, rejoice!
  'The world is grown to one vast drysaltery!
  'So munch on, crunch on, take your nuncheon,
140 'Breakfast, dinner, supper, luncheon!'
 And just as a bulky sugar puncheon,
 All ready staved, like a great sun shone
 Glorious, scarce an inch before me,
 Just as methought it said, 'Come, bore me!'
145 —I found the Weser rolling o'er me."

126. COMMENTARY—An account of his experiences.
136. PSALTERY (sôl'tĕr-ĭ)—An ancient musical instrument.
138. DRYSALTERY—The store of a drysalter, a drysalter being a person who
deals in dried and salted meats, pickles, etc.
139. NUNCHEON—A light luncheon between meals.
141. PUNCHEON—A great cask or hogshead. 142. STAVED—Broken open.

VIII

G   You should have heard the Hamelin people
    Ringing the bells till they rocked the steeple.
B(♯ 1) "Go," cried the Mayor, "and get long poles,
    Poke out the nests, and block up the holes!
150 Consult with carpenters and builders,
     And leave in our town not even a trace
     Of the rats!" when suddenly, up the face
     Of the Piper perked in the market place,
    With a, "First, if you please, my thousand guilders!"

IX

B 155 A thousand guilders!   The Mayor looked blue;
    So did the Corporation, too.
    For council dinners made rare havoc
    With Claret, Moselle, Vin-de-Grave, Hock;
    And half the money would replenish
160 Their cellar's biggest butt with Rhenish.
    To pay this sum to a wandering fellow,
    With a gypsy coat of red and yellow!
B(♯ 1) "Beside," quoth the Mayor, with a knowing wink,
    "Our business was done at the river's brink;
165 We saw with our eyes the vermin sink,
    And what's dead can't come to life, I think.
    So, friend, we're not the folks to shrink
    From the duty of giving you something to drink,
    And a matter of money to put in your poke;
170 But, as for the guilders, what we spoke
    Of them, as you very well know, was in joke.
    Besides, our losses have made us thrifty.
    A thousand guilders! come, take fifty!"

158. CLARET, MOSELLE (mō-zĕl'), VIN-DE-GRAVE (văn'-dĕ-gräv), HOCK (hŏk)
Names of wines.
160. BUTT—Cask.
160. RHENISH (rĕn'ĭsh)—Wine from the vineyards along the Rhine.
169. A MATTER OF MONEY—That is, a reasonable amount.
169. POKE—Pouch or pocket.

X

1B(#2)   The Piper's face fell. and he cried,

175   "No trifling!   I can't wait, beside!

I've promised to visit by dinner time

Bagdad, and accept the prime

Of the Head Cook's pottage, all he's rich in,

For having left, in the Caliph's kitchen,

180   Of a nest of scorpions no survivor.

With him I proved no bargain driver;

With you, don't think I'll bate a stiver!

And folks who put me in a passion

May find me pipe after another fashion."

XI

1B(#1) 185   "How!" cried the Mayor, "d'ye think I'll brook

Being worse treated than a cook?

Insulted by a lazy ribald

With idle pipe and vesture piebald!

You threaten us, fellow!   Do your worst;

190   Blow your pipe there till you burst!"

XII

G   Once more he stept into the street,

     And to his lips again

     Laid his long pipe of smooth, straight cane;

And ere he blew three notes (such sweet

195   Soft notes as yet musician's cunning

Never gave the enraptured air)

There was a rustling that seemed like a bustling,

Of merry crowds justling at pitching and hustling,

Small feet were pattering, wooden shoes clattering,

200   Little hands clapping and little tongues chattering,

177. PRIME—That is, the first dish.
182. BATE—Deduct, reduce.
182. STIVER—A Dutch coin worth about two cents.
187. RIBALD—A coarse jester.
188. PIEBALD—Of mottled colors, pied.

And, like fowls in a farmyard when barley is scat-
    tering,
  Out came the children running.
And all the little boys and girls,
With rosy cheeks and flaxen curls,
205 And sparkling eyes and teeth like pearls,
Tripping and skipping ran merrily after
The wonderful music with shouting and laughter.

XIII

B   The Mayor was dumb, and the Council stood
      As if they were changed into blocks of wood,
210 Unable to move a step, or cry
      To the children merrily skipping by,
      —Could only follow with the eye
      That joyous crowd at the Piper's back.

And now the Mayor was on the rack,

215 And the wretched Council's bosoms beat,
As the Piper turned from the High Street
To where the Weser rolled its waters
Right in the way of their sons and daughters!
However he turned from south to west,

220 And to Koppelberg Hill his steps addressed,
And after him the children pressed;
Great was the joy in every breast.
"He never can cross that mighty top!
He's forced to let the piping drop,

225 And we shall see our children stop!"
When, lo, as they reached the mountain side,
A wondrous portal opened wide,
As if a cavern was suddenly hollowed;
And the Piper advanced, and the children followed,

230 And when all were in to the very last,
The door in the mountain side shut fast.
Did I say all? No! One was lame,
And could not dance the whole of the way;
And in after years, if you would blame

235 His sadness, he was used to say—

1B(#4) "It's dull in our town since my playmates left!
I can't forget that I'm bereft
Of all the pleasant sights they see
Which the Piper also promised me:

240 For he led us, he said, to a joyous land,
Joining the town and just at hand,
Where waters gushed and fruit trees grew,
And flowers put forth a fairer hue,
And everything was strange and new;

245 The sparrows were brighter than peacocks here,
Their dogs outran our fallow deer,

214. ON THE RACK—That is, in torture. The rack was an instrument of torture used in the Middle Ages.

284

And honey bees had lost their stings,
And horses were born with eagles' wings:
And just as I became assured
250 My lame foot would be speedily cured,
The music stopped, and I stood still,
And found myself outside the hill,
Left alone against my will,
To go now limping as before,
255 And never hear of that country more!"

XIV

B   Alas, alas for Hamelin!
    There came into many a burgher's pate
    A text which says that Heaven's gate
    Opes to the rich at an easy rate
260 As the needle's eye takes a camel in!
The Mayor sent east, west, north, and south,
To offer the Piper, by word of mouth,
    Wherever it was man's lot to find him,
Silver and gold to his heart's content,
265 If he'd only return the way he went,
    And bring the children behind him,
But when they saw 'twas a lost endeavor,
And Piper and dancers were gone forever,
They made a decree that lawyers never
270   Should think their records dated duly
If, after the day of the month and the year,
These words did not as well appear,
G   "And so long after what happened here
    On the Twenty-second of July,
275 Thirteen hundred and seventy-six":
And the better in memory to fix

257. BURGHER'S PATE—Townsman's head.
258. TEXT—Matthew 19:24. "And again I say unto you, it is easier for a camel to go through the eye of a needle, than for a rich man to enter into the kingdom of God."

The place of the children's last retreat,
They called it, the Pied Piper's street—
Where any one playing on pipe or tabor
280   Was sure for the future to lose his labor.
Nor suffered they hostelry or tavern
        To shock with mirth a street so solemn;
But opposite the place of the cavern
        They wrote the story on a column,
285   And on the great church window painted
The same, to make the world acquainted
How their children were stolen away,
And there it stands to this very day.
And I must not omit to say
290   That in Transylvania there's a tribe
Of alien people that ascribe
The outlandish ways and dress
On which their neighbors lay such stress,
To their fathers and mothers having risen
295   Out of some subterraneous prison
Into which they were trepanned
Long ago in a mighty band
Out of Hamelin town in Brunswick land,
But how or why, they don't understand.

xv

B 300   So, Willy, let you and me be wipers
Of scores out with all men—especially pipers!
And, whether they pipe us free from rats or free
        from mice,
If we've promised them aught, let us keep our
        promise!

279. TABOR—A small drum.
281. HOSTELRY (hŏs'tĕl rĭ)—Lodging house, inn.
290. TRANSYLVANIA—The "country beyond the forest," a picturesque region of Hungary.
295. SUBTERRANEOUS—Under the earth.
296. TREPANNED—Trapped, ensnared.
300. WILLY—Willy Macready, the boy for whom Browning wrote the poem.

THE SNOW WITCH

CONSTANCE D'ARCY MACKAY

SCENE. *The home of Marina.*[1] *A bare, plain room. A door in background, left. Beyond it a tiny window. A hearth at right with a chair beside it. Against the left wall a cupboard. Beneath the window a deal table. On it a few cups of earthenware, and a small brass samovar.*[2] *On the platter a loaf of black bread. At the rise of the curtain, Marina is looking out through the tiny frosted window, breathing on it to get a clear space. The samovar is steaming; near it the wick of a squat brass lamp burns with a blue flame; the hooded hearth sends out a cheerful, rosy glow that gives the room an air of comfort, in spite of the meagerness of its furnishing.*

Marina (*rubbing at window*). It is a fine night, and a cold. Ai! How sharp the stars are shining! They are as white as the snow that covers the steppes![3] And the snow—how it is

---

[1] MARINA—Pronounced mä-rē'nà.
[2] SAMOVAR (săm'ô-vär)—A metal urn used in Russia for making tea.
[3] STEPPES (stĕps)—Vast tracts of level, treeless lands in southeastern Europe.

287

whirling whenever the wind passes. Now it blows like a white scarf; now it seems to move and tower as if—(*Turns, facing audience, and rubs her eyes.*) The whiteness must have blinded me; for I thought I saw the snow move like a human shape, a woman with a crown of frost-leaves. (*Turns again to window.*) No! No! I was but dreaming! There are the village lights, and there's no one passing, though I can hear the faint, far sound of music from where the lads and girls are dancing. (*Crosses to hearth.*) Dancing! No! No! Marina, your feet are too old for that! Your youth lies far behind you. You've only the singing steam and the fire to keep you company. (*Wind gives a gust, without.*) There's the wind again! 'Tis like a voice that's calling. (*Returns to window, rubs it, and peers out.*) There's the snow still whirling with the wind, and looking like—(*Starts back from window.*) Nay, I was right! 'Twas something moving! (*Peers again.*) Now, as I live, it is the Snow Witch whom folk call Silver-Sonia—she who goes abroad before the flakes come flying! I wonder why she is looking at my window!

Silver-Sonia (*knocking at the door without*). Marina! Marina! Let me in!

Marina. She knocks! She calls me! (*Hesitates.*) Shall I open the door, or no? All the Snow Witch ever does is to wander about before a storm. (SILVER-SONIA *knocks again.*) I never heard of her working harm to any one; so why should I grudge to lift the latch? (*Opens the door.*)

Silver-Sonia (*crossing the threshold, a white-clad glittering figure, wreathed with frost, and with something very stately in her bearing*). There are good witches and evil witches, Marina. All those who live in Bitter Russia know it well. And they know, too, that I have never used my powers for aught save the sheltering of the furry folk of the forest, and the enlightening of those who live in villages. I am a prophecy, a warning. When folk see me, they say: "A storm is coming. Let us put off our journey till it passes." Sometimes I tread the deserted highway. Sometimes I pause at the hearths of humans. To-night I saw the friendly gleam of your window, and I said: "Marina is alone. She will make me welcome." (*Turns to* MARINA, *who has backed away from her, somewhat over-awed.*) It is not of my will I go a-roving; but when the wild winds blow I feel their echo here in my heart. Then must I forth, whether I will or no.

Marina (*timidly*). Is there to be a storm tonight?

Silver-Sonia. Nay. But tomorrow the clouds will gather, and there will be a snowstorm. Tonight, 'tis sharp and clear! Tomorrow—flakes a-flying! (*As she speaks the silverish gauze that floats from her sleeve whirls as with presage of coming storm as she raises her arm.*)

Marina. You must see strange sights, Silver-Sonia!

Silver-Sonia. I see the great white wastes where never a human stirs! I see the midnight forests black against the stars. I see the huddled villages with tiny lights in their windows. I see the bleak harvest fields, where the drifts lie deeply, and where the lone gray wolf is fleet as a moving shadow.

Marina (*beginning to recover from her awe, and wake to a sense of manners*). Will you not be seated, Silver-Sonia?

Silver-Sonia. Beneath a roof? Nay, nay. I must be with the storm-wind. Yet ere I leave the steppes of the village I will return to you; for I see that my going grieves you, good Marina. And for those who love a hearth what hearth could shine brighter! You must be happy in this home of yours, Marina.

Marina (*bitterly*). Happy! An old woman happy! With all my years behind me, and no joy to come!

Silver-Sonia. Yet you have many comforts, Marina.

Marina. Comforts! To be living here old and lonely? Do you call that comfort? I've had my fill of such! If I were young, now, like some of our village girls, or rich like the Princess Valeska—(*Grumbles.*) There's not a soul hereabout but what must be happier than I!

Silver-Sonia (*quietly*). How would you like to change, Marina?

Marina (*looking at* SILVER-SONIA, *half-fascinated, half-fearful*). Change— Do you mean— Have you power to make me change——

Silver-Sonia. But lay your hand in the hand of the human whom you envy most, and then you will change places. Ah, I see! You only half-believe me. Look into my eyes, Marina. (MARINA *does as she is bid*.) You do not doubt me now.

Marina (*brushing her hand across her own eyes and speaking to herself*). There is magic in her eyes! They are like deep wells with stars in them!

Silver-Sonia. Now you can change your lot, Marina. You can be another than yourself.

Marina (*joyfully*). And someone else will be changed into poor old Marina! (*Suddenly pausing in her delight*.) But what would a neighbor do if she were changed to Marina? Would she look like me? Would she talk like me? And what would the neighbors say if she told them that she was no longer herself, though she stood in my skin?

Silver-Sonia. They would say, "Poor Marina has gone mad today. The White Fox has bitten her."

Marina (*again overjoyed*). So they would! So they would! None would know I had done it! Oh, to think I can change from being myself! It is a great gift you have given me!

Silver-Sonia (*at door*). When I return I will find how you have used my gift. I will know whose lot in life you have chosen for your own! Choose wisely, Marina Machinoff! (*Exit* SONIA.)

Marina. Choose! I've the whole village to choose from! (*Suiting her step and actions to the words*.) Young women, old women, middle-aged! I can be what I like! Only to lay my hand in the hand of the one I envy most! (*A light breaking over her face*.) Why, I can be a man! (*Again suiting her action to the word as she walks up and down*.) A soldier, a sledge-driver, a mojuk! [4] And when we have changed places, how the soldier will rage to find himself in petticoats! Knitting instead of marching! (*Laughs to herself.*) Ai! What a jest it would be! I'll place my hand in his, so! And then— (*Laughs to herself, and then wipes her eyes.*) But, after all, it is better to stay a woman. (*Sits by hearth.*) Now, let me see, who shall I be? (*Telling off her neighbors on her fingers.*) Marya Topliff? No! No! Her nose is far too long! Alla Povlova? But her step is halting. Besides, they're poor. And to be happy one must be rich and noble. Hark! (*Nearer and nearer come the sounds of sleighbells.*) Sleighbells! And of silver! Who can be passing? Can it be some one with whom I might change places?

[*There comes the sound of a whip-handle knocking on the door.* MARINA *hastens to open it, and* PAUL, *the sledge-driver, stands on the threshold, wrapped in furs.*]

Paul. Have you a fire here? Fire and shelter for the Princess Valeska?

Marina (*overcome*). The Princess! (PAUL *stands back. The Princess enters. She is richly garbed, and, after a glance about the room, sweeps to the fire at left.*) Excellency, all that I have is at your Excellency's service. (*Looks at* PAUL.) Your Excellency's sledge-driver?

Princess Valeska. Let him wait without. [*Exit* PAUL.]

Marina (*to herself*). To be a sledge-driver! Not for a thousand kopecs [5] would I lay my hand in his!

Princess Valeska (*at fire*). Good peasant——

Marina (*starting forward*). Can I serve your Excellency?

Princess Valeska (*who has unfastened her cloak*). The warmth of your fire has served me, good peasant, and I must be going on. How do they call you?

Marina (*bowing humbly*). They call me Marina, Excellency. Will your Excellency taste my tea? It is all that I have to offer.

---

[4] MOJUK—Pronounced mō′jŭk.   [5] KOPEC (kō′pĕk)—A small Russian coin.

Princess Valeska (more to herself than to MARINA). No!
No! I only want the warmth. I am afraid of the night. I
shiver through my furs.

Marina. You fear the night, Excellency?

Princess Valeska. The night and the robbers.

Marina (startled). Robbers!

Princess Valeska. It comes of having gold and jewels. Always they follow me. Sometimes they start like shadows from
the edge of the forest, and sometimes they gallop after me to
my very doors.

Marina (gasping). Shield us! Have mercy! I should die
of terror!

Princess Valeska (shuddering). Even in my dreams I see
them—their greedy, cruel eyes. Why, have *you* never shaken
in your sleep, good mother!

Marina (vehemently). Oh, never, never, never!

Princess Valeska. Have you never driven homeward with
your heart thudding with fear? Ah, I see! Peace dwells beneath your roof! A Princess must go like a Princess; but a
peasant is safe from danger. It is a free and happy moment I
have spent with you, Marina, and therefore you may take my
fingers within your own. You may kiss my hand.

*Marina (starting forward, and then drawing back as she re-
members).* Oh, no, no, no! I mean—I kiss your fingers, Excellency! (*With her hands held tightly behind her back,*
MARINA *bends over the* PRINCESS'S *outstretched hand.*) How
should I touch so snowy a hand as yours with a palm that is as
rough as mine! (*Kisses the* PRINCESS'S *hand.*) The honor
overcomes me!

Princess Valeska. My cloak, Marina.

Marina (assisting her). May your Excellency speed well
and safely!

Princess Valeska. I thank you. (*Exit* VALESKA. *Sleighbells
grow fainter and fainter.*)

Marina If she had made me put my hand in hers — Ah, I

shiver to think of it! Darkness and robbers! (*Shivers again.*)
I would not be the Princess for a thousand rubles! (*Dance music begins outside, drawing nearer and nearer.*) It is always ill luck to be a woman. If I were only a lad, with the world before me! There's Ivan now— So tall, so strong, so handsome! He'd be the match for a dozen robbers!

Ivan (*laughing in doorway*). Why, so he would, dushenka,[6] unless they were a match for him. (*Dance music grows nearer.*)

Marina. Oh, Ivan, how you startled me!

Ivan. Did you not hear me knock? The world is full of surprises!

Marina. It is, indeed. What would you say, now, Ivan, if you should find yourself turned into an old woman like me? (*Folds her arms and regards him.*)

Ivan (*folding his arms and regarding her*). And what would *you* say if you found yourself a soldier? Ah, you think I look wonderful now with the cloak and the clanking sword; but you should see us on the march with our shoes frozen to our feet, and nothing to eat except crusts and snow! You would not envy us then, I give you my hand upon it! (*Stretches out his hand.*)

Marina (*starting back*). No! No! Do not give me your hand. I will take your word. I will take your word. Listen! There's music, Ivan. The dancers must be coming here!

[*With a gay shout* MARINA'S *door is opened, and the dancers dance in and fill the room, lads and girls in peasant costumes. As they pass* MARINA *she reaches out her hand and stays one of the girls.*]

Marina. There is no one here as beautiful, as light of foot as you, pretty Foma. Will you lay your hand in mine and take a step or two with an old woman?

Foma (*stretching out her hand, and then pausing as there comes the far-off howl of a wolf*) What sound is that?

---

[6] DUSHENKA—Pronounced dōō-shĕn′kȧ.

Ivan (*jesting*). The Were Wolf [7] is calling you, Foma.

Marina (*starting back*). Heaven save us! You cannot mean what you are saying! It is not true that the wicked powers of the forest have cast a spell on Foma?

Foma (*holding out her hand*). Come, neighbor Marina, the music is calling us!

Marina (*drawing back*). No! No! My feet are too old for dancing. I spoke in jest, pretty Foma. (FOMA *turns away, laughing, and joins the other dancers. The village fiddler has been unflagging in his music, and* FOMA, *with the others, turns towards the door. One by one all the dancers cross the threshold and disappear into the night, save* IVAN, *who lingers for a moment with* MARINA.

Marina (*anxiously*). And you, too, spoke in jest, did you not, Ivan? It is not true that the powers of the forest have put a spell on Foma?

Ivan (*half-smiling, half-serious*). You cannot tell about another's life, good neighbor. There are dark spells woven in the shadow, and bright spells woven in the sun. No life is all sun or all shadow. (*Exit* IVAN.)

Marina (*coming slowly and thoughtfully back to the center of the room*). I do not know whether he be in jest or in earnest; but of one thing am I certain: I will not try to change places with any. The Princess is always in terror; Ivan must suffer as he marches; and Foma— Was it true about the Were Wolf or was Ivan jesting, I wonder? Well, be that as it may, I am glad I did not lay my hand in hers. No! No! It is better to be just one's self, with one's own burdens!

Silver-Sonia (*entering softly*). Well spoken, Marina! I see you have learned true wisdom. See you, the fire has burned low, and the charm has ended. You may lay your hand in mine without fear. Look once again in my eyes, Marina. (MARINA *does as she is bid.* SONIA *slips a white ring into* MARINA'S *hand, and then goes softly out the door.*)

[7] WERE WOLF (wĕr' wŏŏlf)—A person transformed into a wolf in form.

Marina (*delighted*).   A ring!   A gift from Silver-Sonia!
What says it?   (*Reads.*)

> Choose not another's lot or pelf,
> Happiness lies within thyself!

I am thinking the Snow Witch speaks truly!

CURTAIN

THE BROKEN NOTE

ERIC P. KELLY

1241 A.D.

It was in the spring of the year 1241 that rumors began to
travel along the highroad from Kiev [1] in the land of Rus that
the Tartars of the East were again upon the march.   Men trembled when they heard that news and mothers held their chil-

[1] KIEV (kē′yĕf)—A city in the Ukraine.   Rus is an abbreviation of Russia.

295

dren close to their breasts, for the name "Tartar" was one that froze folks' blood in their veins. As the weeks went on, the rumors grew thicker and there began to come through to Poland, our land of the fields, the news that the country lands of the Ukraine [2] were ablaze. Then it was heard that Kiev had fallen, then Lwow,[3] the city of the Lion, and now there was naught between the savage band of warriors and the fair city of Krakow,[4] save a few peaceful villages and fertile fields.

The Tartars came through the world like a horde of wild beasts. They left not one thing alive nor one green blade of wheat standing. They were short, dark men of shaggy beards and long hair twisted into little braids, and they rode on small horses which they covered with trophies they had gained in war. Brave they were as lions, courageous they were as great dogs, but they had hearts of stone and knew not mercy, nor pity, nor tenderness, nor God. On their horses they carried round shields of leather and iron, and long spears often trailed from their saddles. About their shoulders and thighs they wore skins of animals. Some decorated their ears with golden rings—here and there one wore a gold ring in the nose. When they traveled, the dust rose high into the sky from beneath the hoofs of their little horses, and the thunder of the hoofbeats could be heard many miles away. They were so numerous that it took days for the whole horde to pass any one given point, and for miles behind the army itself rumbled carts bearing slaves, provisions, and booty—usually gold.

Before them went always a long, desperate procession of country people driven from their humble homes by the news of the coming terror; they had already said farewell to the cottages where they lived, the parting from which was almost as bitter as death. So it has always been in time of war that the innocent suffer most—these poor, helpless peasants with their carts and horses and geese and sheep trudging along

[2] THE UKRAINE (ū'krān)—A province of southwest Russia.
[3] LWOW—Pronounced lĕ-vŏŏf'. A city in Poland.
[4] KRAKOW (krä'kow)—A city in southwest Poland.

through the dust to escape, if God so willed, the terrible fate which would befall them were they left behind. There were old people in that procession too feeble to be stirring even about a house, mothers nursing children, women weak with sickness, and men broken-hearted at the loss of all that a lifetime of labor had brought. Children dragged themselves wearily along beside them, often bearing their pets in their arms.

To this company Krakow opened her gates, and prepared for defense. Many of the nobility and rich citizens had, in the meantime, fled to the west or taken refuge in monasteries far to the north. The brothers of the monastery at Zvierzyniec,[5] a short distance outside the city, took in all the refugees that the building could accommodate, and then prepared to stand siege. But the great, weary, terror-mad mob that had fled ahead of the band of Tartars was content enough to make the city itself its destination. And once within its walls all turned their faces toward the south. For there, in the south of the city, towering on its rocky hill high over the Vistula [6] River, was the great, irregular, turreted mass that was the Wawel— the fortress and castle of the kings of Poland from the time of Krakus, the legend king, and the home of the dukes and nobles who formed the king's court.

It had been decided to make no attempt to defend the city outside the castle gates, since that would entail a great loss of life; and so for several days the city dwellers who remained and these refugees from all the country about poured into the fortification and were housed inside its walls. The old castle gates which were then on Castle Highway opposite the Church of St. Andrew were at last shut and barricaded, and the walls were manned with citizen soldiery prepared to give their lives for the protection of the city and their families.

The Tartars fell upon the city in the night and, after burning the outlying villages, pillaged the districts that lay about the churches of St. Florian, St. John, and the Holy Cross. The

[5] ZVIERZYNIEC—Pronounced tsfēr'tsnyĕk.   [6] VISTULA—Pronounced wĭstá.

whole night long was one of hideous sounds—the crackling and fury of flames, the snarling and yelling of the enemy when they found that the prey had fled, the roars of triumph when they came upon gold and treasure. As morning dawned the watchers from the Wawel looked out over the town and saw but three churches not already in flames. These were the Church of Our Lady Mary near the great market, the Church of St. Andrew with its stalwart towers at the Castle Gate, and the Church of St. Adalbert in the market place. Already a colony of Jews in the Black Village had perished, also those refugees and town dwellers who had not rushed inside the walls of defense. There remained but one man—or rather a youth—still alive in the midst of all that destruction.

He was the trumpeter of the Church of Our Lady Mary, and he had taken solemn oath to sound the trumpet each hour of the day and night from a little balcony high up on the front of the church. As the first golden rays of the sun changed the Vistula from a dark line to a plash of dancing gold, he mounted this balcony to sound the Heynal [7]—the hymn to Our Lady which every trumpeter in the church had in the past sworn to play each hour of the day and night—"until death." He felt with a strange joy the glow of the sun as it fell upon him that morning, for the night had been very dark both with its own shadow and with the gloomy blackness of men's ruthlessness.

About his feet, down in the town highway, stood groups of short, fierce men gazing up at him curiously. Here and there the roof of a house was shooting upward in flames and belching forth clouds of black smoke. Hundreds of dwellings lay charred and ruined by the conflagration. He was alone in the midst of a terrible enemy—he might have fled on the previous day and gained the castle with the refugees and the town dwellers, but he had been true to his oath and remained at his post until he should be driven away. Now it was too late to retreat.

He was a very young man, perhaps nineteen or twenty, and

[7] HEYNAL—Pronounced hä′näl.

wore a dark cloth suit that was caught at the knees with buckles, like the knickerbockers of a later generation; dark, thick hose extended from the knees to the tops of his soft, pointed sandals, and a short coat falling just below the waist was held together in front by a belt. The head covering was of leather and something like a cowl; it fell clear to his shoulders and ran up over the head in such a way that only his face and a bit of hair were visible.

"My mother and sister are safe," he thought. "May God be praised for that! They are gone these ten days and must be now with the cousins in Moravia." [8]

It came to him then what a sweet thing life is. The sun over the Vistula was now reflected in the windows of the Cathedral of the Wawel where the priests were already saying mass. At the tops of all the gates he could see guards in full armor upon which the sunlight flashed. A banner with a white eagle hung in the air above the gate at the great draw.

"Poland lives," he thought.

And then it came to him, young as he was, that he was part of the glorious company of Polish men that was fighting for all Christendom against brutal and savage invaders. He had not seen much of death before that minute—he had heard of it only as something vague. And now, he himself was perhaps going out to meet it, because of his oath, because of his love for the Church, because of his love for Poland.

"I shall keep my word," he mused. "If I die it shall be for that. My word is as good as my life."

Had a painter caught his expression then, he would have caught only the expression of a very great peace—an expression that signified somehow that God was very close. There was no moment of weakness, no faltering, no suffering even— for he did not think of what might come after his duty was performed. The sand in the hourglass already marked the hour for the trumpet to sound.

[8] MORAVIA (mŏ-rā′vĭ-ȧ)—A province in Czechoslovakia.

"Now, for Poland and Our Lady I will sound the Heynal," he said, and raised the trumpet to his lips.

Softly he blew at first—then, thrilled with a sense of triumph, he felt in his heart a joy that was almost ecstatic. He seemed to see in a vision that though he might now die alone and for naught save what perhaps some scoffing ones might call a foolish honor, still that bravery was to descend as a heritage to the people to whom he belonged, and was to become a part of their spirit, their courage, their power of everlasting—all this that moment brought.

A Tartar below crouched to his bow and drew back the arrow as far as he could draw. The string whirred. The dark shaft flew like a swift bird straight for the mark. It pierced

the breast of the young trumpeter when he was near the end of his song—it quivered there a moment and the song ceased. But still holding to the trumpet the youth fell back against the supporting wall and blew one last glorious note; it began strongly, trembled, and then ceased—broken like the young life that gave it birth, and at that moment those below applied the torch to the wooden church and it, too, rose in flames to Heaven, with the soul of the youth among them.

1461 A.D.

On a hot July day in the year 1461 many wagons wended their way along the Krakow, Tarnov, Lwow, Kiev route. It was market day, and among the travelers were a fifteen-year-old lad and his father and mother. The Charnetskis, however, were not bound for the market-place. They were fleeing from the Cossacks who had set upon their home in the Ukraine. Reaching Krakow, Pan Andrew [1] Charnetski sought out his influential cousin only to learn of the latter's death and of the seizure of the family estates. He found himself destitute and surrounded by enemies. In the midst of his difficulties he was be-friended by a scholar-priest, a much-loved man of the community. Through him Pan Andrew, who was an accomplished musician, ob-tained work as the watchman-trumpeter in the Church of Our Lady Mary. Like the scores of trumpeters who had preceded him, he took the ancient oath: "I swear on my honor as a Pole, as a servant of the King of the Polish people, that I will faithfully and unto the death, if there be need, sound upon the trumpet the Heynal in honor of Our Lady each hour in the tower of the church which bears Her name."

One of the great sights of Central Europe, even in those far-away days, which men came from all parts of the world to see, was the Church of Our Lady Mary in Krakow. Now though this church rose majestically over the medieval city, its towers visible from afar, and its red-brick walls as substantial and as solid as the very rock base of the Wawel Hill itself, it was not from the outside such an imposing sight as was its more aristocratic sister, the Wawel Cathedral. It lacked flying buttresses and distinct Gothic ornamentation such as huge gargoyles and flowers and saints carved in stone, though its graceful form indicated a solid and magnificent strength. It was not a church such as one might gaze upon in sunny France where the mild breezes and sweet sunshine permit delicate carvings and pinnacles upon the outside walls, but it was built

---

[1] PAN ANDREW—Pan is a formal Polish term signifying Sir or Mr.

like a solid fortress to withstand the mighty storms that sometimes sweep over Poland from the wild steppes or from the
Baltic Sea. It was the interior of this church, however, that
drew men to it, for within, it was a very miracle of beauty, a
crystal hidden in a shapely stone.

It was to this church, then, that Pan Andrew and Joseph
wended their way after darkness fell on their first day in the
new dwelling. Pan Andrew carried the trumpet under his right
arm. Near the base of the higher tower a watchman spied
them as they approached, and unlocked a small, heavy door
that led to the tower stairs. They went up a narrow staircase,
winding about in the darkness, until it reached a platform
where the interior of the tower loomed suddenly above them.
Just at the right, as they began their ascent in the main body
of the tower, was a door that led to a little chapel in which, as
Joseph learned afterward, prisoners condemned to death spent
their last hours on earth.

A man carrying a lantern shouted to them from above; they
waited then until he had descended—he was the day watchman whom Pan Andrew relieved. He paused to kiss Pan Andrew upon the cheek in welcome, and to speak a few words
in explanation of his duties above. Then he placed in his hand
the lantern and a key to the room which the trumpeter was to
occupy in the high tower. He wished them luck on their first
night and then descended by the side staircase to the ground
where the watchman let him out. Joseph and his father in
the meantime began to climb the steps of the scaffolding that
led up into the tower. This scaffolding was held in place by
cross beams, and at its edge ran the steps, so built that as a
man ascended he passed constantly from one of the four sides
of the tower to another side. The staircase was steep and narrow, but very solid, so solid that the stairs did not creak as
they ascended.

They climbed and climbed, past five levels of windows,
glassed in with small white globes of solid crystal. Up and

up went father and son until they reached the level where there was a room for the watchman. This octagonal room was divided into two sections, one being the room where the trumpeter might keep warm between watches, the other being the open space around it from which the turret windows looked out over the city. Here hung extra trumpets, here were the ropes which connected the great bell hanging in the lower tower, and here were the red flags and the lanterns which were hung out when a fire was perceived from the tower.

For it was the duty of the trumpeter to watch constantly for fires. He was also to watch for troops approaching the city, for tumults or disturbances of any kind, but he was especially the guardian against fires. Conflagrations had done the city much harm in the past; many of the older buildings were of wood, although fronted with stone, and roofs were often of thatch or soft wood that easily caught fire from sparks. When a fire was discovered, the trumpeter or watchman, for he was both, hung a red flag from the window which faced the direction in which the blaze lay. At night he would hang out a lantern with a red-glass front instead of the flag.

It was his duty also to sound the alarm bell if any danger whatever came to threaten the lives of citizens. In the very month previous to the coming of Pan Andrew and his family to Krakow, the watchman had rung loud and long upon the bell to alarm the watch and the city when the riot against the Tenczynski [2] family took place. In the coming year the bell was to be tolled at the execution, in the town square just below the tower, of the four men charged with causing the riot. The tower was indeed the very center of Krakow activity.

Pan Andrew fitted his key to the lock of the door leading into the inner room and threw back the bolt. Entering after his father, Joseph found himself in a small, comfortable room, containing a table, a bed, a small stove, and a lighted lantern hanging on the wall. About the table were three chairs, wedged

---

[2] TENCZYNSKI—Pronounced těn-chĭn'skĭ.

rather tightly because of the lack of space, and upon the table was a huge hourglass, one of the largest that Joseph had ever seen. The sand pouring through it in a fine stream had filled the lower section almost to a level graded on the glass with a Latin "X" to designate the tenth hour. The glass was in reality a twelve-hour glass, and lines and Latin numerals had been marked upon it just after the maker had blown it into shape, when the material was still soft. This was the trumpeter's official clock. There was on the south side of the nave roof, where the sun touched at all hours of the day, a large sundial which was read each noon, and on the north wall of the tower was a clock with one hand. This hand, which indicated the hours, was in truth a hand—a piece of metal shaped like a doubled fist —with fingers curled and the index pointing out to the hours.

When the sand had reached the level of the glass at which the "X" was cut, Pan Andrew hastened out to the open section of the tower and released a coil of rope that hung on a pillar in the center of the space. This rope ran down through a hole in the flooring until it reached the level of the lower tower, when it swung about over a piece of round wood that served as a pulley and leaped from there to the lower tower through an aperture that was originally designed as a narrow window through which to shoot arrows in time of defense. In the lower tower the rope was connected with one end of an iron hammer that was suspended above the great bell. When the rope was pulled the hammer descended, but it sprang quickly back to its original position when the rope was loosed, a spring of twisted metal and leather serving to draw it back. Pan Andrew pulled once—the hammer descended—boom—the stroke of the bell sounded over the whole city. He pulled again and again until the full quota of ten strokes was made.

Next he went to the side of the tower nearest the entrance to the little room, and swung back a small glass window. Through this space he thrust the trumpet and began to play. It was on the west side, the side toward the Cloth Hall, with

the university in the distance. Then he moved to another window but one and began to play toward the south. Likewise he
played toward the east, and finally toward the north, according to the instructions which he had received. Lights were
twinkling now all over the city below him, the air was soft and
smelled of the freshly cut grass which the peasants gather into
piles. In the direction of the university a group of men were
chanting a hymn. A clashing of iron hoofs on the stones of
Grodzka Street betokened the presence of some armed men,
perhaps the servitors of some nobles' houses at the castle, or
perhaps members of the royal guard. Men of the night watch
could be heard banging at doors of shops with the butts of their
spears to be sure that no careless apprentice or servant had
left the door ajar. Down below in the graveyard the white
stones were just perceptible, dim and gray in the dusk, and
over the way the lamplighter was enkindling the huge wicks of
the lamps that hung under the Cloth Hall roof. The stars were
coming out, one after another, in the sky where a touch of
blue still lingered—across this world rang the notes of the
hymn which Pan Andrew had just played exquisitely, the
Heynal or Hymn to the Holy Mother.

"It is wondrous sweet," said Joseph.

"It is so, my son," replied the father. Thereupon he told
the boy of the morning, years before, when the square below
them had been full of hostile Tartars; of the lad who had kept
his oath, even with the last breath of life itself; and of the
honor paid him from that day to this by the tower trumpeters
who end the Heynal at the broken note.

And Joseph, listening, with eyes shining and heart throbbing, realized more at that moment than ever before how dear
to him was his native land and all the customs that had been
bequeathed by brave men and women who had made it great
forever among all nations; it seemed as if tears were forcing
themselves to his eyes as he thought of the sacrifice of that
young life so many years before, but a thrill of pride drove

back the tears when he thought of the nobility of the deed, as he stood silently gazing out of the little tower window.

1926 A.D.

It is the year 1926. The Vistula River now no longer turns at the Wawel Hill and plunges straight through the Krakow plain dividing the city of Kazimierz [1] from the city of Krakow, but instead swings far to the left and surrounds the whole plain, now the new city. The castles and towers and cathedral of the Wawel still rise proudly on the hill as in former days; St. Andrew's which has defied fire, siege, and war for eight centuries raises its head—two towers—above Grodzka Street; the old Cloth Hall, beautified during the Renaissance, [2] still stands in the middle of the central Rynek. And although the glory of former days is departed from the city and the kings no longer sit in the castle on the hill, there has come with the years the growth of a new glory, the glory of culture as seen in the university of fourteenth century origin, in the schools of fine arts and music and handicraft and trade. From all Poland come students to study and to live in this venerable city, which is Gothic in every corner and every gable save where here and there a bit of Romanesque wall or arch has survived the Tartar, [3] or the Cossack, or the Swede.

But the chief glory of the city is the Church of Our Lady Mary. It no longer stands apart, a monument visible from afar as of old—other palaces and buildings have shut it in, and one sees its towers only, until one is close upon it. Then the sudden magnificence leaps upon the visitor. A splendid silence lurking in its high roof descends suddenly like the thousands of pigeons that thunder down for particles of bread. Beneath one's feet is the old city cemetery; there on the walls are the tablets and shrines; there at the south doorway are the iron collars that

[1] KAZIMIERZ—Pronounced kå-zē'mēr.
[2] RENAISSANCE (rĕn-ĕ-säns')—A period in medieval history marked by a revival of interest in the arts and sciences.
[3] TARTAR . . . COSSACK . . . SWEDE—Successive conquerors.

306

once clasped the throats of petty criminals as they stood sup-
plicating the prayers and pennies of the faithful. Inside, the
church is a veritable miracle of beauty. Above its exquisite
wood carvings and choir rises a vaulted roof of sky blue,
studded with stars. Images of stone look down from breaks in
the Gothic fluting—tablets, banners, altars, shrines all strike
alike upon the sight in amazing beauty.

But listen: is the organ playing? Whence come those notes
that float down from above like God's own music from heaven?
They come from the towers, for the hour is striking on the bell,
and a trumpeter is playing at one of the open tower windows.
And that tune? It is the Heynal, the same tune played by a
young man so many centuries ago when the Tartars burned
the city—and listen, the trumpeter breaks off his song in the
middle of a note. . . . Four times he sounds the Heynal, once
at each of the four windows, west, south, east, north. And
many a man or woman or child on hearing that song thinks of
the days when the young life was given to country and God and
duty. . . . Poland has been through many fires since that time
—she has had centuries of war, a century of extinction. But
in all that time the Heynal has sounded with each passing
hour and men have sworn each year to keep the custom unto
the very end of time. Hark, it is sounding now.

May it bring in an epoch of peace to all men!

Joining in fun and laughter from everywhere.

HOW TOM SAWYER WHITE-WASHED THE FENCE

MARK TWAIN

SATURDAY morning was come, and all the summer world was bright and fresh, and brimming with life. There was a song in every heart; and if the heart was young the music issued at the lips. There was cheer in every face and a spring in every step. The locust trees were in bloom and the fragrance of the blossoms filled the air. Cardiff Hill, beyond the village and above it, was green with vegetation, and it lay just far enough away to seem a Delectable Land, dreamy, reposeful, and inviting.

Tom appeared on the sidewalk with a bucket of whitewash and a long-handled brush. He surveyed the fence, and all gladness left him and a deep melancholy settled down upon his spirit. Thirty yards of board fence nine feet high. Life to him seemed hollow, and existence but a burden. Sighing he dipped his brush and passed it along the topmost plank; repeated the operation; did it again; compared the insignificant whitewashed streak with the far-reaching continent of unwhitewashed fence, and sat down on a tree-box discouraged. Jim came skipping out at the gate with a tin pail, and singing "Buffalo Gals." Bringing water from the town pump had always been hateful work in Tom's eyes, before, but now it did not strike him so. He remembered that there was company at the pump. White, mulatto, and Negro boys and girls were always there waiting their turns, resting, trading playthings, quarreling, fighting, skylarking. And he remembered that although the pump was only a hundred and fifty yards off, Jim never got back with a bucket of water under an hour—and even then somebody generally had to go after him.   Tom said:

"Say, Jim, I'll fetch the water if you'll whitewash some."

Jim shook his head and said:

"Can't, Mars Tom.   Ole missis, she tole me I got to go an' git dis water an' not stop foolin' roun' wid anybody.   She say she spec' Mars Tom gwine to ax me to whitewash, an' so she tole me go 'long an' 'tend to my own business—she 'lowed she'd 'tend to de whitewashin'."

"Oh, never you mind what she said, Jim.   That's the way she always talks.   Gimme the bucket—I won't be gone only a minute.   She won't ever know."

"Oh, I dasn't, Mars Tom.   Ole missis she'd take an' tar de head off'n me.   'Deed she would."

"She!   She never licks anybody—whacks 'em over the head with her thimble—and who cares for that, I'd like to know.   She talks awful, but talk don't hurt—anyways it don't if she don't cry.   Jim, I'll give you a marvel.[1]   I'll give you a white alley!"

Jim began to waver.

"White alley, Jim!   And it's a bully taw."

"My!   Dat's a mighty gay marvel, I tell you!   But Mars Tom I's powerful 'fraid ole missis——"

"And besides, if you will I'll show you my sore toe."

Jim was only human—this attraction was too much for him. He put down his pail, took the white alley, and bent over the toe with absorbing interest while the bandage was being unwound.   In another moment he was flying down the street with his pail and a tingling rear, Tom was whitewashing with vigor, and Aunt Polly was retiring from the field with a slipper in her hand and triumph in her eye.

But Tom's energy did not last.   He began to think of the fun he had planned for this day, and his sorrows multiplied. Soon the free boys would come tripping along on all sorts of

[1] MARVEL—Marble.   A white alley was a choice marble, and a taw the marble with which the player shoots.

delicious expeditions, and they would make a world of fun of him for having to work—the very thought of it burnt him like fire. He got out his worldly wealth and examined it—bits of toys, marbles, and trash; enough to buy an exchange of work, maybe, but not half enough to buy so much as half an hour of pure freedom. So he returned his straitened means to his pocket, and gave up the idea of trying to buy the boys. At this dark and hopeless moment an inspiration burst upon him! Nothing less than a great, magnificent inspiration.

He took up his brush and went tranquilly to work. Ben Rogers hove in sight presently—the very boy, of all boys, whose ridicule he had been dreading. Ben's gait was the hop-skip-and-jump—proof enough that his heart was light and his anticipations high. He was eating an apple, and giving a long, melodious whoop, at intervals, followed by a deep-toned ding-dong-dong, ding-dong-dong, for he was personating a steamboat. As he drew near, he slackened speed, took the middle of the street, leaned far over to starboard [2] and rounded-to ponderously and with laborious pomp and circumstance—for he was personating the *Big Missouri,* and considered himself to be drawing nine feet of water. He was boat and captain and engine-bells combined, so he had to imagine himself standing on his own hurricane-deck giving the orders and executing them:

"Stop her, sir! Ting-a-ling-ling!" The headway ran almost out and he drew up slowly toward the sidewalk.

"Ship up to back! Ting-a-ling-ling!" His arms straightened and stiffened down his sides.

"Set her back on the stabboard! Ting-a-ling-ling! Chow! Ch-chow-wow! Chow!" His right hand, meantime, describing stately circles—for it was representing a forty-foot wheel. [3]

---

[2] STARBOARD—To the right. This and other nautical expressions were common, for Tom lived on the Mississippi River, and the chief delight of the boys was to watch the riverboats as they plied their way north and south.

[3] FORTY-FOOT WHEEL—In early days, steamboats were propelled by large wheels on each side of the boat and hence were called "side-wheelers." In this case, the size of the wheel is represented as being forty feet in diameter.

"Let her go back on the labboard! Ting-a-ling-ling! Chow-ch-chow-chow!" The left hand began to describe circles.

"Stop the stabboard! Ting-a-ling-ling! Stop the labboard! Come ahead on the stabboard! Stop her! Let your outside turn over slow! Ting-a-ling-ling! Chow-ow-ow! Get out that head-line! Lively now! Come—out with your spring-line! What're you about there! Take a turn round that stump with the bight [4] of it! Stand by that stage, now—let her go! Done with the engines, sir! Ting-a-ling-ling! Sh't! s'h't! sh't!"

Tom went on whitewashing—paid no attention to the steam-boat. Ben stared a moment and then said:

"Hi-yi! You're up a stump, ain't you!"

No answer. Tom surveyed his last touch with the eye of an artist, then he gave his brush another gentle sweep and surveyed the result, as before. Ben ranged up alongside of him.

[4] BIGHT—The loop of a rope.

Tom's mouth watered for the apple, but he stuck to his work. Ben said:

"Hello, old chap, you got to work, hey?"

Tom wheeled suddenly and said:

"Why, it's you, Ben! I warn't noticing."

"Say—I'm going in a-swimming, I am. Don't you wish you could? But of course you'd druther work—wouldn't you? Course you would!"

Tom contemplated the boy a bit, and said:

"What do you call work?"

"Why, ain't that work?"

Tom resumed his whitewashing, and answered carelessly:

"Well, maybe it is, and maybe it ain't. All I know, is, it suits Tom Sawyer."

"Oh, come, now, you don't mean to let on that you like it?"

The brush continued to move.

"Like it. Well, I don't see why I oughtn't to like it. Does a boy get a chance to whitewash a fence every day?"

That put the thing in a new light. Ben stopped nibbling his apple. Tom swept daintily back and forth—stepped back to note the effect—added a touch here and there—criticized the effect again—Ben watching every move and getting more and more interested, more and more absorbed. Presently he said:

"Say, Tom, let me whitewash a little."

Tom considered, was about to consent; but he altered his mind:

"No—no—I reckon it wouldn't hardly do, Ben. You see, Aunt Polly's awful particular about this fence—right here on the street, you know—but if it was the back fence I wouldn't mind and she wouldn't. Yes, she's awful particular about this fence; it's got to be done very careful; I reckon there ain't one boy in a thousand, maybe two thousand, that can do it the way it's got to be done."

"No—is that so? Oh, come, now—lemme just try. Only just a little—I'd let you, if you was me, Tom."

"Ben, I'd like to, honest injun; but Aunt Polly—well, Jim wanted to do it, but she wouldn't let him; Sid wanted to do it, and she wouldn't let Sid. Now don't you see how I'm fixed. If you was to tackle this fence and anything was to happen to it——"

"Oh, shucks, I'll be just as careful. Now lemme try. Say— I'll give you the core of my apple."

"Well, here—No, Ben, now don't. I'm afeared——"

"I'll give you all of it!"

Tom gave up the brush with reluctance in his face, but alacrity in his heart. And while the late steamer *Big Missouri* worked and sweated in the sun, the retired artist sat on a barrel in the shade close by, dangled his legs, munched his apple, and planned the slaughter of more innocents. There was no lack of material; boys happened along every little while; they came to jeer, but remained to whitewash. By the time Ben was fagged out, Tom had traded the next chance to Billy Fisher for a kite, in good repair; and when he played out, Johnny Miller bought in for a dead rat and a string to swing it with—and so on, and so on, hour after hour. And when the middle of the afternoon came, from being a poor, poverty-stricken boy in the morning, Tom was literally rolling in wealth. He had beside the things before mentioned, twelve marbles, part of a jew's-harp, a piece of blue bottle-glass to look through, a spool cannon, a key that wouldn't unlock anything, a fragment of chalk, a glass stopper of a decanter, a tin soldier, a couple of tadpoles, six firecrackers, a kitten with only one eye, a brass door-knob, four pieces of orange-peel, and a dilapidated old window-sash.

He had had a nice, good, idle time all the while—plenty of company—and the fence had three coats of whitewash on it! If he hadn't run out of whitewash, he would have bankrupted every boy in the village.

Tom said to himself that it was not such a hollow world, after all. He had discovered a great law of human action, without knowing it—namely, that in order to make a man or a boy covet a thing, it is only necessary to make the thing difficult to attain. If he had been a great and wise philosopher, like the writer of this story, he would now have comprehended that Work consists of whatever a body is *obliged* to do, and that Play consists of whatever a body is *not* obliged to do. And this would help him to understand why constructing artificial flowers or performing on a treadmill is work, while rolling tenpins or climbing Mont Blanc[5] is only amusement. There are wealthy gentlemen in England who drive four-horse passenger-coaches twenty or thirty miles on a daily line, in the summer, because the privilege costs them considerable money; but if they were offered wages for the service, that would turn it into work and then they would resign.

The boy mused awhile over the substantial change which had taken place in his worldly circumstances, and then wended toward headquarters to report.

[5] MONT BLANC (mông bläng')—The highest mountain in Europe, located in the Alps near the France-Switzerland border. Mountain climbers from all over the world perform the notable feat of climbing Mont Blanc.

GODFREY GORDON GUSTAVUS GORE

WILLIAM BRIGHTY RANDS

U　　GODFREY GORDON GUSTAVUS GORE—
　　　No doubt you have heard the name before—
　　　Was a boy who would not shut a door!

1G(#1)　　The wind might whistle, the wind might roar,
1G(#2)　5　And teeth be aching, and throats be sore,
　G　　But still he would never shut the door.

B(#1) His father would beg, his mother implore,
 U   "Godfrey Gordon Gustavus Gore,
    We really do wish you would shut the door!"

 G 10 Their hands they wrung, and their hair they tore;
    But Godfrey Gordon Gustavus Gore
    Was deaf as the buoy out at the Nore.

 B   When he walked forth the folks would roar,
 U   "Godfrey Gordon Gustavus Gore,
  15 Why don't you think to shut the door?"

    They rigged out a Shutter with sail and oar,
    And threatened to pack off Gustavus Gore
    On a voyage of penance to Singapore.

B(#2) But he begged for mercy and said, "No more!
  20 Pray do not send me to Singapore
    On a Shutter, and then I will shut the door!"

 ₁B "You will?" said his parents; "then keep on shore!
 U   But mind you do! for the plague is sore
    On a fellow that never will shut the door,
  25 Godfrey Gordon Gustavus Gore!"

THE MODERN HIAWATHA

GEORGE A. STRONG

 B   HE KILLED the noble Mudjokivis,
    With the skin he made him mittens,
 ₁B Made them with the fur side inside,
 ₁G Made them with the skin side outside,
 B 5 He, to get the warm side inside,

Put the inside skin side outside:
G   He, to get the cold side outside,
Put the warm side fur side inside:
U   That's why he put the fur side inside,
10   Why he put the skin side outside,
Why he turned them inside outside.

THE LOBSTER MARATHON

ROBERT P. TRISTRAM COFFIN

B   AMERICANS love so to race,
1B(♯1)   They drive their horses breakneck pace,
1B(♯2)   Their jumping-frogs, their boats, their bees,
1B(♯3)   Their homing pigeons, autos, fleas.

1G(♯1)   5   They race raindrops down a pane,
1G(♯2)   They race their wives and growing grain,
1G(♯3)   Bet on their babies as they creep,
1G(♯4)   And race the sheep they count to sleep.

1B(♯1)   Dan'l Prince and Hen McCue
10   Raced their boys on lobster stew,
Hen got his wife to cook a lot,
They set their sons each side the pot.

1B(♯2)   They had kept all grub away
From their hopefuls all that day,
15   Each was a freckled ten-year-old,
And goodness knew what he could hold!

1B(♯3)   Dan ladled out the bowls to eat
Till Hen discovered much more meat

In his son's bowl, seized the dipper,
20   And became the race's skipper.

B(#4)   Dan Jr. had a one-bowl lead,
But Hen's boy upped and ran full speed
Around the shack and made great holes
For three more brimming buttery bowls.

G   25   The boys stood ten all, no man durst
Say which boy would burst the first,
Had not their mothers come upon
And stopped the lobster marathon.

THE CENTIPEDE

SAMUEL HOPKINS ADAMS

I'M VERY, very glad indeed
I need not feed a centipede;
But I would rather, could I choose,
Feed him than buy his boots and shoes.

THE FROG

HILAIRE BELLOC

G   BE KIND and tender to the Frog,
      And do not call him names,
1G(#1)   As "Slimy-Skin," or "Polly-wog,"
      Or likewise, "Uncle James,"
1G(#2)   5   Or "Gape-a-grin," or "Toad-gone-wrong,"
      Or "Billy-Bandy-knees;"
1G(#3)   The Frog is justly sensitive
      To epithets like these.

G No animal will more repay
10 A treatment kind and fair,
At least, so lonely people say
Who keep a frog (and, by the way,
They are extremely rare.)

LIMERICKS

ANONYMOUS

THERE was a young lady of Niger
Who smiled as she rode on a Tiger;
They came back from the ride
With the lady inside,
And a smile on the face of the Tiger.

There was a young maid who said, "Why
Can't I look in my ear with my eye?
If I give my mind to it,
I'm sure I can do it,
You never can tell till you try."

A silly young man had a knack
Of jumping off cliffs in a sack,
He jumped off one day,
In his usual way,
His widow looks charming in black.

There was a young fellow named Fisher,
Who was fishing for fish in a fissure,
When a cod with a grin
Pulled the fisherman in;
Now they're fishing the fissure for Fisher.

CONAL AND DONAL AND TAIG

SEUMAS MACMANUS

ONCE there were three brothers named Conal, Donal and Taig,[1] and they fell out regarding which of them owned a field of land. One of them had as good a claim to it as the other, and the claims of all of them were so equal that none of the judges, whomsoever they went before, could decide in favor of one more than the other.

At length they went to one judge who was very wise indeed and had a great name, and every one of them stated his case to him.

He sat on the bench, and heard Conal's case and Donal's case and Taig's case all through, with very great patience. When the three of them had finished, he said he would take a day and a night to think it all over, and on the day after, when they were all called into court again, the Judge said that he had weighed the evidence on all sides, with all the deliberation it was possible to give it, and he decided that one of them

[1] CONAL, DONAL AND TAIG—Pronounced kō'nȧl, dō'nȧl, tāg.

319

hadn't the shadow of a shade of a claim more than the others, so that he found himself facing the greatest puzzle he had ever faced in his life.

"But," says he, "no puzzle puzzles me long. I'll very soon decide which of you will get the field. You seem to me to be three pretty lazy-looking fellows, and I'll give the field to whichever of the three of you is the laziest."

"Well, at that rate," says Conal, "it's me gets the field, for I'm the laziest man of the lot."

"How lazy are you?" says the Judge.

"Well," said Conal, "if I were lying in the middle of the road, and there was a regiment of troopers come galloping down it, I'd sooner let them ride over me than take the bother of getting up and going to the one side."

"Well, well," says the Judge, says he, "you are a lazy man surely, and I doubt if Donal or Taig can be as lazy as that."

"Oh, faith," says Donal, "I'm just every bit as lazy."

"Are you?" says the Judge. "How lazy are you?"

"Well," said Donal, "if I was sitting right close to a big fire, and you piled on it all the turf in a town-land and all the wood in a barony, sooner than have to move I'd sit there till the boiling marrow would run out of my bones."

"Well," says the Judge, "you're a pretty lazy man, Donal, and I doubt if Taig is as lazy as either of you."

"Indeed, then," says Taig, "I'm every bit as lazy."

"How can that be?" says the Judge.

"Well," says Taig, "if I was lying on the broad of my back in the middle of the floor and looking up at the rafters, and if soot drops were falling as thick as hailstones from the rafters into my open eyes, I would let them drop there for the length of the lee-long day sooner than take the bother of closing the eyes."

"Well," says the Judge, "that's very wonderful entirely, and," says he, "I'm in as great a quandary as before, for I see you are the three laziest men that ever were known since the world began, and which of you is the laziest it certainly beats me to say. But I'll tell you what I'll do," says the Judge. "I'll give the field to the oldest man of you."

"Then," says Conal, "it's me gets the field."

"How is that?" says the Judge; "how old are you?"

"Well, I'm that old," says Conal, "that when I was twenty-one years of age I got a shipload of awls and never lost nor broke one of them, and I wore out the last of them yesterday mending my shoes."

"Well, well," says the Judge, says he, "you're surely an old man, and I doubt very much that Donal and Taig can catch up to you."

"Can't I?" says Donal. "Take care of that."

"Why," said the Judge, "how old are you?"

"When I was twenty-one years of age," says Donal, "I got a shipload of needles, and yesterday I wore out the last of them mending my clothes."

"Well, well, well," says the Judge, says he, "you're two very, very old men, to be sure, and I'm afraid poor Taig is out of his chance anyhow."

"Take care of that," says Taig.

"Why," said the Judge, "how old are you, Taig?"

Says Taig, "When I was twenty-one years of age I got a shipload of razors, and yesterday I had the last of them worn to a stump shaving myself."

"Well," says the Judge, says he, "I've often heard tell of old men," he says, "but anything as old as what you are never was known since Methusalem's [2] cat died. The like of your ages," he says, "I never heard tell of, and which of you is the oldest, that surely beats me to decide, and I'm in a quandary again. But I'll tell you what I'll do," says the Judge, says he, "I'll give the field to whichever of you minds (remembers) the longest."

"Well, if that's it," says Conal, "it's me gets the field, for I

---

[2] METHUSALEM—Methuselah (mĕ-thū′sĕ-là) was a Hebrew patriarch who lived to be 969 years old.

mind the time when if a man tramped on a cat he usen't to give it a kick to console it."

"Well, well, well," says the Judge, "that must be a long mind entirely; and I'm afraid, Conal, you have the field."

"Not so quick," says Donal, says he, "for I mind the time when a woman wouldn't speak an ill word of her best friend."

"Well, well, well," says the Judge, "your memory, Donal, must certainly be a very wonderful one, if you can mind that time. Taig," says the Judge, says he, "I'm afraid your memory can't compare with Conal's and Donal's."

"Can't it?" says Taig, says he. "Take care of that, for I mind the time when you wouldn't find nine liars in a crowd of ten men."

"Oh, oh, oh!" says the Judge, says he, "that memory of yours, Taig, must be a wonderful one." Says he: "Such memories as you three men have were never known before, and which of you has the greatest memory it beats me to say. But I'll tell you what I'll do now," says he; "I'll give the field to whichever of you has the keenest sight."

"Then," says Conal, says he, "it's me gets the field; because," says he, "if there was a fly perched on the top of yon mountain, ten miles away, I could tell you every time he blinked."

"You have wonderful sight, Conal," says the Judge, says he, "and I'm afraid you've got the field."

"Take care," says Donal, says he, "but I've got as good. For I could tell you whether it was a mote[3] in his eye that made him blink or not."

"Ah, ha, ha!" says the Judge, says he. "This is wonderful sight surely. Taig," says he, "I pity you, for you have no chance for the field now."

"Have I not?" says Taig. "I could tell you from here whether that fly was in good health or not by counting his heart beats."

[3] MOTE—A minute speck.

"Well, well, well," says the Judge, says he, "I'm in as great a quandary as ever. You are three of the most wonderful men that ever I met, and no mistake. But I'll tell you what I'll do," says he; "I'll give the field to the supplest man of you."

"Thank you," says Conal. "Then the field is mine."

"Why so?" says the Judge.

"Because," says Conal, says he, "if you filled that field with hares, and put a dog in the middle of them, and then tied one of my legs up my back, I would not let one of the hares get out."

"Then, Conal," says the Judge, says he, "I think the field is yours."

"By the leave of your judgeship, not yet," says Donal.

"Why, Donal," says the Judge, says he, "surely you are not as supple as that?"

"Am I not?" says Donal. "Do you see that old castle over there without door, or window, or roof in it, and the wind blowing in and out through it like an iron gate?"

"I do," says the Judge. "What about that?"

"Well," says Donal, says he, "if on the stormiest day of the year you had that castle filled with feathers, I would not let a feather be lost, or go ten yards from the castle until I had caught and put it in again."

"Well, surely," says the Judge, says he, "you are a supple man, Donal, and no mistake. Taig," says he, "there's no chance for you now."

"Don't be too sure," says Taig, says he.

"Why," says the Judge. "You couldn't surely do anything to equal these things, Taig?"

Says Taig, says he: "I can shoe the swiftest race horse in the land when he is galloping at his topmost speed, by driving a nail every time he lifts his foot."

"Well, well, well," says the Judge, says he, "surely you are the three most wonderful men that ever I did meet. The likes of you never was known before, and I suppose the likes of you never will be on the earth again. There is only one other trial," says he, "and if this doesn't decide, I'll have to give it up. I'll give the field," says he, "to the cleverest man amongst you."

"Then," says Conal, says he, "you may as well give it to me at once."

"Why? Are you that clever, Conal?" says the Judge, says he.

"I am that clever," says Conal. "I am that clever, that I would make a skin-fit suit of clothes for a man without any more measurement than to tell me the color of his hair."

"Then, boys," says the Judge, says he, "I think the case is decided."

"Not so quick, my friend," says Donal, "not so quick."

"Why, Donal," says the Judge, says he, "you are surely not cleverer than that?"

"Am I not?" says Donal.

"Why," says the Judge, says he, "what can you do, Donal?"

"Why," says Donal, says he, "I would make a skin-fit suit for a man and give me no more measurement than let me hear him cough."

"Well, well, well," says the Judge, says he, "the cleverness of you two boys beats all I ever heard of. Taig," says he, "poor Taig, whatever chance either of these two may have for the field, I'm very, very sorry for you, for you have no chance."

"Don't be so very sure of that," says Taig, says he.

"Why," says the Judge, says he, "surely, Taig, you can't be as clever as either of them. How clever are you, Taig?"

"Well," says Taig, says he, "if I was a judge, and too stupid to decide a case that came up before me, I'd be that clever that I'd look wise and give some decision."

"Taig," says the Judge, says he, "I've gone into this case and deliberated upon it, and by all the laws of right and justice, I find and decide that you get the field."

JOURNEYS

WITH INTERESTING PEOPLE

Recognizing perseverance and initiative.

ABE DISCOVERS A NEW WORLD

ENID LAMONTE MEADOWCROFT

ABE stepped out of the cow-shed, carrying the pail full of foaming milk carefully. Beyond the clearing he could hear his father's voice as Tom Lincoln and Dennis [1] set off to look at their traps, and deep in the forest the sharp bark of a fox. The ground under his moccasined feet was powdered with snow. Smoke curled from the cabin chimney against a gray morning sky. He walked quickly to the little log house and, once inside, set the pail gently on the wooden floor.

"Cold enough to freeze your nose off," he announced to his stepmother who was dishing hot cornmeal mush into the bowls which Sally was setting on the long plank table.

Sarah Lincoln nodded, smiling.

"Reckon it is," she agreed cheerfully. "Too cold for the gals to git to school. You an' Johnny kin make it, though. Abe, do git that boy up. He's the laziest critter that ever breathed."

Abe grinned.

"All right, Mammy, ef you say so," he said. And he clambered up the wooden pegs which were sunk into one wall of the cabin, and pulled himself into the loft to arouse Johnny, who still slept soundly in his warm feather bed.

Two years had passed since that day in December when Tom Lincoln had brought home a new wife. And those two years had wrought many changes in the lives of Abe and Sally, and in the home in which they lived.

Tom Lincoln had been very sure what he was about when

[1] DENNIS—Dennis Hanks, Abe's cousin.

he had traveled to Kentucky to ask Sarah Bush Johnston to marry him. He had known and liked her since her girlhood. And when, some time after Nancy Lincoln's death he had learned that Sarah's husband, too, was dead, he had decided that life might be happier for himself and Sarah and for their children if they spent the rest of it together. Fortunately Sarah Johnston agreed with him and Abe and Sally found themselves with a stepmother who was loving, kindly, understanding, and full of fun.

She was a hard worker, too, and before she had been long in the dirty, forlorn cabin she had transformed it into a comfortable home. First she and the girls cleaned it inside and out. Next she demanded that Tom Lincoln and Dennis lay a real wooden floor in place of the earthen one, hang a door at the entrance in place of the smoke-grimed deerskin, and cut windows over which greased paper could be stretched to let in the light. Then she arranged in the cabin all the things she had brought with her—a table; a set of chairs with backs; a shiny walnut bureau, wonderfully smooth to the touch; a loom; homespun blankets; quilts and feather beds; iron knives, forks, pots, kettles, and crockery dishes.

With three growing girls and three noisy boys about, the little log house was crowded, but the life that went on under its roof was a busy, happy one. For Abe it was especially happy, now that a school had at last been opened on Little Pigeon Creek, only a mile and a half away. As he started off after breakfast with a hot potato in each pocket to keep his hands warm and Johnny trailing along at his heels, he remembered with a grin the argument between his father and stepmother when they had first heard that a schoolmaster had come to the settlement.

"Abe an' Sally don't need no more eddication than they got. It's plumb foolish an' a waste of time an' I'm agin it," Tom Lincoln had announced.

"Schoolin' ain't ever hurt anybody, Tom," Sarah Lincoln

had protested vigorously. "I aim to see that our children git all they can of it, 'specially Abe. That boy is a born learner, if ever I saw one."

And in spite of her husband's grumbling she had packed all the children off the next morning to sit on hard wooden benches in the one-room schoolhouse, studying their lessons aloud, under the watchful eye of Mr. Azel Dorsey, the new schoolmaster.

Abe ambled along the wintry road in silence, remembering all the things that had happened since that first morning in school nearly three weeks before. Suddenly Johnny tugged at his arm.

"Walkin' with you is like havin' nobody around at all," he complained. "Why don't you talk some?"

"I'll do more than talk," Abe laughed. "I'll race you to the schoolhouse door." And he set out across a snowy field in great long-legged strides.

He liked to study and was learning quickly how to write, to read, and to spell. When he was at home he pored over the only book in the house—the old Bible—reading the stories aloud again and again, much to his stepmother's delight. He scrawled his name and all the words he could write in the ashes near the fireplace, or scratched them with a burned pointed stick on the back of his father's wooden shovel. And soon the children were bringing home the news, "Abe is gittin' to be so good in spellin' that there ain't nobody in the school that kin beat him."

But spring came and the boys who had been sitting on benches studying had to go into the fields to plow and plant. The door to the log schoolhouse was shut and latched and the schoolmaster went on his way to another village.

Two years passed before another schoolmaster came to Little Pigeon Creek. They were years in which young Abe Lincoln grew taller and stronger as he hauled dead stumps from the ground and broke the fields with a plow. They were years in which he grew more thoughtful as, day after day, he swung his axe in the forest with only the trees and the birds and the squirrels for company. They were years in which he learned to do a man's work for his father and sometimes for the neighbors too.

One day Jack Carter, one of the settlers who owned a farm some distance down the road, came to the Lincoln cabin. He spoke to Tom Lincoln.

"Tom, I got a field to be cleared an' I can't get enough help," he said. "If your boy, Abe, can use a grub hoe as good as he can tell stories I'll pay you fair wages for him. Aaron Grigsby was sayin' that all the folks at the mill was doubled up a-laughin' the other day at some yarn Abe was tellin' 'em."

Tom Lincoln scowled. "He talks too much, that boy. I don't like it," he declared. "But he works real good too— when he works. I'll send him over to you in the mornin'."

And the following morning Abe set off with his grub hoe over his shoulder for Mr. Carter's farm. All day he hacked and chopped and yanked and pulled, clearing the ground of bushes and young trees. By sundown he was tired and glad to stop. As he left the field and started past the farmhouse toward the road Mrs. Carter appeared in the doorway.

"Reckon you could eat a bite before you start home, Abe?" she called.

Abe grinned. "I'm so hungry I feel like my feet was holler," he said.

"Wash your hands at the pump, then, and come on in."

Abe scrubbed away the grime of the day's work as well as he could. Then he stepped inside the comfortable cabin. His eyes strayed about curiously, for this was the largest and finest home he had ever been in. Suddenly over a table in one corner of the room he spied a shelf on which there were several books.

"Kin I look at 'em?" he asked eagerly. And almost before Mrs. Carter had nodded he had taken one of them in his

330

hands. His lips moved as he spelled out the title, *Aesop's Fables*. Slowly he turned the pages, so absorbed in them that he did not hear Mrs. Carter speak to him, and jumped when she touched his arm.

"There's fresh milk and hot gingerbread over here," she said. Then, seeing how reluctantly he laid aside the book she added, "If you'll wash your hands real good each time before you read it, you can borrow that book and take it home."

Abe looked at her as though he could not believe his ears.

"Take it home!" he repeated, his sallow face crinkling into a smile. "Oh, thank you, ma'am." And without so much as a glance at the food which had been set out on the table he strode out of the cabin.

"Well, that's a queer one!" exclaimed Mrs. Carter, watching him walk off down the road holding the open book before him. "Never knew a boy before that liked books better than eating." And she put away the milk and gingerbread which Abe had left untouched.

As for Abe, he felt as though he had discovered a whole new world. Although he had longed for books he had never had money with which to buy them and it had never occurred to him that he might borrow them. That evening he hurried through his supper and when the meal was over stretched himself on the floor close to the fireplace, with *Aesop's Fables* spread out before him, reading until his father ordered him up to bed.

The following day he carried the book to the fields with him and at the lunch hour read it aloud to himself, between snatches of cornbread and bacon. That night after work he was at it again, and by the time he was forced to return the volume to Mrs. Carter he knew all the fables it contained nearly as well as he knew his own name.

He borrowed *Pilgrim's Progress* next and then *Arabian Nights*. Soon the neighbors became accustomed to seeing him perched on a rail fence or sprawled under a tree oblivious to anyone or anything about him. All this was very distressing to his father.

"That boy ain't goin' to amount to anythin'," Tom Lincoln announced, stamping into the cabin one morning just after Abe had started to the mill with some corn to be ground. "He's got his nose buried in a book half the time and the rest of the time he spends tellin' folks what he's read. John Romine has jes' been sayin' he went to his field yesterday and there wasn't one of his boys at work. They was all gapin' at Abe, who was standin' up on a stump makin' some sort of speech, 'stead of shuckin' the corn. I tell you, Sairey, it's got me plumb worried."

Sarah Lincoln pushed her needle through a piece of linsey-woolsey,[2] and bit off the thread. "Don't fret yourself, Tom," she advised. "It's true Abe don't seem to take to carpenterin' like you do, and mebbe he ain't even cut out to be a farmer, but there's other things he can be if only he can get the learnin'." She sighed as she folded up the dress she was making for Tilda. "I wish somebody would open up that school again," she said.

Before very long her wish was granted. A stranger who announced that he was a teacher and that his name was Andrew Crawford came to Little Pigeon Creek and opened the log schoolhouse. Once again Sarah Lincoln sent Abe and Sally, Johnny, Sairey, and little Tilda off to school.

It did not take Mr. Crawford long to find out that Abe Lincoln was the most eager and intelligent student he had, as well as the best speller in the class. In fact the tall, lanky boy with the shock of black hair spelled so well that the schoolmaster was forced at last to exclude him from the spelling matches, and often had to send him from the room so that he could not help the others by whispering or by signs, to spell the words they had forgotten.

---

[2] LINSEY-WOOLSEY (lĭn'zĭ-wŏol'zĭ)—Coarse cloth made of linen and wool.

All too swiftly the winter passed and the school was closed. But during the days that followed, Abe found time to read, to think, and now that he could spell so well, to put his thoughts in writing. He made himself a scrapbook from a few sheets of foolscap paper. Sprawled on the floor he chuckled as he scrawled these words on the first page:

> *"Abraham Lincoln*
> *his hand and pen.*
> *he will be good but*
> *god knows When."*

Then he set to work to copy carefully some examples from an arithmetic book which he had borrowed. When he had no paper on which to figure or to set down his thoughts he used a smooth board or the old wooden fire-shovel, shaved clean with his father's drawing knife. And even when the cabin was filled with noisy chattering children he managed to do some studying. If Johnny or one of the girls begged him to lay aside his book for one reason or another, Sarah Lincoln always came to the rescue.

"Don't pester Abe, he's learnin'," she would say. And that seemed to settle the matter.

Soon the word spread about among the people of Little Pigeon Creek that Tom Lincoln's boy was an odd one, but a pretty smart fellow, as well, for he could tell better stories and recite longer pieces and make funnier speeches than anyone for miles around.

"He's as strong as an ox, too," a farmer named Richardson announced one summer night when some men at the blacksmith shop were discussing the boy. "Last fall we was buildin' a corn-crib and while we was figurin' how to move the big posts it was to set on, that Abe, he jes' picked one of them up like it was a little stick and carried it to where it belonged."

Josiah Crawford, a man who had recently come to the village, looked up sharply.

"Ought to be a good boy to have around when I build my new cabin," he said. And the next morning he sought out Tom Lincoln to ask him to bring Abe with him when he came to work on the cabin.

"I'll pay you twenty-five cents a day fer the lad, as long as he works steady," he promised.

To Abe's chagrin, Josiah Crawford meant exactly what he said. In return for each full day's work twenty-five cents was turned over to Tom Lincoln, but if the boy stopped to chat with a passer-by, or to tell a joke to the farm hands, or to stare un-seeingly ahead while he reviewed in his mind what he had read the night before, Mr. Crawford promptly docked his wages. He was good about one thing, though. He had books and was willing to lend them.

One afternoon late in September as Sarah Lincoln was pre-paring to go to the home of a neighbor to help her with some quilting, she heard someone singing in the road beyond the clearing.

> *"Oh the terrible Turk that scorns the world*
> *And struts about with his whiskers curled,*
> *With his whiskers curled, with his whiskers curled."*

Over and over again a thin high-pitched voice chanted the words. "Why, that's Abe," Mrs. Lincoln exclaimed. "What's he doin' home at this time of day?"

At that very moment Abe himself answered the question.

"Hi, Mammy," he cried, flinging open the cabin door. "Ol' man Crawford didn't have any more work fer me today so he sent me home. And look—he let me borrow this."

He held up a small brown book.

"What's it about?" asked his stepmother, studying curiously the title, which she could not read.

"It's *The Life of George Washington,* written by a man named Weems," Abe replied. "It tells about Washington's life an' the battles he fought an' how he got to be the first presi-dent an'——"

"Abe Lincoln!" There was a note of annoyance in Mrs. Lincoln's voice as she interrupted him. "Jes' look at your feet. You've tracked in mud enough to start a potato patch."

"I'm sorry." The boy glanced at his feet so ruefully that Sarah Lincoln laughed.

"Don't fret yourself about it," she said, reaching up to pat his cheek. "I reckon I shouldn't mind cleanin' up the dirt you git on the floor, ef you jes' keep your head clean so's you don't mark up my nice whitewashed rafters."

Abe chuckled. "I'll try," he promised. Then, helping himself to a piece of cornbread from the cupboard, he tipped a chair upside down so that he could lean against its back, settled himself on the floor with one long leg cocked over the other, and began to read. But no sooner had his stepmother left the cabin than he put down his book and went outside where three small boys were playing in the road near the log house.

"Hi, Jack," he called to one of them. "Did you ever walk upside down?"

The boy named Jack looked puzzled and shook his head.

"Well, you're goin' to now. Come over here a minute." When Jack reached his side Abe bent down and held a long whispered conversation with him. Then the younger boy laughed aloud, ran to a large mud-puddle near the cow shed, and dragged his feet through it.

"That's enough," said Abe.

He swooped the youngster up in his arms and carried him into the cabin. The other boys followed in bewildered silence.

"Put your hands on my shoulders," Abe commanded. With one motion he turned Jack upside down so that his feet waved wildly near the ceiling.

"Now, walk, young 'un," Abe said. "That's right. Put another footprint there. And one there. That's enough."

He set the red-faced giggling boy on the floor.

"Anyone else want to try it?" he asked the other two.

Of course they both did, and for several minutes the cabin was filled with shouts and laughter.

When Sarah Lincoln came home an hour later she found Abe just where she had left him, apparently buried in his book. It was not until she had hung up her cape that she caught sight of the ceiling, which was covered with muddy footprints.

"Abe Lincoln!" she gasped. Then she sank on the bench near the fireplace and rocked back and forth, laughing until the tears came.

"You crazy young Injun," she cried at last, wiping her eyes on the corner of her apron. "There ain't nobody on earth but you could have figgered out such foolishment."

Abe's eyes were twinkling. "I thought you'd get a real good laugh out of that, Mammy," he said. "I'll clean it all up fer you tonight, so's not one mark will show." And he went back to his book.

From now on for many weeks he spent every spare minute of the day with *The Life of George Washington*. At night he carried the book to bed with him. One morning he brought it down from the loft, wet and muddy.

"Rain leaked in through the cracks," he said gloomily to Sally, who was frying pork in the long-handled skillet. "Looks like it's kind of spoiled the book. Tell Pappy I'll have to take it over to Mr. Crawford an' see what he wants me to do about it." And without waiting for his breakfast he set off for Josiah Crawford's farm. It was long after dark when he returned and the family was at supper.

"Ol' Bluenose was as mad as a wet hen at first," he told them. "Then he reckoned that ef I pulled fodder fer him fer three days, that would pay for it."

"Three days pullin' fodder jes fer an old book!" Dennis Hanks exclaimed in disgust.

Abe nodded. "It's fair enough, Dennis, an' once I git

through, Mr. Crawford says the book will be mine for keeps," he said.

For two days more he pulled fodder and then came home with the news that Josiah Crawford and his wife both expected to need help in the near future, and wanted to know if Tom Lincoln would let Abe and Sally hire out to them for a while.

"We'll have to sleep there and eat there, too," Abe explained, adding with a twinkle in his eye, "Tonight they were havin' chicken an' gravy an' all the fixin's, so it won't be so bad fer me, but it will be hard on Sally when she can't have Aaron Grigsby around sparkin' her."

Sally Lincoln colored to the tips of her ears and laughed. She was eighteen now and for some time she and Aaron Grigsby, the son of a wealthy farmer, had been planning to marry. Although she knew that he could not call on her often while she was working for the Crawfords, she was glad to go, for money was scarce and her father sometimes found it difficult to feed and clothe his large family. For many weeks she and Abe worked on the Crawford farm, she helping in the kitchen and around the house, he in the fields and barn.

As the weeks passed, Mrs. Crawford grew very fond of the homely, lanky Lincoln boy, who was so tall that he had to stoop to get through the back door, and who always remembered to lift his hat and say "Howdy," when he met her on the road or in the fields. But there were moments when she wished he were not quite so full of fun and good spirits. One night when she and Sally were in the kitchen trying to get supper and he was in their way, teasing, joking, and playing tricks on them, she turned on him.

"Abe Lincoln, whatever is going to become of you?"

"Of me?" Abe looked surprised. · Then he laughed. "Why I'm going to be president of the United States some day," he boasted. And picking up an empty bucket he loped out to milk the cows, untying Sally's apron strings as he passed by her.

WINGS FOR WORDS

DOUGLAS C. MCMURTRIE

More than five hundred years ago a ten-year-old boy in Mainz,[1] Germany, learned from his grandfather the art of cutting woodblocks. Then and there the idea of printing was born. If woodblocks of playing cards could be printed, thought small Johann Gutenberg,[2] why could not the letters of the Latin alphabet be printed and made into books? The years went on and slowly the dream grew. By patient experiment Johann taught himself how to cast a carefully carved letter in brass and how to hammer it deep into a bar of lead. By pouring liquid metal into the lead mold he could make a letter exactly like its model. This lead mold he called a "matrix" because it was the "mother" to the letters cast from it. By 1438 he and his associates, Hans Riffe, and Herr Heilmann,[3] were still searching for a way to make the lead "types" square enough to make straight lines across the page. But the dream persisted—the dream of giving wings to words, the dream that all men might share the world of books.

As JOHANN plodded down Furriers' Street one day early in 1440, his calloused and ink-stained hands clasped behind him,

---

[1] MAINZ—Pronounced mīnts.

[2] JOHANN GUTENBERG—Pronounced yō'hän gōō'tĕn-bĕrk.

[3] HANS RIFFE . . . HERR HEILMANN—Pronounced häns rĭf'ĕ, hĕr hīl'män.

his eyes on the ground, he was so lost in his problems that he did not see his friend, the Bishop of Strasbourg, approaching. The bishop turned and touched his arm.

"Wait, Johann, my son."

"I am sorry."   Johann bowed.   "I was thinking . . ."

"It is good for a man to think, Johann.   But not of one thing only.   Come, forget the thoughts of your invention for a while. It is long since I have talked with you."

The bishop listened, once they had reached his quarters next to the almost completed cathedral.   That had been his business for fifty years—listening while men talked.   It was not the first time the two had discussed Johann's attempts to print, for the bishop was one of the few who shared Johann's secret.   Again Johann, discouraged, worn and tired from working day and night, poured out his story.   He went back to his days in Mainz and told of his attempts, with Relf, to copy the Donatus [4] by hand, of his printing from woodblocks, then of his more recent efforts to solve the problems facing one who would print books.

When he had finished, the bishop leaned forward.

"You should rest, Johann.   A little time away from your work would do you good. . . .   And Herr Heilmann and Herr Riffe, too.   Every day the brothers work in the scriptorium, copying valuable books from our library.   It is a place of peace and quiet, and you three could rest there while you become familiar with our beautiful books.   When you are able to print you will wish to design many of your books after those we and others have.   What better time than now to study them?"

For a month, Gutenberg, Riffe, and Heilmann spent much of their time in the scriptorium, examining the more than one hundred handwritten books that made up the cathedral library. It was time well spent, both for themselves and for the invention.   It rested and clarified their minds and gave them fresh

[4] DONATUS (dō-nā'tŭs)—A Latin grammar.

vigor to attack their problems. If man could produce such beauty through his pen, they felt that surely they must be able eventually to reproduce it by a much cheaper and simpler method. A monk, they knew, would work a year to copy a book of several hundred pages. And because of this, the world did not possess many books, and no one without wealth could own even a few.

Surrounded by the dozen monks in their brown robes, their backs bent over the slanted desks, Johann turned to Herr Riffe. "The labor of love," he whispered. "Look you at this parchment page." He pointed to the open volume before him. "See the dark stain at the bottom, from the wrist of the one who worked hours in copying words upon it during a hot summer day? Yet we can print it in a few moments, when we have learned just how it can be done. Printing will open the doors to a new world, Hans. We must go on and on until we succeed."

The picture of those bent brown backs remained uppermost in the minds of the three men, a challenge that must be accepted. The cathedral, started in the year 1176, was in itself a challenge. They had watched its west tower grow, almost stone by stone to its 465 feet of height—one of the tallest towers in all Christendom. Destined to a place among the most famous cathedrals in Germany, it had at last been completed. As they saw stonecutters and metalworkers from all over Germany creating beautiful figures and designs for it, their imagination was fired. By inventing flying buttresses a way had been found to support a vast arched roof, yet leave spaces for windows towering sixty feet high. If men could do this, then they could invent many other things, equally difficult. And if men could find a way to make stained glass to fill those towering windows with colors that rivaled the sunset, then a way would be discovered to duplicate the beauty that lay in handwritten books—books that were the result of centuries of artistic effort by the scribes of many countries.

Besides trying to discover a harder metal for the types than lead alone, the partners were attempting to do something still more important. It was to work out a better mold to place over the matrix when the types were being cast. They wanted something that would shape the sides of the type more truly than the oblong brass mold they were using, and which would make the types different widths for the narrow and for the wide letters. They must also find some way of making the types of exactly the same height. Because if there was any difference at all in the height of the types, when printing, some of them pressed deeply into the paper, making heavy letters, while others touched it so lightly that the letters could hardly be read.

Johann had worked all morning on this business of a mold. It was a drowsy day in 1440, a day when it would have been much more pleasant to be out strolling. From the narrow slit of the back window he gazed over the city roofs, his hands clasped behind him, his mind methodically sorting and discarding the various ways in which he had tried to solve this problem. To cast the types and then even up the sides of each one and cut them all down to a standard height, was a never-ending task. He must find a way . . .

Behind him Herr Riffe stood near the charcoal forge, on which was a pot of melted lead. Johann turned to watch Hans fill the iron dipper with the liquid metal and pour it quickly into the brass casting mold which guided it into the letter in the lead matrix.

"You do that well!" Johann commented as Hans, in almost the same motion with which he poured the melted lead, flipped the matrix and mold toward him to force the hot metal evenly into every corner of the letter, then pushed the piece of type out of the opening in the mold.

"I do it faster than when I started," Hans observed. "But what good is that when we still have to stop to cut off the overhang at the top? Some day I will get mad and invent a quicker way to make a finished type!"

"Go to it, Hans," Johann laughed good-naturedly. "Someone has to invent it, and I do not seem to be wise enough to do it."

Johann brought some rye bread and ale from an adjoining room, setting Han's share on the bench beside him.

"We may as well have lunch, Hans. Herr Heilmann will be here soon to help you."

Johann pulled his knife from his belt and hacked off a piece of the black rye bread, tossing the knife on the bench near where Hans had dumped the newly made types. A few of them lay along the handle where the guard, separating the blade from the handle, made a right angle; Johann's eyes were thoughtlessly fixed on a piece of type resting in the right-angled corner. Suddenly his mind began to race.

Characteristically, he held himself in check, considering every side of this new idea that had come to him so suddenly. With ink-stained finger he carefully set one of the types on end and pushed it slowly into the angle of the knife guard. Then he moved the knife back and forth, toward and away from the type.

"Hans," he said intensely, without looking up, "I think I've found it!"

For an hour he worked feverishly. Then he called the men. "See!" he said jubilantly. "Here are two L-shaped pieces of metal, of exactly the same height. When I put the short side of one L against the long side of the other, it makes a rectangular opening, or well, which is just as high as the metal pieces are, but which can be made wider or narrower just by pulling the L's farther apart or pushing them closer together."

Hans whistled. "So! To make our type for an 'i' we put the pieces close together and for an 'm' we pull them apart. Johann, you are the wise one, after all!"

When the partners saw that the L-shaped metal pieces really made a perfect mold, as Johann said they would do, they spent days casting new types and comparing them. Each type was now accurate in size and shape, and all the letters of one kind were exactly the same, no matter how many of them they made. From now on, letters cast from lead could be more uniform than any letters made with quills. The only trouble was that there was still a slight variation in the height of the types, causing the impression on the page to be uneven. This was because the ends of the type at the top of the mold had to be smoothed off by hand and were not exactly uniform.

But rather than work any longer on this problem of exact height, Johann decided to spend his time redesigning the type faces to make them more beautiful.

"You see," he told his partners, "it is only afterward that we know whether or not a thing is important." He produced from under his arm a beautiful handwritten volume which he had brought from the cathedral scriptorium. "We spend much time with the monks, studying their beautifully written books. Then we discover a way to make our types perfect. So I go to the monks and secure their work. Now we will design our types to match it. The monks spend their lives learning to make perfect letters and then we use what they have done. We spend our lives learning how to reproduce their work in printing, and they will have our books. . . . Yes, the bishop knew—the work of any man, if it is good, will help the work of other men."

His new type face designed, Johann decided not to wait any longer. They must not delay until they could find a perfect metal for types. They must start to print.

Johann's dream was becoming reality. The Donatus lay open on the bench before him—the same copy from which he had learned his first lessons in Latin grammar when he was ten years old. Twenty-eight handwritten pages, this copy of the thin volume that had been in use for a thousand years to instruct the young in Latin was to be used for Johann's first major attempt to print a book. He had pulled trial proofs of other things, a few lines of type held together in slipshod fashion, with irregular type faces that made a poor impression when printed. But here was the real test that would prove whether or not the invention he had worked on so many years was to be successful.

His two partners watched at his elbow that summer afternoon in 1440. Johann's experienced fingers deftly picked the Latin types from the slanting many-sectioned case that Herr Riffe had devised to sort the types into. One by one he placed them together to form the words and sentences of the Donatus. For months all three men had been memorizing the exact design of letters in reverse until they could tell at a glance a "b" from a "d" and an "l" from an "i." Now they watched, eagle-eyed, to see that no errors crept into the spelling of the words.

The heat was intense in the close room. Perspiration dropped from Johann's chin as he bent over the types. When he had set ten lines he paused and straightened up. "I cannot set any more," he said, wiping his face on his bare arm. "We have waited too long for this moment to delay until the whole page is set. Hans, look to the press. Herr Heilmann, see that the ink is not too thick and spread it evenly on the types while I put the paper in the frame. . . . We print, at last!"

Johann carried the lead types to the window, checking them once more against the handwritten Donatus. Satisfied, he walked slowly across the room to the waiting press. Herr Heilmann tapped an inked sheepskin ball stuffed with wool on the faces of the types. A last, light tap, and he nodded to Johann.

With the help of Hans, the lines of types were fastened securely upon the bed of the press. Johann placed the dampened paper in its frame and pushed it into position, directly above the types, then stopped to give one final look.

"It is ready," he said. "Turn the screw, Hans."

The upper plate of the press came down slowly. The plate touched the paper. Only the heavy breathing of Hans broke the silence as the screw tightened.

"Now reverse the screw," Johann ordered.

Slowly the plate retreated upward from the paper.

Johann carefully lifted the paper from the types and released it from its frame.

"Your hand shakes," Hans said softly.

"Here is printing!" Johann's voice was intense. "Quick now, ink the types again. We shall see if we can get another proof as good. I promise you, my friends, we shall long remember this day!"

One of the few to whom Johann showed the trial proof of the ten lines of the Donatus was the bishop.

"My blessing is yours!" The bishop gazed at the single sheet of paper, then looked at Johann. "It has required courage to accomplish this. But I need not tell you that. The years have taken much from you, Johann, but your courage has given more to the world. It may even be that our world has been waiting for this invention—even more anxiously than you have labored to accomplish it." He paused a moment, then went on, "Remember, my son, now that you are sure of what you can do, there is one book that you must print."

"I know," Johann smiled. "The Bible. But that cannot be done at once. There are still many problems to be solved before we can print so many words."

"But what is to be done about it, Johann?"

"I have heard," Johann said, "that when the cathedral was started men said it would not be finished. But you know that when something truly worth doing is started, it is always finished."

"I know that, Johann," the bishop replied.

"And so it will be with printing. But casting and setting the type and printing so large a book as the Bible—over a thousand pages—is a little like building a cathedral. Not only will it take time; it will also take a great deal of money and I do not know where I would get so much. . . . But first I must finish printing the Donatus."

The partners, encouraged by the successful trial proofs and by the interest of the bishop, went ahead with Johann's idea of producing printed copies of the Donatus cheaply enough so that the fathers of poor boys in Strasbourg could purchase them. The venture would also prove whether, as the bishop had suggested, the world was waiting for the invention of printing.

Arranging or "setting up" the metal letters according to the Latin words of the Donatus, word by word and line by line, was a genuine pleasure to Johann. When a page was ready the partners placed it in its frame, inked it, and put it into position in the press. One hundred copies of the page were printed—some on parchment and some on paper. Then the types were taken out of the frame and sorted into the many-sectioned type case, each letter finding its place with the others like it. Then the second page was set up, letter by letter, and word by word, and it was printed. And so on, until all twenty-eight pages of the Donatus were printed and there were seven piles of sheets stacked on the long table, a hundred sheets in each stack. On each sheet were four printed pages—two on each side.

This took months. Often the soft lead types wore down and had to be thrown aside and new types cast and put into their right places in the page. Often the ink dried out and new ink must be ground and mixed to the right consistency. But in spite of these delays, the making of the hundred copies of the Donatus required only a tenth of the time that a scribe would have taken to write them.

Thoughtfully, Johann selected one sheet from each stack, until he held in his hand a complete Donatus. "These are for the Bishop. And now, at last, our secret belongs to the world. Now we shall see if the world is interested in it and if our book will be purchased. Go you, Hans, to the town hall with a complete Donatus and give it to the mayor with our compliments. Herr Heilmann, do you take a copy to Herr Dunne. Tomorrow we shall give copies to a few boys. It will not take long for the word to get around that we have something for sale at a reasonable price."

The mayor accepted the Donatus sheets but scoffed at the story Hans told about the printing. Calling other city officials into his office he showed them the sheets.

"Herr Riffe, gentlemen, claims that by some magic this book has been produced without the work of a scribe."

"Your honor, I did not mention magic," Hans protested. "Come you to our shop and we will show you that there is no magic. There is only the result of a man's years of work. Herr Gutenberg has invented . . ."

Strasbourg's former interest in Johann Gutenberg was revived. Its citizens stopped in to see this invention that could make better books than the scribes could make and in a tenth of the time. The scribes themselves protested violently at having their work taken from them. But when the Bishop of Strasbourg issued a statement defending the invention, there was none who dared speak publicly against it or against Johann Gutenberg and his partners. Instead of selling the copies to parents, Johann was forced to sell his Donatus to the wealthy, who offered large prices for it.

"It is well," Johann assured his partners. "We know now that men want our books. Now we shall print one hundred more copies, and this time they will be for the boys."

But it was not just one hundred more copies that the partners printed during the next year and the next. In all, more than fifteen editions of the Donatus were printed. Travelers and traders leaving Strasbourg often took a copy or two with them in their packs. They were in sheet form, and each purchaser would have them bound in his favorite material, as had been the custom with handwritten volumes.

Wings for words!

The "magic" of Gutenberg, Riffe, and Heilmann was revising men's ideas all over Europe and bringing about a change in their thinking. The excitement of the great universities on learning of these printed books knew no bounds, for they saw here a way to reproduce the few, precious books in their libraries in almost endless quantities. Such a thing was truly magic! In Paris a trader was thrown into jail when he offered two copies of the printed Donatus for sale. For the officials declared that only one who dealt in black art could make two copies exactly alike!

Toward the end of 1441, the Bishop of Strasbourg induced the parish of Saint Thomas to lend Herr Gutenberg money with which to prepare to print the Bible.

"You understand that first we must cast the types," Johann pointed out to the bishop when he was told of the loan. "That is a huge task. Nor can it be done at once, for I am not satisfied with the types we are using in the Donatus. They will need refining to make them . . ."

"I know, Johann," the bishop nodded. "More beautiful. That is right. The Church believes in beautiful ceremonies and robes, so it is right that her book should also be beautiful. We leave that in your hands."

WILBUR WRIGHT AND ORVILLE WRIGHT

1867–1912   1871–

ROSEMARY AND STEPHEN VINCENT BENÉT

1B(#1)   SAID Orville Wright to Wilbur Wright,
            "These birds are very trying.

348

I'm sick of hearing them cheep-cheep
About the fun of flying.
5   A bird has feathers, it is true.
That much I freely grant.
But, must that stop us, W?"

1B(#2)   Said Wilbur Wright, "It shan't."

B   And so they built a glider, first,
10   And then they built another.
—There never were two brothers more
Devoted to each other.
They ran a dusty little shop
For bicycle-repairing,
15   And bought each other soda-pop
And praised each other's daring.

They glided here, they glided there,
They sometimes skinned their noses,
—For learning how to rule the air
20   Was not a bed of roses—
But each would murmur, afterward,
While patching up his bro.

1B(#1)   "Are we discouraged, W?"
1B(#2)   "Of course we are not, O!"

B 25   And finally, at Kitty Hawk
In Nineteen-Three (let's cheer it!),
The first real airplane really flew
With Orville there to steer it!
—And kingdoms may forget their kings
30   And dogs forget their bites,
But not till Man forgets his wings,
Will men forget the Wrights.

25. KITTY HAWK—A small town in North Carolina, on Albemarle Sound

JOHNNY APPLESEED

1775–1847

ROSEMARY AND STEPHEN VINCENT BENÉT

U   *Of Jonathan Chapman*
Two things are known,
That he loved apples,
That he walked alone.

B   5   At seventy-odd
He was gnarled as could be,
But ruddy and sound
As a good apple tree.

G   For fifty years over
   10   Of harvest and dew,
He planted his apples
Where no apples grew.

The winds of the prairie
Might blow through his rags,
15 But he carried his seeds
In the best deerskin bags.

B   From old Ashtabula
To frontier Fort Wayne,
He planted and pruned
20 And he planted again.

He had not a hat
To encumber his head.
He wore a tin pan
On his white hair instead.

G 25 He nested with owl,
And with bear-cub and possum,
B   And knew all his orchards
Root, tendril and blossom.

G   A fine old man,
30 As ripe as a pippin,
His heart still light,
And his step still skipping.

B   The stalking Indian,
The beast in its lair
35 Did no hurt
While he was there.

For they could tell,
As wild things can,
That Jonathan Chapman
40 Was God's own man.

351

G   Why did he do it?
         We do not know.
B   He wished that apples
         Might root and grow.

G   45 He has no statue.
         He has no tomb.
B   He has his apple trees
         Still in bloom.

U   *Consider, consider,*
     50 *Think well upon*
         The marvelous story
         Of Appleseed John.

TOM WAS JUST A LITTLE BOY

ROBERT P. TRISTRAM COFFIN

₁G(♯₁)   Tom was just a little boy,
₁G(♯₂)   He took his small glass jug
                Out in the July night to catch
                A pretty lightning-bug.

₁G(♯₁)   5   There was thunder roundabout,
₁G(♯₂)   At times he saw white flowers,
                When the lightning was turned on,
                Round him tall as towers.

₁G(♯₁)   He got his handful of the small
            10 Lightning in the grass,

1G(#2)   He took it in, he watched it spark
             Against the wall of glass.

1G(#1)   It lit the life-lines in his hand,
             Turned on and off its light,
1G(#2) 15 And this small boy sat wondering
             In the big dark night.

   G   Why couldn't he catch lightning, too,
             And turn it off and on,
             And light up cities of the earth
          20 Till they shone and shone?

1G(#1)   He went to bed, but through his head
             The question ran and ran,
1G(#2)   In his sleep he planned to light
             The world up as a man.

   G   25 And what the little nightgowned boy
             Dreamed that night is so,
             Around the world behind the sun
             Tom Edison's lightnings go.

N-1

Saluting courage and resourcefulness.

KELLY COURAGEOUS

JOHN J. FLOHERTY

THE purple shadows of the sawtooth hills lay heavy on a certain airfield in the Bataan [1] Peninsula. The skeletons of hangars and barracks stood gaunt against the darkening sky. Great pockmarks dotted the neighborhood of the chaos created by Jap bombs. A huge plane drumming slowly in from the east, its ponderous landing gear already down, seemed to feel for a safe footing in the gathering darkness. Her wheels touched the ground with the lightness of thistledown.

As she rolled to a stop two machinists, one with a bandage on his head, approached the pulsing plane, her propellers still turning. "That was a Kelly landing if I ever saw one," said one of the men. "Sure enough," said the other with a southern drawl. "I reckon it must be Colin Kelly himself."

A lithe figure climbed out of the plane and slid out of his parachute harness. Of medium height, he had broad shoulders and a well-set head. A shock of wavy brown hair made him seem taller than he really was.

He approached the mechanics who were already placing blocks under the wheels. "I'm Captain Kelly," he said. The tone of command that West Point imparts to its men was in his voice. "Any place left standing where I could put my men up for the night?"

"No, sir," replied one of the mechanics. "Everything is shot to bits."

The crew of the bomber—a B-17—were already piling out

"Kelly Courageous" is reprinted by permission of J. B. Lippincott Company from *The Courage and the Glory* by John B. Floherty.

[1] BATAAN—Pronounced bä-tän'.

through the door near the tail of the plane. A slender second lieutenant, co-pilot Donald Robins, brought up the rear.

"Well, men," said Captain Kelly cheerily, "we've got to make the best of it for the night. Our boudoir[2] will be under the wing. Lots of fresh air to get the gasoline out of our lungs."

A crusty sergeant, the flight engineer, spoke out. "Sir," he said, "a little gasoline in the tanks wouldn't hurt any."

Captain Kelly was thoughtful for a moment as he recalled the nightmare of the preceding two days during which they had hopped from one bombed field to another eluding Jap attacks. "Don't worry Sergeant," he said encouragingly, "we will take off for Clark Field early in the morning. Your last fuel reading showed that we have about enough to reach it."

Night brought with it a star-studded sky and a gentle breeze from the south. A death-like stillness had settled over the shattered airfield. The seven men huddled under the left wing of the bomber soon forgot the strain they had been under for two tragic days and were unworried about the future. Their

[2] BOUDOIR (boo'dwär)—Retiring room.

commanding officer was known as one of the best in the service; he would fight for his men at the drop of a hat.

Some of the crew sat on their parachute packs, others used them as pillows, while they listened to the sergeant who told hair-raising stories of crash landings, downwind take-offs, of planes afire and planes out of gas in the dimly distant days of the late thirties when he was attached to fields from New York to Texas. One by one they sprawled on the baked ground and slept.

Captain Kelly sat long after his men had slipped off to sleep. With chin in hands he gazed off into the soft Philippine night. The men who lay around him must be safeguarded; so, too, must the plane under which they slept. The tradition of West Point and of Randolph and Kelly Fields where he got his training must be upheld. The boys and girls at Madison High from which he had been graduated must not be let down. And then there were his wife and his eighteen-month-old son, Colin P. Kelly, III, waiting for his early return in their Brooklyn, New York, home.

His unwavering faith in his men and in his plane made him yearn for a task that would be worthy of them. Playing hare to the Japanese hounds was not to his liking. The heavy breathing of the sleeping men reminded him that it was late and that the morning take-off must be at sunup. Pillowing his head on his parachute pack, he fell into a restless sleep.

Daybreak came with a fanfare of color above the magenta hills. A molten sun rising over the peaks touched the sleeping men with coppery light.

Captain Kelly sat upright, rubbed the sleep from his eyes and looked over the six men sprawled around him. He hated to disturb them. Shaking Lieutenant Robins who lay beside him, he snapped, "Come on, Lieutenant; let's go." In a few moments all the men were struggling into their parachute harnesses. The sergeant climbed to the cockpit and soon had the motors warming up.

During the hop to Clark Field, north of Manila, the B-17 was not molested; there was not a Jap in sight. As the plane banked Captain Kelly looked down and was appalled at the wanton destruction. Picking out a course between bomb craters he set the plane down as if he had been landing on bombed airfields all his life. He reported to headquarters at once and learned that, as deputy Squadron leader, he was chosen for a task of immediate importance. He was to destroy a Japanese aircraft carrier believed to be off the northern coast of Luzon,[3] a menace to the entire northern end of the island.

As the operations officer laid down the pencil with which he had indicated the probable position and course of the vessel, he paused for a moment as if he were thinking of some final instructions. Then turning to the young officer, he said quietly, "Captain, I'm sorry we have no escort fighters to give you on this job. You will have to go it alone. Do not take unnecessary chances; neither planes nor men are plentiful. Good luck!"

Captain Kelly saluted. "I'll do my best, sir," he replied.

As he returned to the plane the fuel truck was already rolling into position and refueling began at once. A tractor trundled out from somewhere hauling behind it a miniature train of trucks loaded with bombs. As it came to a halt beside the plane the sergeant's leathery face rippled in a broad smile. "Boy!" he exclaimed as he eyed the sleek metal cylinders, "they're big babies," and hurried under the belly of the plane where the bomb racks were already exposed.

Captain Kelly busied himself both outside and inside the plane. No detail escaped his inspection. Although he had an efficient co-pilot and his flight engineer, the crusty little sergeant, was one of the best mechanics in the service, he considered them but parts of the whole for which he alone was responsible. He waggled the elevators, worked the rudder and tested the ailerons and flaps. He inspected bomb releases and

---

[3] LUZON (loō-zŏn′)—Chief island of the Philippines.

guns and went from tail to cockpit with the keen eye of a craftsman looking over his tools before beginning a critical job.

Fuel and oil tanks had been filled and three of the comple-
ment of bombs had already been slung in the racks when the
air was shattered by the excruciating wail of an air raid siren.

The plane crew scrambled to their stations in the plane, the
co-pilot started the four motors and revved them for a short
warming. Captain Kelly, cool but alert as a fox, took his seat
on the left side of the cockpit, signaled to have the blocks withdrawn, and taxied to the only runway left unscarred by bombs.
The breeze, though light, was enough to make the crosswind
take-off hazardous with so large a plane.

The B-17 roared down the runway with her four motors
blasting out their last ounce of power. This was no time for
gentle take-offs. The Japs might pounce on him at any moment and ruin his first big opportunity to bring glory to his
crew and to his plane. With full confidence in the plane's ability to make a quick take-off he pulled back on the stick. The
bumping wheels touched the ground more lightly with each
revolution until they spun in air. The nose of the bomber
tipped as she became air-borne. In a matter of seconds she
was banking high over the field and straightening out on her
course which lay due north.

The lieutenant and navigator were scanning the skies from
all angles; every man was at his station.

As the plane gained altitude the green wrinkles on the face
of the island grew smaller and disappeared. Villages, towns
and subprovinces crept into view and slipped slowly behind.
When they had reached seven thousand feet Captain Kelly leveled off. Lieutenant Robins swept the sky with glasses. In
spite of a head wind the plane was cruising at nearly two hundred miles an hour. Three quarters of an hour after the take-
off the seven-thousand-five-hundred-foot summit of Mount
Secapoo was sighted resting on a pillow of morning mist.
Kelly, always a safe flyer, passed over it at ten thousand feet.

At that height the sizable town of Solsona looked like a handful of hemp seed spilled near the base of the mountain.

The ocean came into view dimly through a filmy haze on the horizon. The sky was a dome of indigo without so much as a fleck of a cloud. Soon the surf line was immediately below, looking curiously like flounces of white lace on blue velvet. Claveria, a town of some ten thousand inhabitants, nestled close along the shore line and melted into the green vegetation. To the northeast the island of Fuga lay on the sea basking luxuriously in the morning sun. The scene below made it hard to believe that war existed.

Turning the controls over to his co-pilot, Kelly made a rapid tour of inspection. His eyes had their usual friendly twinkle as he checked each man and found him alert and eager.

Bombardier Corporal Levin, a little anxious because of an untried bombsight, crouched beside the device deep in the study of its intricacies. He was startled by the captain's strong voice

close to his ear.   "How do you like the new sight, Corporal?"
The young man straightened and shouted above the bedlam of
the motors.   "I guess it's all right, sir."

"Guess nothing!   It's the best doggone bombsight in the
world and you are going to prove it by laying one right on the
Japs' button!"   As he finished Kelly smiled encouragingly.

The bombardier caught the captain's assurance and replied
with new confidence, "O.K., sir, *right* on the button."

As Captain Kelly returned to the control room and took over
the controls, the navigator who had been sweeping the sea with
the glasses reported, "Two vessels dead ahead, sir."   The co-
pilot also trained his glasses on the ships which were rapidly
growing larger with the fast approach of the bomber.   "Look
like small transports," he said without lowering the binoculars.

"We will take a closer look and make sure," the captain replied.   Presently the bomber was circling above the vessels
with the left wing down so that the pilot could get an unob-
structed view of them.   Their decks were swarming with men,
in evident confusion at the prospect of being bombed.

The crew of the plane waited expectantly for the order that
would begin the action, but none came.   The lieutenant looked
at his captain enquiringly.

Captain Kelly straightened out the plane and smiled a little
disdainfully.   "Small fry," he said grimly.   "We're after bigger
fish.   Remember we have only three bombs in the racks."

The plane, now well to the north of Luba Island, was put on
a southeasterly course that took it between Luba and Camiguin [4] Islands and over Babuyan Channel [5] which separated
them from the Luzon mainland by some thirty miles of open
water.

The sea was empty as the cloudless sky, not a vessel was in
sight.   The specter of failure began to haunt Kelly.   What if

[4] LUBA (lōō′bȧ) AND CAMIGUIN (kä-mê-gēn′) ISLANDS—Islands of the
Babuyan group, north of Luzon.
[5] BABUYAN (bä-bōō-yän′) CHANNEL—Channel between Babuyan and Luzon.

he could not find the carrier, a target as large as three city blocks. It was unlikely that the reconnaissance would have reported a phantom ship. The thought of returning without completing his mission was unthinkable. He had already begun to doubt the wisdom of his southerly course; the quarry might have sailed north among the Babuyan Islands. He was weighing the advisability of putting about and retracing his course when the lieutenant shouted, "Fleet of vessels ahead."

Kelly took the glasses, turning the controls over to his copilot. He looked long and searchingly at the group of hazy gray dots on the far horizon. At their speed of three and a half miles a minute the distance between the plane and the fleet was quickly shortened. The dots grew bigger and blacker, three large ones, two smaller and one that dwarfed the rest. It must be the carrier!

Unflurried as a telephone operator, he cut in all intercommunicating phones and said, "Prepare for action!"

The command was picked up by the sergeant who was already hurrying from one station to another in a final check-up. "Hit 'em first and hit 'em hard and don't spare the hot lead," he admonished each gunner.

Handing the glasses to the navigator, Kelly took over. He could feel his heart tick a little faster and his breath come a trifle more quickly. In the pit of his stomach was a heavy feeling such as he had often felt before a stiff examination. There was neither fear nor doubt within him. His hands were steady, his brain was clear. He was filled to elation with a transcendent sense of duty.

The bomb bay doors opened leaving a dark gash in the belly of the plane and exposing three three-hundred-pound bombs.

Lieutenant Robins and the navigator were probing the sky with glasses. The sergeant was scrutinizing dial after dial in one of his periodical surveys. There was a tenseness among the crew but there was also a confidence born of their complete trust in the ability of their commanding officer.

"Three pursuits coming right at us from dead ahead." The navigator shouted his report without lowering the glasses. Coolly as if he were putting down a dinner fork, Captain Kelly reached for the throttles and drew back on the "stick." The nose of the plane shot upward with an augmented snarl in the roar of the engines. Safety lay in altitude. He flashed the gunner in the nose of the plane. "Commence firing as soon as they are in range," he said quietly.

The attacking planes could now be seen with the naked eye. They, too, were climbing. This placed them at a disadvantage temporarily since their guns were in a fixed position and could be aimed only along the line of the planes' flight. They soon leveled out, their guns spitting fire as they came on. The gunner in the bomber's nose opened up with hyphenated bursts, the last of which found its mark on the leading edge of one of the enemy's wings. Before he could correct his aim the planes banked away and dived under the bomber with the evident intention of coming up under her from the rear. Soon the belly and tail guns of the B-17 were chattering away like magpies.

Meantime the bomber was rapidly gaining altitude. The indicator on the altimeter ticked off thousands of feet as steadily as the hand of a split-second watch. The air was becoming rarer, the superchargers gulped great quantities of air to the motors to appease their craving for oxygen. Already the smaller planes of the enemy were laboring against their ceiling a thousand feet below. As the altimeter pointed to twenty thousand feet Captain Kelly banked the plane into a long easy circle, and cut down the motors. The sergeant-engineer heaved a sigh of relief at the respite for his engines. "Boy! I'm glad that's over," he shouted to the navigator. "Cruising is O.K. with me, but gunning these engines in a hot scramble upstairs like we've just done tears the heart out of them." A red flash on the board interrupted the sergeant. He went forward to the control room in time to hear the co-pilot shout, "Captain!—the big baby isn't a carrier, *it's a battleship!*" Kelly took the

BOATS AWAY!

Lt. William F. Draper, U.S.N.R.

LIEUTENANT WILLIAM F. DRAPER

American School

A native of Hopedale, Massachusetts, Lieutenant William F. Draper first studied to be a concert pianist, but later gave up music to study sculpture and painting. He worked under some of the best teachers in New York and Boston and studied both in Spain and in Paris.

In June, 1942, Draper was commissioned a Lieutenant (jg) in the U. S. Naval Reserve, and after working at the Anti-Submarine Warfare Unit was transferred to the art section and assigned to do a series of forty-two oil paintings on the islands of the Aleutian chain. There he worked under the severe difficulties of high winds and freezing weather, but succeeded in depicting many scenes of historic importance such as the initial Japanese attack on Amchitka Island. Sixteen reproductions of these Aleutian paintings can be found in the August 1943 issue of the National Geographic Magazine.

Promoted to Lieutenant in May, 1943, Draper has continued to render valuable service to the Navy. For the permanent records of the U. S. Naval Academy at Annapolis, Maryland, he painted a portrait of its superintendent. Recently he has been occupied in depicting scenes and events of historic character in the South Pacific. "Boats Away" shows dive bombers and ships' guns covering the landing forces streaking shoreward in Empress Augusta Bay. The painting is owned by the Navy Department and hangs in Washington, D. C.

glasses as the co-pilot took the controls. At the first glance at the fleet now less than six miles away, the captain's face seemed to lose its youthful contour, his nostrils distended and his lips became a thin line. His voice, usually touched with the warmth of his Celtic ancestry, became cold as chilled steel as he spoke to the bombardier over the interphone. "Corporal," he said, "give the battleship all three bombs. I will approach her from the east. That will put the sun at your back. Do not release until the plane is exactly where you want it with relation to the target. Do you understand?"

"Yes sir," came back from Levin at the bombsight.

As the plane circled out to sea for an ample run down on the target, Kelly had regained full composure. Never had he seen a bluer sky, a smoother sea, a more complete absence of haze, nor a finer target. For once luck was with him.

The interphone flashed. "Yes?" snapped the captain into the mouthpiece. It was the bombardier. "Can you fly right over the smoke stack, sir? I'd like to drop an egg in it."

Captain Kelly smiled. "Right over the stack," he repeated and eased the plane to the course requested by the corporal at the bomb release.

Two escorting destroyers and the battleship opened a lively antiaircraft fire, the smaller calibers falling short and the heavier shells bursting wide of their target.

A pleading call from the bombardier came through the commanding pilot's headphones. "Hold her as she is, Captain; please hold her!" A second later three bombs slipped from the racks and began their parabolic course downward. The bombardier reported, "String released, sir." The sergeant and corporal watched the cylinders diminish to pinpoints and disappear. The ships were more than three and a half miles below. After an interminable wait they saw a flash stab through a great mushroom of smoke on the starboard side of the battleship's deck. It was followed almost immediately by another explosion at the base of the funnel that made the entire ship shudder. It struck deep into her vitals and was as effective as if it had actually gone down through the stack. The third bomb landed squarely on the deck on the port side. Almost instantly the big battleship *Haruna* burst into flames and soon was burning fiercely. Even as the plane circled beyond the range of the anti-aircraft guns the Jap warship seemed to heave as with a stupendous hiccough and disintegrate in a blast of fire and flying debris.

As the plane headed back to Luzon the bewildered bombardier shouted to the sergeant. "The old man is a great pilot, Sarge. He put me on the target so fair I could not have missed if I had tried."

Captain Kelly sat pensively at the segmented wheel as he let down to ten thousand feet for his homing flight to Clark Field. Now that his mission had been finished his interest in his success was purely professional. He had one of the world's finest planes and one of the army's best crews; anything short of what had been accomplished would have been stark failure. He remained silent for a long time and then sent for the bombardier.

"You did well with that new bombsight, Levin," he said. "Keep up the good work."

"Thank you, sir," the corporal replied and returned to his station bubbling over with satisfaction. Praise from Kelly was beyond price to his crew.

Patches of cirrus clouds hanging lazily in the sky ahead gave the pilot concern; they were ideal hiding places from which the enemy could dart without warning. He switched the intercommunication on to every headphone and spoke calmly into the receiver. "I want every man at his station alert and ready for trouble, particularly the nose, sky and tail guns." As he put the receiver back in its place he ordered the radio operator to call the field for landing instructions. Below them the town of San Miguel was slowly slipping into the distance. If all went well they would make a landing in less than ten minutes.

The operator manipulating the dials on the radio outfit was calling the field in sing-song repetition, listening intently for the voice from the control tower between calls. During a pause the instrument panel seemed to explode in his face, a spatter of machine-gun bullets whipped through the top of the cabinet and blasted diagonally through the front, shattering the dial on which his hand rested. The sky gun close by instantly went into action spitting rapid bursts at the Jap pursuit ships that had suddenly come out of a cloud five hundred feet above.

Kelly threw the plane into a sharp bank, nosing her down simultaneously, and was about to go into a climb when a flight of bullets pulverized half a dozen of his instruments. He threw the plane into an ascent so sharp it was within but a few degrees of the stalling angle. With a steady hand on the throttle he whipped the last ounce from the 4500 horsepower at his command. He was thrilled at the response as the plane leaped skyward to take cover in a large cloud mass a thousand feet above.

As the first wisps of vapor drifted by the plane shot into the cloud, a flanking fire from one of the Japs ripped through the transparent blister that housed the gun on the right side. The gunner slumped with a bullet through his neck. The sergeant, seeing the lad collapse, took over. He noted that the wound, while serious was not fatal.

Kelly kept the plane climbing through the mile high cloud in an attempt to gain altitude and get above the attackers' ceiling. When he came through the dark murk of heavy vapor and burst out into the sunlight he was startled to find two of the enemy planes flying parallel to his course, less than four hundred feet away on his right. "Give 'em the works, Sergeant," he shouted into the phone. Almost simultaneously the sergeant's gun began to hammer away. Kelly looked relieved for he knew the sergeant to be an expert machine gunner.

The first and second bursts were long and steady. The third burst began and ended almost simultaneously. A mere whiff of fire had stabbed from the gun when it became silent.

The radioman hurried to the control room and reported, "They got the sergeant, sir." Kelly kicked his rudder over and pushed on the stick, throwing the great plane into a vertical bank as it dived back into the cloud. As the plane was about to disappear into the gray mass a heavy projectile from a cannon on one of the Jap planes ripped through the roof and struck the oxygen tanks. There was a rending explosion that staggered the plane; fragments of the tanks flew like shrapnel through the metal sides. The crew were stunned but none was seriously injured.

As soon as the plane was hidden in the cloud bank Kelly looked back over his shoulder. The men at their stations were as alert as hunters approaching a covey of game. Their eyes were on the sights and impatient fingers lay lightly on the triggers. The radioman had taken over the right blister gun beside which lay the wounded gunner and the dead sergeant.

Clark Field was only a few minutes away when Kelly shot the plane out of the underside of the cloud. The Japs had come down also and were buzzing around like hornets and peppering the bomber apparently at will. These enemy pilots were much more skillful than the Japs Kelly had been eluding for two days. They seemed to be thoroughly familiar with all the advanced maneuvers and aerobatic movements as taught at the best American flying fields. Chandelles, wingovers, half rolls, vertical cartwheels and double snap rolls were done with a precision that Kelly had to admire.

This showing-off by the Japs irritated him. He shouted into the interphone. "What's the matter with you fellows back there? Forgotten how to shoot?"

He had scarcely finished when he saw one of the attacking planes on the left roll over and hurtle down out of control. He phoned the gunner. "Good work, Mac. Knew you could do it." Kelly never forgot to give his men credit.

He was now streaking for the field with all motors wide

open. As he took his hand from the throttle he felt the left wing shudder violently at the impact of one of the Japs' heavy caliber projectiles. The motor nacelle had been ripped open like a tin can. The motor itself was a flailing mass of metal. Instantly the motors and wing were enveloped in streaking flame as from a giant blowtorch. Sideslipping to the right in order to throw the flame away from the fuselage, he flashed the interphone. "Get ready to bail out!" His voice was calm but commanding. The crew lined up. The lieutenant gave a quick inspection of their harness and stood near the door which had been thrown open. "Bail out!" he shouted. The first man to jump was Levin, the bombardier. He released the pilot chute that pulls the parachute from the pack and was still with the cloud of silk trailing behind him as one of the Japs roared by and opened fire on him as the chute opened. "Next," shouted the lieutenant. One by one the men jumped, including the wounded man who had received first aid.

The lieutenant stood in the doorway watching the silken life-rafts-of-the-air grow smaller in the distance, while the Jap planes milled around them firing burst after burst at the helpless men. Then he hurried forward to where Kelly sat stolidly at the controls. The fire had crept close to the control room, the air was heavy with the smell of burning rubber. The flames, fed by the high-octane gasoline and supercharged with oxygen by the two-hundred-mile speed of the plane, roared in a high-pitched key above the exhaust of the three uninjured motors.

The propeller of the burning motor windmilled madly, literally tearing the engine to bits. Kelly threw a quick glance back over his shoulder. The stations were empty, only the still form of the sergeant remained, resting peacefully in the passageway. As he saw the lieutenant approach he yelled, "I ordered you to bail out." His voice was stern for even then obedience to orders superseded the other articles of his soldier's creed.

The loyal lieutenant forgot their difference in rank. "For God's sake, Kelly," he yelled, "let the ship go. They need you." Even as he pleaded he could see the white-hot flames lick along the bullet-torn metal immediately over the wing fuel tank. He could also see knots of excited people watching the staggering plane from the airfield below.

Kelly turned to speak; there was affection for his officer in his eyes.

At that instant the watchers in the field saw the plane burst apart in a mass of rolling flame. A limp figure was hurtled through the side of the plane. It plummeted down for several hundred feet. The parachute opened miraculously. Why it did so no one knows to this day for on the end of its silken lines the lieutenant hung unconscious.

The great bomber fell like a wounded bird. In the seat of honor on the left side of the cockpit sat a young American, trapped; calm and without fear to the end. Captain Colin P. Kelly, Jr., had flown forever into the hearts of his countrymen.

CHILD PIONEER

HONORÉ WILLSIE MORROW

LET me tell you the epic story of thirteen-year-old John Sager, as I gleaned it from letters and diaries of Oregon pioneers.

In the fall of 1844, John appeared at the gate of Dr. Whitman's medical mission, in what is now the State of Washington, carrying a starving five-months-old baby sister. He was staggering before an emaciated[1] cow on whose back were perched a sister aged eight, with a broken leg, and a sister of five who helped support the leg. A sister of three and one of seven walked beside his eleven-year-old brother, Francis.

[1] EMACIATED (ê-mā'shĭ-āt-ed)—Very thin.

Unaccompanied, John Sager and his five sisters and a brother, all younger than himself, had made their way from Fort Hall, five hundred miles to the east, over the Oregon Trail, then little more than a horse track.

The trail was frequented by predatory [2] Indians and was so difficult that the migration of 1844, which John's parents had joined, went to pieces. Some died en route; others turned southwest into California. But John came through.

The record of this strange children's expedition starts in early July, when Kit Carson [3] came across the Sagers' camping place near the Green River Rendezvous in what is today eastern Idaho.

He rode at a gallop into the camp, two fresh scalps hanging at his belt, flung himself from his horse and told John to put out the fire—a band of Sioux was on the warpath. John sent his brother and little sisters scurrying into the Conestoga

[2] PREDATORY (prĕd′à-tō-rĭ)—Plundering.
[3] KIT CARSON—An American frontiersman.

wagon,[4] kicked out the tiny blaze of buffalo chips, then looked to Carson for further orders.

Carson described John as a sandy-haired, freckle-faced boy, clad in a hunter's red flannel shirt which came to his knees. His snakeskin belt carried a knife and powder-horn. In reply to Carson's questions he said his father and mother were in the wagon, sick with the bloody flux;[5] that the remnant of the caravan to which they had attached themselves was two days' travel ahead. Carson told John to hitch the oxen at once and move forward all night and as long the next day as his strength would permit.

We next pick up the Sagers approaching Soda Springs on the Bear River. There were a half-dozen families in this camp and one of the men was a veterinary. On the edge of the camp John halted the oxen and asked for a doctor. He said that for two days his mother had been too sick to nurse the baby and that he couldn't make the little thing drink cow's milk. The veterinary climbed into the wagon. He was out in a few moments. Both the Sagers were dead, he told the waiting crowd. John called the doctor a liar and tried to climb into the wagon, but was held back by a dozen pitying hands.

The Sager orphans stayed with the caravan until it reached Fort Hall, a British trading post owned by the Hudson's Bay Company. The factor[6] in charge of the post was trying to prevent American emigrants from entering the Columbia Valley by deflecting them into California. Great Britain was then beginning her final struggle to retain her hold on Oregon Territory. He told them that the wagon trail to Oregon, made the year before by Marcus Whitman, the missionary doctor, was impassable. The members of the caravan, already worn and discouraged and terribly afraid of Indian massacre, decided to go down into California.

John Sager, squatting by the campfire, listened without a

[4] CONESTOGA (kŏn-ĕs-tō'gȧ) WAGON—Large covered wagon.
[5] BLOODY FLUX—Dysentery, a disease of the large intestine
[6] FACTOR—Agent.

word to the council of elders. His grief for his father and mother had merged into one immense desire. Ever since he could remember, he had heard his father talk of making a great farm in the valley of the Columbia, of helping to keep Oregon Territory for America. John determined to go on to the Columbia, to complete his father's life for him.

He would abandon the wagon; the oxen and cow could carry the packs of food and bedding. He had learned from an old woman in the camp how to feed the baby. The next morning he was gone, leaving this note: "I have taken the family back to the States with Kit Carson. He is in a hurry. John Sager." By this false information he made sure he would not be followed and prevented from pushing on westward.

There is a break here of several weeks while John and the rest of the children crept along the valley of the Snake River to Fort Boise, nearly three hundred miles beyond. The Snake writhes through a tremendous canyon that slashes Idaho from east to west. Barren plains, brutal mountains, scorching heat by day and chill by night, a pestilence of mosquitoes and fleas —a heartbreaking test for seasoned adults. Yet, one September afternoon there crept up to the gates of Fort Boise a boy holding a baby in his arms. Except for ragged buckskin pants and still more ragged moccasins, the boy was naked. His sun-faded hair fell to his shoulders in tangled profusion.

The factor in this one-man post was inured to all sorts of hardships, but when he saw John he uttered an oath of shocked surprise. John asked with fierce eagerness if there was a white woman in the fort. Something had to be done for the baby: she vomited everything she ate. The factor, with increasing horror in his eyes, looked down on the unsavory atom in the boy's arms. There was no white woman, and the factor suggested a nursing Indian mother. John declared that nothing could induce him to allow a squaw to wet-nurse the baby. Someone had warned him of the diseases a child would contract through such measures.

At this point Francis came up with the pack-train and there disembarked such a rabble of wild, half-naked little girls as the Scotchman had never seen even among Indians. He ordered his cook to feed the youngsters, and watched while they devoured the venison stew, gobbling and fighting like puppies. John stood aloof and chewed down a hunk of venison which he held in one hand, supporting the baby with the other.

The factor suggested that John leave the baby and the two next sisters at the fort. John shook his head. The baby's one chance, he decided, was to get through to Dr. Whitman's mission with all speed. The factor warned the lad that the baby looked ready to die any minute, anyhow. John's face flamed; he cursed the factor and began to sob.

The Scotch factor afterward set down his feelings in a letter to his mother.

"My letters to you have contained many strange tales, but none that twisted me like this. They were a scourge to have about, I assure you, but nothing could lessen the pathos of them. That lad John! Surely our Heavenly Father must have been moved by this lad's vicarious fatherhood! Not that he was a gentle guardian. He took no nonsense from any of them. When the girl of eight protested against holding the baby, he jerked the sister across his knees and clouted her until she begged to take the baby. The strain had told on him. He was all nerves and unable to throw off the torture of responsibility. By Jove, he ruled me too, for I sent them on, after a night's sleep, under the care of a pair of good Indians and fresh horses."

They may have been good Indians once, but evidently they regarded the job of guiding white papooses across the difficult Blue Mountains as beneath their dignity. A few days out they disappeared, accompanied by the horses.

We have few details of the crossing of the Blue Mountains. The oldest sister slipped under a ponderously moving ox and broke her leg. John used hard-packed snowballs to keep down the swelling. The baby was very low and John was sometimes not sure she was breathing at all. He had to abandon the starving oxen. The cow, which still yielded a small quantity of milk for the baby and transportation for the oldest sister, must come along. With frosted feet, with festering sores due to dirt and emaciation, the children began the last lap of the journey. They made five or six miles a day, huddling together at night like stricken lambs under the lee of a rock or backed against a fallen tree, warmed by huge fires. A thousand times during the trip the younger children shrieked that they would go no farther. John forced them to go on.

It would have wrung my heart, but I wish I might have witnessed the last lap of that immortal journey, though after my many days with the diaries I can see it as clearly as if I had actually come upon them in those mountain fastnesses.

Now they have topped the last crest, and as they stand gazing into the vast valley to the west, the snow is blood-stained beneath their feet. Behind them is a chaos of range and canyon over which they have crept like infinitesimal snails. Before them, a wide, undulating plain cut by the black and silver ribbon of the Columbia River. A moment to gaze, to shiver, then John moves with fumbling feet down the mountain. His legs are tied in strips of buffalo hide. His long hair is bound back from his eyes by a twist of leather around his forehead. On his back is the two-year-old sister. In his arms the baby, wrapped in a wolfskin, lies motionless as death.

Staggering back of John moans the cow, her hoofs split to the quick. On her back the eight-year-old girl huddles under a bit of blanket which she shares with the five-year-old. Francis, his gray eyes dull with hunger and exertion, buckskin pants reduced to a mere clout and flannel shirt only a fluttering decoration across his chest, brings up the rear with the others.

Stumbling, rising, panting, but in a silence more tragic than weeping, they move down into the valley of the blest and stand at last before the Whitman mission. Narcissa Whitman gave a little cry when she saw them and held out her arms toward the bundle in John's arms. Her only child, a little girl of two, had been drowned a few years before. She groaned as she turned back the wolfskin and saw what lay beneath.

Dr. Whitman looked with her, while the six young derelicts waited in breathless silence. The doctor thought that perhaps the baby was still alive and Narcissa took her into the house and laid her in a warm bath while her husband herded the others into an outbuilding and began the unsavory job of turning them into human children. All but John. He shook his head on hearing the doctor's order and followed Mrs. Whitman into the house. Bathed, rubbed with warm oil, wrapped in soft wool, the baby showed no sign of life until Narcissa began to drop hot, diluted milk between the blue lips. After several moments of this the little throat contracted and a whimper, something less than a mouse squeak, came forth. At this sound John dropped to the floor, wrapped his arms around Narcissa's knees, laughed, groaned, then limped from the room.

All that night Narcissa sat with the baby on her lap. John, washed and in decent garments, slept on a blanket on the floor beside her. The doctor dozed on a cot nearby. What thoughts passed through Narcissa Whitman's mind that night we cannot know. We do know that she was already worn with anxiety and overwork, and the prospect of adding seven more to her household must have been staggering. Toward dawn she roused the doctor and told him that she wanted to keep the Sager children at the mission. The next morning Doctor and Mrs. Whitman invited the little orphans to become their adopted children.

And so the heroic Odyssey [7] came to an end. Little John Sager had fulfilled his father's dream of making a home for the Sager family in the Columbia Valley, and of helping save Oregon for America.

---

[7] ODYSSEY—A long wandering. From Homer's *Odyssey* which tells of the ten years' wanderings and adventures of Odysseus.

SONG OF THE NIGHTINGALE

MAURICE HINDUS

Immediately after the dinner hour German troops swung into the village. In reality there was no village any more. Petras Tsvirka,[1] who wrote this story in *Izvestia*,[2] assures us that not a house was left standing—nothing but heaps of ashes and rubble and blackened brush and burned trees. Not a soul was around—not even a dog. All life seemed emptied out of it as completely as though no one had ever lived there.

Tired and sweaty, the Germans halted for a rest. The lieutenant took out his binoculars and searched the country-side in all directions. He was seeking to locate the village for which he was bound.

Suddenly there broke into the air the song of a nightingale. On and on the nightingale sang with increasing zest and me-lodiousness. The lieutenant and the soldiers turned their eyes in the direction of the near-by grove, but they saw no bird. Instead they beheld a bareheaded, barefoot boy sitting beside a ditch. He was whittling a stick and whistling.

The Germans came toward him and he looked up, frightened. Hastily he thrust his knife into his pocket and pressed the stick inside his clothing. The lieutenant ordered him to come over, and when he did the lieutenant saw him rolling something in his mouth.

"Let me see what it is," demanded the lieutenant.

The boy took out of his mouth a birch whistle, small and soaked with saliva. It was with this whistle that he had been imitating the nightingale. The lieutenant and the soldiers gathered around and scrutinized the whistle with deep curiosity. For once the lieutenant's stern expression gave way to a smile of satisfaction and he said: "Splendid, splendid, my boy." He asked the boy to whistle again. The boy, only thirteen years of age, was happy to oblige the German officer. "I can

[1] PETRAS TSVIRKA (pě′träs tsvēr′kȧ)—A reporter.
[2] *Izvestia* (ĭz-věs′tĭ-ȧ)—A Russian periodical.

imitate a cuckoo too," he said, and forthwith produced a perfect imitation of that bird.

The soldiers were amused, but the officer, bent on an important military errand, asked the boy whether he knew the road to the village of Surmontas.

"Yes," said the boy, "I used to go fishing in the millpond there with my uncle."

The officer took out a shiny cigarette lighter, held it before the boy, and promised to give it to him if he would lead them to the village of Surmontas. "But if you fool me," threatened the lieutenant, "I'll twist your head off your shoulders."

With the German field kitchen in the van and the boy marching beside the lieutenant, the company started. As they walked, the officer asked more questions. Pointing to some trees, he said:

"Are there *partisans*[3] in the birch woods?"

With an innocent mien the boy asked:

"You mean mushrooms?" Without waiting for an answer he enumerated the kinds of mushrooms that grew in the birch woods.

The officer asked no more questions.

Out of seeming playfulness the boy started to whistle again, thirty-two times like a nightingale, twice like a cuckoo. The Germans marching along liked the joviality of their youthful companion and said nothing. But deep in the woods the lurking guerrillas knew the meaning of the bird songs. They knew that thirty-two Germans and two machine guns were on the road.

As the party wound along the road and entered the woods, the boy, fleet as a startled rabbit, darted away; and from the concealing birches came a hail of bullets. Not one of the Germans remained alive

[3] *Partisans*—Soviet guerrillas.

THE POTATO HARVEST

Jean François Millet

JEAN FRANCOIS MILLET

French School

Born in 1814, Jean François Millet grew up in the little village of Gruchy, France. His father was a peasant, and the young Millet began early to help with the plowing, sowing, and reaping. When he was eighteen his father consented to send him to study under a famous artist at Cherbourg. He later studied in Paris, but he did not like city life and could not get along with his teachers. Other artists, however, encouraged him and by 1848 he had won a mild success. He decided to settle at Barbizon and there for twenty-seven years he painted simple pictures of the dignity of peasant life. He painted with great sympathy and honesty for he had known the hard labor of the fields and understood the character of the French peasant.

"The Potato Harvest," like most of Millet's works, illustrates his love of people. The scene is dominated by human figures engaged in the simple duties of everyday life. Millet mastered the difficult effects of changing light during different hours of the day and during seasons of the year. First exhibited in Paris in 1867, "The Potato Harvest" now hangs in the Walters Art Gallery in Baltimore, Maryland.

CLARA BARTON OF
THE RED CROSS

JEANETTE COVERT NOLAN

On the afternoon of March 16, 1882, the long struggle of a valiant woman ended in triumph. With the ratification by the United States Senate of the Geneva treaty, the "Association of the American Red Cross" came into being. Its founder in this country, Clara Barton, tasted the reward of years of patient, selfless labor. Looking back over those years she thought of the early months of the Civil War, when, all unknowingly, she had laid the difficult groundwork of her organization. Her one desire then and always had been to go "into the field"—into the midst of suffering. Denied at first, by the second year of the war she had won her fight for the right to carry aid and comfort to the wounded on the battlefield. She was to demonstrate then and on many other occasions that "the Red Cross means not national aid for the needs of the people, but the people's aid for the needs of the nation."

In December, after an autumn of trailing the troops through Maryland and into Virginia, Clara went to Falmouth, where a large portion of the Army of the Potomac was encamped on the Rappahannock River overlooking Fredericksburg. For this expedition Major Rucker had allotted her six wagons and an ambulance. She had eight men to accompany her, but the ruddy, good-humored Pete had been transferred elsewhere—and Clara missed him. That the eight were civilians rather than soldiers, hucksters and mule breakers hired by the government as drivers, she knew. She was to learn that they could be both sullen and fractious.

It was winter, very cold, and Clara rode in the ambulance, shielded by the buttoned-down canvas roof. On the first day out from Washington, at four o'clock in the afternoon, her conveyance was pulled into a little gully and halted. Glancing out, she saw that all the wagons had been formed into a circle, the mules unhitched, the men had dismounted and were raking up sticks and dried grass, as if for a fire.

But why should they have stopped? She called to the ambulance driver, George, who seemed to be the leader of the squad.

"Night," George said laconically. "We ain't owls."

"You have two hours more of daylight. You can go on that long."

"We only drive," George stated, "when we feel like it."

She was somewhat taken aback. "I think," she said, "you drive when *I* feel like it. And I feel like it now. We'll go on."

He regarded her insolently a minute, then strolled to his friends in the center of the circle. Clara had withdrawn behind the curtains, but she could see that a consultation was in progress. There were mutterings and grumbled curses and much cracking of the teamsters' whips. Presently the mules were put into the shafts and the caravan jolted again onto the road.

Clara smiled to herself and thought that the tiff, such as it was, had been settled. But then she was not so positive, for the two hours elapsed, the sun sank, darkness came on. It was six o'clock, and seven, and eight—and George drove on as though he meant never to stop! His behavior was that of a perverse child. His rigid back and the tilt of his cap seemed to say, "Well, if you're so fond of this, you shall have an abundance!"

"And he *is* a child," thought Clara. "An impudent bully. I've had his kind in my classes. He wants me to ask him to stop. I'll not do it."

She was beginning to be hungry, and she knew that George and his fellows must be, too. But she said nothing. Finally, after nine-thirty, with a prodigious squealing of brakes, the wheels were stilled.

Clara got down. She was chilled through, stiff from her cramped attitude, a little apprehensive of what the night might hold. But she had mapped her course of action. She laid a fire. The men lounged near by, making no pretense of helping. She hung a stewpan on a spit and heated soup. She fried eggs and bacon. She had no table, but she spread a cloth upon the ground and set it neatly with plates, forks, and spoons. She opened a glass of crabapple jelly, a jar of blackberry jam, and placed them in the middle of the cloth. She brewed a huge pot of coffee. The men were watching. Each of them had his own food box containing eight days' rations of salted meat and bread. They unfastened the lids of their boxes, looked in—and then at the attractive prospect of Clara's luxurious fare.

"Gentlemen," Clara said, "supper is served."

They came reluctantly, one at a time, edging up, sheepishly taking plates and the cups of coffee which she poured. When all were seated, Clara sat down with them and began to chat casually. Probably she had never indulged in more difficult conversation than that, for there were few responses, but she could not doubt that the supper was appreciated. They ate largely, grunting and casting funny sidelong glances at their amiably smiling hostess.

As the last morsel vanished, Clara collected the dishes, washed them and stowed them away. The fire had dwindled to a bed of coals lighting the surrounding trees with a rosy and almost theatrically beautiful glow. As if by common consent, the drivers had sauntered into the shadows, out of sight. Had she not heard occasionally the guttural rumble of their voices, Clara might have thought they were gone for good.

After a while, and just as she had turned toward her blankets in the ambulance, George emerged.

"Miss Barton?" With the firelight on his black hair and eyes, his rugged countenance and burly, rough-clad figure, he looked sinister as a bandit. The other seven were at his heels, like a bandit's cohorts. "Miss Barton, we got something to say."

"Well," Clara said, "that's fine. Come up where you'll be warm and comfortable, George."

He came a pace closer. "The thing is, we think mebbe we've been—mistaken. None of us ever seen a wagon train bossed by a lady before, an' we didn't hanker ever to see one. When we found out that you was in charge of this'n, we was mad. We thought we'd act mean an' contrary, an' bust it up. But—Miss Barton, that was the best grub I've et in two years! An' you called us *gentlemen*."

"Why not? You are gentlemen, and I shall always treat you as such. I can understand your feeling about being directed by a woman, but in these dreadful days we all have to do things we don't just fancy. I think you'll become accustomed to me. In fact, since you approve of my cooking, I think we shall get along splendidly together and be fast friends. It would be too bad if we weren't, wouldn't it? Because we may have a big job facing us. Good night, George. I'm going to bed now."

She started for the ambulance. But George, the gentleman, was before her, hurrying to assist her, rolling a keg into position for her to step upon, buttoning the canvas down once she she was inside.

"I'll mend the fire, Miss Barton. Don't you fret about it. An' me an' the boys will sleep right here. If you should want us, all you got t' do is holler."

Next morning, Clara was awakened by a succession of muffled sounds. She lifted the curtain and peeped out at great activity. The men were bustling about, spreading the cloth on the ground, setting out dishes. The fire crackled blithely, the mules were hitched. George was walking up from the creek, a bucket in his hand.

"This is for the boss," he asserted. "Don't none o' you touch it. An' pipe down that infernal yawpin' or you'll be sorry! I know about ladies, even if you don't. They got to get their beauty sleep.   Gosh!   Mebbe we'll have flapjacks for breakfast."

At Falmouth, Clara was established in the Lacy House, an old mansion of magnificent architecture and landscaped gardens, abandoned now by its owner, and within a stone's throw of the Rappahannock.   From the piazza, she could see the muddy, ice-bordered river, with the town of Fredericksburg on the far side, and, on the Falmouth shore, a city of tents wherein Union soldiers awaited the command to storm Fredericksburg. There was no bridge over the water.   When the command, long anticipated and often postponed, should be issued, a pontoon bridge must be constructed.

The Lacy House had twelve spacious rooms, all empty now except for Miss Barton and her small staff.   Clara devoutly wished that they might always be so, that there would never be a battle to fill them with pain and horror—and knew that the wish was vain.   This dreadful drama of a nation in travail must play itself out to the end; and already, in the North, certain people were criticizing General Burnside [1] for his delay. "Cross that river!" said newspaper editorials.   "Occupy those brick houses on the other bank!   What if it is winter?   This is war!"   Still Burnside hesitated.

Then on a day of hazy, moderate weather, the engineers began working with the pontoons, lashing the boats, flinging down planks and timber.   Above, on the Fredericksburg heights, was the stirring of suspense, as the Confederates girded themselves to defend.

From the portico Clara saw the first Union squads march out upon the bridge, to be mowed down by batteries of hidden cannon.   She saw the second venture and heard General Burnside's shout, "Bring the guns to bear.   We'll shell them out!"

[1] BURNSIDE—General Ambrose Everett Burnside, in charge of the Northern forces.

Clara left the portico then, for musketry made a fiendish clamor. Bullets whizzed, windows in the Lacy House were crashing and splintering. The engineers were furiously trying to complete the span of pontoons, despite the enemy's scything. They did it at last, and their troops trotted over to the far shore, where men in gray were swarming out of every building in Fredericksburg, surging through every street, solidifying into a wall of rifles and artillery along the Rappahannock's cliffs. This was the battle. . . .

The days and weeks spent at Falmouth were different from anything she had known, for now she had the cold to contend with. Snow and sleet fell; often the men picked up were partially frozen and must be thawed before they could be bandaged. Clara kept fires on every hearth in the big house, tea and broth always simmering on the kitchen stoves. She wrapped hot bricks in rags with which to warm the cots and straw pallets. The rooms soon were overflowing, even though wagons plied steadily toward the railroad which took the more hopeful cases to Washington. Besides nursing, Clara also had the responsibility of supervising the orderlies, and every few hours she must cross into Fredericksburg for those injured detailed to her by the surgeons.

On one of these sorties, she stood on the curb to watch a regiment of infantrymen tramping through the street toward the front line on the heights. As always, she was touched by the sight. How young they were, how browned and vigorous. And how many would be so tomorrow?

An officer, glimpsing her, pulled up his horse, bent from his saddle. "Madam, you are within the range of a thousand rifles, in terrible peril! What on earth are you doing here? Do you want protection?"

She smiled up at him. "No, General. I believe I am the best-protected woman in the United States."

A pert little corporal had overheard. "That's so!" he bellowed, and cheered lustily. "Ain't that so?" *"What's* so?" someone cried. "Ain't she the best-protected woman in the United States?" The cheer echoed to the next rank, through all the ranks. *"That's* so!"

"I believe," said the blinking general, baring his head, "you are right, madam."

Two Confederate prisoners were brought to the Lacy House, one a lieutenant of cavalry, the other an eighteen-year-old private; both seemed to have the chance to survive. Clara

bedded them side by side in an alcove. She felt a special pity for the boy. His name was Donald, his home in a Georgia village.

"Am I going to die?" he queried as she sponged his face.

"Oh, no. You have a nasty saber gash, but it will heal, Donald."

"What *will* become of me?"

"I imagine you'll be sent to some Northern camp and, after the war's over, exchanged for a Union man who is now a Confederate prisoner."

"Who'll tell my family?" He stared at her. "What if I die in that Northern camp? My mother and my dad, they'll wait —and what if they never know? That would be mighty hard on 'em."

"Yes, it would." She thought a minute. "I live in Washington. I'll give you my address. Whatever happens, whatever they do with you, you'll surely be allowed to write to me, Donald. Then I'll communicate with your family."

His eyes brightened—and were dour again. "How could you? The mails are out."

"When we're at peace once more, the mails will be resumed. But if they shouldn't be— Well, there'll be some way for me to notify your parents."

"Gosh! I hope so. Uncertainty can be crueler than out-and-out bad news, Miss Barton." As she rose, the basin in her hands, he murmured, " 'When we're at peace.' I like the sound o' that. But will it ever be true? Will we ever have peace?"

"Yes," she said. "That's one thing we can count on, Donald. We must live for that."

On the day that Clara had twelve hundred people under the roof of the Lacy House, she told George that she regretted the amount of furniture which the previous occupants had left behind them. "These chairs and whatnots and taborets.[2] They're beautiful. But not *useful*. We're all cluttered up with them."

George had an excellent idea. Why not dismember the superfluous things and use the wood to convert the corner cupboards into tiers of bunks? He got hammer and saw and built the tiers, and also more bunks in the halls, under the tables, over the beds, and on the stair landings. Even so, the nurses must step cautiously lest they jostle an arm or a leg in splints.

Whenever Clara's fortitude seemed almost to ebb away, some

[2] TABORET (tăb'ô-rĕt)—A small table or stand.

388

incident would ensue to spur her on—and one such incident was the coming of Mrs. Fales.

"Well, Miss Barton?" she strode in, her old hat cocked at a ridiculous angle. "I got here. By hook or crook."

"Oh, Mrs. Fales!" Joy was in Clara's ejaculation.

"How are things? What shall I do first?" She tied on her apron. At noon, she said, "There's a poor child downstairs. Shot through the lungs. His breathing's shallow, he can't last long. He's sitting on the floor, straight as a ramrod against the wall. I asked an orderly to move him. But he said no, he wouldn't be touched. And he wants a milk punch."

"I'll mix the punch," Clara said. "We have fresh milk and eggs and brandy."

As she spooned the frothy beverage between the boy's lips, Clara asked him his name.

"Riley Faulkner," he gasped. "Ohio. Ashtabula County."

She thought, with Mrs. Fales, that he could not draw those tortured inhalations much longer. But in the evening he was still breathing.

"And stronger," said Mrs. Fales. "I wouldn't have believed it if I hadn't seen with my own eyes."

Next morning Mrs. Fales announced, "That Faulkner boy may pull through yet."

"He should be in a more accessible spot," Clara said.

"Not him. He won't budge. And he wants another milk punch."

"He shall have it!"

If there could have been a subject for joking in that grim place, Riley Faulkner of Ashtabula was such a phenomenon. For two solid weeks he was to sit there in his corner, not budging, growing always a bit stronger, always demanding milk punch. Even when he was finally persuaded to let the orderlies carry him on a stretcher to the Washington train, he had a bottle of his favorite drink tucked into his blouse under the blankets.

After a four-day truce, the batteries at Fredericksburg boomed again. On the morning of the fiercest fighting, when the Lacy House trembled to its foundations, the Confederate lieutenant gripped Clara's hand as she passed his cot.

"You've been kind to me, Miss Barton, and to my comrade, the Georgia lad. You're rendering a stupendous service here. I entreat you not to cross the river today."

"Why not?"

"I can't tell you. But you must not go. Perhaps it is a disloyalty for me to say this much, and if so, I pray I may be pardoned. Please, please, Miss Barton, don't go!"

She thanked him—and went, as usual. She could not disappoint those who were expecting her.

At dusk she returned, knowing why the Confederate had warned her. A trap had been set for Burnside. When the trap was sprung, Burnside had been overwhelmed and Fredericksburg lost.

The South might be weakening. It was not yet conquered.

Clara alighted from a Washington streetcar, stumbled through the muddy street and up the flight of stairs to her apartment. The day was dreary and raw, late in January. She unlocked her door and just avoided falling over a wooden box which stood in the center of the floor. She slammed the door and, sitting down on the box, gazed around her at the chill, somewhat dirty room. How strange it seemed, this silence, after the months of noise and frenzied confusion of the Lacy House. She had the sensation of unreality—and she was weary to the marrow of her bones.

In a mirror on the opposite wall she saw herself, damp and bedraggled, bonnet awry, mantle and skirt shabby, shoes scuffed and unpolished.

"I look like a beggar," she thought. "A scarecrow. A wet hen. And I have no better clothes than these. Everything I own is in shreds."

And she had very little money either. Disconsolately she computed: her salary would be paid in February. But from that must be subtracted the sum with which she hired her substitute at the Patent Office. If she spent the remainder for clothing, she could not replenish her stores—not unless she drew further upon her savings, and she feared to do that.

She had not shed a tear in Fredericksburg or Falmouth. Now her composure dissolved. Somehow the deluge of weeping eased her. After a while she wiped her eyes, got up and struck a match to the gas jet. And then she noticed the box upon which she had been sitting.

It was addressed to her. Underneath her name was the intriguing word "Personal." What was in the box? She ran for a hatchet and pried loose the lid. Inside were folds of tissue and a card: FROM FRIENDS IN OXFORD. She lifted the paper——

Skirts, jackets, collars, handkerchiefs, shoes, boots, gloves! And petticoats, aprons, a knitted hood, stockings! An entire wardrobe, all for her, from her dear friends back home!

The tears welled again, but she smiled through them.

She wore the lovely new things that afternoon in February when she was summoned to the Lincoln Hospital. The messenger had been rather mysterious, she didn't know who wanted her, or why. She was told to go to Ward 17. Still baffled, she entered.

Seventy men were there, facing toward the door, saluting. Every one had been at Falmouth, every one her patient. A young chap, pink complexioned and husky looking, came and took her hand.

"Hello, Miss Barton. Don't you recognize me? I'm Faulkner."

"You're surely not!"

"Guess I was a skeleton when you coaxed me onto that train, eh? Well, I didn't die. And the milk punch lasted all the way to Washington."

A MESSAGE TO GARCIA

ELBERT HUBBARD

IN ALL this Cuban business there is one man stands out on the horizon of my memory like Mars at perihelion.[1]

When war [2] broke out between Spain and the United States it was very necessary to communicate quickly with the leader of the Insurgents.[3] Garcia was somewhere in the mountain fastnesses of Cuba—no one knew where. No mail or telegraph message could reach him. The President [4] must secure his co-operation, and quickly.

What to do!

Some one said to the President, "There's a fellow by the name of Rowan will find Garcia for you, if anybody can."

Rowan was sent for and given a letter to be delivered to Garcia. How "the fellow by the name of Rowan" took the let-

[1] MARS AT PERIHELION (pĕr-ĭ-hē′lĭ-ŏn)—When the planet Mars is at that point in its orbit which is nearest to the sun. Mars is conspicuous for its redness which is the more vivid when it is at perihelion.

[2] WAR—The Spanish-American War which broke out in 1898.

[3] INSURGENTS—The native Cubans who had rebelled against Spanish rule. General Garcia was their commander.

[4] PRESIDENT—The president of the United States was at that time William McKinley.

ter, sealed it up in an oilskin pouch, strapped it over his heart, in four days landed by night off the coast of Cuba from an open boat, disappeared into the jungle, and in three weeks came out on the other side of the island, having traversed a hostile country on foot, and delivered his letter to Garcia—are things I have no special desire to tell in detail now. The point I wish to make is this: McKinley gave Rowan a letter to be delivered to Garcia; Rowan took the letter and did not ask, "Where is he at?" By the Eternal! there is a man whose form should be cast in deathless bronze and the statue placed in every college in the land! It is not book learning young men need, nor instruction about this or that, but a stiffening of the vertebræ that will cause them to be loyal to a trust, to act promptly, concentrate their energies: do the thing—"Carry a message to Garcia."

General Garcia is dead now, but there are other Garcias.

No man who has endeavored to carry out an enterprise wherein many hands were needed, but has been well-nigh appalled at times by the imbecility of the average man—the inability or unwillingness to concentrate on a thing and do it.

Slipshod assistance, foolish inattention, dowdy indifference, and half-hearted work seem the rule; and no man succeeds unless, by hook or crook or threat, he forces or bribes other men to assist him; or mayhap, God in his goodness performs a miracle, and sends him an Angel of Light for an assistant. You, reader, put this matter to a test: You are sitting now in your office—six clerks are within call. Summon any one and make this request: "Please look in the encyclopedia and make a brief memorandum of Correggio."

Will the clerk quietly say, "Yes, sir," and go to the task?

On your life he will not! He will look at you out of a fishy eye and ask one or more of the following questions:

Who is he?

Which encyclopedia?

Where is the encyclopedia?

Was I hired for that?

Don't you mean Bismarck?

What's the matter with Charlie doing it?

Is he dead?

Is there any hurry?

Shall I bring you the book and let you look it up for yourself?

What do you want to know for?

And I will lay you ten to one that after you have answered the questions, and explained how to find the information, and why you want it, the clerk will go off and get one of the other clerks to help him try to find Garcia—and then come back and tell you there is no such man. Of course I may lose my bet, but according to the Law of Average, I will not.

Now if you are wise you will not bother to explain to your "assistant" that Correggio is indexed under the C's, not in the K's, but you will smile sweetly and say, "Never mind," and go look it up yourself.

The dread of "getting the bounce" Saturday night holds many a worker in his place. Advertise for a stenographer, and nine out of ten who apply can neither spell nor punctuate—and do not think it necessary to.

Can such a one write a letter to Garcia?

"You see that bookkeeper?" said a foreman to me in a large factory.

"Yes; what about him?"

"Well, he's a fine accountant, but if I'd send him uptown on an errand, he might accomplish the errand all right, and on the other hand, might stop on the way, and when he got to Main Street would forget what he had been sent for."

Can such a man be entrusted to carry a message to Garcia?

We have recently been hearing much maudlin sympathy expressed for the "downtrodden denizens [5] of the sweatshop" and the "homeless wanderer searching for honest employment," and

---

[5] DENIZENS—Inhabitants, usually aliens in their adopted country.

with it all often go many hard words for the men in power.

Nothing is said about the employer who grows old before his time in a vain attempt to get frowsy ne'er-do-wells to do intelligent work; and his long, patient striving with "help" that does nothing but loaf when his back is turned. In every store and factory there is a constant weeding-out process going on. The employer is constantly sending away "help" that have shown their incapacity to further the interests of the business, and others are being taken on.

No matter how good times are, this sorting continues, only if times are hard and work is scarce, the sorting is done finer— but out and forever out the incompetent and unworthy go. It is the survival of the fittest. Self-interest prompts every employer to keep the best—those who can carry a message to Garcia.

I know one man of really brilliant parts who has not the ability to manage a business of his own, and yet who is absolutely worthless to any one else, because he carries with him constantly the insane suspicion that his employer is oppressing, or intending to oppress him. He cannot give orders; and he will not receive them. Should a message be given him to take to Garcia, his answer would probably be, "Take it yourself!"

Tonight this man walks the streets looking for work, the wind whistling through his threadbare coat. No one who knows him dare employ him, for he is a regular firebrand of discontent.

Of course I know that one so morally deformed is no less to be pitied than a physical cripple; but in our pitying, let us drop a tear, too, for the men who are striving to carry on a great enterprise, whose working hours are not limited by the whistle, and whose hair is fast turning white through the struggle to hold in line dowdy indifference, slipshod imbecility, and the heartless ingratitude which, but for their enterprise, would be both hungry and homeless.

Have I put the matter too strongly? Possibly I have; but when all the world has gone a-slumming I wish to speak a word of sympathy for the man who succeeds—the man who, against great odds, has directed the efforts of others, and having succeeded, finds there's nothing in it—nothing but bare board and clothes. I have carried a dinner pail and worked for day's wages, and I have also been an employer of labor, and I know there is something to be said on both sides. There is no excellence, *per se*,[6] in poverty; rags are no recommendation; and all employers are not rapacious [7] and high-handed, any more than all poor men are virtuous.

My heart goes out to the man who does his work when the "boss" is away, as well as when he is at home. And the man who, when given a letter for Garcia, quietly takes the missive, without asking any idiotic questions, and with no lurking intention of chucking it into the nearest sewer, or of doing aught else but delivering it, never gets "laid off." Civilization is one long, anxious search for just such individuals. Anything such a man asks shall be granted. His kind is so rare that no employer can afford to let him go. He is wanted in every city, town, and village—in every office, shop, store, and factory.

The world cries out for such; he is needed, and needed badly —the man who can carry A MESSAGE TO GARCIA.

[6] *Per se*—By itself.
[7] RAPACIOUS—Greedy, avaricious.

JOURNEYS

INTO OURSELVES

VI

Finding rewards in nature.

OH FAIR ENOUGH ARE SKY AND PLAIN

A. E. HOUSMAN

OH FAIR enough are sky and plain,
   But I know fairer far:
Those are as beautiful again
   That in the water are;

5   The pools and rivers wash so clean
   The trees and clouds and air,
The like on earth was never seen,
   And oh that I were there.

These are the thoughts I often think
10   As I stand gazing down
In act upon the cressy brink
   To strip and dive and drown;

But in the golden-sanded brooks
   And azure meres I spy
15   A silly lad that longs and looks
   And wishes he were I.

MOCKERY

KATHARINE DIXON RIGGS

HAPPENED that the moon was up before I went to bed,
Poking through the bramble-trees her round gold head.

399

I didn't stop for stocking,
I didn't stop for shoe,
5   But went running out to meet her—oh, the night was blue!

Barefoot down the hill road, dust beneath my toes;
Barefoot in the pasture smelling sweet of fern and rose!
Oh, night was running with me,
Tame folk were all in bed—
10   And the moon was just showing her wild gold head.

But before I reached the hilltop where the bramble-trees
    are tall,
I looked to see my lady moon—she wasn't there at all!—
Not sitting on the hilltop,
Nor slipping through the air,
15   Nor hanging in the brambles by her bright gold hair!

I walked slowly down the pasture and slowly up the hill,
Wondering and wondering, and very, very still.
1 wouldn't look behind me,
I went at once to bed—
20   And poking through the window was her bold gold head!

WINTER STREAMS

BLISS CARMAN

D   Now the little rivers go
           Muffled safely under snow,

           And the winding meadow streams
           Murmur in their wintry dreams,

5   While a tinkling music wells
           Faintly from their icy bells,

Telling how their hearts are bold
Though the very sun be cold.

L
10   Oh, but wait until the rain
Comes a-sighing once again,

Sweeping softly from the Sound,
Over ridge and meadow ground!

Then the little streams will hear
April calling far and near,—

15   Slip their snowy bands and run
Sparkling in the welcome sun.

THEME IN YELLOW

CARL SANDBURG

I SPOT the hills
With yellow balls in autumn.
I light the prairie cornfields
Orange and tawny gold clusters
5   And I am called pumpkins.
On the last of October
When dusk is fallen
Children join hands
And circle round me
10   Singing ghost songs
And love to the harvest moon:
I am a jack-o'-lantern
With terrible teeth
And the children know
15   I am fooling.

THE PASTURE

ROBERT FROST

I'M GOING out to clean the pasture spring;
I'll only stop to rake the leaves away
(And wait to watch the water clear, I may):
I shan't be gone long.—You come too.

5   I'm going out to fetch the little calf
That's standing by the mother. It's so young,
It totters when she licks it with her tongue.
I shan't be gone long.—You come too.

A BOY'S SUMMER SONG

PAUL LAURENCE DUNBAR

B   'TIS fine to play
          In the fragrant hay,
    And romp on the golden load;
1B   To ride old Jack
5   To the barn and back,
    Or tramp by a shady road.
        To pause and drink,
        At a mossy brink;
B   Ah, that is the best of joy,
10   And so I say
        On a summer's day,
    What's so fine as being a boy?
        Ha, Ha!

B   With line and hook
15   By a babbling brook,

The fisherman's sport we ply;
And list the song
Of the feathered throng
That flit in the branches nigh.
At last we strip
For a quiet dip;
Ah, that is the best of joy.
For this I say
On a summer's day,
What's so fine as being a boy?
Ha, Ha!

APRIL

THEODOSIA GARRISON

SOMETHING tapped at my window pane,
Someone called me without my door,
Someone laughed like the tinkle o' rain,
The robin echoed it o'er and o'er.

5   I threw the door and the window wide;
Sun and the touch of the breeze and then—
"Oh, *were* you expecting me, dear?" she cried,
And here was April come back again.

ROBERT OF LINCOLN

WILLIAM CULLEN BRYANT

G   MERRILY swinging on brier and weed,
    Near to the nest of his little dame,
Over the mountain side or mead,
    Robert of Lincoln is telling his name:
5   Bob-o'-link, bob-o'-link,
1G   Spink, spank, spink;
Snug and safe is that nest of ours,
Hidden among the summer flowers.
    Chee, chee, chee.

B   10   Robert of Lincoln is gayly drest,
    Wearing a bright black wedding-coat;
White are his shoulders and white his crest.
    Hear him call in his merry note:
1B   Bob-o'-link, bob-o'-link,
15   Spink, spank, spink,
Look, what a nice new coat is mine,
Sure there was never a bird so fine.
    Chee, chee, chee.

G   Robert of Lincoln's Quaker wife,
20   Pretty and quiet, with plain brown wings,
Passing at home a patient life,
    Broods in the grass while her husband sings:
1B   Bob-o'-link, bob-o'-link,
    Spink, spank, spink;

25   Brood, kind creature; you need not fear
Thieves and robbers while I am here.
Chee, chee, chee.

G   Modest and shy as a nun is she;
One weak chirp is her only note.

B 30   Braggart and prince of braggarts is he,
Pouring boasts from his little throat:

1B   Bob-o'-link, bob-o'-link,
Spink, spank, spink;
Never was I afraid of man;

35   Catch me, cowardly knaves, if you can!
Chee, chee, chee.

G   Six white eggs on a bed of hay,
Freckled with purple, a pretty sight!
There as the mother sits all day,

40   Robert is singing with all his might:

1B   Bob-o'-link, bob-o'-link,
Spink, spank, spink;
Nice good wife that never goes out,
Keeping house while I frolic about.

45   Chee, chee, chee.

G   Soon as the little ones chip the shell,
Six wide mouths are open for food;
Robert of Lincoln bestirs him well,
Gathering seeds for the hungry brood.

1B 50   Bob-o'-link, bob-o'-link,
Spink, spank, spink;
This new life is likely to be
Hard for a gay young fellow like me.
Chee, chee, chee.

B 55   Robert of Lincoln at length is made
Sober with work, and silent with care;

          Off is his holiday garment laid,
            Half-forgotten that merry air:

1B
               Bob-o'-link, bob-o'-link,
60
               Spink, spank, spink;
          Nobody knows but my mate and I
          Where our nest and our nestlings lie.
             Chee, chee, chee.

U
          Summer wanes; the children are grown;
65
            Fun and frolic no more he knows;
          Robert of Lincoln's a humdrum crone;
            Off he flies, and we sing as he goes:

1B
               Bob-o'-link, bob-o'-link,
               Spink, spank, spink;
70
          When you can pipe that merry old strain,
          Robert of Lincoln, come back again.
             Chee, chee, chee.

THE SNOW

EMILY DICKINSON

G
          IT SIFTS from leaden sieves,   *1G(#1)*
          It powders all the wood,   *1G(#2)*
          It fills with alabaster wool   *1G(#3)*
          The wrinkles of the road.

B   5
          It makes an even face   *B*
          Of mountain and of plain,—
          Unbroken forehead from the east
          Unto the east again.

G
          It reaches to the fence,   *1G(#1)*
10
          It wraps it, rail by rail,   *1G(#2)*

Till it is lost in fleeces;
B   It flings a crystal veil   *B*

On stump and stack and stem,—
The summer's empty room,
15   Acres of seams where harvests were,
Recordless, but for them.

U   It ruffles wrists of posts,   *U*
As ankles of a queen,—
Then stills its artisans like ghosts,
20   Denying they have been.

SOMETHING TOLD THE WILD GEESE

RACHEL FIELD

B   SOMETHING told the wild geese
It was time to go.
G   Though the fields lay golden
Something whispered,—"Snow."
B 5 Leaves were green and stirring,
Berries, luster-glossed,
G   But beneath warm feathers
Something cautioned,—"Frost."
B   All the sagging orchards
10   Steamed with amber spice,
G   But each wild breast stiffened
At remembered ice.
B   Something told the wild geese
It was time to fly,—
G 15 Summer sun was on their wings,
Winter in their cry.

407

ANOTHER APRIL

JESSE STUART

"Now, Pap, you won't get cold," Mom said as she put a heavy wool cap over his head.

"Huh, what did ye say?" Grandpa asked, holding his big hand cupped over his ear to catch the sound.

"Wait until I get your gloves," Mom said, hollering real loud in Grandpa's ear. Mom had forgotten about his gloves until he raised his big bare hand above his ear to catch the sound of Mom's voice.

"Don't get 'em," Grandpa said, "I won't ketch cold."

Mom didn't pay attention to what Grandpa said. She went on to get the gloves anyway. Grandpa turned toward me. He saw that I was looking at him.

"Yer Ma's a-puttin' enough clothes on me to kill a man," Grandpa said, then he laughed a coarse laugh like March wind among the pine tops at his own words. I started laughing but not at Grandpa's words. He thought I was laughing at them and we both laughed together. It pleased Grandpa to think that I had laughed with him over something funny that he had said. But I was laughing at the way he was dressed. He looked like a picture of Santa Claus. But Grandpa's cheeks were not cherry-red like Santa Claus' cheeks. They were covered with white thin beard—and above his eyes were long white eyebrows almost as white as percoon petals and very much longer.

Grandpa was wearing a heavy wool suit that hung loosely about his big body but fitted him tightly round the waist where he was as big and as round as a flour barrel. His pant legs were as big round his pipe-stem legs as emptied meal sacks. And his big shoes, with his heavy wool socks dropping down over their tops, looked like sled runners. Grandpa wore a heavy wool shirt and over his wool shirt he wore a heavy wool sweater and then his coat over the top of all this. Over his coat he wore a heavy overcoat and about his neck he wore a wool scarf.

The way Mom had dressed Grandpa you'd think there was a heavy snow on the ground but there wasn't. April was here instead and the sun was shining on the green hills where the wild plums and the wild crab apples were in bloom enough to make you think there were big snowdrifts sprinkled over the green hills. When I looked at Grandpa and then looked out the window at the sunshine and the green grass I laughed more. Grandpa laughed with me.

"I'm a-goin' to see my old friend," Grandpa said just as Mom came down the stairs with his gloves.

"Who is he, Grandpa?" I asked, but Grandpa just looked at my mouth working. He didn't know what I was saying. And he hated to ask me the second time.

Mom put the big wool gloves on Grandpa's hands. He stood there just like I had to do years ago, and let Mom put his gloves on. If Mom didn't get his fingers back in the glove-fingers exactly right Grandpa quarreled at Mom. And when

Mom fixed his fingers exactly right in his gloves the way he wanted them Grandpa was pleased.

"I'll be a-goin' to see 'im," Grandpa said to Mom. "I know he'll still be there."

Mom opened our front door for Grandpa and he stepped out slowly, supporting himself with his big cane in one hand. With the other hand he held to the door facing. Mom let him out of the house just like she used to let me out in the spring. And when Grandpa left the house I wanted to go with him, but Mom wouldn't let me go. I wondered if he would get away from the house—get out of Mom's sight—and pull off his shoes and go barefooted and wade the creeks like I used to do when Mom let me out. Since Mom wouldn't let me go with Grandpa, I watched him as he walked slowly down the path in front of our house. Mom stood there watching Grandpa too. I think she was afraid that he would fall. But Mom was fooled; Grandpa toddled along the path better than my baby brother could.

"He used to be a powerful man," Mom said more to herself than she did to me. "He was a timber cutter. No man could cut more timber than my father; no man in the timber woods could sink an ax deeper into a log than my father. And no man could lift the end of a bigger saw log than Pap could."

"Who is Grandpa goin' to see, Mom?" I asked.

"He's not goin' to see anybody," Mom said.

"I heard 'im say that he was goin' to see an old friend," I told her.

"Oh, he was just a-talkin'," Mom said.

I watched Grandpa stop under the pine tree in our front yard. He set his cane against the pine tree trunk, pulled off his gloves and put them in his pocket. Then Grandpa stooped over slowly, as slowly as the wind bends down a sapling, and picked up a pine cone in his big soft fingers. Grandpa stood fondling the pine cone in his hand. Then, one by one, he pulled the little chips from the pine cone—tearing it to pieces like he was hunting for something in it—and after he had torn it to pieces he threw the pine-cone stem on the ground. Then he pulled pine needles from a low hanging pine bough and he felt of each pine needle between his fingers. He played with them a long time before he started down the path.

"What's Grandpa doin'?" I asked Mom.

But Mom didn't answer me.

"How long has Grandpa been with us?" I asked Mom.

"Before you's born," she said. "Pap has been with us eleven years. He was eighty when he quit cuttin' timber and farmin'; now he's ninety-one."

I heard her say that when she was a girl he'd walk out on the snow and ice barefooted and carry wood in the house to put on the fire. He had shoes but he wouldn't bother to put them on. And I heard her say that he would cut timber on the coldest days without socks on his feet but with his feet stuck down in cold brogan shoes and he worked stripped above the waist so his arms would have freedom when he swung his double bitted ax. I had heard her tell how he'd sweat and how the sweat in his beard would be icicles by the time he got home from work on the cold winter days. Now Mom wouldn't let him get out of the house for she wanted him to live a long time.

As I watched Grandpa go down the path toward the hog pen he stopped to examine every little thing along his path. Once he waved his cane at a butterfly as it zigzagged over his head, its polka-dot wings fanning the blue April air. Grandpa would stand when a puff of wind came along, and hold his face against the wind and let the wind play with his white whiskers. I thought maybe his face was hot under his beard and he was letting the wind cool his face. When he reached the hog pen he called the hogs down to the fence. They came running and grunting to Grandpa just like they were talking to him. I knew that Grandpa couldn't hear them trying to talk to him but he could see their mouths working and he knew they were trying to say something. He leaned his cane against the hog pen, reached over the fence, and patted the hogs' heads. Grandpa didn't miss patting one of our seven hogs.

As he toddled up the little path alongside the hog pen he stopped under a blooming dogwood. He pulled a white blossom from a bough that swayed over the path above his head, and he leaned his big bundled body against the dogwood while he tore each petal from the blossoms and examined it carefully. There wasn't anything his dim eyes missed. He stopped under a redbud tree before he reached the garden to break a tiny spray of redbud blossoms. He took each blossom from the spray and examined it carefully.

"Gee, it's funny to watch Grandpa," I said to Mom, then I laughed.

"Poor Pap," Mom said, "he's seen a lot of Aprils come and go. He's seen more Aprils than he will ever see again."

I don't think Grandpa missed a thing on the little circle he took before he reached the house. He played with a bumblebee that was bending a windflower blossom that grew near our corn-crib beside a big bluff. But Grandpa didn't try to catch the bumblebee in his big bare hand. I wondered if he would and if the bumblebee would sting him, and if he would holler. Grandpa even pulled a butterfly cocoon from a blackberry briar that grew beside his path. I saw him try to tear it into shreds but he couldn't. There wasn't any butterfly in it, for I'd seen it before. I wondered if the butterfly with the polka-dot wings, that Grandpa waved his cane at when he first left the house, had come from this cocoon. I laughed when Grandpa couldn't tear the cocoon apart.

"I'll bet I can tear that cocoon apart for Grandpa if you'd let me go help him," I said to Mom.

"You leave your Grandpa alone," Mom said. "Let 'im enjoy April."

Then I knew that this was the first time Mom had let

Grandpa out of the house all winter. I knew that Grandpa
loved the sunshine and the fresh April air that blew from the
redbud and dogwood blossoms. He loved the bumblebees, the
hogs, the pine cones, and pine needles. Grandpa didn't miss a
thing along his walk. He'd stop along and look at everything
as he had done summers before. But each year he didn't take
as long a walk as he had taken the year before. Now this
spring he didn't go down to the lower end of the hog pen as he
had done last year. And when I could first remember Grandpa
going on his walks he used to go out of sight. He'd go all over
the farm. And he'd come to the house and take me on his knee
and tell me about all that he had seen. Now Grandpa wasn't
getting out of sight. I could see him from the window along
all of his walk.

Grandpa didn't come back into the house at the front door.
He tottled around back of the house toward the smokehouse
and I ran through the living room to the dining room so I could
look out at the window and watch him.

"Where's Grandpa goin'?" I asked Mom.

"Now never mind," Mom said. "Leave your Grandpa alone.
Don't go out there and disturb him."

"I won't bother 'im, Mom," I said. "I just want to watch
'im."

"All right," Mom said.

But Mom wanted to be sure that I didn't bother him so she
followed me into the dining room. Maybe she wanted to see
what Grandpa was going to do. She stood by the window and
we watched Grandpa as he walked down beside our smokehouse where a tall sassafras tree's thin leaves fluttered in the
blue April sky—so high you couldn't see the sky-roof. It was
just blue space and little white clouds floated upon this
blue.

When Grandpa reached the smokehouse he leaned his cane
against the sassafras tree. He let himself down slowly to his

knees as he looked carefully at the ground. Grandpa was looking at something and I wondered what it was. I just didn't
think or I would have known.

"There you are, my good old friend," Grandpa said.

"Who is his friend, Mom?" I asked.

Mom didn't say anything. Then I saw.

"He's playin' with that old terrapin, Mom," I said.

"I know he is," Mom said.

"The terrapin doesn't mind if Grandpa strokes his head with
his hand," I said.

"I know it," Mom said.

"But the old terrapin won't let me do it," I said. "Why does
he let Grandpa?"

"The terrapin knows your Grandpa."

"He ought to know me," I said, "but when I try to stroke
his head with my hand, he closes up in his shell."

Mom didn't say anything. She stood by the window watching Grandpa and listening to Grandpa talk to the terrapin.

"My old friend, how do you like the sunshine?" Grandpa
asked the terrapin.

The terrapin turned his fleshless-face to one side like a hen
does when she looks at you in the sunlight. He was trying to
talk to Grandpa; maybe the terrapin could understand what
Grandpa was saying.

"Old fellow, it's been a hard winter," Grandpa said. "How
have you fared under the smokehouse floor?"

"Does the terrapin know what Grandpa is sayin'?" I asked
Mom.

"I don't know," she said.

"I'm awfully glad to see you, old fellow," Grandpa said.

He didn't offer to bite Grandpa's big soft hand as he stroked
his head.

"Looks like the terrapin would bite Grandpa," I said.

"That terrapin has spent the winters under the smokehouse
for fifteen years," Mom said. "Pap has been acquainted with

him for eleven years. He's been talkin' to that terrapin every spring."

"How does Grandpa know the terrapin is old?" I asked Mom.

"It's got 1847 cut on its shell," Mom said. "We know he's ninety-five years old. He's older than that. We don't know how old he was when that date was cut on his back."

"Who cut 1847 on his back, Mom?"

"I don't know, child," she said, "but I'd say whoever cut that date on his back has long been under the ground."

Then I wondered how a terrapin could get that old and what kind of a looking person he was who cut the date on the terrapin's back. I wondered where it happened—if it happened near where our house stood. I wondered who lived here on this land then, what kind of a house they lived in, and if they had a sassafras with tiny thin April leaves on its top growing in their yard, and if the person that cut the date on the terrapin's back was buried at Plum Grove, if he had farmed these hills where we lived today and cut timber like Grandpa had—and if he had seen the Aprils pass like Grandpa had seen them and if he enjoyed them like Grandpa was enjoying this April. I wondered if he had looked at the dogwood blossoms, the redbud blossoms, and talked to this same terrapin.

"Are you well, old fellow?" Grandpa asked the terrapin.

The terrapin just looked at Grandpa.

"I'm well as common for a man of my age," Grandpa said.

"Did the terrapin ask Grandpa if he was well?" I asked Mom.

"I don't know," Mom said. "I can't talk to a terrapin."

"But Grandpa can."

"Yes."

"Wait until tomatoes get ripe and we'll be in the garden together," Grandpa said

"Does a terrapin eat tomatoes?" I asked Mom.

"Yes, that terrapin has been eatin' tomatoes from our garden for fifteen years," Mom said. "When Mick was tossin' the terrapins out of the tomato patch, he picked up this one and found the date cut on his back. He put him back in the patch and told him to help himself. He lives from our garden every year. We don't bother him and don't allow anybody else to bother him. He spends his winters under our smokehouse floor buried in the dry ground."

"Gee, Grandpa looks like the terrapin," I said.

Mom didn't say anything; tears came to her eyes. She wiped them from her eyes with the corner of her apron.

"I'll be back to see you," Grandpa said. "I'm a-gettin' a little chilly; I'll be gettin' back to the house."

The terrapin twisted his wrinkled neck without moving his big body, poking his head deep into the April wind as Grandpa pulled his bundled body up by holding to the sassafras tree trunk.

"Good-by, old friend."

The terrapin poked his head deeper into the wind, holding one eye on Grandpa, for I could see his eye shining in the sinking sunlight.

Grandpa got his cane that was leaned against the sassafras tree trunk and hobbled slowly toward the house. The terrapin looked at him with first one eye and then the other.

Appreciating friends and families.

ALAS! POOR ANNABELLE!

CAROL RYRIE BRINK

Caddie Woodlawn was a real person. To the author of our story she was "Gram" at whose feet she often sat and begged for "just one more story"—a story of the days when Caddie was a little girl. Caddie had been born in Boston but when she was four years old the family had moved to the big house on the prairie in western Wisconsin. There, due to her father's insistence, Caddie had been allowed to run the woods with her brothers, Tom and Warren. At eleven, she was frankly a tomboy, but every day's experiences were rich and wonderful. Her elder sister, Clara, was a well-behaved young lady, but Caddie swam and climbed and scampered over the countryside in joyous delight. Then one day an exciting event occurred. There came a letter from Cousin Annabelle Grey in Boston who, in a most elegant fashion, had accepted "Aunty Harriet's" invitation to visit the Woodlawns. During all the long hot weeks of early summer the family looked forward to the coming of their guest.

THERE were rains after that and things grew green again. And presently it was time for cousin Annabelle to arrive on the Little Steamer. Mrs. Hyman and Katie [1] had come out to help make the girls' new summer dresses, and Clara and Mother had been in their element, turning the pages of the *Godey's Lady's Book* [2] and talking of muslin, bodices, buttons, and braids.

"Of course," said Clara sadly, "anything we can make here will be sure to be six months behind the fashions in Boston, to say the least; and I do wish I might have hoops for every day."

"I don't!" cried Caddie, "Good gracious, every time I sit down in hoops they fly up and hit me in the nose!"

"That's because you don't know how to manage them," said

---

[1] MRS. HYMAN AND KATIE—Neighbors of the Woodlawns.
[2] *Godey's Lady's Book*—A popular ladies' magazine of the day.

Clara. "There's an art to wearing hoops, and I suppose you're too much of a tomboy ever to learn it."

"I suppose so," said Caddie cheerfully. But to herself she added: "I'm not really so much of a tomboy as they think. Perhaps I *shall* wear hoops some day, but only when I get good and ready."

Then one day Cousin Annabelle came. The Little Steamer seemed full of her little round-topped trunks and boxes, and, after they had all been carried off, down the gangplank tripped Annabelle Grey herself in her tiny buttoned shoes, with her tiny hat tilted over her nose and its velvet streamers floating out behind. Clara and Caddie had been allowed to come with Mother and Father to meet her, and Caddie suddenly felt all clumsy hands and feet when she saw this delicate apparition.

"Dearest Aunty Harriet, what a pleasure this is!" cried Annabelle in a voice as cultivated as her penmanship. "And this is Uncle John? And these the little cousins? How quaint and rustic it is here! But, just a moment, let me count my boxes. There ought to be seven. Yes, that's right. They're all here. Now we can go."

Father piled the seven boxes in the back of the wagon and Clara and Caddie climbed in on top of them, while Annabelle sat between Mother and Father, her full skirts billowing over their knees. Above the rattle of the wagon wheels her cultivated voice ran on and on. Clara leaned forward to catch what they were saying and sometimes put in a word of her own, but Caddie sat tongue-tied and uncomfortable, conscious only of her own awkwardness and of a sharp lock on one of Annabelle's boxes which hurt her leg whenever they went over a bump.

When they reached the farm Hetty, Minnie, and the boys ran out and stood in a smiling row beside the wagon. Tom held baby Joe in his arms.

"Dear me!" said Cousin Annabelle," are these children all yours, Aunty Harriet?"

"There are only seven," said Mother, "and every one is precious."

"Of course! Mother told me there were seven. But they do look such a lot when one sees them all together, don't they?"

"I picked you a nosegay," said Hetty, holding out a rather wilted bunch of flowers which she had been clutching tightly in her warm hands for a long time.

"How very thoughtful of you, little girl," said Annabelle. "But do hold it for me, won't you? I should hate to stain my mitts. You've no idea what a dirty journey this has been, and what difficulty I have had in keeping clean."

"You look very sweet and fresh, my dear," said Mother, "but I'm sure that you must be tired. Come in and take a cup of tea."

Caddie stayed outside a moment to put a quick arm about Hetty's shoulders. "That was an awful pretty nosegay you made, anyway, Hetty," she said.

Hetty's downcast face suddenly shone bright again. "Yes, it was, wasn't it, Caddie? Would you like it?"

"Why, yes, I would. I think it would look real nice here on my new dress, don't you?"

"Oh, it would be lovely, Caddie!"

That evening everyone listened to Annabelle telling about Boston. Mother's eyes shone and her cheeks were pinker than usual. It had been a good many years now since she had seen one of her own kin direct from home. Now she could find out whether Grandma Grey's rheumatism was really better or whether they only wrote that to reassure her. She could find out what pattern of silk Cousin Kitty had chosen for her wedding gown, who had been lecturing in Boston this winter, what new books had come out since the end of the war, why Aunt Phoebe had forgotten to write to her, and a hundred other things that she longed to know, but could never get them to put into letters. From time to time Father glanced at her happy face, over the old newspapers which Annabelle had brought him. It was only at moments such as this that Father understood how much Mother had given up when she left Boston to come with him to Wisconsin.

But after an hour or so of Boston gossip, Tom grew restless. Both he and Caddie were well tired of Annabelle's city airs.

"Well, I guess Boston's a pretty good place all right, but how about Dunnville?" Tom said.

Cousin Annabelle's silvery laughter filled the room. "Why, Tom, Boston is one of the world's great cities—the only one *I'd* care to live in, I am sure; and Dunnville—well, it's just too quaint and rustic, but it isn't even on the maps yet."

"Why, Tom," echoed Hetty seriously, "you hadn't ought to have said that. I guess Boston is just like—like Heaven, Tom." Everyone burst out laughing at this, and Cousin Annabelle rose and shook out her flounces, preparatory to going to bed.

"But really, Tom," she said, "I want you to show me *everything* in your savage country. I want to be just as *uncivilized* as you are while I am here. I shall learn to ride horseback and milk the cows—and—and salt the sheep, if that is what you do —and—turn somersaults in the haymow—and—what else do you do?"

"Oh, lots of things," said Tom, and suddenly there was an impish twinkle in his eyes.

"And you, Caroline," said Annabelle, turning to Caddie. "I suppose that you do all of those amusing things, too?"

"Yes, I'm afraid I do, Cousin Annabelle," replied Caddie. She tried to avoid Tom's eyes, but somehow it seemed impossible, and for just an instant an impish twinkle in her own met and danced with the impish twinkle in Tom's.

"You must begin to teach me tomorrow," said Annabelle sweetly. "I'm sure that it will be most interesting, and now, if you will excuse me, I am really quite fatigued."

"Yes, of course, dear Annabelle, and you're to sleep with me," said Clara, linking her arm through Annabelle's and leading her upstairs.

The next morning Tom, Caddie, and Warren had a brief consultation behind the straw stack. They ran through the list of practical jokes which they were used to playing when Uncle Edmund was among them.

"We can make up better ones than most of those," said Tom confidently. "It'll do her good."

"Let's see," said Caddie dreamily. "She wants to ride horseback and salt the sheep and turn somersaults in the haymow. Yes, I think we can manage."

"Golly! What fun!" chirped Warren, turning a handspring.

When they entered the house, Annabelle had just come bouncing down the stairs, resolved upon being uncivilized for the day. She wore a beautiful new dress which was of such novel style and cut that Mother and Clara could not admire it enough. Up and down both front and back of the fitted bodice was a row of tiny black jet buttons that stood out and sparkled at you when you looked at them.

"Golly!" said Warren, "you don't need all those buttons to fasten up your dress, do you?"

"Of course not," laughed Annabelle. "They are for decoration. All the girls in Boston are wearing them now, but none of them have as many buttons as I have. I have eight and eighty, and that's six more than Bessie Beaseley and fourteen more than Mary Adams."

"You don't say!" said Tom, and once again he and Caddie exchanged a twinkling glance.

"When shall I have my riding lesson?" asked Annabelle after breakfast.

"Right away, if you like," said Caddie pleasantly.

Clara stayed to help Mother, and Minnie was playing with baby Joe, but Hetty came with the others.

"Hadn't you better stay with Mother, Hetty?" said Tom in his kindest voice.

But, no, Hetty wanted to see the riding lesson.

Annabelle chattered vivaciously of how much better everything was done in Boston, while Tom went into the barn to bring out the horse.

"Why, Tom," cried Hetty, when he returned, "that's not Betsy, that's Pete."

Pete was perfectly gentle in appearance, but he had one trick which had kept the children off his back for several years.

"Hetty," said Caddie firmly, "we must have perfect quiet while anyone is learning to ride. If you can't be perfectly quiet, we'll have to send you right back to the house."

"I suppose he bucks," said Cousin Annabelle. "All Western horses do, don't they? Shall I be hurt?"

"He's pretty gentle," said Tom. "You better get on and you'll find out."

"Bareback and astride?" quavered Annabelle. "Dear me! how quaint and rustic!"

Caddie and Tom helped her on.

"He hasn't started bucking yet," said Annabelle proudly. "I *knew* that I should be a good rider!"

"Just touch him with the switch a little," advised Tom.

At the touch of the switch, Pete swung into a gentle canter, but instead of following the road, he made for a particular shed at the back of the barn. It was Pete's one accomplishment.

"How do I pull the rein to make him go the other way?" queried Annabelle, but already Pete was gathering momentum and, before they could answer, he had swung in under the low shed, scraped Annabelle neatly off into the dust, and was standing peacefully at rest inside the shed picking up wisps of hay.

Annabelle sat up in a daze. The little straw sun hat which she had insisted on wearing was over one ear and she looked very comical indeed.

"I don't yet understand what happened," she said politely. "I thought that I was going along so well. In Boston, I'm sure the horses never behave like that."

"Would you like to try another horse?" said Tom.

"Oh, no!" said Annabelle hastily. "Not today, at least. Couldn't we go and salt the sheep now, perhaps?"

"Do you think we could, Tom?" asked Caddie doubtfully.

"Why, yes, I believe we could," said Tom kindly. "Here, let me help you up, Cousin Annabelle."

"I'll get the salt," shouted Warren, racing into the barn.

Hetty looked on in silence, her eyes round with surprise. Annabelle rose, a bit stiffly, and brushed the back of her beautiful dress.

"She's not a cry-baby at any rate," thought Caddie to herself. "Maybe it's kind of mean to play another trick on her."

But Warren had already returned with the salt, and he and Tom, with Annabelle between them, were setting out for the woodland pasture where Father kept the sheep. Caddie hastened to catch up with them, and Hetty, still wondering, tagged along behind.

"Will they eat it out of my hand, if I hold it for them?" asked Annabelle, taking the chunk of salt from Warren.

"Sure," said Tom, "they're crazy about salt."

"But you mustn't *hold* it," said Hetty, coming up panting. "You must lay it down where the sheep can get it."

"Now, Hetty," said Caddie, "what did I tell you about keeping perfectly quiet?"

"You do just as you like, Annabelle," said Tom kindly.

"Well, of course," said Annabelle, "I should prefer to hold it and let the cunning little lambs eat it right out of my hands."

"All right," said Tom, "you go in alone then, and we'll stay outside the fence here where we can watch you."

"It's so nice of you to let me do it," said Cousin Annabelle. "How do you call them?"

Tom uttered a low persuasive call—the call to salt. He uttered it two or three times, and sheep began coming from all parts of the woods into the open pasture.

Annabelle stood there expectantly, holding out the salt, a

424

bright smile on her face. "We don't have sheep in Boston," she said. But almost immediately the smile began to fade.

The sheep were crowding all around her, so close that she could hardly move; they were treading on her toes and climbing on each other's backs to get near her. Frightened, she held the salt up out of their reach, and then they began to try to climb up *her* as if she had been a ladder. There was a perfect pandemonium of bleating and baaing, and above this noise rose Annabelle's despairing shriek.

"Drop the salt and run," called Tom, himself a little frightened at the success of his joke. But running was not an easy matter with thirty or forty sheep around her, all still believing that she held the salt. At last poor Annabelle succeeded in breaking away and they helped her over the fence. But, when she was safe on the other side, everybody stopped and looked at her in amazement. The eight and eighty sparkling jet buttons had disappeared from her beautiful frock. The sheep had eaten them!

"Oh! my buttons!" cried Annabelle. "There were eight and eighty of them—six more than Bessie Beaseley had! And where is my sun hat?"

Across the fence in the milling crowd of sheep, the wicked Woodlawns beheld with glee Annabelle's beautiful sun hat rakishly dangling from the left horn of a fat old ram.

If Annabelle had rushed home crying and told Mother, the Woodlawn children would not have been greatly surprised. But there seemed to be more in Annabelle than met the eye.

"What a quaint experience!" she said. "They'll hardly believe it when I tell them about it in Boston." Her voice was a trifle shaky, but just as polite as ever, and she went right upstairs without speaking to Clara or Mother, and changed to another dress. That evening she was more quiet than she had been the night before and she had almost nothing to say about the superiority of her native city over the rest of the uncivilized world. Caddie noticed with remorse that Annabelle walked a little stiffly, and she surmised that the ground had not been very soft at the place where Pete had scraped her off.

"I wish I hadn't promised Tom to play that next trick on her," Caddie thought to herself. "Maybe he'll let me off."

But Tom said, no, it was a good trick and Annabelle had asked for it, and Caddie had promised to do her part, and she had better go through with it.

"All right," said Caddie.

After all it *was* a good trick and Annabelle *had* asked for it.

"Let's see," said Tom the next day. "You wanted to turn somersaults in the haymow, didn't you, Cousin Annabelle?"

"Well, I suppose that's one of the things one always does on a farm, isn't it?" said Cousin Annabelle, a trifle less eagerly than she had welcomed their suggestions of the day before. The beautiful eight-and-eighty-button dress had not appeared today. Annabelle had on a loose blouse over a neat, full skirt. "Of course, I never turn somersaults in Boston, you understand. It's so very quaint and rustic."

"Of course we understand that," said Caddie.

"But out here where you have lots of hay——"

"It's bully fun!" yelled Warren.

"Now, Hetty," directed Tom, "you better stay at home with Minnie. A little girl like you might fall down the ladder to the mow and hurt herself."

"Me fall down the haymow ladder?" demanded Hetty in amazement. "Why, Tom Woodlawn, you're just plumb crazy!"

"Well, run into the house then and fetch us some cookies," said Tom, anxious to be rid of Hetty's astonished eyes and tattling tongue. Hetty departed reluctantly with a deep conviction that she was missing out on something stupendous.

When she returned a few moments later with her hands full of cookies, she could hear them all laughing and turning somersaults in the loft above. She made haste to climb the ladder and peer into the loft. It was darkish there with dust motes dancing in the rays of light that entered through the chinking. But Hetty could see quite plainly, and what she saw was Caddie slipping an egg down the back of Annabelle's blouse, just as Annabelle was starting to turn a somersault.

"I can turn them every bit as well as you can already," said Annabelle triumphantly, and then she turned over, and she sat up with a surprised and stricken look upon her face, and then she began to cry!

"Oh, it's squishy!" she sobbed. "You're horrid and mean. I didn't mind falling off the horse or salting the sheep, but oh, this—this—*this* is *squishy!*"

Hetty climbed down from the haymow and ran to the house as fast as she could go.

"Mother, if you want to see something, you just come here with me as fast as you can," she cried.

On the way to the barn she gave Mrs. Woodlawn a brief but graphic account of the riding lesson and the sheep salting. When they reached the haymow, Annabelle was still sobbing.

"Oh, Aunty Harriet!" she cried. "I don't know what it is, but it's squishy. I can't— Oh dear! I *can't* bear squishy things!"

"You poor child!" said Mrs. Woodlawn, examining the back of Annabelle's blouse, and then, in an ominous voice, she announced: "It's egg." With a good deal of tenderness Mother got Annabelle to the house and put her into Clara's capable hands. Then she turned with fury on the three culprits. But it was Caddie whom she singled out for punishment.

"Caroline Woodlawn, stand forth!" she cried. Caddie obeyed. "It was only a joke, Mother," she said in a quivering voice. Mrs. Woodlawn took a little riding whip which hung behind the kitchen door and struck Caddie three times across the legs.

"Now go to your bed and stay until morning. You shall have no supper."

"Ma, it was as much my fault as hers," cried Tom, his ruddy face gone white.

"No, Tom," said Mrs. Woodlawn. "I cannot blame *you* so much. But that a *daughter* of mine should so far forget herself in her hospitality to a guest—that she should be such a hoyden as to neglect her proper duties as a lady! Shame to her! Shame! No punishment that I can invent would be sufficient for her."

As Caddie went upstairs, she saw Father standing in the kitchen door and she knew that he had witnessed her disgrace. But she knew too, that he would do nothing to soften the sentence which Mother had spoken, for it was an unwritten family law that one parent never interfered with the justice dealt out by the other.

For hours Caddie tossed about on her bed. The upper room was hot and close, but an even hotter inner fire burned in Caddie. She had some of her mother's quick temper, and she was stung by injustice. She would have accepted punishment without question if it had been dealt out equally to the boys. But the boys had gone free! All the remorse and the resolves to do better, which had welled up in her as soon as she had seen Annabelle's tears, were dried up now at the injustice of her punishment. Hot and dry-eyed, she tossed about on the little bed where she had spent so many quiet hours. At last she got up and tied a few things which she most valued into a towel. She put them under the foot of her mattress and lay down again. Later she would slip down to the kitchen and get a loaf of bread and Father's old water bottle which she would fill at the spring. At least they could not begrudge her that much. They would soon cease to miss her. Perhaps they would adopt Annabelle in her place.

Her anger cooled a little in the fever of making plans. It would have been much easier if she had known just where the

Indians were. But at this season the woods were full of berries and there would soon be nuts. John's dog [1] would protect
her and she could live a long time in the woods until she could
join the Indians. She knew that they would take her in, and
then she would never have to grow into that hateful thing
which Mother was always talking about—a lady. A lady with

fine airs and mincing walk who was afraid to go out into the
sun without a hat or a sunshade! A lady, who made samplers
and wore stays and was falsely polite no matter how she
felt!

A soft blue twilight fell, and still Caddie tossed, hot, resentful, and determined. There was the clatter of supper dishes
down below, and no one relented enough to send her a bite of
bread. A velvet darkness followed the twilight and, through
the window, summer stars began to twinkle. Presently Hetty
and Minnie came up to bed. Hetty came and stood by Caddie's bed and looked at her. Caddie could feel the long, wistful
look, but she did not stir or open her eyes. Hetty was a tattle-
tale. It was torture to have to lie so still, but at last the little

---

[1] JOHN'S DOG—A dog given to Caddie by a friendly Indian.

sisters were breathing the regular breath of sleep, and Caddie could toss and turn again as much as she pleased. She must keep awake now until the house was all still and the lights out, and then she would be free to run away. Her heart beat fast, and with every beat something hot and painful seemed to throb in her head. A cooler breeze began to come in at the window. How long it took the house to grow quiet tonight! How tiresome they were! They wouldn't even go to bed and let her run away!

Then the door creaked a little on its hinges, there was a glimmer of candlelight, and Father came in. He went first and looked at Minnie and Hetty. He put a lock of hair back from Minnie's forehead and pulled the sheet up over Hetty's shoulder. Then he came and stood by Caddie's bed. She lay very still with tightly closed eyes so that Father should think her asleep. It had fooled Hetty, but Father knew more than most people did. He put the candle down and sat on the side of the bed and took one of Caddie's hot hands in his cool ones. Then he began to speak in his nice quiet voice, without asking her to wake up or open her eyes or look at him.

"Perhaps Mother was a little hasty today, Caddie," he said. "She really loves you very much, and, you see, she expects more of you than she would of someone she didn't care about. It's a strange thing, but somehow we expect more of girls than of boys. It is the sisters and wives and mothers, you know, Caddie, who keep the world sweet and beautiful. What a rough world it would be if there were only men and boys in it, doing things in their rough way! A woman's task is to teach them gentleness and courtesy and love and kindness. It's a big task, too, Caddie—harder than cutting trees or building mills or damming rivers. It takes nerve and courage and patience, but good women have those things. They have them just as much as the men who build bridges and carve roads through the wilderness. A woman's work is something fine and noble to grow up to, and it is just as important as a man's. But no

man could ever do it so well. I don't want you to be the silly
affected person with fine clothes and manners, whom folks
sometimes call a lady. No, that is not what I want for you,
my little girl. I want you to be a woman with a wise and understanding heart, healthy in body and honest in mind. Do
you think you would like to be growing up into that woman
now? How about it, Caddie, have we run with the colts long
enough?"

There was a little silence, and the hot tears which had not
wanted to come all day were suddenly running down Caddie's
cheeks unheeded into the pillow.

"You know, Caddie," added Father gently and half-apolo-
getically, "you know I'm sort of responsible for you, Honey.
I was the one who urged Mother to let you run wild, because
I thought it was the finest way to make a splendid woman of
you. And I still believe that, Caddie."

Suddenly Caddie flung herself into Mr. Woodlawn's arms.
"Father! Father!"

It was all she could say, and really there was nothing more
that needed saying. Mr. Woodlawn held her a long time, his
rough beard pressed against her cheek. Then with his big
hands, which were so delicate with clockwork, he helped her
to undress and straighten the tumbled bed. Then he kissed her
again and took his candle and went away. And now the room
was cool and pleasant again, and even Caddie's tears were not
unpleasant, but part of the cool relief she felt. In a few moments she was fast asleep.

But something strange had happened to Caddie in the night.
When she awoke she knew that she need not be afraid of growing up. It was not just sewing and weaving and wearing stays.
It was something more thrilling than that. It was a responsibility, but, as Father spoke of it, it was a beautiful and precious one, and Caddie was ready to go and meet it. She looked
at the yellow sunshine on the floor and she knew that she had
slept much longer than she usually did. Both Hetty's and

Minnie's beds were empty, but as soon as Caddie began to stir around, Hetty came in as if she had been waiting outside the door.

"Oh, say, Caddie," she said, "I'm awful sorry I went and told on you yesterday. Honest, I am. I never thought you'd get it so hard, and I'll tell you what, I'm not going to be a tattler ever any more, I'm not. But, say, Caddie, I wanted to be the first to tell you Father took Tom and Warren out to the barn yesterday afternoon and he gave 'em both a thrashing. He said it wasn't fair that you should have all the punishment when the same law had always governed you all, and Tom said so, too, although he yelled good and plenty when he was being thrashed."

"It's all right, Hetty," said Caddie. "I guess we won't be playing any more silly jokes on people."

"What's this?" asked Hetty, pulling at the corner of a queer bundle that stuck out under the corner of Caddie's mattress. Out came a knotted towel with an odd assortment of Caddie's treasures rattling around inside.

"Oh, that!" said Caddie, untying the knots and putting the things away. "Those are just some things I was looking at yesterday when I had to stay up here alone."

TWO RIVERS

WALLACE STEGNER

His father's voice awakened him. Stretching his back, arching against the mattress, he looked over at his parents' end of the sleeping porch. His mother was up too, though he could tell from the flatness of the light outside that it was still early. He lay on his back quietly, letting complete wakefulness come on, watching a spider that dangled on a golden, shining thread from the rolled canvas of the blinds. The spider came down in tiny jerks, his legs wriggling, then went up again in the beam of sun. From the other room the father's voice rose loud and cheerful:

> "Oh I'd give every man in the army a quarter
> If they'd all take a shot at my mother-in-law."

The boy slid his legs out of bed and yanked the nightshirt over his head. He didn't want his father's face poking around the door, saying, "I plough deep while sluggards sleep." He didn't want to be joked with. Yesterday was too sore a spot in his mind. He had been avoiding his father ever since the morning before, and he was not yet ready to accept any joking or attempts to make up. Nobody had a right hitting a person for nothing, and you bet they weren't going to be friends. Let him whistle and sing out there, pretending nothing was the matter. The whole business yesterday was the matter, the Ford that wouldn't start was the matter, the whole lost Fourth of July was the matter, the missed parade, the missed ball game in Chinook were the matter. The cuff on the ear his father had given him when he got so mad at the Ford he had to have something to hit was the matter.

In the other room, as he pulled on his overalls, the bacon was snapping in the pan, and he smelled its good morning smell. His father whistled, sang.

The boy pulled the overall straps over his shoulders and went into the main room. His father stopped singing and looked at him. "Hello, Cheerful," he said. "You look like you'd bit into a wormy apple."

The boy mumbled something and went outside to wash at the bench. It wasn't any fun waking up today. You kept thinking about yesterday, and how much fun it had been waking then, when you were going to do something special and exciting, drive fifty miles to Chinook and spend the whole day just having fun. Now there wasn't anything but the same old thing to do you did every day. Run the trap line, put out some poison for the gophers, read the mail-order catalog.

At breakfast he was glum, and his father joked him. Even his mother smiled, as if she had forgotten already how much wrong had been done the day before. "You look as if you'd been sent for and couldn't come," she said. "Cheer up."

"I don't want to cheer up."

They just smiled at each other, and he hated them both.

After breakfast his father said, "You help your Ma with the dishes, now. See how useful you can make yourself around here."

Unwillingly, wanting to get out of the house and away from them, he got the towel and swabbed off the plates. He was rubbing a glass when he heard the Ford sputter and race and roar and then calm down into a steady mutter. His mouth opened, and he looked at his mother. Her eyes were crinkled with smiling.

"It goes!" he said.

"Sure it goes." She pulled both his ears, rocking his head. "Know what we're going to do?"

"What?"

"We're going to the mountains anyway. Not to Chinook— there wouldn't be anything doing today. But to the mountains, for a picnic. Pa got the car going yesterday afternoon, when you were down in the field, so we decided to go today. If you want to, of course."

"Yay!" he said. "Shall I dress up?"

"Put on your shoes, you'd better. We might climb a mountain."

The boy was out into the porch in three steps. With one shoe on and the other in his hand he hopped to the door. "When?" he said.

"Soon as you can get ready."

He was trying to run and tie his shoelaces at the same time

as he went out of the house. There in the Ford, smoking his pipe, with one leg over the door and his weight on the back of his neck, his father sat. "What detained you?" he said. "I've been waiting a half hour. You must not want to go very bad."

"Aw!" the boy said. He looked inside the Ford. There was the lunch all packed, the fat wet canvas waterbag, even Spot with his tongue out and his ears up. Looking at his father, all his sullenness gone now, the boy said, "When did you get all this ready?"

His father grinned. "While you slept like a sluggard we worked like a buggard," he said. Then the boy knew that everything was perfect, nothing could go wrong. When his father started rhyming things he was in his very best mood, and not even breakdowns and flat tires could make him do more than puff and blow and play-act.

He clambered into the front seat and felt the motor shaking under the floorboards. "Hey, Ma!" he yelled. "Hurry up! We're all ready to go!"

Their own road was a barely marked trail that wiggled out over the burnouts along the east side of the wheat field. At the line it ran into another coming down from the homesteads to the east, and at Cree, a mile inside the Montana boundary, they hit the straight sectionline road to Chinook. On that road they passed a trotting team pulling an empty wagon, and the boy waved and yelled, feeling superior, feeling as if he were char-ioted on pure speed and all the rest of the world were earth-footed.

"Let's see how fast this old boat will go," the father said. He nursed it down through a coulee and onto the flat. His fingers pulled the gas lever down, and the motor roared. Look-ing back with the wind-stung tears in his eyes, the boy saw his mother hanging on to her hat, and the artificial cherries on the hat bouncing. The Ford leaped and bucked, the picnic box tipped over, the dog leaned out and the wind blew his eyes shut and his ears straight back. Turning around, the boy saw the blue sparks leaping from the magneto box and heard his father wahoo. He hung onto the side and leaned out to let the wind tear at him, tried to count the fence posts going by, but they were ahead of him before he got to ten.

The road roughened, and they slowed down. "Good land!" his mother said from the back seat. "We want to get to the Bearpaws, not wind up in a ditch."

"How fast were we going, Pa?"

"Forty or so, I guess. If we'd been going any faster you'd have hollered 'nuff. You were looking pretty peaked."

"I was not."

"Looked pretty scared to me. I guess Ma was hopping around back there like corn in a popper. How'd you like it, Ma?"

"I liked it all right," she said, "but don't do it again."

They passed a farm, and the boy waved at three open-mouthed kids in the yard. It was pretty good to be going somewhere, all right. The mountains were plainer now in the south.

He could see dark canyons cutting into the slopes, and there was snow on the upper peaks.

"How soon'll we get there, Pa?"

His father tapped the pipe out and put it away and laughed. Without bothering to answer, he began to sing:

> "Oh, I dug Snoqualmie River,
> And Lake Samamish too,
> And paddled down to Kirklan
> In a little birch canoe.
>
> "I built the Rocky Mountains,
> And placed them where they
>   are. . . ."

It was then, with the empty flat country wheeling by like a great turntable, the wheat fields and the fences and the far red peaks of barns rotating slowly as if in a dignified dance, wheeling and slipping behind and gone, and his father singing, that the strangeness first came over the boy. Somewhere, sometime . . . and there were mountains in it, and a stream, and a swing that he had fallen out of and cried, and he had mashed ripe blackberries in his hand and his mother had wiped him off, straightening his stiff finger and wiping hard.

. . . His mind caught on that memory from a time before there was any memory, he rubbed his finger tips against his palm and slid a little down in the seat.

His father tramped on both pedals hard and leaned out of the car, looking. He swung to stare at the boy as a startled idiot might have looked, and in a voice heavy with German gutturals he said, "Vot it iss in de crass?"

"What?"

"Iss in de crass somedings. Besser you bleiben right here."

He climbed out, and the boy climbed out after him. The dog jumped over the side and rushed, and in the grass by the side of the road the boy saw the biggest snake he had ever seen, long and fat and sleepy. When it pulled itself in and faced the stiff-legged dog he saw that the hind legs and tail of a gopher stuck out of the stretched mouth.

"What is it?" the mother said from the car, and the boy yelled back, "A snake, a great big snake, and he's got a whole gopher in his mouth!"

The father chased the pup away, found a rock, and with one careful throw crushed the big flat head. The body, as big around as the boy's ankle, tightened into a rigid convulsion of muscles, and the tail whipped back and forth.

The father lifted the snake by the tail and held it up. "Look," he said. "He's no longer than I am." But the mother made a face and turned her head while he fastened it in the forked top of a fence post. It trailed almost two feet on the ground. The tail still twitched.

"He'll twitch till the sun goes down," the father said. He climbed into the car again, and the boy followed.

"What was it, Pa?"

"Milk snake. They come into barns sometimes and milk the cows dry. You saw what he did to that gopher. Milk a cow dry as powder in ten minutes."

"Gee," the boy said. He sat back and thought about how long and slick the gopher had been, and how the snake's mouth was all stretched, and it was a good feeling to have been along and to have shared something like that with his father. It was a trophy, a thing you would remember all your life, and you could tell about it. And while he was thinking that already, even before they got to the mountains at all, he had something to remember about the trip, he remembered that just before they saw the snake he had been remembering something else, and he puckered his eyes in the sun thinking. He had been right on the edge of it, it was right on the tip of his tongue, and then his father had tramped on the pedals. But it was something a long time ago, and there was a strangeness about it, something bothersome and a little scary, and it hurt his head the way it hurt his head sometimes to do arithmetical sums without pencil and paper. When you did them in your head something went round and round, and you had to keep looking inside to make sure you didn't lose sight of the figures that were pasted up there somewhere, and if you did it very long at a time you got a sick headache out of it. It was something like that when he had almost remembered just a while ago, only he hadn't quite been able to see what he knew was there. . . .

By ten o'clock they had left the graded road and were chugging up a winding trail with toothed rocks embedded in the ruts. Ahead of them the mountains looked low and disappointing, treeless, brown. The trail ducked into a narrow gulch and the sides rose up around them, reddish gravel covered with bunch grass and sage.

"Gee whiz," the boy said. "These don't look like mountains."

"What'd you expect?" his father said. "Expect to step out onto a glacier or something?"

"But there aren't any trees," the boy said. "Gee whiz, there isn't even any water."

He stood up to look ahead. His father's foot went down on on the low pedal, and the Ford growled at the grade. "Come on, Lena," his father said. He hitched himself back and forward in the seat, helping the car over the hill, and then, as they barely pulled over the hump and sides of the gully fell away, there were the real mountains, high as heaven, the high slopes spiked and tufted with trees, and directly ahead of them a magnificent V-shaped door with the sun touching gray cliffs far back in, and a straight-edged violet shadow streaming down from the eastern peak clear to the canyon floor.

"Well?" the father's voice said. "I guess if you don't like it we can drop you off here and pick you up on the way back."

The boy turned to his mother. She was sitting far forward

439

on the edge of the seat. "I guess we want to come along all right," she said, and laughed as if she might cry. "Anything as beautiful as that! Don't we, sonny?"

'You bet," he said. He remained standing all the way up over the gentle slope of the alluvial fan that aproned out from the canyon's mouth, and when they passed under the violet shadow, not violet any more but cool gray, he tipped his head back and looked up miles and miles to the broken rock above.

The road got rougher. "Sit down," his father said. "First thing you know you'll fall out on your head and sprain both your ankles."

He was in his very best mood. He said funny things to the car, coaxing it over steep pitches. He talked to it like a horse, patted it on the dashboard, promised it an apple when they got there. Above them the canyon walls opened out and back, went up steeply high and high and high, beyond the first walls that the boy had thought so terrific, away beyond those, piling peak on peak, and the sun touched and missed and touched again.

"Yay!" the boy said. He was standing up, watching the deep insides of the earth appear behind the angled rock, and his mind was soaring again, up into the heights where a hawk or eagle circled like a toy bird on a string.

"How do you like it?" his mother shouted at him. He turned around and nodded his head, and she smiled at him, wrinkling her eyes. She looked excited herself. Her face had color in it and the varnished cherries bouncing on her hat gave her a reckless, girlish look.

"Hi, Ma," he said, and grinned.

"Hi yourself," she said, and grinned right back. He lifted his face and yelled for the very pressure of happiness inside him.

They lay on a ledge high up on the sunny east slope and looked out to the north through the notch cut as sharply as a wedge out of a pie. Far below them the golden plain spread level, golden-tawny grass and golden-green wheat checkerboarded in a pattern as wide as the world. Back of them the spring they had followed up the slope welled out of the ledge, spread out in a small swampy spot, and trickled off down the hill. There were trees, a thick cluster of spruce against the bulge of the wall above them, a clump of twinkling, sunny aspen down the slope, and in the canyon bottom below them a dense forest of soft maple. The mother had a bouquet of leaves in her hand, a little bunch of pine cones on the ground beside her. The three lay quietly, looking down over the steeply dropping wall to the V-shaped door, and beyond that to the interminable plain.

The boy wriggled his back against the rock, put his hand down to shift himself, brought it up again prickled with brown spruce needles. He picked them off, still staring out over the canyon gateway. They were far above the world he knew. The air was cleaner, thinner. There was cold water running from the rock, and all around there were trees. And over the whole canyon, like a haze in the clear air, was that other thing, that memory or ghost of a memory, a swing he had fallen out of, a feel of his hands sticky with crushy blackberries, his skin drinking cool shade, and his father's anger—the reflection of ecstasy and the shadow of tears.

"I never knew till this minute," his mother said, "how much I've missed the trees."

Nobody answered. They were all stuffed with lunch, pleasantly tired after the climb. The father lay staring off down the canyon, and the sour smell of his pipe, in that air, was pleasant and clean. The boy saw his mother put the stem of a maple leaf in her mouth and make a half-pleased face at the bitter taste.

The father rose and dug a tin cup from the picnic box, walked to the spring and dipped himself a drink. He made a breathy sound of satisfaction. "So cold it hurts your teeth," he said. He brought the mother a cup, and she drank.

"Brucie?" she said, motioning with the cup.

He started to get up, but his father filled the cup and brought it, making believe he was going to pour it on him. The boy ducked and reached for the cup. With his eyes on his father over the cup's rim, he drank, testing the icy water to see if it really did hurt the teeth. The water was cold and silvery in his mouth, and when he swallowed he felt it cold clear down to his stomach.

"It doesn't either hurt your teeth," he said. He poured a little of it on his arm, and something jumped in his skin. It was his skin that remembered. Something numbingly cold, and then warm. He felt it now, the way you waded in it.

"Mom," he said.

"What?"

"Was it in Washington we went on a picnic like this and picked blackberries and I fell out of a swing and there were big trees, and we found a river that was half cold and half warm?"

His father was relighting his pipe. "What do you know about Washington?" he said. "You were only knee-high to a grasshopper when we lived there."

"Well, I remember," the boy said. "I've been remembering it all day long, ever since you sang that song about building the Rocky Mountains. You sang it that day, too. Don't you remember, Mom?"

"I don't know," she said doubtfully. "We went on picnics in Washington."

"What's this about a river with hot and cold running water?" his father said. "You must remember some time you had a bath in a bathtub."

"I do not!" the boy said. "I got blackberries mashed all over my hands and Mom scrubbed me off, and then we found that river and we waded in it and half was hot and half was cold."

"Oh-h-h," his mother said. "I believe I do. . . . Harry, you remember once up in the Cascades, when we went out with the Curtises? And little Bill Curtis fell off the dock into the lake." She turned to the boy. "Was there a summer cottage there, a brown shingled house?"

"I don't know," the boy said. "I don't remember any Curtises. But I remember blackberries and that river and a swing."

"Your head is full of blackberries," his father said. "If it was the time we went out with the Curtises there weren't any blackberries. That was in the spring."

"No," the mother said. "It was in the fall. It was just before we moved to Redmond. And I think there was a place where one river from the mountains ran into another one from the valley, and they ran alongside each other in the same channel. The mountain one was a lot colder. Don't you remember that trip with the Curtises, Harry?"

"Sure I remember it," the father said. "We hired a buckboard and saw a black bear and I won six bits from Joe Curtis pitching horseshoes."

"That's right," the mother said. "You remember the bear, Brucie."

The boy shook his head. There wasn't any bear in what he remembered. Just feelings, and things that made his skin prickle.

His mother was looking at him, a little puzzled wrinkle between her eyes. "It's funny you should remember such different things than we remember," she said. "Everything means something different to everybody, I guess." She laughed, and the boy thought her eyes looked very odd and bright. "It makes me feel as if I didn't know you at all," she said. She brushed her face with the handful of leaves and looked at the father, gathering up odds and ends and putting them in the picnic box. "I wonder what each of us will remember about today?"

"I wouldn't worry about it," the father said. "You can depend on Bub here to remember a lot of things that didn't happen."

"I don't think he does," she said. "He's got a good memory."

The father picked up the box. "It takes a good memory to remember things that never happened," he said. "I remember once a garter snake crawled into my cradle and I used it for a belt to keep my breechclout on. They took it away from me and I bawled the crib so full of tears I had to swim for shore. I drifted in three days later on a checkerboard raft with a didie for a sail."

The boy stood up and brushed off his pants. "You do too remember that river," he said.

His father grinned at him. "Sure. Only it wasn't quite as hot and cold as you make it out."

It was evening in the canyon, but when they reached the mouth again they emerged into full afternoon, with two hours of sun left them. The father stopped the car before they dipped into the gravelly wash between the foothills, purpling in the shadows, the rock glowing golden-red far back on the faces of the inner peaks. The mother still held her bouquet of maple leaves in her hand.

"Well, there go the Mountains of the Moon," she said. The moment was almost solemn. In the front seat the boy stood looking back. He felt the sun strong against the side of his face, and the mountains sheering up before him were very real.

In a little while, as they went forth, they would begin to melt together, and the patches of snow would appear far up on the northern slopes. His eyes went curiously out of focus, and he saw the mountains as they would appear from the homestead on a hot day, a ghostly line on the horizon.

He felt his father twist to look at him, but the trance was so strong on him that he didn't look down for a minute. When he did he caught his mother and father looking at each other, the look they had sometimes when he had pleased them and made them proud of him.

"Okay," his father said, and stabbed him in the ribs with a hard thumb. "Wipe the black bears out of your eyes."

He started the car again, and as they bounced down the rocky trail toward the road he sang at the top of his voice, bellowing into the still, hot afternoon——

> "I had a kid and his name was Brucie,
> Squeezed black bears and found them juicy,
> Washed them off in a hot-cold river,
> Now you boil and now you shiver,
> Caught his pants so full of trout
> He couldn't sit down till he got them out.
> Trout were boiled from the hot-side river,
> Trout from the cold side raw as liver.
> Ate the boiled ones, ate the raw,
> And then went howling home to Maw."

The boy looked up at his father, his laughter bubbling up, everything wonderful, the day a swell day, his mother clapping hands in time to his father's fool singing.

"Aw, for gosh sakes," he said, and ducked when his father pretended he was going to swat him one.

OUT TO OLD AUNT MARY'S

JAMES WHITCOMB RILEY

WASN'T it pleasant, O brother mine,
In those old days of the lost sunshine
    Of youth—when the Saturday's chores were
       through,
    And the "Sunday's wood" in the kitchen, too,
5   And we went visiting, "me and you,"
       Out to old Aunt Mary's?

It all comes back so clear today!
Though I am as bald as you are gray—
    Out by the barn-lot, and down the lane
10   We patter along in the dust again,
    As light as the tips of the drops of the rain,
       Out to old Aunt Mary's.

We cross the pasture and through the wood,
Where the old gray snag of the poplar stood,
15   Where the hammering "red-heads" hopped awry,
    And the buzzard "raised" in the "clearing" sky,
    And lolled and circled, as we went by
       Out to old Aunt Mary's.

And then in the dust of the road again,
20   And the teams we met, and the countrymen;
    And the long highway, with sunshine spread
    As thick as butter on country bread,
    Our cares behind, and our hearts ahead
       Out to old Aunt Mary's.

25   And the romps we took, in our glad unrest!
    Was it the lawn that we loved the best,

With its swooping swing in the locust trees,
Or was it the grove, with its leafy breeze,
Or the dim hay-mow with its fragrancies—
30   Out to old Aunt Mary's?

Far fields, bottom-lands, creek-banks—all,
We ranged at will.—Where the waterfall
    Laughed all day as it slowly poured
    Over the dam by the old mill-ford,
35   While the tail-race writhed, and the mill-wheel
      roared—
      Out to Old Aunt Mary's.

Why I see her now, in the open door
Where the little gourds grew up the sides and o'er
    The clapboard roof!   And her face—ah, me!
40   Wasn't it good for a boy to see—
    And wasn't it good for a boy to be
      Out to old Aunt Mary's?

Ah! was there, ever, so kind a face
And gentle as hers, or such a grace
45   Of welcoming, as she cut the cake
    Or the juicy pies that she joyed to make
    Just for the visiting children's sake—
      Out to Old Aunt Mary's.

For, O my brother so far away,
50   This is to tell you—she waits *today*
    To welcome us.   Aunt Mary fell
    Asleep this morning, whispering, "Tell
    The boys to come." . . .   And all is well
      Out to old Aunt Mary's.

A CHRISTMAS CAROL

CHARLES DICKENS

STAVE [1] ONE—MARLEY'S GHOST

MARLEY was dead, to begin with. There is no doubt whatever about that. The register of his burial was signed by the clergyman, the clerk, the undertaker, and the chief mourner. Scrooge signed it. And Scrooge's name was good upon 'Change [2] for anything he chose to put his hand to. Old Marley was as dead as a doornail.

Scrooge never painted out Old Marley's name. There it stood years afterwards, SCROOGE AND MARLEY, above the warehouse door. The firm was known as Scrooge and Marley. Sometimes people new to the business called Scrooge, Scrooge, and sometimes Marley, but he answered to both names. It was all the same to him.

Nobody ever stopped him in the street to say, with glad-

[1] STAVE—A stanza. A carol is a song, so the word "stave" is used to indicate the divisions of the story, rather than the word "part."

[2] 'CHANGE—Exchange, a place where men meet to transact business.

448

some looks, "My dear Scrooge, how are you? When will you come to see me?" No beggars implored him to bestow a trifle, no children asked him what it was o'clock, no man or woman ever once in all his life inquired the way to such and such a place, of Scrooge. Even the blind men's dogs appeared to know him; and when they saw him coming on, would tug their owners into doorways and up courts; and then would wag their tails as though they said, "No eye at all is better than an evil eye, dark master!"

Oh! But he was a tight-fisted hand at the grindstone. Scrooge! A squeezing, wrenching, grasping, scraping, clutching, covetous, old sinner! Hard and sharp as flint, from which no steel had ever struck out generous fire; secretive, and self-contained, and solitary as an oyster. The cold within him froze his old features, nipped his pointed nose, shriveled his cheek, stiffened his gait; made his eyes red, and his thin lips blue.

Once upon a time—of all the good days in the year, on Christmas Eve—old Scrooge sat busy in his countinghouse. It was cold, bleak, biting weather: foggy withal: and he could hear the people in the court outside go wheezing up and down, beating their hands upon their breasts, and stamping their feet upon the pavement stones to warm them. The city clocks had only just gone three, but it was quite dark already—it had not been light all day—and candles were flaring in the windows of the neighboring offices, like ruddy smears upon the palpable [3] brown air. The fog came pouring in at every chink and key-hole, and was so dense without, that although the court was of the narrowest, the houses opposite were mere phantoms. To see the dingy cloud come drooping down, obscuring everything, one might have thought that Nature lived hard by, and was brewing on a large scale.

The door of Scrooge's countinghouse was open, that he might

---

[3] PALPABLE—Capable of being touched or felt. Hence, the air was thick with fog.

keep his eye upon his clerk, who in a dismal little cell beyond, a sort of tank, was copying letters. Scrooge had a very small fire, but the clerk's fire was so very much smaller that it looked like one coal. But he couldn't replenish it, for Scrooge kept the coal box in his own room; and so surely as the clerk came in with the shovel, the master predicted that it would be necessary for them to part. Wherefore the clerk put on his white comforter, and tried to warm himself at the candle; in which effort, not being a man of strong imagination, he failed.

"A Merry Christmas, Uncle! God save you!" cried a cheerful voice. It was the voice of Scrooge's nephew, who came upon him so quickly that this was the first intimation he had of his approach.

"Bah!" said Scrooge. "Humbug!"

He had so heated himself with rapid walking in the fog and frost, this nephew of Scrooge's, that he was all in a glow; his face was ruddy and handsome; his eyes sparkled, and his breath smoked again.

"Christmas a humbug, Uncle!" said Scrooge's nephew. "You don't mean that, I am sure?"

"I do," said Scrooge. "Merry Christmas! What right have you to be merry? What reason have you to be merry? You're poor enough."

"Come, then," returned the nephew gayly. "What right have you to be dismal? What reason have you to be morose? [4] You're rich enough."

Scrooge having no better answer ready on the spur of the moment, said "Bah!" again; and followed it up with "Humbug!"

"Don't be cross, Uncle!" said the nephew.

"What else can I be," returned the uncle, "when I live in such a world of fools as this? Merry Christmas! Out upon merry Christmas! What's Christmas time to you but a time for paying bills without money; a time for finding yourself a

---

[4] MOROSE—Ill-humored.

year older, but not an hour richer; a time for balancing your books and having every item in 'em through a round dozen of months presented dead against you? If I could work my will," said Scrooge indignantly, "every idiot who goes about with 'Merry Christmas' on his lips, should be boiled with his own pudding, and buried with a stick of holly through his heart. He should!"

"Uncle!" pleaded the nephew.

"Nephew!" returned the uncle, sternly, "keep Christmas in your own way, and let me keep it in mine."

"Keep it!" repeated Scrooge's nephew. "But you don't keep it."

"Let me leave it alone, then," said Scrooge. "Much good may it do you! Much good it has ever done you!"

"There are many things from which I might have derived good, by which I have not profited, I dare say," returned the nephew. "Christmas among the rest. But I am sure I have always thought of Christmas time, when it has come round— apart from the veneration [5] due to its sacred name and origin, if anything belonging to it can be apart from that—as a good time; a kind, forgiving, charitable, pleasant time; the only time I know of, in the long calendar of the year, when men and women seem by one consent to open their shut-up hearts freely, and to think of people below them as if they really were fellow-passengers to the grave, and not another race of creatures bound on other journeys. And, therefore, Uncle, though it has never put a scrap of gold or silver in my pocket, I believe that it *has* done me good, and *will* do me good; and I say, God bless it!"

The clerk involuntarily [6] applauded. Becoming immediately sensible of the impropriety,[7] he poked the fire, and extinguished the last frail spark forever.

"Let me hear another sound from *you*," said Scrooge, "and

[5] VENERATION—Respect.
[6] INVOLUNTARILY—Automatically; without thinking what he was doing.
[7] IMPROPRIETY—An act not in keeping, out of place.

you'll keep your Christmas by losing your situation. You're quite a powerful speaker, sir," he added, turning to his nephew. "I wonder you don't go into Parliament."

"Don't be angry, Uncle. Come! Dine with us tomorrow."

"Good afternoon," said Scrooge.

"I am sorry, with all my heart, to find you so resolute. We have never had any quarrel to which I have been a party. But I have made the trial in homage to Christmas, and I'll keep my Christmas humor to the last. So a Merry Christmas, Uncle!"

"Good afternoon!" said Scrooge.

"And a Happy New Year!"

"Good afternoon!" said Scrooge.

His nephew left the room without any angry word, notwithstanding. He stopped at the outer door to bestow the greetings of the season on the clerk, who, cold as he was, was warmer than Scrooge; for he returned them cordially.

"There's another fellow," muttered Scrooge, who overheard him: "my clerk, with fifteen shillings a week, and a wife and family, talking about a merry Christmas. I'll retire to Bedlam." [8]

This lunatic, in letting Scrooge's nephew out, had let two other people in. They were portly gentlemen, pleasant to behold, and now stood, with their hats off, in Scrooge's office. They had books and papers in their hands, and bowed to him.

"Scrooge and Marley's, I believe," said one of the gentlemen, referring to his list. "Have I the pleasure of addressing Mr. Scrooge, or Mr. Marley?"

"Mr. Marley has been dead these seven years," Scrooge replied. "He died seven years ago, this very night."

"We have no doubt his liberality is well represented by his surviving partner," said the gentleman, presenting his credentials.

It certainly was; for they had been two kindred spirits. At

---

[8] BEDLAM—The hospital of St. Mary of Bethlehem, in London, long used as a hospital for lunatics. Bedlam is a corrupt pronunciation of Bethlehem.

the ominous word "liberality," Scrooge frowned, and shook his head, and handed the credentials back.

"At this festive season of the year, Mr. Scrooge," said the gentleman, taking up a pen, "it is more than usually desirable that we should make some slight provision for the poor and destitute, who suffer greatly at the present time. Many thousands are in want of common necessaries; hundreds of thousands are in want of common comforts, sir."

"Are there no prisons?" asked Scrooge.

"Plenty of prisons," said the gentleman, laying down the pen again.

"And the Union workhouses?" demanded Scrooge. "Are they still in operation?"

"They are. Still," returned the gentleman, "I wish I could say they were not."

"The Treadmill [9] and the Poor Law [10] are in full vigor, then?" said Scrooge.

"Both very busy, sir."

"Oh! I was afraid, from what you said at first, that something had occurred to stop them in their useful course," said Scrooge. "I'm very glad to hear it."

"Under the impression that they scarcely furnish Christian cheer of mind or body to the multitude," returned the gentleman, "a few of us are endeavoring to raise a fund to buy the poor some meat and drink, and means of warmth. We choose this time, because it is a time, of all others, when Want is keenly felt, and Abundance rejoices. What shall I put you down for?"

"Nothing!" Scrooge replied.

"You wish to be anonymous?"

"I wish to be left alone," said Scrooge. "Since you ask me what I wish, gentlemen, that is my answer. I don't make merry myself at Christmas, and I can't afford to make idle

[9] TREADMILL—A mill worked by persons treading on a wide, cylinder-like wheel. It was used in prison discipline in olden times.
[10] POOR LAW—Law regulating public support of the poor.

453

people merry. I help to support the establishments I have mentioned—they cost enough; and those who are badly off must go there."

"Many can't go there; and many would rather die."

"If they would rather die," said Scrooge, "they had better do it, and decrease the surplus population. Good afternoon, gentlemen!"

Seeing clearly that it would be useless to pursue their point, the gentlemen withdrew. Scrooge resumed his labors with an improved opinion of himself, and in a more facetious [11] temper than was usual with him.

Meanwhile the fog and darkness thickened so, that people ran about with flaring links,[12] proffering their services to go before horses and carriages, and conduct them on their way. The ancient tower of a church, whose gruff old bell was always peeping slyly at Scrooge out of a gothic [13] window in the wall, became invisible, and struck the hours and quarters in the clouds, with tremulous vibrations afterwards as if its teeth were chattering in its frozen head up there. The cold became intense. The brightness of the shops, where holly sprigs and berries crackled in the lamp heat of the windows, made pale faces ruddy as they passed. Poulterers' and grocers' trades became a splendid joke: a glorious pageant, with which it was next to impossible to believe that such dull principles as bargain and sale had anything to do.

Foggier yet, and colder! Piercing, searching, biting cold. The owner of one scant young nose, gnawed and mumbled by the hungry cold as bones are gnawed by dogs, stooped down at Scrooge's keyhole to regale him with a Christmas carol: but at the first sound of

> "God bless you, merry gentlemen,
> May nothing you dismay!"

---

[11] FACETIOUS (fȧ-sē'shŭs)—Humorous, good-natured.
[12] LINKS—Torches.
[13] GOTHIC—A style of architecture characterized by pointed arches.

Scrooge seized the ruler with such energy of action that the singer fled in terror, leaving the keyhole to the fog and even more congenial frost.

At length the hour of shutting up the countinghouse arrived. With an ill-will Scrooge dismounted from his stool and tacitly [14] admitted the fact to the expectant clerk, who instantly snuffed his candle out, and put on his hat.

"You'll want to be off all day tomorrow, I suppose?" said Scrooge.

"If quite convenient, sir."

"It's not convenient," said Scrooge, "and it's not fair. If I was to stop half-a-crown for it, you'd think yourself ill-used, I'll be bound?"

The clerk smiled faintly.

"And yet," said Scrooge, "you don't think *me* ill-used, when I pay a day's wages for no work."

The clerk observed that it was only once a year.

"A poor excuse for picking a man's pocket every twenty-fifth of December!" said Scrooge, buttoning his greatcoat to the chin. "But I suppose you must have the whole day. Be here all the earlier next morning."

The clerk promised that he would; and Scrooge walked out with a growl. The office was closed in a twinkling, and the clerk, with the long ends of his white comforter dangling below his waist (for he boasted no greatcoat), ran home to Camden Town as hard as he could pelt, to play at blindman's-buff.

Scrooge took his melancholy dinner in his usual melancholy tavern; and having read all the newspapers, and beguiled the rest of the evening with his banker's book, went home to bed. He lived in chambers which had once belonged to his deceased partner. They were a gloomy suite [15] of rooms, in an open lumber yard. The house was old enough now, and dreary enough, for nobody lived in it but Scrooge, the other rooms being all let

---

[14] TACITLY (tăs'ĭt-lĭ)—Silently.
[15] SUITE—Pronounced swēt.

out as offices. The yard was so dark that even Scrooge, who knew its every stone, was fain to grope with his hands. The fog and frost so hung about the black old gateway of the house, that it seemed as if the Genius of the Weather sat in mournful meditation on the threshold.

Now it is a fact that there was nothing at all particular about the knocker on the door, except that it was very large. It is also a fact that Scrooge had seen it, night and morning, during his whole residence in that place; also that Scrooge had as little of what is called fancy about him as any man in the City of London. Let any man explain to me, if he can, how it happened that Scrooge, having his key in the lock of the door, saw in the knocker, without its undergoing any intermediate process of change—not a knocker, but Marley's face.

Marley's face. It was not in impenetrable [16] shadow as the other objects in the yard were, but had a dismal light about it. It was not angry or ferocious, but looked at Scrooge as Marley used to look. The hair was curiously stirred, as if by breath or hot air; and, though the eyes were wide open, they were perfectly motionless. That, and its livid [17] color, made it horrible; but its horror seemed to be in spite of the face and beyond its control, rather than a part of its own expression.

As Scrooge looked fixedly at this phenomenon,[18] it was a knocker again.

To say that he was not startled, or that his blood was not conscious of a terrible sensation to which it had been a stranger from infancy, would be untrue. But he put his hand upon the key he had relinquished, turned it sturdily, walked in, and lighted his candle.

He *did* pause, with a moment's irresolution, before he shut the door; and he *did* look cautiously behind it first, as if he half expected to be terrified with the sight of Marley's pigtail sticking out into the hall. But there was nothing on the back

[16] IMPENETRABLE—Incapable of being pierced or penetrated.
[17] LIVID—Ashy-pale.
[18] PHENOMENON—Something which appears unaccountable.

of the door, except the screws and nuts that held the knocker on, so he said "Pooh, pooh!" and closed it with a bang.

The sound resounded through the house like thunder. Every room above, and every cask in the wine-merchant's cellars below, appeared to have a separate peal of echoes of its own. Scrooge was not a man to be frightened by echoes. He fastened the door, and walked across the hall, and up the stairs; slowly, too: trimming his candle as he went.

Up Scrooge went. Darkness is cheap, and Scrooge liked it. But before he shut his heavy door, he walked through his rooms to see that all was right. He had just enough recollection of the face to desire to do that.

Sitting room, bedroom, lumber room.[19]   All as they should be. Nobody under the table, nobody under the sofa; a small fire in the grate; spoon and basin ready; and the little saucepan of gruel (Scrooge had a cold in his head) upon the hob.[20] Nobody under the bed; nobody in the closet; nobody in his dressing gown, which was hanging up in a suspicious attitude against the wall. Lumber room as usual. Old fireguard,[21] old shoes, two fish baskets, washing stand on three legs, and a poker, all in their places.

Quite satisfied, he closed his door, and locked himself in; double-locked himself in, which was not his custom. Thus secured against surprise, he took off his cravat,[22] put on his dressing gown and slippers, and his nightcap; and sat down before the fire to take his gruel.

It was a very low fire indeed; in fact, no fire at all on such a bitter night. He was obliged to sit close to it, and brood over it, before he could extract the least sensation of warmth from such a handful of fuel. The fireplace was an old one, built by some Dutch merchant long ago, and paved all around with

[19] LUMBER ROOM—Storage room.
[20] HOB—A projection at the back or side of a fireplace on which food might be kept warm.
[21] FIREGUARD—A screen placed in front of fireplace to keep the sparks from flying into the room.
[22] CRAVAT (krȧ-vǎt)—Necktie.

quaint Dutch tiles, designed to illustrate the Scriptures. If each smooth tile had been a blank at first, with power to shape some picture on its surface from the disjointed fragments of his thoughts, there would have been a copy of old Marley's head on every one.

"Humbug!" said Scrooge; and walked across the room.

After several turns, he sat down again. As he threw his head back in the chair, his glance happened to rest upon a bell, a disused bell, that hung in the room, and communicated for some purpose now forgotten with a chamber in the highest story of the building. It was with great astonishment, and with a strange, inexplicable [23] dread, that as he looked, he saw this bell begin to swing. It swung so softly in the outset that it scarcely made a sound; but soon it rang out loudly, and so did every bell in the house.

This might have lasted half a minute, or a minute, but it seemed an hour. The bells ceased as they had begun, together. They were succeeded by a clanking noise, deep down below; as if some person were dragging a heavy chain over the casks in the wine-merchant's cellar. Scrooge then remembered to have heard that ghosts in haunted houses were described as dragging chains.

The cellar door flew open with a booming sound, and then he heard the noise much louder, on the floors below; then coming up the stairs; then coming straight towards his door.

"It's humbug still!" said Scrooge. "I won't believe it."

His color changed though, when, without a pause, it came on through the heavy door, and passed into the room before his eyes. Upon its coming in, the dying flame leaped up, as though it cried "I know him! Marley's Ghost!" and fell again.

The same face: the very same. Marley in his pigtail, usual waistcoat, tights and boots; the tassels on the latter bristling, like his pigtail, and his coat skirts, and the hair upon his head. The chain he drew was clasped about his middle. It was long,

---

[23] INEXPLICABLE (ĭn-ĕks'plĭ-kȧ-b'l)—Unexplainable.

and wound about him like a tail; and it was made (for Scrooge observed it closely) of cash boxes, keys, padlocks, ledgers, deeds, and heavy purses wrought in steel. His body was transparent; so that Scrooge, observing him, and looking through his waistcoat, could see the two buttons on his coat behind.

Though he looked the phantom through and through, and saw it standing before him; though he felt the chilling influence of its death-cold eyes, and marked the very texture of the folded kerchief bound about its head and chin, which wrapper he had not observed before; he was still incredulous, and fought against his senses.

"How now!" said Scrooge, caustic and cold as ever. "What do you want with me?"

"Much!"—Marley's voice, no doubt about it.

"Who are you?"

"Ask me who I *was*."

"Who *were* you then?" said Scrooge, raising his voice.

"In life I was your partner, Jacob Marley."

"Can you—can you sit down?" asked Scrooge, looking doubtfully at him.

"I can."

"Do it, then."

Scrooge asked the question, because he didn't know whether a ghost so transparent might find himself in a condition to take a chair; and felt that in the event of its being impossible, it might involve the necessity of an embarrassing explanation. But the Ghost sat down on the opposite side of the fireplace, as if he were quite used to it.

"You don't believe in me," observed the Ghost.

"I don't," said Scrooge.

"What evidence would you have of my reality beyond that of your own senses?"

"I don't know," said Scrooge.

"Why do you doubt your senses?"

"Because," said Scrooge, "a little thing affects them. A slight disorder of the stomach makes them cheats. You may be an undigested bit of beef, a blot of mustard, a crumb of cheese, a fragment of an underdone potato. There's more of gravy than of grave about you, whatever you are!"

Scrooge was not much in the habit of cracking jokes, nor did he feel, in his heart, by any means waggish then. The truth is, that he tried to be smart, as a means of distracting his own attention, and keeping down his terror; for the specter's voice disturbed the very marrow in his bones. To sit, staring at those fixed, glazed eyes, in silence for a moment, would play, Scrooge felt, the very deuce with him.

"You see this toothpick?" said Scrooge, returning quickly to the charge, and wishing, though it were only for a second, to divert the vision's stony gaze from himself.

"I do," replied the Ghost.

"You are not looking at it," said Scrooge.

"But I see it," said the Ghost, "notwithstanding."

"Well!" said Scrooge, "I have but to swallow this, and be for the rest of my days persecuted by a legion of goblins, all of my own creation. Humbug, I tell you! humbug!"

At this the spirit raised a frightful cry and shook its chain with such a dismal and appalling noise, that Scrooge held on tight to his chair, to save himself from falling in a swoon. But how much greater was his horror, when, the phantom's taking off the bandage round its head, as if it were too warm to wear indoors, its lower jaw dropped down upon its breast!

Scrooge fell upon his knees, and clasped his hands before his face. "Mercy!" he said. "Dreadful apparition, why do you trouble me?"

"Man of the worldly mind!" replied the Ghost, "do you believe in me or not?"

"I do," said Scrooge. "I must. But why do spirits walk the earth, and why do they come to me?"

"It is required of every man," the Ghost returned, "that the spirit within him should walk abroad among his fellow men, and travel far and wide; and if that spirit goes not forth in life, it is condemned to do so after death. It is doomed to wander through the world—oh, woe is me!—and witness what it cannot share, but might have shared on earth, and turned to happiness!"

Again the specter raised a cry, and shook its chain, and wrung its shadowy hands.

"You are fettered," said Scrooge, trembling. "Tell me why?"

"I wear the chain I forged in life," replied the Ghost. "I made it link by link, and yard by yard; I girded it on of my own free will, and of my own free will I wore it. Is its pattern strange to *you?*"

Scrooge trembled more and more.

"Or would you know," pursued the Ghost, "the weight and length of the strong coil you bear yourself? It was full as heavy and as long as this, seven Christmas Eves ago. You have labored on it, since. It is a ponderous chain!"

Scrooge glanced about him on the floor, in the expectation of finding himself surrounded by some fifty or sixty fathoms of iron cable: but he could see nothing.

"Jacob," he said imploringly. "Old Jacob Marley, tell me more. Speak comfort to me, Jacob!"

"I have none to give," the Ghost replied. "It comes from other regions, Ebenezer Scrooge, and is conveyed by other ministers, to other kinds of men. Nor can I tell you what I would. A very little more is all permitted to me. I cannot rest, I cannot stay, I cannot linger anywhere. My spirit never walked beyond our countinghouse—mark me!—in life my spirit never roved beyond the narrow limits of our money-changing hole; and weary journeys lie before me!"

"You travel fast?" said Scrooge.

"On the wings of the wind," replied the Ghost.

"You might have got over a great quantity of ground in the seven years you have been dead," said Scrooge.

The Ghost, on hearing this, set up another cry, and clanked its chain hideously in the dead silence of the night.

"Oh! captive, bound, and double-ironed," cried the phantom, "not to know that any Christian spirit working kindly in its little sphere, whatever it may be, will find its mortal life too short for its vast means of usefulness. Not to know that no space of regret can make amends for one life's opportunity misused! Yet such was I! Oh! such was I."

"But you were always a good man of business, Jacob," faltered Scrooge, who now began to apply this to himself.

"Business!" cried the Ghost, wringing its hands again. "Mankind was my business. The common welfare was my business; charity, mercy, forbearance, and benevolence, were, all, my business. The dealings of my trade were but a drop of water in the comprehensive ocean of my business!"

It held up its chain at arm's length, as if that were the cause of all its unavailing grief, and flung it heavily upon the ground again.

"At this time of the rolling year," the specter said, "I suffer most. Why did I walk through crowds of fellow beings with my eyes turned down, and never raise them to that blessed Star which led the Wise Men to a poor abode! Were there no poor homes to which its light would have conducted *me?*"

Scrooge was very much dismayed to hear the specter going on at this rate, and began to quake exceedingly.

"Hear me!" cried the Ghost. "My time is nearly gone."

"I will," said Scrooge. "But don't be hard upon me! Don't be flowery, Jacob! Pray!"

"How it is that I appear before you in a shape that you can see, I may not tell. I have sat invisible beside you many and many a day."

It was not an agreeable idea. Scrooge shivered, and wiped the perspiration from his brow.

"That is no light part of my penance," pursued the Ghost. "I am here tonight to warn you, that you have yet a chance and hope of escaping my fate.   A chance and hope of my procuring, Ebenezer."

"You were always a good friend to me," said Scrooge. "Thank'ee!"

"You will be haunted," resumed the Ghost, "by Three Spirits. Without their visits, you cannot hope to shun the path I tread. Expect the first tomorrow, when the bell tolls One.   Expect the second on the next night at the same hour.   The third upon the next night when the last stroke of Twelve has ceased to vibrate.   Look to see me no more; and look that, for your own sake, you remember what has passed between us!"

When it had said these words, the specter took its bandage from the table, and bound it round its head, as before.   Scrooge knew this by the smart sound its teeth made, when the jaws were brought together by the bandage.   He ventured to raise his eyes again, and found his supernatural visitor confronting him in an erect attitude, with its chain wound over its arm.

The apparition walked backward from him; and at every step it took, the window raised itself a little, so that when the specter reached it, it was wide open.   It beckoned Scrooge to approach, which he did.   When they were within two paces of each other, Marley's Ghost held up its hand, warning him to come no nearer.   Scrooge stopped.

Not so much in obedience, as in surprise and fear: for on the raising of the hand, he became sensible of confused noises in the air; incoherent sounds of lamentation and regret; wailings inexpressibly sorrowful and self-accusatory.   The specter, after listening for a moment, joined in the mournful dirge, and floated out upon the bleak, dark night.

Scrooge followed to the window: desperate in his curiosity. He looked out.   The air was filled with phantoms, wandering hither and thither in restless haste, and moaning as they went. Every one of them wore chains like Marley's Ghost; some few were linked together; none were free.   Many had been personally known to Scrooge in their lives.

Scrooge closed the window, and examined the door by which the Ghost had entered. It was double-locked, as he had locked it with his own hands, and the bolts were undisturbed. He tried to say "Humbug!" but stopped at the first syllable. And being much in need of repose, he went straight to bed, without undressing, and fell asleep upon the instant.

STAVE TWO—-THE FIRST OF THE THREE SPIRITS

When Scrooge awoke, it was so dark that, looking out of bed, he could scarcely distinguish the transparent window from the opaque [1] walls of his chamber. He was endeavoring to pierce the darkness with his ferret eyes, when the chimes of a neighboring church struck four quarters. So he listened for the hour.

To his great astonishment the heavy bell went on from six to seven, and from seven to eight, and regularly up to twelve; then stopped. Twelve! It was past two when he went to bed. The clock was wrong. An icicle must have got into the works. Twelve!

"Why, it isn't possible," said Scrooge, "that I can have slept through a whole day and far into another night. It isn't possible that anything has happened to the sun, and this is twelve at noon!"

The idea being an alarming one, he scrambled out of bed, and groped his way to the window. He was obliged to rub the frost off with the sleeve of his dressing gown before he could see anything; and could see very little then. All he could make out was, that it was still very foggy and extremely cold, and that there was no noise of people running to and fro, and making a great stir, as there unquestionably would have been if night had beaten off bright day, and taken possession of the world.

Scrooge went to bed again, and thought, and thought, and thought it over and over, and could make nothing of it. The more he thought, the more perplexed he was; and the more he endeavored not to think, the more he thought.

[1] OPAQUE—The opposite of transparent—dense.

Marley's Ghost bothered him exceedingly. Every time he resolved within himself, after mature inquiry, that it was all a dream, his mind flew back again, like a strong spring released, to its first position, and presented the same problem to be worked all through, "Was it a dream or not?"

Scrooge lay in this state until the chimes had gone three quarters more, when he remembered on a sudden, that the Ghost had warned him of a visitation when the bell tolled One. He resolved to lie awake until the hour was passed; and, considering that he could no more go to sleep than go to Heaven, this was perhaps the wisest resolution in his power.

The quarter was so long, that he was more than once convinced he must have sunk into a doze unconsciously, and missed the clock. At length it broke upon his listening ear.

"Ding, dong!"

"A quarter-past," said Scrooge, counting.

"Ding, dong!"

"Half-past!" said Scrooge.

"Ding, dong!"

"A quarter to it," said Scrooge.

"Ding, dong!"

"The hour itself," said Scrooge, triumphantly, "and nothing else!"

He spoke before the hour bell sounded, which it now did with a deep, dull, hollow, melancholy ONE. A light flashed up in the room upon the instant, and the curtains of his bed were drawn aside.

The curtains of his bed were drawn aside, I tell you, by a hand. Not the curtains at his feet, nor the curtains at his back, but those to which his face was addressed. The curtains of his bed were drawn aside; and Scrooge, starting up into a half-recumbent attitude, found himself face to face with the unearthly visitor who drew them.

It was a strange figure—like a child: yet not so like a child as like an old man, viewed through some supernatural medium, which gave him the appearance of having receded from the view, and being diminished to a child's proportions. Its hair, which hung about its neck and down its back, was white as if with age; and yet the face had not a wrinkle in it, and the ten-

derest bloom was on the skin. The arms were very long and muscular; the hands the same, as if its hold were of uncommon strength. Its legs and feet, most delicately formed, were, like those upper members, bare. It wore a tunic of the purest white; and round its waist was bound a lustrous belt, the sheen of which was beautiful. It held a branch of fresh green holly in its hand; and, in singular contradiction of that wintry emblem, had its dress trimmed with summer flowers. But the strangest thing about it was, that from the crown of its head there sprung a bright clear jet of light, by which all this was visible.

"Are you the Spirit, sir, whose coming was foretold to me?" asked Scrooge.

"I am!" The voice was soft and gentle. Singularly low, as if instead of being so close beside him, it were at a distance.

"Who, and what are you?" Scrooge demanded.

"I am the Ghost of Christmas Past."

"Long Past?" inquired Scrooge, observant of its dwarfish stature.

"No. *Your* past."

Scrooge then made bold to inquire what business brought the Spirit there.

"*Your* welfare!" said the Ghost.

Scrooge expressed himself much obliged, but could not help thinking that a night of unbroken rest would have been more conducive to that end. The Spirit must have heard him thinking, for it said immediately:

"Your reclamation,² then. Take heed!"

It put out its strong hand as it spoke, and clasped him gently by the arm.

"Rise! and walk with me!"

It would have been in vain for Scrooge to plead that the weather and the hour were not adapted to pedestrian purposes; that the bed was warm, and the thermometer a long way below freezing; that he was clad but lightly in his slippers, dressing gown, and nightcap; and that he had a cold upon him at that time. The grasp, though gentle as a woman's hand, was not to be resisted. He rose: but finding that the Spirit made toward the window, clasped its robe in supplication.

"I am a mortal," Scrooge remonstrated, "and liable to fall."

"Bear but a touch of my hand *there*," said the Spirit, laying it upon his heart, "and you shall be upheld in more than this!"

As the words were spoken, they passed through the wall, and stood upon an open country road, with fields on either hand. The city had entirely vanished. Not a vestige of it was to be seen. The darkness and the mist had vanished with it, for it was a clear, cold, winter day, with snow upon the ground.

² RECLAMATION—Reform, restoration.

"Good Heaven!" said Scrooge, clasping his hands together, as he looked about him. "I was bred in this place. I was a boy here!"

The Spirit gazed upon him mildly. Its gentle touch, though it had been light and instantaneous, appeared still present to the old man's sense of feeling. He was conscious of a thousand odors floating in the air, each one connected with a thousand thoughts, and hopes, and joys, and cares long, long forgotten.

"You recollect the way?" inquired the Spirit.

"Remember it!" cried Scrooge, with fervor; "I could walk it blindfolded."

"Strange to have forgotten it for so many years!" observed the Ghost. "Let us go on."

They walked along the road; Scrooge recognizing every gate, and post, and tree; until a little market town appeared in the distance, with its bridge, its church, and winding river. Some shaggy ponies now were seen trotting toward them with boys upon their backs, who called to other boys in country gigs [3] and carts, driven by farmers. All these boys were in great spirits, and shouted to each other, until the broad fields were so full of merry music that the crisp air laughed to hear it.

"These are but shadows of the things that have been," said the Ghost. "They are not conscious of us."

The jocund travelers came on; and as they came, Scrooge knew and named them every one. Why was he rejoiced beyond all bounds to see them? Why did his cold eye glisten, and his heart leap up as they went past? Why was he filled with gladness when he heard them give each other Merry Christmas, as they parted at crossroads and byways, for their several homes? What was merry Christmas to Scrooge? Out upon merry Christmas! What good had it ever done to him?

"The school is not quite deserted," said the Ghost. "A solitary child, neglected by his friends, is left there still."

Scrooge said he knew it. And he sobbed.

[3] GIGS—Light, two-wheeled, one-horse carriages.

They left the highroad, by a well-remembered lane, and soon approached a mansion of dull red brick, with a little weather-cock-surmounted cupola on the roof, and a bell hanging in it. It was a large house, but one of broken fortunes; for the spacious offices were little used, their walls were damp and mossy, their windows broken, and their gates decayed. Fowls clucked and strutted in the stables; and the coach houses and sheds were overrun with grass. Nor was it more retentive of its ancient state, within; for entering the dreary hall, and glancing through the open doors of many rooms, they found them poorly furnished, cold, and vast. There was an earthy savor in the air, a chilly bareness in the place, which associated itself somehow with too much getting up by candlelight, and not too much to eat.

They went, the Ghost and Scrooge, across the hall, to a door at the back of the house. It opened before them, and disclosed a long, bare, melancholy room, made barer still by lines of plain deal forms [4] and desks. At one of these a lonely boy was reading near a feeble fire; and Scrooge sat down upon a form, and wept to see his poor forgotten self as he used to be.

Not a latent [5] echo in the house, not a squeak and scuffle from the mice behind the paneling, not a drip from the half-thawed water-spout in the dull yard behind, not a sigh among the leafless boughs of one despondent poplar, not the idle swinging of an empty storehouse-door, no, not a clicking in the fire, but fell upon the heart of Scrooge with a softening influence, and gave a freer passage to his tears.

The Spirit touched him on the arm, and pointed to his younger self, intent upon his reading. Then, with a rapidity of transition very foreign to his usual character, he said, in pity for his former self, "Poor boy!"

"I wish," Scrooge muttered, putting his hand in his pocket,

[4] DEAL FORMS—Fir or pine benches.
[5] LATENT (lā′tĕnt)—Hidden, concealed.

and looking about him, after drying his eyes with his cuff: "but it's too late now."

"What is the matter?" asked the Spirit.

"Nothing," said Scrooge. "Nothing. There was a boy singing a Christmas carol at my door last night. I should like to have given him something; that's all."

The Ghost smiled thoughtfully, and waved its hand: saying as it did so, "Let us see another Christmas!"

Scrooge's former self grew larger [6] at the words, and the room became a little darker and more dirty. The panels shrank, the windows cracked; fragments of plaster fell out of the ceiling, and the naked laths were shown instead; but how all this was brought about, Scrooge knew no more than you do. He only knew that it was quite correct: that everything had happened so; that there he was, alone again, when all the other boys had gone home for the jolly holidays.

He was not reading now, but walking up and down despairingly. Scrooge looked at the Ghost, and, with a mournful shaking of his head, glanced anxiously toward the door.

It opened; and a little girl, much younger than the boy, came darting in, and putting her arms about his neck, and often kissing him, addressed him as her "Dear, dear brother."

"I have come to bring you home, dear brother!" said the child, clapping her tiny hands, and bending down to laugh. "To bring you home, home, home!"

"Home, little Fan?" returned the boy.

"Yes!" said the child, brimful of glee. "Home, for good and all. Home, for ever and ever. Father is so much kinder than he used to be, that home's like Heaven. He spoke so gently to me one dear night when I was going to bed, that I was not afraid to ask him once more if you might come home; and he said 'Yes, you should'; and sent me in a coach to bring you. And you're to be a man!" said the child, opening her eyes; "and are never to come back here; but first, we're to be to-

[6] GREW LARGER—Scrooge, as a boy, grew older but was attending the same school.

gether all the Christmas long, and have the merriest time in all the world."

"You are quite a woman, little Fan!" exclaimed the boy.

She clapped her hands and laughed, and tried to touch his head; but being too little, laughed again, and stood on tiptoe to embrace him. Then she began to drag him, in her childish eagerness, toward the door; and he, nothing loath to go, accompanied her.

A terrible voice in the hall cried, "Bring down Master Scrooge's box [7] there!" and in the hall appeared the schoolmaster himself, who glared on Master Scrooge with a ferocious condescension, and threw him into a dreadful state of mind by shaking hands with him. He then conveyed him and his sister into the old, shivering best-parlor, where the maps upon the wall, and the celestial and terrestrial globes [8] in the windows were waxy with cold. Master Scrooge's trunk being by this time tied on to the top of the chaise, the children bade the schoolmaster good-by right willingly; and getting into it, drove gayly down the garden sweep: the quick wheels dashing the hoarfrost and snow from off the dark leaves of the evergreens like spray.

"Always a delicate creature, whom a breath might have withered," said the Ghost. "But she had a large heart!"

"So she had," cried Scrooge. "You're right. I will not gainsay it, Spirit. God forbid!"

"She died a woman," said the Ghost, "and had, as I think, children."

"One child," Scrooge returned.

"True," said the Ghost. "Your nephew!"

Scrooge seemed uneasy in his mind; and answered briefly, "Yes."

Although they had but that moment left the school behind them, they were now in the busy thoroughfares of a city, where

[7] BOX—Trunk.
[8] CELESTIAL AND TERRESTRIAL GLOBES—Globes showing respectively the heavenly bodies and the continents.

shadowy passengers passed and repassed; where shadowy carts and coaches battled for the way, and all the strife and tumult of a real city were. It was made plain enough, by the dressing of the shops, that here, too, it was Christmas time again; but it was evening, and the streets were lighted up.

The Ghost stopped at a certain warehouse door, and asked Scrooge if he knew it.

"Know it!" said Scrooge. "Was I not apprenticed here?"

They went in. At sight of an old gentleman in a Welsh wig, sitting behind such a high desk that if he had been two inches taller he must have knocked his head against the ceiling, Scrooge cried in great excitement:

"Why, it's old Fezziwig! Bless his heart; it's Fezziwig alive again!"

Old Fezziwig laid down his pen, and looked up at the clock, which pointed to the hour of seven. He rubbed his hands; adjusted his capacious waistcoat; laughed all over himself, from his shoes to his organ of benevolence; and called out in a comfortable, oily, rich, fat jovial voice:

"Yo-ho, there! Ebenezer! Dick!"

Scrooge's former self, now grown a young man, came briskly in, accompanied by his fellow 'prentice.

"Dick Wilkins, to be sure!" said Scrooge to the Ghost. "Bless me, yes. There he is. He was very much attached to me, was Dick. Poor Dick! Dear, dear!"

"Yo-ho, my boys!" said Fezziwig. "No more work tonight. Christmas Eve, Dick. Christmas, Ebenezer! Let's have the shutters up," cried old Fezziwig, with a sharp clap of his hands, "before a man·can say Jack Robinson!"

You wouldn't believe how those two fellows went at it! They charged into the street with the shutters—one, two, three—had 'em up in their places—four, five, six—barred 'em and pinned 'em—seven, eight, nine—and came back before you could have got to twelve, panting like racehorses.

"Hilli-ho!" cried old Fezziwig, skipping down from the high

desk, with wonderful agility. "Clear away, my lads, and let's have lots of room here! Hilli-ho, Dick! Chirrup, Ebenezer!"

Clear away! There was nothing they wouldn't have cleared away, or couldn't have cleared away, with old Fezziwig looking on. It was done in a minute. Everything movable was packed off, as if it were dismissed from public life for evermore; the floor was swept and watered, the lamps were trimmed, fuel was heaped upon the fire; and the warehouse was as snug, and warm, and dry, and bright a ballroom as you would desire to see upon a winter's night.

In came a fiddler with a music book, and went up to the lofty desk, and made an orchestra of it. In came Mrs. Fezziwig, one vast, substantial smile. In came the three Miss Fezziwigs, beaming and lovable. In came the six young followers whose hearts they broke. In came all the young men and women employed in the business. In came the housemaid, with her cousin, the baker. In came the cook, with her brother's particular friend, the milkman. In came the boy from over the way, who was suspected of not having board enough from his master; trying to hide himself behind the girl from next door but one, who was proved to have had her ears pulled by her mistress. In they all came, one after another; some shyly, some boldly, some gracefully, some awkwardly, some pushing, some pulling; in they all came, anyhow and every how.

There were dances, and there were forfeits, and more dances, and there was cake, and there was negus,[9] and there was a great piece of Cold Roast,[10] and there was a great piece of Cold Boiled, and there were mince pies. But the great effect of the evening came after the Roast and Boiled, when the fiddler struck up *Sir Roger de Coverley*.[11] Then old Fezziwig stood out to dance with Mrs. Fezziwig. Top couple, too; with a good stiff piece of work cut out for them; three or four and twenty pair of partners; people who were not to be trifled with;

[9] NEGUS—A beverage of wine, hot water, sugar, nutmeg, and lemon.
[10] COLD ROAST . . . COLD BOILED—Roast beef; boiled ham.
[11] *Sir Roger de Coverley*—A sprightly dance.

people who *would* dance, and had no notion of walking.

When the clock struck eleven, this domestic ball broke up. Mr. and Mrs. Fezziwig took their stations, one on either side the door, and shaking hands with every person individually as he or she went out, wished him or her a Merry Christmas. When everybody had retired but the two 'prentices, they did the same to them; and thus the cheerful voices died away, and the lads were left to their beds, which were under a counter in the back shop.

During the whole of this time, Scrooge had acted like a man out of his wits. His heart and soul were in the scene, and with his former self. He corroborated everything, remembered everything, enjoyed everything, and underwent the strangest agitation. It was not until now, when the bright faces of his former self and Dick were turned from them, that he remembered the Ghost, and became conscious that it was looking full upon him.

"A small matter," said the Ghost, "to make these silly folks so full of gratitude."

"Small!" echoed Scrooge.

The Spirit signed to him to listen to the two apprentices, who were pouring out their hearts in praise of Fezziwig: and when he had done so, said:

"Why! Is it not? He has spent but a few pounds of your mortal money: three or four, perhaps. Is that so much that he deserves this praise?"

"It isn't that," said Scrooge, heated by the remark, and speaking unconsciously like his former, not his latter, self. "It isn't that, Spirit. He has the power to render us happy or unhappy; to make our service light or burdensome; a pleasure or a toil. Say that his power lies in words and looks; in things so slight and insignificant that it is impossible to add and count 'em up: what then? The happiness he gives is quite as great as if it cost a fortune."

He felt the Spirit's glance, and stopped.

"What is the matter?" asked the Ghost.

"Nothing particular," said Scrooge.

"Something, I think?" the Ghost insisted.

"No," said Scrooge, "No. I should like to be able to say a word or two to my clerk just now. That's all."

"My time grows short," observed the Spirit. "Quick!"

This was not addressed to Scrooge, or to anyone whom he could see, but it produced an immediate effect. For again Scrooge saw himself. He was older now; a man in the prime of life. His face had not the harsh and rigid lines of later years; but it had begun to wear signs of care and avarice.[12] There was an eager, greedy, restless motion in the eye, which showed the passion that had taken root, and where the shadow of the growing tree would fall.

He was not alone, but sat by the side of a fair young girl in a mourning dress: in whose eyes there were tears, which sparkled in the light that shone out of the Ghost of Christmas Past.

"It matters little," she said softly. "To you, very little. Another idol has displaced me; and if it can cheer and comfort you in time to come, as I would have tried to do, I have no just cause to grieve."

"What idol has displaced you?" he rejoined.

"A golden one."

"This is the even-handed dealing of the world!" he said. "There is nothing on which the world is so hard as poverty; and there is nothing it professes to condemn with such severity as the pursuit of wealth."

"You fear the world too much," she answered, gently. "All your other hopes have merged into the hope of being beyond the chance of its sordid reproach. I have seen your nobler aspirations fall off one by one, until the master passion, Gain, engrosses you. Have I not?"

"What then?" he retorted. "Even if I have grown so much wiser, what then? I am not changed toward you."

---

[12] AVARICE—Covetousness, greed.

"Our contract is an old one. It was made when we were both poor and content to be so, until, in good season, we could improve our worldly fortune by our patient industry. You *are* changed. When it was made, you were another man."

"I was a boy," he said impatiently.

"Your own feeling tells you that you are not what you were," she returned. "I am. That which promised happiness when we were one in heart, is fraught [13] with misery now that we are two. How often and how keenly I have thought of this, I will not say. It is enough that I *have* thought of it, and can release you."

"Have I ever sought release?"

"In words? No. Never."

"In what, then?"

"In a changed nature; in an altered spirit; in another atmosphere of life; another Hope as its great end. In everything that made my love of any worth or value in your sight. If this had never been between us," said the girl, looking mildly, but with steadiness, upon him; "tell me, would you seek me out and try to win me now? Ah, no!"

He seemed to yield to the justice of this supposition, in spite of himself. But he said with a struggle, "You think not."

"I would gladly think otherwise if I could," she answered. "But if you were free today, tomorrow, yesterday, can even I believe that you would choose a dowerless [14] girl—you who, in your very confidence with her, weigh everything by Gain: or, choosing her, if for a moment you were false enough to your one guiding principle to do so, do I not know that your repentance and regret would surely follow? I do; and I release you. With a full heart, for the love of him you once were."

He was about to speak; but with her head turned from him, she resumed.

"You may—the memory of what is past half makes me hope

[13] FRAUGHT—Full of, laden.
[14] DOWERLESS—Without property, without money.

you will—have pain in this. A very, very brief time, and you will dismiss the recollection of it, gladly, as an unprofitable dream, from which it happened well that you awoke. May you be happy in the life you have chosen!"

She left him, and they parted.

"Spirit!" said Scrooge, "show me no more! Conduct me home. Why do you delight to torture me?"

"One shadow more!" exclaimed the Ghost.

"No more!" cried Scrooge. "No more. I don't wish to see it. Show me no more!"

But the relentless Ghost pinioned [15] him in both his arms, and forced him to observe what happened next.

They were in another scene and place; a room, not very large or handsome, but full of comfort. Near to the winter fire sat a beautiful young girl, so like that last that Scrooge believed it was the same, until he saw *her,* now a comely [16] matron, sitting opposite her daughter. The noise in this room was perfectly tumultuous, for there were more children there than Scrooge in his agitated state of mind could count; and, unlike the celebrated herd in the poem, they were not forty children conducting themselves like one, but every child was conducting itself like forty. The consequences were uproarious beyond belief; but no one seemed to care; on the contrary, the mother and daughter laughed heartily, and enjoyed it very much; and the latter, soon beginning to mingle in the sports, got pillaged [17] by the young brigands [18] most ruthlessly.

But now a knocking at the door was heard, and such a rush immediately ensued that she with laughing face and plundered dress was borne toward it in the center of a flushed and boisterous group, just in time to greet the father, who came home attended by a man laden with Christmas toys and presents. Then the shouting and the struggling, and the onslaught that

[15] PINIONED—Bound, held.
[16] COMELY (kŭm'lĭ)—Attractive.
[17] PILLAGED—Robbed, despoiled.
[18] BRIGANDS—Thieves. The allusion is to the story from *The Arabian Nights* of Ali Baba and the forty thieves.

was made on the defenseless porter! [19]   The scaling him, with chairs for ladders, to dive into his pockets, despoil him of brown-paper parcels, hold on tight by his cravat, hug him round the neck, pommel his back, and kick his legs in irrepressible affection!   The shouts of wonder and delight with which the development of every package was received!   The joy, and gratitude, and ecstasy!   They are all indescribably alike.   It is enough that by degrees the children and their emotions got out of the parlor and by one stair at a time, up to the top of the house; where they went to bed, and so subsided.

And now Scrooge looked on more attentively than ever, when the master of the house, having his daughter leaning fondly on him, sat down with her and her mother at his own fireside; and when he thought that such another creature, quite as graceful and as full of promise, might have called him father, and been a springtime in the haggard winter of his life, his sight grew very dim indeed.

"Belle," said the husband, turning to his wife with a smile,· "I saw an old friend of yours this afternoon."

"Who was it?"

"Guess!"

"How can I?   Tut, don't I know," she added in the same breath, laughing as he laughed.   "Mr. Scrooge."

"Mr. Scrooge it was.   I passed his office window; and as it was not shut up, and he had a candle inside, I could scarcely help seeing him.   His partner lies upon the point of death, I hear; and there he sat alone.   Quite alone in the world, I do believe."

"Spirit!" said Scrooge in a broken voice, "remove me from this place."

"I told you these were shadows of the things that have been," said the Ghost.   "That they are what they are, do not blame me!"

"Remove me!" Scrooge exclaimed, "I cannot bear it!"

---

[19] PORTER—One who carries luggage.

He was conscious of being exhausted, and overcome by an irresistible drowsiness; and, further, of being in his own bed-room. He had barely time to reel to bed, before he sank into a heavy sleep.

STAVE THREE—THE SECOND OF THE THREE SPIRITS

Awakening in the middle of a prodigiously tough snore, and sitting up in bed to get his thoughts together, Scrooge had no occasion to be told that the bell was again upon the stroke of One.

Now, being prepared for almost anything, he was not by any means prepared for nothing; and, consequently, when the bell struck One, and no shape appeared, he was taken with a violent fit of trembling. Five minutes, ten minutes, a quarter of an hour went by, yet nothing came. All this time, he lay upon his bed, the very core and center of a blaze of ruddy light, which streamed upon it when the clock proclaimed the hour; and which, being only light, was more alarming than a dozen ghosts, as he was powerless to make out what it meant.

At last, however, he began to think that the source and secret of this ghostly light might be in the adjoining room, from whence, on further tracing it, it seemed to shine. This idea taking full possession of his mind, he got up softly and shuffled in his slippers to the door.

The moment Scrooge's hand was on the lock, a strange voice called him by his name, and bade him enter. He obeyed.

It was his own room. There was no doubt about that. But it had undergone a surprising transformation. The walls and ceiling were so hung with living green, that it looked a perfect grove; from every part of which, bright gleaming berries glistened. The crisp leaves of holly, mistletoe, and ivy reflected back the light, as if so many little mirrors had been scattered there; and such a mighty blaze went roaring up the chimney, as that hearth had never known in Scrooge's time, or Marley's, or for many and many a winter season gone. Heaped upon the floor, to form a kind of throne, were turkeys, geese, game, poultry, brawn, great joints of meat, little pigs, long wreaths of sausages, mince pies, plum puddings, barrels of oysters, red-hot chestnuts, cherry-cheeked apples, juicy oranges, luscious pears, immense twelfth-cakes,[1] and seething bowls of punch, that made the chamber dim with their delicious steam.   In easy state upon this couch, there sat a jolly Giant, glorious to see; who bore a glowing torch, in shape not unlike Plenty's horn, and held it up, high up, to shed its light on Scrooge, as he came peeping round the door.

"Come in!" exclaimed the Ghost.   "Come in! and know me better, man!"

Scrooge entered timidly, and hung his head before this Spirit. He was not the dogged Scrooge he had been; and though the Spirit's eyes were clear and kind, he did not like to meet them.

"I am the Ghost of Christmas Present," said the Spirit. "Look upon me!"

Scrooge reverently did so.   It was clothed in one simple deep green robe, or mantle, bordered with white fur.   This garment hung so loosely on the figure that its capacious breast was bare, as if disdaining to be warded or concealed by any artifice.   Its feet, observable beneath the ample folds of the garment, were also bare; and on its head it wore no other covering than a holly wreath, set here and there with shining icicles.   Its dark brown curls were long and free; free as its genial face, its sparkling eye, its open hand, its cheery voice, its unconstrained demeanor, and its joyful air.   Girded round its middle was an antique scabbard; but no sword was in it, and the ancient sheath was eaten up with rust.

"You have never seen the like of me before!" exclaimed the Spirit.

"Never," Scrooge made answer to it.

The Ghost of Christmas Present rose.

"Spirit," said Scrooge, submissively, "conduct me where you

[1] TWELFTH-CAKE—For Twelfth-tide, the twelfth day after Christmas.

will. I went forth last night on compulsion, and I learned a lesson which is working now. Tonight if you have aught to teach me, let me profit by it."

"Touch my robe!"

Scrooge did as he was told, and he held it fast.

Holly, mistletoe, red berries, ivy, turkeys, geese, game, poultry, brawn, meat, pigs, sausages, oysters, pies, puddings, fruits, and punch all vanished instantly. So did the room, the fire, the ruddy glow, the hour of night, and they stood in the city streets on Christmas morning, where (for the weather was severe) the people made a rough, but brisk and not unpleasant kind of music, in scraping the snow from the pavement in front of their dwellings, and from the tops of their houses, whence it was mad delight to the boys to see it come plumping down into the road below, and splitting into artificial little snowstorms.

The house fronts looked black enough, and the windows blacker, contrasting with the smooth white sheet of snow upon the roofs, and with the dirtier snow upon the ground. The sky was gloomy, and the shortest streets were choked up with a dingy mist, half-thawed, half-frozen, whose heavier particles descended in a shower of sooty atoms, as if all the chimneys in Great Britain had, by one consent, caught fire, and were blazing away to their dear hearts' content. There was nothing very cheerful in the climate or the town, and yet was there an air of cheerfulness abroad that the clearest summer air and brightest summer sun might have endeavored to diffuse in vain.

For, the people who were shoveling away on the housetops were jovial and full of glee; calling out to one another from the parapets, and now and then exchanging a facetious [2] snowball—better-natured missile far than many a wordy jest—laughing heartily if it went right and not less heartily if it went wrong. The poulterers' shops were still half open, and the fruiterers' were radiant in their glory. There were great,

[2] FACETIOUS (fà-sē'shŭs)—Pleasant, jocose, jolly.

round, pot-bellied baskets of chestnuts, and ruddy, brown-faced, broad-girthed Spanish onions; there were pears and apples, clustered high in blooming pyramids; there were bunches of grapes, and piles of filberts, there were Norfolk biffins,[3] big and swarthy, setting off the yellow of the oranges and lemons, and, in the great compactness of their juicy persons, urgently entreating and beseeching to be carried home in paper bags and eaten after dinner.

But soon the steeples called good people all, to church and chapel, and away they came, flocking through the streets in their best clothes, and with their gayest faces. And at the same time there emerged from scores of by-streets, lanes, and nameless turnings, innumerable people, carrying their dinners to the bakers' shops. The sight of these poor revelers appeared to interest the Spirit very much, for he stood with Scrooge beside him in a baker's doorway, and taking off the covers as their bearers passed, sprinkled incense on their dinners from his torch. And it was a very uncommon kind of torch, for once or twice when there were angry words between some dinner-carriers who jostled each other, he shed a few drops of water on them from it, and their good humor was restored directly. For they said, it was a shame to quarrel upon Christmas Day. And so it was! God love it, so it was!

Scrooge and the Spirit went on, invisible, as they had been before, into the suburbs of the town. It was a remarkable quality of the Ghost, that notwithstanding his gigantic size, he could accommodate himself to any place with ease; and that he stood beneath a low roof quite as gracefully and like a supernatural creature, as it was possible he could have done in any lofty hall.

And perhaps it was the pleasure the good Spirit had in showing off this power of his, or else it was his own kind, generous, hearty nature, and his sympathy with all poor men, that led him straight to Scrooge's clerk's; for there he went, and took

[3] NORFOLK BIFFINS—A variety of apple.

Scrooge with him, holding to his robe; and on the threshold of the door the Spirit smiled, and stopped to bless Bob Cratchit's dwelling with the sprinklings of his torch.   Think of that!   Bob had but fifteen "Bob" [4] a-week himself; he pocketed on Saturdays but fifteen copies of his Christian name; and yet the Ghost of Christmas Present blessed his four-roomed house!

Then up rose Mrs. Cratchit, dressed out but poorly in a twice-turned gown, but brave in ribbons, which are cheap and make a goodly show for sixpence; and she laid the cloth, assisted by Belinda Cratchit, second of her daughters, also brave in ribbons; while Master Peter Cratchit plunged a fork into the saucepan of potatoes, and getting the corners of his monstrous shirt collar (Bob's private property, conferred upon his son and heir in honor of the day) into his mouth, rejoiced to find himself so gallantly attired.   And now two smaller Cratchits, boy and girl, came tearing in, screaming that outside the baker's they had smelled the goose, and known it for their own; and basking in luxurious thoughts of sage and onions, these young Cratchits danced about the table, and exalted Master Peter Cratchit to the skies, while he (not proud, although his collars nearly choked him) blew the fire, until the slow potatoes, bubbling up, knocked loudly at the saucepan lid to be let out and peeled.

"What has ever got your precious father then?" said Mrs. Cratchit.   "And your brother, Tiny Tim!   And Martha warn't as late last Christmas Day by half an hour!"

"Here's Martha, Mother," said a girl, appearing as she spoke.

"Here's Martha, Mother!" cried the two young Cratchits.   "Hurrah!   There's *such* a goose, Martha!"

"Why, bless your heart alive, my dear, how late you are!" said Mrs. Cratchit, kissing her a dozen times, and taking off her shawl and bonnet for her with officious zeal.

"We'd a deal of work to finish up last night," replied the girl, "and had to clear away this morning, mother!"

[4] BOB—Shilling.

"Well! Never mind so long as you are come," said Mrs. Cratchit. "Sit ye down before the fire, my dear, and have something warm, Lord bless ye!"

"No, no! There's Father coming," cried the two young Cratchits, who were everywhere at once. "Hide, Martha, hide!"

So Martha hid herself, and in came Bob, the father, with at least three feet of comforter exclusive of the fringe, hanging down before him; and his threadbare clothes darned up and brushed, to look seasonable; and Tiny Tim upon his shoulder. Alas for Tiny Tim, he bore a little crutch, and had his limbs supported by an iron frame!

"Why, where's our Martha?" cried Bob Cratchit, looking round.

"Not coming," said Mrs. Cratchit.

"Not coming!" said Bob, with a sudden declension [5] in his high spirits; for he had been Tim's race horse all the way from church, and had come home rampant.[6] "Not coming upon Christmas Day!"

Martha didn't like to see him disappointed, if it were only in joke; so she came out prematurely [7] from behind the closet door, and ran into his arms, while the two young Cratchits hustled Tiny Tim, and bore him off into the washhouse, that he might hear the pudding singing in the copper.

"And how did little Tim behave?" asked Mrs. Cratchit, when she had rallied Bob on his credulity,[8] and Bob had hugged his daughter to his heart's content.

"As good as gold," said Bob, "and better. Somehow he gets thoughtful, sitting by himself so much, and thinks the strangest things you ever heard. He told me, coming home, that he hoped the people saw him in the church, because he was a cripple, and it might be pleasant to them to remember upon Christ-

[5] DECLENSION—Descent.
[6] RAMPANT—Exuberant.
[7] PREMATURELY—Too early.
[8] CREDULITY—Belief that Martha had not come.

485

mas Day, who made lame beggars walk, and blind men see."

Bob's voice was tremulous when he told them this, and trembled more when he said that Tiny Tim was growing strong and hearty.

His active little crutch was heard upon the floor, and back came Tiny Tim before another word was spoken, escorted by his brother and sister to his stool before the fire; and while Bob, turning up his cuffs—as if, poor fellow, they were capable of being made more shabby—compounded some hot mixture in a jug and stirred it round and round and put it on the hob to simmer, Master Peter and the two ubiquitous [9] young Cratchits went to fetch the goose, with which they soon returned in high procession.

Such a bustle ensued that you might have thought a goose the rarest of all birds; a feathered phenomenon, to which a black swan was a matter of course—and in truth it was something very like it in that house. Mrs. Cratchit made the gravy (ready beforehand in a little saucepan) hissing hot; Master Peter mashed the potatoes with incredible vigor; Miss Belinda

[9] UBIQUITOUS (û-bĭk'wĭ-tŭs)—Omnipresent, everywhere at the same time.

sweetened up the apple-sauce; Martha dusted the hot plates;
Bob took Tiny Tim beside him in a tiny corner at the table;
the two young Cratchits set chairs for everybody, not forgetting themselves, and mounting guard upon their posts, crammed
spoons into their mouths, lest they should shriek for goose before their turn came to be helped. At last the dishes were set
on, and grace was said. It was succeeded by a breathless
pause, as Mrs. Cratchit, looking slowly all along the carving-
knife, prepared to plunge it in the breast; but when she did,
and when the long expected gush of stuffing issued forth, one
murmur of delight arose all around the board, and even Tiny
Tim, excited by the two young Cratchits, beat on the table with
the handle of his knife, and feebly cried "Hurrah!"

There never was such a goose. Bob said he didn't believe
there ever was such a goose cooked. Its tenderness and flavor,
size and cheapness, were the themes of universal admiration.
Eked out by the apple-sauce and mashed potatoes, it was a
sufficient dinner for the whole family, and the youngest Cratchits, in particular, were steeped in sage and onion to the eyebrows! But now, the plates being changed by Miss Belinda,
Mrs. Cratchit left the room alone—too nervous to bear wit-
nesses—to take the pudding up and bring it in.

Suppose it should not be done enough! Suppose it should
break in turning out! Suppose somebody should have got over
the wall of the backyard, and stolen it, while they were merry
with the goose—a supposition at which the two young Cratchits became livid! All sorts of horrors were supposed.

In half a minute Mrs. Cratchit entered—flushed, but smiling proudly—with the pudding, like a speckled cannon-ball, so
hard and firm, bedight [10] with Christmas holly stuck into the
top.

Oh, a wonderful pudding! Bob Cratchit said, and calmly
too, that he regarded it as the greatest success achieved by
Mrs. Cratchit since their marriage. Everybody had something

[10] BEDIGHT—Bedecked, decorated, trimmed.

to say about it, but nobody said or thought it was at all a small pudding for a large family. Any Cratchit would have blushed to hint at such a thing.

At last the dinner was all done, the cloth was cleared, the hearth swept, and the fire made up. The compound in the jug being tasted, and considered perfect, apples and oranges were put upon the table, and a shovel-full of chestnuts on the fire. Then all the Cratchit family drew around the hearth, in what Bob Cratchit called a circle, meaning half a one; and at Bob Cratchit's elbow stood the family display of glass, two tumblers, and a custard cup without a handle.

These held the hot stuff from the jug, however, as well as golden goblets would have done; and Bob served it out with beaming looks, while the chestnuts on the fire sputtered and cracked noisily. Then Bob proposed:

"A merry Christmas to us all, my dears. God bless us!" Which all the family reëchoed.

"God bless us every one!" said Tiny Tim, the last of all. He sat very close to his father's side upon his little stool. Bob held his withered little hand in his, as if he loved the child, and wished to keep him by his side, and dreaded that he might be taken from him.

"Spirit," said Scrooge, with an interest he had never felt before, "tell me if Tiny Tim will live."

"I see a vacant seat," replied the Ghost, "in the poor chimney corner, and a crutch without an owner, carefully preserved. If these shadows remain unaltered by the Future, the child will die."

"No, no," said Scrooge. "Oh, no, kind Spirit! say he will be spared."

"If these shadows remain unaltered by the Future, none other of my race," returned the Ghost, "will find him here. What then? If he be like to die, he had better do it, and decrease the surplus population."

Scrooge hung his head to hear his own words quoted by the Spirit, and was overcome with penitence and grief.

"Man," said the Ghost, "will you decide what men shall live, what men shall die? It may be, that in the sight of Heaven, you are more worthless and less fit to live than millions like this poor man's child."

Scrooge bent before the Ghost's rebuke, and trembling cast his eyes upon the ground. But he raised them speedily, on hearing his own name.

"Mr. Scrooge!" said Bob; "I'll give you Mr. Scrooge, the Founder of the Feast!"

"The Founder of the Feast, indeed!" cried Mrs. Cratchit, reddening. "I wish I had him here. I'd give him a piece of my mind to feast upon, and I hope he'd have a good appetite for it."

"My dear," said Bob, "the children! Christmas Day."

"It should be Christmas Day, I am sure," said she, "on which one drinks the health of such an odious, stingy, hard, unfeeling man as Mr. Scrooge. You know he is, Robert! Nobody knows it better than you do, poor fellow!"

"My dear," was Bob's mild answer, "Christmas Day."

"I'll drink his health for your sake and the Day's," said Mrs. Cratchit, "not for his. Long life to him! A Merry Christmas and a Happy New Year! He'll be very merry and very happy, I have no doubt!"

The children drank the toast after her. It was the first of their proceedings which had no heartiness, and the mention of his name cast a dark shadow on the party, which was not dispelled for full five minutes.

After it had passed away, they were ten times merrier than before, from the mere relief of Scrooge being done with. Bob Cratchit told them how he had a situation in his eye for Master Peter, which would bring in, if obtained, full five-and-sixpence [11]

---

[11] FIVE-AND-SIXPENCE—About $1.30 in our money.

weekly. Martha, who was a poor apprentice at a milliner's, then told them what kind of work she had to do, and how many hours she worked at a stretch, and how she meant to lie abed tomorrow morning for a good long rest; tomorrow being a holiday she passed at home. All this time the chestnuts and

the jug went round and round; and by-and-by they had a song, about a lost child traveling in the snow, from Tiny Tim, who had a plaintive little voice, and sang it very well indeed.

There was nothing of high mark in this. They were not a handsome family; they were not well dressed; their shoes were far from being waterproof; their clothes were scanty; and Bob might have known, and very likely did, the inside of a pawn-broker's. But they were happy, grateful, pleased with one another, and contented with the time; and when they faded, and looked happier yet in the bright sprinklings of the Spirit's torch at parting, Scrooge had his eye upon them, and especially on Tiny Tim, until the last.

By this time it was getting dark, and snowing pretty heavily;

and as Scrooge and the Spirit went along the streets, the brightness of the roaring fire in kitchens, parlors, and all sorts of rooms, was wonderful. Here, the flickering of the blaze showed preparations for a cozy dinner, with hot plates baking through and through before the fire, and deep red curtains, ready to be drawn to shut out cold and darkness. There, all the children of the house were running out into the snow to meet their married sisters, brothers, cousins, uncles, aunts, and be the first to greet them. Here, again, were shadows on the window blind of guests assembling; and there a group of handsome girls, all hooded and fur-booted, and all chattering at once, tripped lightly off to some near neighbor's house.

But if you had judged from the numbers of people on their way to friendly gatherings, you might have thought that no one was at home to give them welcome when they got there, instead of every house expecting company, and piling up its fires half-chimney high. Blessings on it, how the Ghost exulted! How it bared its breadth, and opened its capacious palm, and floated on, outpouring, with a generous hand, its bright and harmless mirth on everything within its reach!

And now, without a word of warning from the Ghost, they stood upon a bleak and desert moor, where monstrous masses of rude stone were cast about, as though it were the burial place of giants; and water spread itself wheresoever it listed or would have done so, but for the frost that held it prisoner; and nothing grew but moss and furze,[12] and coarse rank grass. Down in the west the setting sun had left a streak of fiery red, which glared upon the desolation for an instant, like a sullen eye, and frowning lower, lower, lower yet, was lost in the thick gloom of darkest night.

"What place is this?" asked Scrooge.

"A place where Miners live, who labor in the caves of the earth," returned the Spirit. "But they know me. See!"

A light shone from the window of a hut, and swiftly they

[12] FURZE—A spiny evergreen shrub.

advanced toward it. Passing through the wall of mud and stone, they found a cheerful company assembled round a glowing fire. An old, old man and woman, with their children and their children's children, and another generation beyond that, all decked out gayly in their holiday attire. The old man, in a voice that seldom rose above the howling of the wind upon the barren waste, was singing them a Christmas song—it had been a very old song when he was a boy—and from time to time they all joined in the chorus. So surely as they raised their voices, the old man got quite blithe and loud; and so surely as they stopped, his vigor sank again.

The Spirit did not tarry here, but bade Scrooge hold his robe, and passing on above the moor, sped—whither? Not to sea? To sea. To Scrooge's horror, looking back, he saw the last of the land, a frightful range of rocks, behind them; and his ears were deafened by the thundering of water, as it rolled, and roared, and raged among the dreadful caverns it had worn, and fiercely tried to undermine the earth.

Built upon a dismal reef of sunken rocks, some league or so from shore, on which the waters chafed and dashed, the wild year through, there stood a solitary lighthouse. Great heaps of seaweed clung to its base, and storm birds—born of the wind one might suppose, as seaweed of the water—rose and fell about it, like the waves they skimmed.

But even here, two men who watched the light had made a fire, that through the loophole in the thick stone wall shed out a ray of brightness on the awful sea. Joining their horny hands over the rough table at which they sat, they wished each other Merry Christmas; and one of them—the elder, too, with his face all damaged and scarred with hard weather, as the figurehead of an old ship might be—struck up a sturdy song that was like a gale in itself.

Again the Ghost sped on, above the black and heaving sea— on, on,—until, being far away, as he told Scrooge, from any shore, they lighted on a ship. They stood beside the helmsman at the wheel, the lookout in the bow, the officers who had the watch; dark, ghostly figures in their several stations; but every man among them hummed a Christmas tune, or had a Christmas thought, or spoke below his breath to his companion of some bygone Christmas Day, with homeward hopes belonging to it. And every man on board, waking or sleeping, good or bad, had had a kinder word for one another on that day than on any day in the year; and had shared to some extent in its festivities; and had remembered those he cared for at a distance, and had known that they delighted to remember him.

It was a great surprise to Scrooge, while listening to the moaning of the wind, and thinking what a solemn thing it was to move on through the lonely darkness over an unknown abyss,[13] whose depths were secrets as profound as death, to hear a hearty laugh. It was a much greater surprise to Scrooge to recognize it as his own nephew's, and to find himself in a bright, dry, gleaming room, with the Spirit standing smiling by his side, and looking at that same nephew with an approving affability!

"Ha! ha!" laughed Scrooge's nephew. "Ha, ha, ha!"

When Scrooge's nephew laughed in this way: holding his sides, rolling his head, and twisting his face into the most extravagant contortions, Scrooge's niece, by marriage, laughed as heartily as he. And their assembled friends being not a bit behindhand, roared out lustily.

"Ha, ha! Ha, ha, ha, ha!"

"He said that Christmas was a humbug, as I live!" cried Scrooge's nephew. "He believed it too!"

"More shame for him, Fred!" said Scrooge's niece indignantly.

She was very pretty: exceedingly pretty. With a dimpled, surprised-looking, capital face; a ripe little mouth, that seemed made to be kissed—as no doubt it was; all kinds of good little

---

[13] ABYSS (à-bĭs')—Deep, immeasurable space.

dots about her chin, that melted into one another when she laughed; and the sunniest pair of eyes you ever saw in any little creature's head.

"He's a comical old fellow," said Scrooge's nephew, "that's the truth; and not so pleasant as he might be. However, his offenses carry their own punishment, and I have nothing to say against him."

"I'm sure he is very rich, Fred," hinted Scrooge's niece. "At least you always tell *me* so."

"What of that, my dear?" said Scrooge's nephew. "His wealth is of no use to him. He doesn't do any good with it. He doesn't make himself comfortable with it. He hasn't the satisfaction of thinking—ha, ha, ha!—that he is ever going to benefit *Us* with it."

"I have no patience with him," observed Scrooge's niece. Scrooge's niece's sisters, and all the other ladies expressed the same opinion.

"Oh, I have!" said Scrooge's nephew. "I am sorry for him; I couldn't be angry with him if I tried. Who suffers by his ill whims? Himself, always. Here he takes it into his head to dislike us, and he won't come and dine with us. And the consequence of his taking a dislike to us, and not making merry with us, is, as I think, that he loses some pleasant moments, which could do him no harm. I am sure he loses pleasanter companions than he can find in his own thoughts, either in his moldy old office, or his dusty chambers. I mean to give him the same chance every year, whether he likes it or not, for I pity him. He may rail at Christmas till he dies, but he can't help thinking better of it—I defy him—if he finds me going there, in good temper, year after year, and saying, 'Uncle Scrooge, how are you?' If it only puts him in the vein to leave his poor clerk fifty pounds, *that's* something; and I think I shook him yesterday."

It was their turn to laugh now at the notion of his shaking Scrooge. But being thoroughly good-natured and not much

THE GULF STREAM

Winslow Homer

WINSLOW HOMER

American School

"*Winslow Homer was a plain American, a cantankerous Yankee opposed to cosmopolitan refinements, a native artist entitled to a seat among the master painters of the sea,*" states Thomas Craven, one of the foremost critics of modern art. Homer was born and grew up in Boston, taught himself the rudiments of drawing, and began his career as an illustrator and correspondent for Harper's Weekly. His first serious pictures grew out of the sketches he made while covering the front during the Civil War.

In 1881 Homer went on a holiday to Europe and spent two summers living among the fishermen along the English seacoast. There he discovered that his true genius lay in painting the sea. Returning to America, he built himself a cottage on the wild coast of Maine near the village of Prout's Neck. For twenty-six years he lived the life of a recluse, kept house for himself, saw few people, and devoted himself to the sea.

Homer seldom left his secluded retreat except for occasional trips to Florida and the West Indies. In 1899, after one of these vacations, he painted "The Gulf Stream," one of his most famous and characteristic works. The tragedy of the stalwart Negro sailor is evident in the hideous sharks waiting for their prey, in the helpless sliding of the boat into the trough of the sea, in the distant, unseeing ship. The beauty of the deep blue Caribbean waters only enhances the tragic figure. The painting hangs in The Metropolitan Museum of Art in New York City.

caring what they laughed at, so that they laughed at any rate, he encouraged them in their merriment.

After tea, they had some music. For they were a musical family, and knew what they were about, when they sang a Glee or Catch.[14]

But they didn't devote the whole evening to music. After a while they played at forfeits and blind-man's buff; for it is good to be children sometimes, and never better than at Christmas, when its mighty Founder was a child Himself.

There might have been twenty people there, young and old, but they all played, and so did Scrooge; for wholly forgetting, in the interest he had in what was going on, that his voice made no sound in their ears, he laughed and shouted with the rest.

The Ghost was greatly pleased to find him in this mood, and looked upon him with such favor, that he begged like a boy to be allowed to stay until the guests departed. But this the Spirit said could not be done.

"Here is a new game," said Scrooge. "Wait, Spirit!"

It was a Game called *Yes and No,* where Scrooge's nephew had to think of something, and the rest must find out what; he only answering to their questions, yes or no, as the case was. The brisk fire of questioning to which he was exposed, elicited from him that he was thinking of an animal, a live animal, rather a disagreeable animal, a savage animal, an animal that growled and grunted sometimes, and talked sometimes, and lived in London, and walked about the streets, and wasn't made a show of, and wasn't led by anybody, and didn't live in a menagerie, and was never killed in a market, and was not a horse, or a cow, or a tiger, or a dog, or a pig, or a cat, or a bear. At every fresh question that was put to him, this nephew burst into a fresh roar of laughter; and was so inexpressibly tickled, that he was obliged to get up off the sofa. At last the plump sister, falling into a similar state, cried out:

---

[14] GLEE OR CATCH—A Glee is an unaccompanied piece for three or more voices, usually men's. A Catch is a kind of round.

"I have it! I know what it is, Fred! I know what it is!'

"What is it?" cried Fred.

"It's your uncle Scro-o-o-o-oge!"

Which it certainly was. Admiration was the universal sentiment, though somebody objected that the reply to "Is it a bear?" ought to have been "Yes"; inasmuch as an answer in the negative was sufficient to have diverted their thoughts from Mr. Scrooge, supposing they had ever had any tendency that way.

"He has given us plenty of merriment, I am sure," said Fred, "and it would be ungrateful not to drink his health. I say 'Uncle Scrooge'!"

"Well! Uncle Scrooge!" they cried.

"A Merry Christmas and a Happy New Year to the old man, whatever he is!" said Scrooge's nephew. "He wouldn't take it from me, but may he have it, nevertheless. Uncle Scrooge!"

Uncle Scrooge had imperceptibly become so gay and light of heart, that he would have pledged the unconscious company in return, and thanked them in an inaudible speech, if the Ghost had given him time. But the whole scene passed off in the breath of the last word spoken by his nephew; and he and the Spirit were again upon their travels.

Much they saw, and far they went, and many homes they visited, but always with a happy end. The Spirit stood beside sick beds, and they were cheerful; on foreign lands, and they were close at home; by struggling men, and they were patient in their greater hope; by poverty, and it was rich. In almshouse, hospital and jail, in misery's every refuge, where vain man in his little brief authority had not made fast the door, and barred the Spirit out, he left his blessing. It was a long night and it was strange that while Scrooge remained unaltered in his outward form, the Ghost grew older, clearly older. Scrooge had observed this change, but never spoke of it, until they left a children's Twelfth Night party, when, looking at the Spirit as they stood together in an open place, he noticed that its hair was gray.

"Are spirits' lives so short?" asked Scrooge.

"My life upon this globe, is very brief," replied the Ghost. "It ends tonight."

"Tonight!" cried Scrooge.

"Tonight at midnight. Hark! The time is drawing near." The bell struck twelve.

Scrooge looked about him for the Ghost, and saw it not. As the last stroke ceased to vibrate, he remembered the prediction of old Jacob Marley, and lifting up his eyes, beheld a solemn Phantom, draped and hooded, coming, like a mist along the ground, toward him.

STAVE FOUR—THE LAST OF THE SPIRITS

The Phantom slowly, gravely, silently approached. When it came near him, Scrooge bent down upon his knee; for in the very air through which this Spirit moved it seemed to scatter gloom and mystery.

It was shrouded in a deep black garment, which concealed its head, its face, its form, and left nothing of it visible save one outstretched hand. But for this it would have been difficult to detach its figure from the night, and separate it from the darkness by which it was surrounded.

He felt that it was tall and stately when it came beside him, and that its mysterious presence filled him with a solemn dread. He knew no more, for the Spirit neither spoke nor moved.

"I am in the presence of the Ghost of Christmas Yet-To-Come?" said Scrooge.

The Spirit answered not, but pointed onward with its hand.

"You are about to show me shadows of the things that have not happened, but will happen in the time before us," Scrooge pursued. "Is that so, Spirit?"

The upper portion of the garment was contracted for an instant in its folds, as if the Spirit had inclined his head. That was the only answer he received.

"Ghost of the Future!" Scrooge exclaimed, "I fear you more than any specter I have seen. But as I know your purpose is to do me good, and as I hope to live to be another man from what I was, I am prepared to bear you company, and do it with a thankful heart. Will you not speak to me?"

It gave him no reply. The hand was pointed straight before them.

"Lead on!" said Scrooge. "Lead on! The night is waning fast, and it is precious time to me, I know. Lead on, Spirit!"

The Phantom moved away as it had come toward him. Scrooge followed in the shadow of its dress, which bore him up, he thought, and carried him along.

They scarcely seemed to enter the city; for the city rather seemed to spring up about them, and encompass them of its own act. But there they were, in the heart of it; on 'Change, amongst the merchants, who hurried up and down, and chinked the money in their pockets, and conversed in groups, and looked at their watches, and trifled thoughtfully with their great gold seals; and so forth, as Scrooge had seen them often.

The Spirit stopped beside one little knot of business men. Observing that the hand was pointed to them, Scrooge advanced to listen to their talk.

"No," said a great fat man with a monstrous chin, "I don't know much about it, either way. I only know he's dead."

"When did he die?" inquired another.

"Last night, I believe."

"Why, what was the matter with him?" asked a third, taking a vast quantity of snuff out of a very large snuffbox. "I thought he'd never die."

"God knows," said the first, with a yawn.

"What has he done with his money?" asked a red-faced gentleman.

"I haven't heard," said the man with the large chin, yawning again. "Left it to his Company, perhaps. He hasn't left it to *me*. That's all I know."

This pleasantry was received with a general laugh.

"It's likely to be a cheap funeral," said the same speaker; "for upon my life I don't know of anybody to go to it. Suppose we make up a party and volunteer?"

"I don't mind going if a lunch is provided," observed one gentleman.

Another laughed.

"Well, I am the most disinterested among you, after all," said the first speaker, "for I never wear black gloves, and I never eat lunch. But I'll offer to go, if anybody else will. When I come to think of it, I'm not at all sure that I wasn't his most particular friend; for we used to stop and speak whenever we met. Bye, bye!"

Speakers and listeners strolled away, and mixed with other groups. Scrooge knew the men, and looked toward the Spirit for an explanation.

Scrooge was at first inclined to be surprised that the Spirit should attach importance to conversations apparently so trivial; but feeling assured that they must have some hidden purpose, he set himself to consider what it was likely to be. They could scarcely be supposed to have any bearing on the death of Jacob, his old partner, for that was Past, and this Ghost's province was the Future. Nor could he think of any one immediately connected with himself, to whom he could apply them. But nothing doubting that to whomsoever they applied they had some latent moral for his own improvement, he resolved to treasure up every word he heard, and everything he saw; and especially to observe the shadow of himself when it appeared. For he had an expectation that the conduct of his future self would give him the clue he missed, and would render the solution of these riddles easy.

He looked about in that very place for his own image; but another man stood in his accustomed corner, and though the

clock pointed to his usual time of day for being there, he saw
no likeness of himself among the multitudes that poured in.
It gave him little surprise, however; for he had been revolving
in his mind a change of life, and thought and hoped he saw his
newborn resolutions carried out in this.

They left the busy scene, and went into an obscure part of
the town, where Scrooge had never penetrated before, although
he recognized its situation, and its bad repute. The ways were
foul and narrow; the shops and houses wretched; the people
half naked, drunken, slipshod, ugly. Alley and archways, like
so many cesspools, disgorged their offenses of smell, and dirt,
and life, upon the straggling streets; and the whole quarter
reeked with crime, with filth, with misery.

Far in this den of infamous resort, there was a low-browed
beetling shop, below a penthouse roof, where iron, old rags,
bottles, and bones, were bought. Upon the floor within, were
piled up heaps of rusty keys, nails, chains, hinges, files, scales,
weights and refuse iron of all kinds. Secrets that few would
like to scrutinize were bred and hidden in mountains of un-
seemly rags, masses of corrupted fat, and sepulchers [1] of bones.
Sitting in among the wares he dealt in, by a charcoal stove,
made of old bricks, was a gray-haired rascal, nearly seventy
years of age; who had screened himself from the cold air without by a frowzy curtaining of miscellaneous tatters, hung upon
a line; and smoked his pipe in all the luxury of calm retire-
ment.

Scrooge and the Phantom came into the presence of this man,
just as a woman with a heavy bundle slunk into the shop. But
she had scarcely entered, when another woman, similarly laden,
came in too; and she was closely followed by a man in faded
black, who was not less startled by the sight of them, than they
had been upon the recognition of each other. After a short
period of blank astonishment, in which the old man with the
pipe had joined them, they all three burst into a laugh.

[1] SEPULCHERS—Graves, tombs.

"Let the charwoman be the first!" cried she who had entered first. "Let the laundress be the second; and let the under-taker's man be the third. Look here, old Joe, here's a chance! If we haven't all three met here without meaning it!"

"You couldn't have met in a better place," said old Joe, removing his pipe from his mouth. "Come into the parlor." The parlor was the space behind the screen of rags. The old man raked the fire together with an old stair rod, and having trimmed his smoky lamp (for it was night) with the stem of his pipe, put it in his mouth again.

While he did this, the woman who had already spoken threw her bundle on the floor and sat down in a flaunting manner on a stool; crossing her elbows on her knees, and looking with a bold defiance at the other two.

"Open that bundle, old Joe," said the woman, "and let me know the value of it. Speak out plain. I'm not afraid to be the first, nor afraid for them to see it. We knew pretty well that we were helping ourselves, before we met here, I believe. It's no sin. Open the bundle, Joe."

But the gallantry of her friends would not allow of this; and the man in faded black, mounting the breach first, produced *his* plunder. It was not extensive. A seal or two, a pencil case, a pair of sleeve buttons, and a brooch of no great value, were all. They were severally examined and appraised by old Joe, who chalked the sums he was disposed to give for each, upon the wall, and added them up into a total when he found there was nothing more to come.

"That's your account," said Joe, "and I wouldn't give another sixpence, if I was to be boiled for not doing it. Who's next?"

Mrs. Dilber was next. Sheets and towels, a little wearing apparel, two old-fashioned silver teaspoons, a pair of sugar-tongs, and a few boots. Her account was stated on the wall in the same manner.

"I always give too much to ladies. It's a weakness of mine, and that's the way I ruin myself," said old Joe. "That's your account. If you asked me for another penny, and made it an open question, I'd repent of being so liberal, and knock off half-a-crown."

"And now undo *my* bundle, Joe," said the first woman.

Joe went down on his knees for the greater convenience of opening it, and having unfastened a great many knots, dragged out a large and heavy roll of some dark stuff.

"What do you call this?" said Joe. "Bed curtains!"

"Ah!" returned the woman, laughing and leaning forward on her crossed arms. "Bed curtains!"

"You don't mean to say you took 'em down, rings and all, with him lying there?" said Joe.

"Yes, I do," replied the woman. "Why not?"

"I hope he didn't die of anything catching? Eh?" said old Joe, stopping in his work, and looking up.

"Don't you be afraid of that," returned the woman. "I ain't so fond of his company that I'd loiter about him for such things, if he did. Ah! You may look through that shirt till your eyes ache; but you won't find a hole in it, nor a thread-bare place. It's the best he had, and a fine one, too. They'd have wasted it, if it hadn't been for me."

"What do you call wasting of it?" asked old Joe.

"Putting it on him to be buried in, to be sure," replied the woman with a laugh. "Somebody was fool enough to do it, but I took it off again. If calico ain't good enough for such a purpose, it isn't good enough for anything. It's quite as be-coming to the body. He can't look uglier than he did in that one."

Scrooge listened to this dialogue in horror. As they sat grouped about their spoil, in the scanty light afforded by the old man's lamp, he viewed them with a detestation and disgust, which could hardly have been greater though they had been obscene demons, marketing the corpse itself.

"Ha, ha!" laughed the same woman, when old Joe, produc-ing a flannel bag with money in it, told out [2] their several gains upon the ground. "This is the end of it, you see! He fright-ened every one away from him when he was alive, to profit us when he was dead! Ha, ha, ha!"

"Spirit!" said Scrooge, shuddering from head to foot. "I see, I see. The case of this unhappy man might be my own. My life tends that way, now."

He recoiled in terror, for the scene had changed, and now he almost touched a bed: a bare, uncurtained bed: on which, beneath a ragged sheet, there lay a something covered up, which though it was dumb, announced itself in awful lan-guage.

The room was very dark, too dark to be observed with any accuracy, though Scrooge glanced around it in obedience to a secret impulse, anxious to know what kind of room it was. A pale light rising in the outer air, fell straight upon the bed; and on it, plundered and bereft, unwatched, unwept, uncared for, was the body of this man.

---

[2] TOLD OUT—Counted out.

Scrooge glanced toward the Phantom. Its steady hand was pointed to the head. The cover was so carelessly adjusted that the slightest raising of it, the motion of a finger upon Scrooge's part, would have disclosed the face. He thought of it, felt how easy it would be to do, and longed to do it; but had no more power to withdraw the veil than to dismiss the specter at his side. He thought, if this man could be raised up now, what would be his foremost thoughts? Avarice, hard-dealing, gripping cares? They have brought him to a rich end, truly!

He lay, in the dark, empty house, with not a man, a woman, or a child to say that he was kind in this or that. A cat was tearing at the door, and there was a sound of gnawing rats beneath the hearthstone. What *they* wanted in the room of death, and why they were so restless and disturbed, Scrooge did not dare to think.

"Spirit!" he said, "this is a fearful place. In leaving it, I shall not leave its lesson, trust me. Let us go!"

Still the Ghost pointed with an unmoved finger to the head.

"I understand you," Scrooge returned, "and I would do it, if I could. But I have not the power, Spirit. I have not the power."

Again it seemed to look upon him.

"If there is any person in the town, who feels emotion caused by this man's death," said Scrooge quite agonized, "show that person to me, Spirit, I beseech you!"

The Phantom spread its dark robe before him for a moment, like a wing; and withdrawing it, revealed a room by daylight, where a mother and her children were.

She was expecting someone, and with anxious eagerness; for she walked up and down the room; started at every sound; looked out from the window; glanced at the clock; tried, but in vain, to work with her needle; and could hardly bear the voices of the children in their play.

At length the long-expected knock was heard. She hurried

to the door, and met her husband; a man whose face was care-worn and depressed, though he was young. There was a remarkable expression in it now; a kind of serious delight of which he felt ashamed, and which he struggled to repress.

He sat down to the dinner that had been hoarding for him by the fire; and when she asked him faintly what news (which was not until after a long silence), he appeared embarrassed how to answer.

"Is it good," she said, "or bad?"

"Bad," he answered.

"We are quite ruined?"

"No. There is hope yet, Caroline."

"If *he* relents," she said, amazed, "there is! Nothing is past hope, if such a miracle has happened."

"He is past relenting," said her husband. "He is dead."

She was a mild and patient creature if her face spoke truth; but she was thankful in her soul to hear it, and she said so, with clasped hands. She prayed forgiveness the next moment, and was sorry, but the first was the emotion of her heart.

"What the half-drunken woman whom I told you of last night, said to me, when I tried to see him and obtain a week's delay; and what I thought was a mere excuse to avoid me; turns out to have been quite true. He was not only very ill, but dying, then."

"To whom will our debt be transferred?"

"I don't know. But before that time we shall be ready with the money; and even though we were not, it would be bad fortune indeed to find so merciless a creditor in his successor. We may sleep tonight with light hearts, Caroline!"

Yes. Soften it as they would, their hearts were lighter. The children's faces, hushed and clustered round to hear what they so little understood, were brighter; and it was a happier house for this man's death! The only emotion that the Ghost could show him, caused by the event, was one of pleasure.

The Ghost conducted him through several streets familiar

to his feet; and as they went along, Scrooge looked here and there to find himself, but nowhere was he to be seen. They entered Bob Cratchit's house; the dwelling he had visited before; and found the mother and the children seated around the fire.

Quiet. Very quiet. The noisy little Cratchits were as still as statues in one corner, and sat looking up at Peter, who had a book before him. The mother and her daughters were engaged in sewing. But surely they were very quiet!

" 'And he took a child, and set him in the midst of them.' "

Where had Scrooge heard those words? He had not dreamed them. The boy must have read them out, as he and the Spirit crossed the threshold. Why did he not go on?

The mother laid her work upon the table, and put her hand up to her face.

Ah, poor Tiny Tim!

"I'm better now again," said the mother. "It makes me weep in candlelight; and I wouldn't show weak eyes to your father when he comes home, for the world. It must be near his time."

"Past it rather," Peter answered, shutting up his book. "But I think he has walked a little slower than he used to, these last few evenings, Mother."

They were very quiet again. At last she said, and in a steady, cheerful voice, that only faltered once:

"I have known him walk with—I have known him walk with Tiny Tim upon his shoulders, very fast indeed."

"And so have I," said Peter. "Often."

"And so have I," exclaimed another. So had all.

"But he was very light to carry," she resumed, intent upon her work, "and his father loved him so, that it was no trouble —no trouble. And there is your father at the door!"

She hurried out to meet him; and Bob in his comforter—he had need of it, poor fellow—came in. His tea was ready for him on the hob, and they all tried who should help him to it most. Then the two young Cratchits got upon his knees and laid, each child, a little cheek against his face, as if they said, "Don't mind it, Father. Don't be grieved!"

Bob was very cheerful with them, and spoke pleasantly to all the family. He looked at the work upon the table, and praised the industry and speed of Mrs. Cratchit and the girls.

"My little, little child!" cried Bob. "My little child!" He broke down all at once. He couldn't help it.

He left the room, and went upstairs into the room above, which was lighted cheerfully, and hung with Christmas. There was a chair set close beside the child, and there were signs of someone having been there lately. Poor Bob sat down in it,

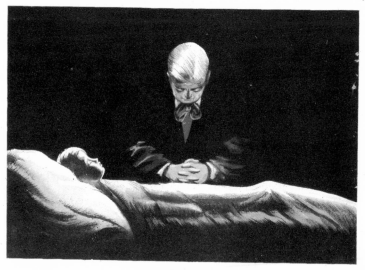

and when he had thought a little and composed himself, he kissed the little face. He was reconciled to what had happened, and went down again.

They drew about the fire, and talked; the girls and mother working still. Bob told them of the extraordinary kindness of Mr. Scrooge's nephew, whom he had scarcely seen but once, and who, meeting him in the street that day, inquired what had happened to distress him. " 'I am heartily sorry for it, Mr. Cratchit,' he said, 'and heartily sorry for your good wife.' By the bye, how he ever knew *that,* I don't know."

"Everybody knows that!" said Peter.

"Very well observed, my boy!" said Bob. "I hope they do. 'Heartily sorry,' he said, 'for your good wife. If I can be of service to you in any way,' he said, giving me his card, 'that's where I live. Pray come to me.' Now, it wasn't," continued Bob, "for the sake of anything he might be able to do for us, so much as for his kind way, that this was quite delightful. It really seemed as if he had known our Tiny Tim, and felt with us. And I know," said Bob, "I know, my dears, that when we recollect how patient and how mild he was, although he was a little, little child, we shall not quarrel easily among ourselves, and forget poor Tiny Tim in doing it."

"No, never, Father!" they all cried again.

Mrs. Cratchit kissed him, his daughters kissed him, the two young Cratchits kissed him, and Peter and himself shook hands.

Spirit of Tiny Tim, thy childish essence was from God!

"Specter," said Scrooge, "something informs me that our parting moment is at hand. I know it, but I know not how. Tell me what man that was whom we saw lying dead!"

The Ghost of Christmas Yet-To-Come conveyed him, as before—though at a different time, he thought: indeed, there seemed no order in these latter visions, save that they were in the Future—into the resorts of business men, but showed him not himself. Indeed, the Spirit did not stay for anything, but went straight on, as to the end just now desired, until besought by Scrooge to tarry for a moment.

"This court," said Scrooge, "through which we hurry now, is where my place of occupation is, and has been for a length of time. I see the house. Let me behold what I shall be, in days to come."

The Spirit stopped; the hand was pointed elsewhere

"The house is yonder," Scrooge exclaimed. "Why do you point away?"

The inexorable [3] finger underwent no change.

Scrooge hastened to the window of his office, and looked in. It was still an office, but not his. The furniture was not the same, and the figure in the chair was not himself. The Phantom pointed as before.

He joined it once again, and wondering why and whither he had gone, accompanied it until they reached an iron gate. He paused to look round before entering.

A churchyard. Here, then, the wretched man whose name he had now to learn, lay underneath the ground. It was a worthy place—walled in by houses; overrun by grass and weeds.

The Spirit stood among the graves, and pointed down to one. He advanced toward it trembling. The Phantom was exactly as it had been, but he dreaded that he saw new meaning in its solemn shape.

"Before I draw nearer to that stone to which you point," said Scrooge, "answer me one question. Are these the shadows of the things that Will be, or are they shadows of things that May be, only?"

Still the Ghost pointed downward to the grave by which it stood.

"Men's courses will foreshadow certain ends, to which, if persevered in, they must lead," said Scrooge. "But if the courses be departed from, the ends will change. Say it is thus with what you show me!"

The Spirit was immovable as ever.

Scrooge crept toward it, trembling as he went; and following the finger, read upon the stone of the neglected grave his own name, EBENEZER SCROOGE.

"Am *I* that man who lay upon the bed?" he cried, upon his knees.

---

[3] INEXORABLE (ĭn-ĕk′sô-rå-b'l)—Unyielding, relentless.

The finger pointed from the grave to him, and back again. "No, Spirit! Oh, no, no!"

The finger still was there.

"Spirit!" he cried, tight clutching at its robe, "hear me! I am not the man I was. I will not be the man I must have been but for this experience. Why show me this, if I am past all hope?"

For the first time the hand appeared to shake.

"Good Spirit," he pursued, as down upon the ground he fell before it: "Your nature intercedes for me, and pities me. Assure me that I yet may change these shadows you have shown me, by an altered life!"

The kind hand trembled.

"I will honor Christmas in my heart, and try to keep it all the year. I will live in the Past, the Present, and the Future. The Spirits of all Three shall strive within me. I will not shut out the lessons that they teach. Oh, tell me I may sponge away the writing on this stone!"

In his agony, he caught the spectral hand. It sought to free itself but he was strong in his entreaty, and detained it. The Spirit, stronger yet, repulsed him.

Holding up his hands in a last prayer to have his fate reversed, he saw an alteration in the Phantom's hood and dress. It shrunk, collapsed, and dwindled down into a bedpost.

STAVE FIVE—THE END OF IT

Yes! and the bedpost was his own. The bed was his own, the room was his own. Best and happiest of all, the Time before him was his own, to make amends in!

"I will live in the Past, the Present, and the Future!" Scrooge repeated, as he scrambled out of bed. "The Spirits of all Three shall strive within me. Oh, Jacob Marley! Heaven, and the Christmas Time be praised for this! I say it on my knees, old Jacob, on my knees!"

He was so fluttered and so glowing with his good intentions, that his broken voice would scarcely answer to his call. He had been sobbing violently in his conflict with the Spirit, and his face was wet with tears.

"They are not torn down," cried Scrooge, folding one of his bed curtains in his arms; "they are not torn down, rings and all. They are here—I am here—the shadows of the things that would have been, may be dispelled. They will be. I know they will!"

His hands were busy with his garments all this time: turning them inside out, putting them on upside down, tearing them, mislaying them, making them parties to every kind of extravagance.

"I don't know what to do!" cried Scrooge, laughing and crying in the same breath. "I am as light as a feather, I am as happy as an angel, I am as merry as a schoolboy. A Merry Christmas to everybody! A Happy New Year to all the world! Hallo here! Whoop! Hallo!"

He had frisked into the sitting room, and was now standing there.

"There's the saucepan that the gruel was in!" cried Scrooge, starting off again, and going round the fireplace. "There's the door by which the Ghost of Jacob Marley entered!   There's the corner where the Ghost of Christmas Present sat!   It's all right, it's all true, it all happened.   Ha, ha, ha!"

Really, for a man who had been out of practice for so many years, it was a splendid laugh, a most illustrious laugh.   The father of a long, long line of brilliant laughs!

"I don't know what day of the month it is!" said Scrooge. "I don't know how long I've been among the Spirits.   I don't know anything.   I'm quite a baby.   Never mind.   I don't care. I'd rather be a baby.   Hallo!   Whoop!   Hallo here!"

He was checked in his transports by the churches ringing out the lustiest peals he had ever heard.   Clash, clang, hammer; ding, dong, bell.   Bell, dong, ding; hammer, clang, clash!   Oh, glorious, glorious!

Running to the window, he opened it, and put out his head. No fog, no mist; clear, bright, jovial, stirring, cold; cold, piping for the blood to dance to; golden sunlight; heavenly sky; sweet fresh air; merry bells.   Oh, glorious!   Glorious!

"What's today?" cried Scrooge, calling downward to a boy in Sunday clothes, who perhaps had loitered in to look about him.

"Eh?" returned the boy, with all his might of wonder.

"What's today, my fine fellow?" said Scrooge.

"Today!" replied the boy.   "Why, CHRISTMAS DAY."

"It's Christmas Day!" said Scrooge to himself.   "I haven't missed it.   The Spirits have done it all in one night.   They can do anything they like.   Of course they can.   Of course they can.   Hallo, my fine fellow!"

"Hallo!" returned the boy.

"Do you know the Poulterer's, in the next street but one, at the corner?" Scrooge inquired.

"I should hope I did," replied the lad.

"An intelligent boy!" said Scrooge.   "A remarkable boy! Do you know whether they've sold the prize Turkey that was hanging up there?—Not the little prize Turkey: the big one?"

"What, the one as big as me?" returned the boy.

FÊTE CHAMPÊTRE
Jean Antoine Watteau

JEAN ANTOINE WATTEAU

French School

Seeking to escape from unpleasant quarrels at home, young Jean Antoine Watteau (1684–1721) left his native town of Valenciennes in Flanders and fled to Paris in search of a career in art. The cold and hunger endured there for several years were to bring on the consumption from which he was to die at the age of thirty-seven. Finally, through influential friends, he was hailed as the creator of a new style in art.

Sensitive and unstable in nature, Watteau lived and painted the prevailing mood of the French court and the ruling class. Their lives were devoted to reckless pleasure, superficial gallantry, light-hearted romance. Watteau excelled in depicting the fashionable social gatherings of the day, such as that seen in "Fête Champêtre," which now hangs in the National Gallery of Scotland in Edinburgh. The sunlit colors and purity of tone for which Watteau is known give the picture unusual charm and delicacy.

"What a delightful boy!" said Scrooge. "It's a pleasure to talk to him. Yes, my lad!"

"It's hanging there now," replied the boy.

"Is it?" said Scrooge. "Go and buy it."

"Walk-ER!" [1] exclaimed the boy.

"No, no," said Scrooge, "I am in earnest. Go and buy it, and tell 'em to bring it here, that I may give them the directions where to take it. Come back with the man, and I'll give you a shilling. Come back with him in less than five minutes and I'll give you half-a-crown!"

The boy was off like a shot. He must have had a steady hand at a trigger who could have got a shot off half so fast.

"I'll send it to Bob Cratchit's!" whispered Scrooge, rubbing his hands, and splitting with a laugh. "He shan't know who sends it. It's twice the size of Tiny Tim."

The hand in which he wrote the address was not a steady one, but write it he did, somehow, and went downstairs to open the street door, ready for the coming of the Poulterer's man. As he stood there, waiting his arrival, the knocker caught his eye.

"I shall love it, as long as I live!" cried Scrooge, patting it with his hand. "I scarcely ever looked at it before. What an honest expression it has in its face! It's a wonderful knocker!—Here's the Turkey. Hallo! Whoop! How are you! Merry Christmas!"

It *was* a Turkey! He never could have stood upon his legs, that bird. He would have snapped 'em short off in a minute, like sticks of sealing wax.

"Why, it's impossible to carry that to Camden Town," said Scrooge. "You must have a cab."

The chuckle with which he said this, and the chuckle with which he paid for the Turkey, and the chuckle with which he paid for the cab, and the chuckle with which he recompensed the boy, were only to be exceeded by the chuckle with which he

[1] WALK-ER—A slang expression meaning "You're joking!"

sat down breathless in his chair again, and chuckled till he cried.

He dressed himself "all in his best," and at last got out into the streets. The people were by this time pouring forth, as he had seen them with the Ghost of Christmas Present; and walking with his hands behind him, Scrooge regarded every one with a delighted smile. He looked so irresistibly pleasant, in a word, that three or four good-humored fellows said, "Good morning, sir! A Merry Christmas to you!" And Scrooge said often afterwards, that of all the blithe sounds he had ever heard, those were the blithest in his ears.

He had not gone far, when coming on toward him he beheld the portly gentleman who had walked into his countinghouse the day before and said, "Scrooge and Marley's, I believe?" It sent a pang across his heart to think how this old gentleman would look upon him when they met; but he knew what path lay straight before him, and he took it.

"My dear sir," said Scrooge, quickening his pace, and taking the old gentleman by both hands. "How do you do? I hope you succeeded yesterday. It was very kind of you. A Merry Christmas to you, sir!"

"Mr. Scrooge?"

"Yes," said Scrooge. "That is my name, and I fear it may not be pleasant to you. Allow me to ask your pardon. And will you have the goodness"—here Scrooge whispered in his ear.

"Lord bless me!" cried the gentleman, as if his breath were taken away. "My dear Mr. Scrooge, are you serious?"

"If you please," said Scrooge. "Not a farthing less. A great many back payments are included in it, I assure you. Will you do me that favor?"

"My dear sir," said the other, shaking hands with him. "I don't know what to say to such munifi——"

"Don't say anything, please," retorted Scrooge. "Will you come and see me?"

"I will!" cried the old gentleman. And it was clear he meant to do it.

"Thank'ee," said Scrooge. "I am much obliged to you. I thank you fifty times. Bless you!"

He went to church, and walked about the streets, and watched the people hurrying to and fro, and patted children on the head, and questioned beggars, and looked down into the kitchens of houses, and up to the windows, and found that everything could yield him pleasure. He had never dreamed that any walk—that anything—could give him so much happiness. In the afternoon he turned his steps toward his nephew's house.

He passed the door a dozen times, before he had the courage to go up and knock. But he made a dash, and did it:

"Is your master at home, my dear?" said Scrooge to the girl. "Yes, sir."

"Where is he, my love?" said Scrooge.

"He's in the dining room, sir, along with my mother. I'll show you upstairs, if you please."

"Thank'ee. He knows me," said Scrooge, with his hand already on the dining-room lock. "I'll go in here, my dear."

He turned it gently, and sidled his face in round the door. They were looking at the table (which was spread out in great array); for these young housekeepers are always nervous on such points, and like to see that everything is right.

"Fred!" said Scrooge.

"Why bless my soul!" cried Fred, "who's that?"

"It's I. Your uncle Scrooge. I have come to dinner. Will you let me in, Fred?"

Let him in! It is a mercy he didn't shake his arm off. He was at home in five minutes. Nothing could be heartier. His niece looked just the same. So did everyone when *they* came. Wonderful party, wonderful games, wonderful unanimity,[2] wonderful happiness!

But he was early at the office next morning. Oh, he was early there. If he could be first, and catch Bob Cratchit coming late! That was the thing he had set his heart upon.

And he did it; yes, he did! The clock struck nine. No Bob. A quarter past. No Bob. He was full eighteen minutes and a half behind his time. Scrooge sat with his door wide open, that he might see him come.

His hat was off, before he opened the door; his comforter too. He was on his stool in a jiffy; driving away with his pen, as if he were trying to overtake nine o'clock.

"Hallo!" growled Scrooge, in his accustomed voice, as near as he could feign it. "What do you mean by coming here at this time of day?"

"I am very sorry, sir," said Bob. "I *am* behind my time."

"You are?" repeated Scrooge. "Yes. I think you are. Step this way, sir, if you please."

"It's only once a year, sir," pleaded Bob, appearing from the Tank.[3] "It shall not be repeated. I was making rather merry yesterday, sir."

---

[2] UNANIMITY (ū-nȧ-nĭm′ĭ-tĭ)—Of one mind, all thinking the same.

[3] TANK—Lower part of the office, workroom.

"Now, I'll tell you what, my friend," said Scrooge, "I am not going to stand this sort of thing any longer. And therefore," he continued, leaping from his stool, and giving Bob such a dig in the waistcoat that he staggered back into the Tank again, "and therefore I am about to raise your salary!"

Bob trembled, and got a little nearer to the ruler. He had a momentary idea of knocking Scrooge down with it, holding him, and calling to the people in the court for help and a strait-waistcoat.[4]

"A Merry Christmas, Bob!" said Scrooge, with an earnestness that could not be mistaken, as he clapped him on the back. "A merrier Christmas, Bob, my good fellow, than I have given you for many a year!   I'll raise your salary, and endeavor to assist your struggling family, and we will discuss your affairs this very afternoon, Bob!   Make up the fires, and buy another scuttle of coal before you dot another *i,* Bob Cratchit!"

Scrooge was better than his word. He did it all, and infinitely more; and to Tiny Tim, who did NOT die, he was a second father. He became as good a friend, as good a master, and as good a man, as the good old city knew, or any other good old city, town, or borough, in the good old world. Some people laughed to see the alteration in him, but he let them laugh, and little heeded them; for he was wise enough to know that nothing ever happened on this globe, for good, at which some people did not have their fill of laughter in the outset; and knowing that such as these would be blind anyway, he thought it quite as well that they should wrinkle up their eyes in grins, as have the malady in less attractive forms. His own heart laughed: and that was quite enough for him.

He had no further experience with Spirits, but lived a happy life ever afterwards; and it was always said of him, that he knew how to keep Christmas well, if any man alive possessed the knowledge. May that be truly said of us, and all of us! And so, as Tiny Tim observed, "God Bless Us, Everyone!"

[4] STRAIT-WAISTCOAT—Strait-jacket for restraining the violently insane.

Realizing our heritage.

AMERICA FOR ME

HENRY VAN DYKE

1B 'Tis fine to see the Old World, and travel up and down
Among the famous palaces and cities of renown,
To admire the crumbly castles and the statues of the kings,
But now I think I've had enough of antiquated things.

U 5 *So it's home again, and home again, America for me!*
My heart is turning home again, and there I long to be,
In the land of youth and freedom beyond the ocean bars,
Where the air is full of sunlight, and the flag is full of stars.

1B Oh, London is a man's town, there's power in the air;
1G 10 And Paris is a woman's town, with flowers in her hair;
G And it's sweet to dream in Venice, and it's great to study
Rome;
U But when it comes to living there is no place like home.

1B I like the German fir woods, in green battalions drilled;
I like the garden of Versailles with flashing fountains
filled;
1G 15 But, oh, to take your hand, my dear, and ramble for a day
In the friendly western woodland where Nature has her
way!

1B I know that Europe's wonderful, yet something seems to
lack;
The Past is too much with her, and her people looking
back.

But the glory of the Present is to make the Future free—
20   We love our land for what she is and what she is to be.

U   *Oh, it's home again, and home again, America for me!*
    I want a ship that's westward bound to plow the rolling
      sea,
    To the blessed Land of Room Enough beyond the ocean
      bars,
    Where the air is full of sunlight and the flag is full of stars.

THE FLAG GOES BY

HENRY HOLCOMB BENNETT

B   HATS off!
      Along the street there comes
      A blare of bugles, a ruffle of drums,
      A flash of color beneath the sky:
    5   Hats off!
      The flag is passing by!

G   Blue and crimson and white it shines,
      Over the steel-tipped, ordered lines.
        Hats off!
  10   The colors before us fly;
      But more than the flag is passing by.

U   Sea fights and land fights, grim and great,
      Fought to make and to save the State:
1B(♯1)   Weary marches and sinking ships;
1B(♯2) 15 Cheers of victory on dying lips;
1G(♯1)   Days of plenty and years of peace;
1G(♯2)   March of a strong land's swift increase;
1B(♯1)   Equal justice, right, and law,

1B(#2)   Stately honor and reverend awe;
   B   20   Sign of a nation, great and strong
                To ward her people from foreign wrong:
G   Pride and glory and honor,—all
                Live in the colors to stand or fall.

U   Hats off!
   25   Along the street there comes
                A blare of bugles, a ruffle of drums;
                And loyal hearts are beating high:
                   Hats off!
                The flag is passing by!

THE BIRTH OF A NATION'S SONG

KATHERINE LITTLE BAKELESS

On August 27, 1814, in the course of the war between England and America, an old man was taken prisoner by the British in the little town of Upper Marlborough, Maryland. Insignificant as the incident seemed, it was to result in an eventful conclusion. The prisoner was the elderly Dr. Beanes, known and loved as the loyal patriot who as a young man had cared for Washington's soldiers at Valley Forge. Upon hearing of his arrest, his fellow townsmen sought help from a young lawyer, Francis Scott Key, who lived near Washington and who knew Dr. Beanes well.

Seeking to procure the Doctor's release, Key learned that the prisoner had been taken on board the British fleet and that it was necessary to apply to Colonel Skinner, agent, for flags of truce and exchange of prisoners. The location of the British fleet was unknown, but Key and Skinner, starting in the cartel boat from Baltimore, found the fleet a week later at the mouth of the Potomac. They boarded the British Admiral's ship and were reluctantly given per-

"The Birth of a Nation's Song" is reprinted by permission of J. B. Lippincott Company, from *The Birth of a Nation's Song* by Katherine L. Bakeless.

mission to take Dr. Beanes back,—*after* the British attack on Baltimore. To their chagrin and dismay, Key and Skinner thus found *themselves* held prisoner. For some days they remained on board the frigate *Surprize* as the fleet sailed up Chesapeake Bay, but on September 11th they were transferred to the truce boat from which they were to watch the attack on Fort McHenry.

Within the Fort itself, Major Armistead was waging a terrific personal battle. He had been ordered to surrender the Fort without fighting, but unless the Fort held the fleet, the loss of Baltimore was certain. Previously he had arranged a sunken barrier of old barges and boats just above the Fort, its object being to hold the fleet under the guns of the Fort. Then on September 13th, the British bombardment began. Major Armistead, looking up at the great flag flying above him, made his decision. For those fifteen stars, two feet across, and those fifteen stripes, he would fight—even against orders!

Boom-boom-boom-boom! The big guns of the frigates discharged whole broadsides at the little Fort. The terrific concussion of the explosions made the ships pull and tug at their anchors. The heaving and swaying of many boats churned up the gray and muddy water into angry waves, upon which the little cartel [1] pitched and tossed. It was not long before smoke obscured the Fort from Mr. Key's view, and all he could see of the Fort was the great star-bespangled banner flying high above the battle.

During the morning the fleet remained at some distance and pounded the Fort with its bombs. To draw in closer might run their ships aground on the muddy bottom. The Fort, whose guns were lighter than those of the enemy, fired only occasionally to show that the Americans were not giving up. Amid the deafening roar of the invader's bombs, these infrequent answers from the Fort were as music to the ears of Skinner, Beanes and Key.

In the afternoon, the fleet moved in more closely. As the semicircle of ships became smaller, the bombardment grew

---

[1] CARTEL (kär'těl)—A ship commissioned in time of war to sail under a safe conduct for the exchange of prisoners or conveyance of proposals between belligerents.

more intense. When several shells were hurled at one time, the sound of the explosions was almost continuous. Sailors fell overboard from rolling decks. Suddenly, as the approaching enemy came within reach of the land batteries so well planned by Major Armistead, the ships became targets for a hail of cannon-balls. Hastily drawing back, the fury of their attack increased anew.

As the day wore on, the very weather fell in sympathy with events and assumed a color to match the affairs of men. A thunderstorm, which had been brewing all afternoon, gathered its dark clouds together as the evening sun went down behind them.

It grew darker and darker. Boom-boom! The Fort was getting it harder than ever. The three helpless Americans, stranded on their rolling boat, strained their anxious eyes as long as it was possible to see the outline of the flag waving in a gust of breeze which, for the moment, blew the smoke away. That flag, thought Mr. Key, *so gallantly streaming*.

Night fell. Dr. Beanes went below. But not the younger men; they remained on deck and watched every shell from the instant it was fired until it fell. They listened for every explosion, trying to account for each hit.

Mr. Key paced the deck, up and down—up and down. There could be no rest for him. What a night for fire-works! The smoke in the atmosphere held a glow of steady brilliance, which was accented by the lightning and thunder from the background of a black night.

Boom! Lights flickered and flashed.

Boom! answered the Fort.

So long as the men could hear the bombs bursting, they knew that the Fort was still in the fight. *The rockets' red glare . . . gave proof through the night that the flag was still there.* Hm-m! Not bad, thought Mr. Key, I ought to write that down.

Suddenly, it ceased. There was no more firing. Sometime in the blackest part of night, all was still. Horribly still. What was the reason? Had the Fort surrendered? Had the enemy abandoned the attack? Ah, that was almost too good to hope for. What would Mr. Key have given to know the answer! There was no way of receiving messages from the enemy's ships. There was no communication whatsoever. They could only wait for daylight—pacing the deck, pacing up and down.

Long-drawn-out suspense! Would daylight never come? Under a dim lamp on the boat the two men peered frequently at their watches. How long must they wait before it became lighter? What time was it? Up and down—in the strange, brooding silence. What did it mean?

Their attention was caught by a sudden flare of fire against which they could see a great activity on several of the enemy's ships. They perceived that the flame served as a screen between the enemy and the Fort, since the men in the Fort could not see through the bright fire, but Key and Skinner being on the other side of it could see as clearly as if it were day. The enemy had kindled the flame for some purpose. What could it be? Anxiously they watched. Then they saw a few of the larger boats, and many barges, containing what appeared to be over a thousand men at least, break away in the silence and sail past the Fort. They were going up the river to attack the Fort from behind, perhaps assail Baltimore itself!

After passing the Fort, the enemy cheered and shouted in noisy glee. But, like Dr. Beanes some weeks before, they celebrated too soon. Their ships ran into the Major's sunken barrier. They could not pass! The Fort and batteries opened fire, and pelted the invaders with bullets and cannon-balls. The "tight little place" was tight indeed. Cries and screams of wounded and drowning men sounded through the night. The heavens were again lit up with the flames of bursting shells. Away in the city, people could feel the houses shake. And then, gradually, the horror subsided.

More anxious than ever, Key and Skinner found the black silence well-nigh unbearable.

What time was it? Would the night never end? It seemed
to be darker, if anything, instead of brighter. Several times
they imagined it was growing lighter in the east.

"Oh say!" Key stood close to his companion. "Can you
see me?"

"Not a bit," answered Skinner, "why?"

"I thought I could see the outline of your head."

"Just imagination."

They continued their pacing—pacing up and down, watching, waiting for the day.

What flag, thought Mr. Key, is flying over the Fort? Oh
God, let it be the Stars and Stripes—the Stars and Stripes.

"There!" said his companion, suddenly. "It *is* getting
lighter in the east. Don't you see that place where it is
brighter?"

Their eager eyes peered and strained through the darkness.
At last, they thought they could begin to see each other, but so
slowly and subtly crept up the early day, that sometimes they
thought, despairingly, it was only their eyes become used to the
darkness. How long? How long?

What time was it?

"It *is* growing lighter!" cried Key, "I can see the gleam of
my watch."

Breathlessly they waited. Yes, at last the day was breaking.
It seemed to grow perceptibly brighter now as they watched.
They went to the ship's telescope, and turned it toward the
Fort. What flag would be flying? Ah, which flag, which flag?
Too dark to see!

Finally, they perceived that they were floating in an early
morning mist. It was rising from the water all around them.
They could see no objects at a distance, it was still too dark,
too foggy. But, there was a breeze blowing; perhaps, as the
day dawned, the mist would be blown away.

Quickly now, the shafts of light were streaking up the east.
The sun could not be far behind.

Mr. Key was excited as he had never been before. After a night of most intense anxiety when his emotions had been whipped and torn, his brain was whirling. He walked off by himself. He took an old envelope out of his pocket, for he

wanted to jot down some thoughts that came to him—*in the dawn's early light,* (better write that down, thought Mr. Key) —some lines that he might arrange into verse. He needed to be alone. What flag would they see? *The broad stripes and bright stars* which they had seen *at the twilight's last gleaming?* (Write that down, thought Mr. Key.) *O say!* His hands clenched into fists, *does that star-spangled banner yet wave?* (Write that down, thought Mr. Key.)

Ah! Now, at last, they could make out shapes *on the shore, dimly seen through the mists of the deep.* (Write that down.) Suddenly Mr. Key was filled with a great happiness. A surge of gladness came over him, almost too deep—too fervent—

after the dreadful fears of recent weeks with the horrible climax of the night before. His right hand moved to his forehead in a long, silent salute. For the flag which he saw *was* the star-spangled banner——

Oh, long may it wave, he breathed.

THE STAR-SPANGLED BANNER

FRANCIS SCOTT KEY

O say, can you see, by the dawn's early light,
    What so proudly we hailed at the twilight's last gleaming?
Whose broad stripes and bright stars, through the perilous fight,
    O'er the ramparts we watched were so gallantly streaming;
5 And the rockets' red glare, the bombs bursting in air,
  Gave proof through the night that our flag was still there:
    O say, does that star-spangled banner yet wave
    O'er the land of the free and the home of the brave?

  On that shore dimly seen through the mist of the deep,
10   Where the foe's haughty host in dread silence reposes,
  What is that which the breeze, o'er the towering steep,
    As it fitfully blows, half conceals, half discloses?
  Now it catches the gleam of the morning's first beam,
  In full glory reflected now shines on the stream;
15 'Tis the star-spangled banner: O long may it wave
    O'er the land of the free and the home of the brave!

  And where is that band who so vauntingly swore
    That the havoc of war and the battle's confusion

A home and a country should leave us no more?
20   Their blood has washed out their foul footsteps' pollu-
        tion;
No refuge could save the hireling and slave
From the terror of flight or the gloom of the grave;
    And the star-spangled banner in triumph doth wave
    O'er the land of the free and the home of the brave.

25 Oh, thus be it ever, when freemen shall stand
    Between their loved homes and the war's desolation!
Blest with victory and peace, may the heaven-rescued
    land
    Praise the Power that hath made and preserved us a
        nation.
Then conquer we must, for our cause it is just,
30 And this be our motto, "In God is our trust."
    And the star-spangled banner in triumph shall wave
    O'er the land of the free and the home of the brave.

AMERICA

SAMUEL FRANCIS SMITH

My country, 'tis of thee,
Sweet Land of Liberty,
    Of thee I sing;
Land where my fathers died,
5   Land of the pilgrims' pride,
From every mountain-side
    Let Freedom ring.

My native country, thee,
Land of the noble free,—
10   Thy name I love;

I love thy rocks and rills,
Thy woods and templed hills,
My heart with rapture thrills
 Like that above.

15 Let music swell the breeze,
And ring from all the trees,
 Sweet Freedom's song;
Let mortal tongues awake;
Let all that breathe partake;
20 Let rocks their silence break,—
 The sound prolong.

Our fathers' God, to Thee,
Author of Liberty,
 To Thee we sing;
25 Long may our land be bright
With Freedom's holy light;
Protect us by Thy might,
 Great God, our King.

THE AMERICAN'S CREED

WILLIAM TYLER PAGE

I BELIEVE in the United States of America as a government of the people, by the people, for the people; whose just powers are derived from the consent of the governed; a democracy in a republic; a sovereign nation of many sovereign states; a perfect Union, one and inseparable; established upon those principles of freedom, equality, justice, and humanity for which American patriots sacrificed their lives and fortunes.

I therefore believe it is my duty to my country to love it; to support its constitution; to obey its laws; to respect its flag; and to defend it against all enemies.

V·IV

Sharing the thoughts of others.

DREAMS

LANGSTON HUGHES

LG   HOLD fast to dreams
DG   For if dreams die
             Life is a broken-winged bird
             That cannot fly.

LG   5   Hold fast to dreams
DG   For when dreams go
             Life is a barren field
             Frozen with snow.

OPPORTUNITY

BERTON BRALEY

1B   WITH doubt and dismay you are smitten,
             You think there's no chance for you, son?
B   Why the best books haven't been written,
             The best race hasn't been run,
     5   The best score hasn't been made yet,
             The best song hasn't been sung,
             The best tune hasn't been played yet;
             Cheer up, for the world is young!
1B   No chance? Why, the world is just eager
    10   For things that you ought to create;
G   Its store of true wealth is still meager,
             Its needs are incessant and great;

It yearns for more power and beauty,
More laughter and love and romance;
15 More loyalty, labor, and duty;
U   No chance—why, there's nothing but chance,
For the best verse hasn't been rhymed yet;
The best house hasn't been planned,
The highest peak hasn't been climbed yet,
20 The mightiest rivers aren't spanned.
Don't worry and fret, faint-hearted,
The chances have just begun.
For the best jobs haven't been started,
The best work hasn't been done.

OPPORTUNITY

EDWARD ROWLAND SILL

1DB THIS I beheld, or dreamed it in a dream:—
B   There spread a cloud of dust along a plain;
And underneath the cloud, or in it, raged
A furious battle, and men yelled, and swords
5 Shocked upon swords and shields.   A prince's banner
Wavered, then staggered backward, hemmed by foes.
G   A craven hung along the battle's edge,
And thought, "Had I a sword of keener steel—
That blue blade that the king's son bears, but this
10 Blunt thing!" he snapt and flung it from his hand,
And lowering crept away and left the field.
B   Then came the king's son, wounded, sore bestead,
And weaponless, and saw the broken sword,
Hilt-buried in the dry and trodden sand,
15 And ran and snatched it, and with battle-shout
Lifted afresh he hewed his enemy down,
And saved a great cause that heroic day.

TODAY

THOMAS CARLYLE

L   So HERE hath been dawning
       Another blue Day:
     Think, wilt thou let it
       Slip useless away?

M   5   Out of Eternity
       This new Day is born;
     Into Eternity,
       At night, will return.

D   Behold it aforetime
   10   No eye ever did:
     So soon· it forever
       From all eyes is hid.

U   Here hath been dawning
         Another blue Day:
15   Think, wilt thou let it
         Slip useless away?

BOY WANTED

FRANK CRANE

WANTED—

1. A boy that stands straight, sits straight, acts straight, and talks straight.

2. A boy whose finger nails are not in mourning, whose ears are clean, whose shoes are polished, whose clothes are brushed, whose hair is combed, and whose teeth are well cared for.

3. A boy who listens carefully when he is spoken to, who asks questions when he does not understand, and does not ask questions about things that are none of his business.

4. A boy that moves quickly and makes as little noise about it as possible.

5. A boy who whistles in the street, but does not whistle where he ought to keep still.

6. A boy who looks cheerful, has a ready smile for everybody, and never sulks.

7. A boy who is polite to every man and respectful to every woman and girl.

8. A boy who does not smoke cigarettes and has no desire to learn how.

9. A boy who is more eager to know how to speak good English than to talk slang.

10. A boy that never bullies other boys nor allows other boys to bully him.

11. A boy, who when he does not know a thing, says "I don't know," and when he has made a mistake says "I'm sorry," and when he is asked to do a thing says "I'll try."

12. A boy who looks you right in the eye and tells the truth every time.

13. A boy who is eager to read good books.

14. A boy who does not want to be "smart" nor in any wise to attract attention.

15. A boy who would rather lose his job or be expelled from school than tell a lie or be a cad.

16. A boy whom other boys like.

17. A boy who is at ease in the company of girls.

18. A boy who is not sorry for himself, and not forever thinking and talking about himself.

19. A boy who loves his mother, and is more intimate with her than with any one else.

20. A boy who makes you feel good when he is around.

21. A boy who is not goody-goody, a prig, or a little Pharisee,[1] but just healthy, happy, and full of life.

This boy is wanted everywhere. The family wants him, the school wants him, the office wants him, the boys want him, the girls want him, all creation wants him.

[1] PHARISEE—A self-righteous or hypocritical person.

THE GREAT STONE FACE

NATHANIEL HAWTHORNE

ONE afternoon, when the sun was going down, a mother and her little boy sat at the door of their cottage, talking about the Great Stone Face. They had but to lift their eyes, and there it was plainly to be seen, though miles away, with the sunshine brightening all its features.

And what was the Great Stone Face?

Embosomed among a family of lofty mountains, there was a valley so spacious that it contained many thousand inhabitants. Some of these good people dwelt in log huts, with the black forest around them, on the steep and difficult hillsides. Others had their homes in comfortable farmhouses, and cultivated the rich soil on the gentle slopes or level surfaces of the valley. Others, again, were congregated into populous villages, where some wild, highland rivulet, tumbling down from its birthplace in the upper mountain region, had been caught and tamed by human cunning, and compelled to turn the machinery of cotton factories. The inhabitants of this valley, in short, were numerous, and of many modes of life. But all of them, grown people and children, had a kind of familiarity with the Great Stone Face, although some possessed the gift of distinguishing this grand natural phenomenon more perfectly than many of their neighbors.

The Great Stone Face, then, was a work of Nature in her mood of majestic playfulness, formed on the perpendicular side of a mountain by some immense rocks, which had been thrown together in such a position as, when viewed at a proper distance, precisely to resemble the features of the human countenance. It seemed as if an enormous giant, or a Titan,[1] had sculptured his own likeness on the precipice. There was the broad arch of the forehead, a hundred feet in height; the nose, with its long bridge; and the vast lips, which, if they

[1] TITAN—In Greek mythology, the Titans were giants.

could have spoken, would have rolled their thunder accents from one end of the valley to the other. True it is, that if the spectator approached too near, he lost the outline of the gigantic visage, and could discern only a heap of ponderous and gigantic rocks piled in chaotic [2] ruin one upon another. Retracing his steps, however, the wondrous features would again be seen; and the farther he withdrew from them, the more like a human face, with all its original divinity intact, did they appear; until, as it grew dim in the distance, with the clouds and glorified vapor of the mountains clustering about it, the Great Stone Face seemed positively to be alive.

It was a happy lot for children to grow up to manhood or womanhood with the Great Stone Face before their eyes, for all the features were noble, and the expression was at once grand and sweet, as if it were the glow of a vast, warm heart, that embraced all mankind in its affections, and had room for more. It was an education only to look at it. According to the belief of many people, the valley owed much of its fertility to this benign [3] aspect that was continually beaming over it, illuminating the clouds, and infusing its tenderness into the sunshine.

As we began with saying, a mother and her little boy sat at their cottage door, gazing at the Great Stone Face, and talking about it. The child's name was Ernest.

"Mother," said he, while the Titanic visage smiled on him, "I wish that it could speak, for it looks so very kindly that its voice must needs be pleasant. If I were to see a man with such a face I should love him dearly."

"If an old prophecy should come to pass," answered his mother, "we may see a man, some time or other, with exactly such a face as that."

"What prophecy do you mean, dear Mother?" eagerly inquired Ernest. "Pray tell me all about it."

So his mother told him a story that her own mother had told

[2] CHAOTIC (kȧ-ŏt'ĭk)—Confused, disordered. [3] BENIGN (bē-nīn')—Gracious.

to her, when she herself was younger than little Ernest; a story, not of things that were past, but of what was yet to come; a story, nevertheless, so very old, that even the Indians, who formerly inhabited this valley, had heard it from their forefathers, to whom, as they affirmed, it had been murmured by the mountain streams, and whispered by the wind among the tree tops. The purport was, that, at some future day, a child should be born hereabouts, who was destined to become the greatest and noblest personage of his time, and whose countenance, in manhood, should bear an exact resemblance to the Great Stone Face. Not a few old-fashioned people, and young ones likewise, in the ardor of their hopes, still cherished an enduring faith in this old prophecy. But others, who had seen more of the world, had watched and waited till they were weary, and had beheld no man with such a face, nor any man that proved to be much greater or nobler than his neighbors, concluded it to be nothing but an idle tale. At all events, the great man of the prophecy had not yet appeared.

"Oh, Mother, dear Mother," cried Ernest, clapping his hands above his head, "I do hope I shall live to see him!" His mother was an affectionate and thoughtful woman, and felt that it was the wisest not to discourage the generous hopes of her little boy. So she only said to him, "Perhaps you may."

And Ernest never forgot the story that his mother told him. It was always in his mind, whenever he looked upon the Great Stone Face. He spent his childhood in the log cottage where he was born, and was dutiful to his mother, and helpful to her in many things, assisting her much with his little hands, and more with his loving heart. In this manner, from a happy yet often pensive child, he grew up to be a mild, quiet, unobtrusive boy, and sunbrowned with labor in the fields, but with more intelligence brightening his aspect than is seen in many lads who have been taught at famous schools. Yet Ernest had had no teacher, save only that the Great Stone Face became one to him. When the toil of the day was over, he would gaze at it for hours, until he began to imagine that those vast features recognized him, and gave him a smile of kindness and encouragement, responsive to his own look of veneration. We must not take upon us to affirm that this was a mistake, although the Face may have looked no more kindly at Ernest than at all the world besides. But the secret was that the boy's tender and confiding simplicity discerned what other people could not see; and thus the love, which was meant for all, became his peculiar portion.

About this time there went a rumor throughout the valley that the great man, foretold from ages long ago, who was to bear a resemblance to the Great Stone Face, had appeared at last. It seems that, many years before, a young man had migrated from the valley and settled at a distant seaport, where, after getting together a little money, he had set up as shopkeeper. His name—but I could never learn whether it was his real one, or a nickname that had grown out of his habits and success in life—was Gathergold. Being shrewd and active, endowed by Providence with that inscrutable faculty [4] which develops itself in what the world calls luck, he became an exceedingly rich merchant, and owner of a whole fleet of bulky-bottomed ships. All the countries of the globe appeared to join hands for the mere purpose of adding heap after heap to the mountainous accumulation of this one man's wealth. The cold regions of the north, almost within the gloom and shadow of the Arctic Circle, sent him their tribute in the shape of furs; hot Africa sifted for him the golden sands of her rivers, and gathered up the ivory tusks of her great elephants out of the forests; the East came bringing him the rich shawls, and spices, and teas, and the effulgence [5] of diamonds, and the gleaming purity of large pearls. The ocean, not to be behindhand with the earth, yielded up her mighty whales, that Mr. Gathergold might sell their oil, and make a profit on it. Be the original commodity what it might, it was gold within his grasp. It might be said of him, as of Midas in the fable, that whatever he touched with his finger immediately glistened, and grew yellow, and was changed at once into sterling metal, or, which suited him still better, into piles of coin. And when Mr. Gathergold had become so very rich that it would have taken him a hundred years only to count his wealth, he bethought himself of his native valley, and resolved to go back thither, and end his days where he was born. With this purpose in view, he sent a skillful architect to build him such a palace as should be fit for a man of his vast wealth to live in.

As I have said above, it had already been rumored in the valley that Mr. Gathergold had turned out to be the prophetic personage so long and vainly looked for, and that his visage was the perfect and undeniable similitude [6] of the Great Stone Face. People were the more ready to believe that this must needs be the fact, when they beheld the splendid edifice that

---

[4] INSCRUTABLE FACULTY—Remarkable power.
[5] EFFULGENCE (ĕ-fŭl'jĕns)—Splendor; radiance.
[6] SIMILITUDE (sĭ-mĭl'ĭ-tūd)—Likeness.

542

rose, as if by enchantment, on the site of his father's old weather-beaten farmhouse. The exterior was of marble, so dazzlingly white that it seemed as though the whole structure might melt away in the sunshine, like those humbler ones which Mr. Gathergold, in his young play-days, before his fingers were gifted with the touch of transmutation,[7] had been accustomed to build of snow. It had a richly ornamented portico, supported by tall pillars, beneath which was a lofty door, studded with silver knobs, and made of a kind of variegated wood that had been brought from beyond the sea. The windows, from the floor to the ceiling of each stately apartment, were composed, respectively, of but one enormous pane of glass, so transparently pure that it was said to be a finer medium than even the vacant atmosphere. Hardly anybody had been permitted to see the interior of this palace; but it was reported, and with good semblance of truth, to be far more gorgeous than the outside, insomuch that whatever was iron or brass in other houses was silver or gold in this; and Mr. Gathergold's bedchamber, especially, made such a glittering appearance that no ordinary man would have been able to close his eyes there. But, on the other hand, Mr. Gathergold was now so inured [8] to wealth, that perhaps he could not have closed his eyes unless where the gleam of it was certain to find its way beneath his eyelids.

In due time the mansion was finished; next came the upholsterers, with magnificent furniture; then a whole troop of black and white servants, the harbingers [9] of Mr. Gathergold, who in his own majestic person, was expected to arrive at sunset.

Our friend Ernest, meanwhile, had been deeply stirred by the idea that the great man, the noble man, the man of prophecy, after so many ages of delay, was at length to be made manifest to his native valley. He knew, boy as he was, that there were a thousand ways in which Mr. Gathergold, with his

[7] TRANSMUTATION—Ability to change one substance into another.
[8] INURED—Accustomed.
[9] HARBINGER (här'bĭn-jēr)—One who is sent forth to provide lodgings.

vast wealth, might transform himself into an angel of beneficence,[10] and assume control over human affairs as wide and benignant [11] as the smile of the Great Stone Face. Full of faith
and hope, Ernest doubted not that what the people said was
true, and that now he was to behold the living likeness of those
wondrous features on the mountain side. While the boy was
still gazing up the valley, and fancying, as he always did, that
the Great Stone Face returned his gaze and looked kindly at
him, the rumbling of wheels was heard, approaching swiftly
along the winding road.

"Here he comes!" cried a group of people who were assembled to witness the arrival. "Here comes the great Mr. Gathergold!"

A carriage drawn by four horses, dashed round the turn of
the road. Within it, thrust partly out of the window, appeared
the physiognomy [12] of a little old man, with a skin as yellow as
if his own Midas hand had transmuted it. He had a low forehead, small sharp eyes, puckered about with innumerable wrinkles, and very thin lips, which he made still thinner by pressing
them forcibly together.

"The very image of the Great Stone Face!" shouted the people. "Sure enough, the old prophecy is true; and here we have
the great man come, at last!"

And, what greatly perplexed Ernest, they seemed actually to
believe that here was the likeness of which they spoke. By the
roadside there chanced to be an old beggar woman and two little beggar children, stragglers from some far-off region, who,
as the carriage rolled onward, held out their hands and lifted
up their doleful voices, most piteously beseeching charity. A
yellow claw—the very same that had clawed together so much
wealth—poked itself out of the coach window, and dropped
some copper coins upon the ground; so that, though the great
man's name seems to have been Gathergold, he might just as

[10] BENEFICENCE (bĕ-nĕf′ĭ-sĕns)—Goodness.
[11] BENIGNANT (bĕ-nĭg′nănt)—Kindly.
[12] PHYSIOGNOMY (fĭz ĭ-ŏg′nô-mĭ)—Face, visage.

suitably have been nicknamed Scattercopper. Still, nevertheless, with an earnest shout, and evidently with as much good
faith as ever, the people bellowed:

"He is the very image of the Great Stone Face!"

But Ernest turned sadly from the wrinkled shrewdness of
that sordid visage, and gazed up the valley, where, amid a
gathering mist, gilded by the last sunbeams, he could still distinguish those glorious features which had impressed themselves into his soul. Their aspect cheered him. What did the
benign lips seem to say? "He will come! Fear not, Ernest;
the man will come!"

The years went on, and Ernest ceased to be a boy. He had
grown to be a young man now. He attracted little notice from
the older inhabitants of the valley, for they saw nothing remarkable in his way of life, save that, when the labor of the
day was over, he still loved to go apart and gaze and meditate
upon the Great Stone Face. According to their idea of the
matter, it was folly, indeed, but pardonable, inasmuch as Ernest

was industrious, kind, and neighborly, and neglected no duty for the sake of indulging this idle habit. They knew not that the Great Stone Face had become a teacher to him, and that the sentiment which was expressed in it would enlarge the young man's heart, and fill it with wider and deeper sympathies than other hearts. They knew not that thence would come a better wisdom than could be learned from books, and a better life than could be molded on the defaced example of other human lives. Neither did Ernest know that the thoughts and affections which came to him so naturally, in the fields, and at the fireside, and wherever he communed with himself, were of a higher tone than those which all men shared with him. A simple soul—simple as when his mother first taught him the old prophecy—he beheld the marvelous features beaming adown the valley, and still wondered that their human counterpart was so long in making his appearance.

By this time poor Mr. Gathergold was dead and buried; and the oddest part of the matter was that his wealth, which was the body and spirit of his existence, had disappeared before his death, leaving nothing of him but a living skeleton, covered over with a wrinkled, yellow skin. Since the melting away of his gold, it had been very generally conceded that there was no such striking resemblance, after all, between the ignoble features of the ruined merchant and that majestic face upon the mountain side. So the people ceased to honor him during his lifetime, and quietly consigned him to forgetfulness after his decease. Once in a while, it is true, his memory was brought up in connection with the magnificent palace which he had built, and which had long ago been turned into a hotel for the accommodation of strangers, multitudes of whom came, every summer, to visit that famous natural curiosity the Great Stone Face. Thus, Mr. Gathergold being discredited and thrown into the shade, the man of prophecy was yet to come.

It so happened that a native-born son of the valley, many years before, had enlisted as a soldier, and after a great deal of hard fighting had now become an illustrious commander. Whatever he may be called in history, he was known in camps and on the battlefield under the nickname of Old Blood-and-Thunder. This war-worn veteran, being now infirm with age and wounds, and weary of the turmoil of a military life, and of the roll of the drum and the clangor of the trumpet, that had so long been ringing in his ears, had lately signified a purpose of returning to his native valley, hoping to find repose where he remembered to have left it. The inhabitants, his old neighbors and their grown-up children, were resolved to welcome the renowned warrior with a salute of cannon and a public dinner; and all the more enthusiastically, it being affirmed that now, at last, the likeness of the Great Stone Face had actually appeared. An aid-de-camp [13] of Old Blood-and-Thunder, traveling through the valley, was said to have been struck with the resemblance. Moreover, the schoolmates and early acquaintances of the general were ready to testify, on oath, that, to the best of their recollection, the aforesaid general had been exceedingly like the majestic image, even when a boy, only that the idea had never occurred to them at that period. Great, therefore, was the excitement throughout the valley; and many people, who had never once thought of glancing at the Great Stone Face for years before, now spent their time in gazing at it, for the sake of knowing exactly how General Blood-and-Thunder looked.

On the day of the great festival, Ernest, with all the other people of the valley, left their work, and proceeded to the spot where the sylvan banquet was prepared. As he approached, the loud voice of the Rev. Dr. Battleblast was heard, beseeching a blessing on the good things set before them, and on the distinguished friend of peace in whose honor they were assembled. The tables were arranged in a cleared space of the woods, shut in by the surrounding trees, except where a vista opened eastward, and afforded a distant view of the Great

[13] AID-DE-CAMP (ãd-dê-kän')—An officer attached to the person of a general to assist him.

Stone Face. Over the general's chair, which was a relic from the home of Washington, there was an arch of verdant boughs, with the laurel profusely intermixed, and surmounted by his country's banner, beneath which he had won his victories. Our friend Ernest raised himself on his tiptoes, in hopes to get a glimpse of the celebrated guest; but there was a mighty crowd about the tables anxious to hear the toasts and speeches, and to catch any word that might fall from the general in reply, and a volunteer company, doing duty as a guard, pricked ruthlessly with their bayonets at any particularly quiet person among the throng. So Ernest being of an unobtrusive character, was thrust quite into the background, where he could see no more of Old Blood-and-Thunder's physiognomy than if it had been still blazing on the battlefield. To console himself, he turned toward the Great Stone Face, which, like a faithful and long-remembered friend, looked back and smiled upon him through the vista of the forest. Meantime, however, he could overhear the remarks of various individuals, who were comparing the features of the hero with the face on the distant mountain side.

" 'Tis the same face, to a hair!" cried one man, cutting a caper for joy. "Wonderfully like, that's a fact!" responded another. "Like! Why, I call it Old Blood-and-Thunder himself, in a monstrous looking-glass!" cried a third. "And why not? He's the greatest man of this or any other age, beyond a doubt."

And then all three of the speakers gave a great shout, which communicated electricity to the crowd, and called forth a roar from a thousand voices, that went reverberating for miles among the mountains, until you might have supposed that the Great Stone Face had poured its thunder breath into the cry. All these comments and this vast enthusiasm served the more to interest our friend; nor did he think of questioning that now, at length, the mountain visage had found its human counterpart. It is true, Ernest had imagined that this long looked-for personage would appear in the character of a man of peace, uttering wisdom, and doing good and making people happy. But, taking an habitual breadth of view, with all his simplicity, he contended that Providence should choose its own method of blessing mankind, and could conceive that this great end might be effected even by a warrior and a bloody sword, should inscrutable wisdom see fit to order matters so.

"The general! The general!" was now the cry. "Hush! Silence! Old Blood-and-Thunder's going to make a speech."

Even so; for, the cloth being removed, the general's health had been drunk amid shouts of applause, and he now stood upon his feet to thank the company. Ernest saw him. There he was, over the shoulders of the crowd, from the two glittering epaulets [14] and embroidered collar upward, beneath the arch of green boughs with intertwined laurel, and the banner drooping as if to shade his brow. And there, too, visible in the same glance, through the vista of the forest, appeared the Great Stone Face! And was there, indeed, such a resemblance as the crowd has testified? Alas, Ernest could not recognize it! He beheld a war-worn and weather-beaten countenance, full of energy, and expressive of an iron will; but the gentle wisdom, the deep, broad, tender sympathies, were altogether wanting in Old Blood-and-Thunder's visage; and even if the Great Stone Face had assumed his look of stern command, the milder traits would still have tempered it.

"This is not the man of prophecy," sighed Ernest to himself, as he made his way out of the throng. "And must the world wait longer yet?"

The mists had congregated about the distant mountain side, and there were seen the grand and awful features of the Great Stone Face, awful but benignant, as if a mighty angel were sitting among the hills, and enrobing himself in a cloud vesture of gold and purple. As he looked, Ernest could hardly believe

---

[14] EPAULETS (ĕp'ô-lĕts)—Shoulder ornaments worn on military and naval uniforms.

but that a smile beamed over the whole visage, with a radiance still brightening, although without motion of the lips. It was probably the effect of the western sunshine melting through the thinly diffused vapors that had swept between him and the object that he gazed at. But—as it always did—the aspect of his marvelous friend made Ernest as hopeful as if he had never hoped in vain.

"Fear not, Ernest," said his heart, even as if the Great Face were whispering to him—"fear not, Ernest; he will come."

More years sped swiftly and tranquilly away. Ernest still dwelt in his native valley, and was now a man of middle age. By imperceptible degrees, he had become known among the people. Now, as heretofore, he labored for his bread, and was the same simple-hearted man that he had always been. But he had thought and felt so much, he had given so many of the best hours of his life to unworldly hopes for some great good to mankind, that it seemed as though he had been talking with the angels, and had imbibed a portion of their wisdom unawares. It was visible in the calm and well-considered beneficence of his daily life, the quiet stream of which had made a wide green margin all along its course. Not a day passed by, that the world was not the better because this man, humble as he was, had lived. He never stepped aside from his own path, yet would always reach a blessing to his neighbor. Almost involuntarily, too, he had become a preacher. The pure and high simplicity of his thought, which, as one of its manifestations, took shape in the good deeds that dropped silently from his hand, flowed also forth in speech. He uttered truths that wrought upon and molded the lives of those who heard him. His auditors,[15] it may be, never suspected that Ernest, their own neighbor and familiar friend, was more than an ordinary man; least of all did Ernest himself suspect it; but inevitably as the murmur of a rivulet, came thoughts out of his mouth that no other human lips had spoken.

---

[15] AUDITORS—Hearers, listeners.

When the people's minds had had a little time to cool, they were ready enough to acknowledge their mistake in imagining a similarity between General Blood-and-Thunder's truculent [16] physiognomy and the benign visage on the mountain side. But now, again, there were reports and many paragraphs in the newspapers, affirming that the likeness of the Great Stone Face had appeared upon the broad shoulders of a certain eminent statesman. He, like Mr. Gathergold and Old Blood-and-Thunder, was a native of the valley, but had left it in his early days, and taken up the trades of law and politics. Instead of the rich man's wealth and the warrior's sword, he had but a tongue, and it was mightier than both together. So wonderfully eloquent was he, that whatever he might choose to say, his auditors had no choice but to believe him; wrong looked like right, and right like wrong; for when it pleased him he could make a kind of illuminated fog with his mere breath, and obscure the natural daylight with it. His tongue, indeed, was a magic instrument; sometimes it rumbled like thunder; sometimes it warbled like the sweetest music. It was the blast of war; the song of peace; and it seemed to have a heart in it, when there was no such matter. In good truth, he was a wondrous man; and when his tongue had acquired him all other imaginable success; when it had been heard in halls of state, and in the courts of princes and potentates,[17] after it had made him known all over the world, even as a voice crying from shore to shore; it finally persuaded his countrymen to select him for the Presidency. Before this time—indeed, as soon as he began to grow celebrated—his admirers had found out the resemblance between him and the Great Stone Face; and so much were they struck by it, that throughout the country this distinguished gentleman was known by the name of Old Stony Phiz.

While his friends were doing their best to make him President, Old Stony Phiz set out on a visit to the valley where he was born. Of course, he had no other object than to shake

---

[16] TRUCULENT (trŭc′ū-lĕnt)—Ferocious.   [17] POTENTATES—Rulers.

hands with his fellow citizens, and neither thought nor cared about any effect which his progress through the country might have upon the election. Magnificent preparations were made to receive the illustrious statesman; a cavalcade of horsemen set forth to meet him at the boundary line of the State, and all the people left their business and gathered along the wayside to see him pass. Among these was Ernest. Though more than once disappointed, as we have seen, he had such a hopeful and confiding nature, that he was always ready to believe in whatever seemed beautiful and good. He kept his heart continually open, and thus was sure to catch the blessing from on high, when it should come. So now again, as buoyantly as ever, he went forth to behold the likeness of the Great Stone Face.

The cavalcade came prancing along the road with a great clattering of hoofs and a mighty cloud of dust, which rose up so dense and high that the visage of the mountain side was completely hidden from Ernest's eyes. All the great men of the neighborhood were there on horseback: militia officers in uniform; the member of Congress; the sheriff of the county; the editors of newspapers; and many a farmer, too, had mounted his patient steed, with his Sunday coat upon his back. It really was a very brilliant spectacle, especially as there were numerous banners flaunting over the cavalcade, on some of which were gorgeous portraits of the illustrious statesman and the Great Stone Face, smiling familiarly at one another, like two brothers. If the pictures were to be trusted, the mutual resemblance, it must be confessed, was marvelous. We must not forget to mention that there was a band of music, which made the echoes of the mountains ring and reverberate with the loud triumph of its strains; so that airy and soul-thrilling melodies broke out among all the heights and hollows, as if every nook of this native valley had found a voice to welcome the distinguished guest. But the grandest effect was when the far-off mountain precipice flung back the music; for then the

Great Stone Face itself seemed to be swelling the triumphant chorus, in acknowledgment that, at length, the man of prophecy was come.

All this while the people were throwing up their hats and shouting with enthusiasm so contagious that the heart of Ernest kindled up, and he likewise threw up his hat, and shouted as loudly as the loudest, "Huzza for the great man! Huzza for Old Stony Phiz!" But as yet he had not seen him.

"Here he is now!" cried those who stood near Ernest. "There! There! Look at Old Stony Phiz and then at the Old Man of the Mountain, and see if they are not as like as two twin brothers!"

In the midst of all this gallant array came an open barouche [18] drawn by four white horses; and in the barouche, with his massive head uncovered, sat the illustrious statesman, Old Stony Phiz himself.

"Confess it," said one of Ernest's neighbors to him, "the Great Stone Face has met its match at last!"

Now, it must be owned that, at his first glimpse of the countenance which was bowing and smiling from the barouche, Ernest did fancy that there was a resemblance between it and the old familiar face upon the mountain side. The brow, with its massive depth and loftiness, and all the other features, indeed, were boldly and strongly hewn, as if in emulation of a more than heroic, of a Titanic model. But the sublimity and stateliness, the grand expression of a divine sympathy, that illuminated the mountain visage, and etherealized [19] its ponderous granite substance into spirit, might here be sought in vain. Something had been originally left out, or had departed. And therefore the marvelously gifted statesman had always a weary gloom in the deep caverns of his eyes, as of a child that has outgrown its playthings, or a man of mighty faculties and little aims, whose life, with all its high performances was vague and

[18] BAROUCHE (bȧ-rōōsh')—A kind of four-wheeled carriage with a folding top.

[19] ETHEREALIZED (ė-thē're̊-ăl-īzd)—Spiritualized.

empty, because no high purpose had endowed it with reality.

Still Ernest's neighbor was thrusting his elbow into his side, and pressing him for an answer.

"Confess!   Confess!   Is not he the very picture of your Old Man of the Mountain?"

"No!" said Ernest, bluntly, "I see little or no likeness."

"Then so much the worse for the Great Stone Face!" answered his neighbor; and again he set up a shout for Old Stony Phiz.

But Ernest turned away, melancholy, and almost despondent: for this was the saddest of his disappointments, to behold a man who might have fulfilled the prophecy, and had not willed to do so.   Meantime, the cavalcade, the banners, the music, and the barouches swept past him, with the vociferous [20] crowd in the rear leaving the dust to settle down, and the Great Stone Face to be revealed again, with the grandeur that it had worn for untold centuries.

[20] VOCIFEROUS (vô-sĭf'ẽr-ŭs)—Clamorous.

"Lo, here I am, Ernest!" the benign lips seemed to say. "I have waited longer than thou, and am not yet weary. Fear not; the man will come."

The years hurried onward, treading in their haste on one another's heels. And now they began to bring white hairs, and scatter them over the head of Ernest; they made reverend wrinkles across his forehead, and furrows in his cheeks. He was an aged man. But not in vain had he grown old; more than the white hairs on his head were the sage thoughts in his mind; his wrinkles and furrows were inscriptions that Time had graved, and in which he had written legends of wisdom that had been tested by the tenor [21] of a life. And Ernest had ceased to be obscure. Unsought for, undesired, had come the thing which so many seek, and made him known in the great world beyond the limits of the valley in which he had dwelt so quietly. College professors, and even the active men of cities, came from afar to see and converse with Ernest; for the report had gone abroad that this simple husbandman had ideas unlike those of other men, not gained from books, but of a higher tone, a tranquil and familiar majesty, as if he had been talking with the angels as his daily friends. Whether it were sage, statesman, or philanthropist,[22] Ernest received these visitors with the gentle sincerity that had characterized him from boyhood, and spoke freely with them of whatever came uppermost, or lay deepest in his heart or their own. While they talked together, his face would kindle unawares, and shine upon them, as with a mild evening light. Pensive with the fullness of such a discourse, his guests took leave and went their way, and passing up the valley, paused to look at the Great Stone Face, imagining that they had seen its likeness in a human countenance, but could not remember where.

While Ernest had been growing up and growing old, a bountiful Providence had granted a new poet to this earth. He,

[21] TENOR—Course.
[22] PHILANTHROPIST (fĭ-lăn'thrŏp-ĭst)—One who loves mankind.

likewise, was a native of the valley, but had spent the greater part of his life at a distance from that romantic region, pouring out his sweet music amid the bustle and din of cities. Often, however, did the mountains which had been familiar to him in his childhood lift their snowy peaks into the clear atmosphere of his poetry. Neither was the Great Stone Face forgotten, for the poet had celebrated it in an ode, which was grand enough to have been uttered by its own majestic lips. This man of genius, we may say, had come down from heaven with wonderful endowments. If he sang of a mountain, the eyes of all mankind beheld a mightier grandeur reposing on its breast, or soaring to its summit, than had before been seen there. If his theme were a lovely lake, a celestial smile had now been thrown over it, to gleam forever on its surface. If it were the vast old sea, even the deep immensity of its dread bosom seemed to swell the higher, as if moved by the emotions of the song. Thus the world assumed another and a better aspect from the hour that the poet blessed it with his happy eyes. The Creator had bestowed him, as the last best touch to his own handiwork. Creation was not finished till the poet came to interpret, and so complete it.

The effect was no less high and beautiful when his human brethren were the subject of his verse. The man or woman, sordid with the common dust of life, who crossed his daily path, and the little child who played in it, were glorified if he beheld them in his mood of poetic faith. He showed the golden links of the great chain that intertwined them with an angelic kindred; he brought out the hidden traits of a celestial birth that made them worthy of such kin. Some, indeed, there were, who thought to show the soundness of their judgment by affirming that all the beauty and dignity of the natural world existed only in the poet's fancy. As respects all things else, the poet's ideal was the truest truth.

The songs of this poet found their way to Ernest. He read them after his customary toil, seated on the bench before his cottage door, where for such a length of time he had filled his repose with thought, by gazing at the Great Stone Face. And now as he read stanzas that caused the soul to thrill within him, he lifted his eyes to the vast countenance beaming on him so benignantly.

"O majestic friend," he murmured, addressing the Great Stone Face, "is not this man worthy to resemble thee?"

The Face seemed to smile, but answered not a word.

Now it happened that the poet, though he dwelt so far away, had not only heard of Ernest, but had meditated much upon his character, until he deemed nothing so desirable as to meet this man, whose untaught wisdom walked hand in hand with the noble simplicity of his life. One summer morning, therefore, he took passage by the railroad, and, in the decline of the afternoon, alighted from the cars, at no great distance from Ernest's cottage. The great hotel which had formerly been the palace of Mr. Gathergold, was close at hand, but the poet, with his carpetbag on his arm, inquired at once where Ernest dwelt, and was resolved to be accepted as his guest.

Approaching the door, he there found the good old man, holding a volume in his hand, which alternately he read, and then, with a finger between the leaves, looked lovingly at the Great Stone Face.

"Good evening," said the poet. "Can you give a traveler a night's lodging?"

"Willingly," answered Ernest; and then he added, smiling, "Methinks I never saw the Great Stone Face look so hospitably at a stranger."

The poet sat down on the bench beside him, and he and Ernest talked together. Often had the poet held intercourse with the wittiest and the wisest, but never before with a man like Ernest, whose thoughts and feelings gushed up with such a natural freedom, and who made great truths so familiar by his simple utterance of them. Angels, as had been so often said, seemed to have wrought with him at his labor in the fields;

angels seemed to have sat with him by the fireside; and, dwelling with angels as friend with friends, he had imbibed the sublimity of their ideas, and imbued it with the sweet and lowly
charm of household words. So thought the poet. And Ernest,
on the other hand, was moved and agitated by the living images
which the poet flung out of his mind, and which peopled all
the air about the cottage door with shapes of beauty, both gay
and pensive. The sympathies of these two men instructed
them with a profounder sense than either could have attained
alone. Their minds accorded into one strain, and made delightful music which neither of them could have claimed as all
his own, nor distinguished his own share from the other's.
They led one another, as it were, into a high pavilion of their
thoughts, so remote and hitherto so dim, that they had never
entered it before and so beautiful that they desired to be there
always.

As Ernest listened to the poet, he imagined that the Great
Stone Face was bending forward to listen too.

He gazed earnestly into the poet's glowing eyes.

"Who are you, my strangely gifted guest?"

The poet laid his finger on the volume that Ernest had been
reading. "You have read these poems," said he. "You know
me, then, for I wrote them."

Again, and still more earnestly than before, Ernest examined the poet's features, then turned toward the Great Stone
Face; then back with an uncertain aspect, to his guest. But
his countenance fell; he shook his head, and sighed.

"Wherefore are you sad?" inquired the poet.

"Because," replied Ernest, "all through life I have awaited
the fulfillment of a prophecy; and when I read these poems, I
hoped that it might be fulfilled in you."

"You hoped," answered the poet, faintly smiling, "to find in
me the likeness of the Great Stone Face. And you are disappointed, as formerly with Mr. Gathergold, and Old Blood-and-
Thunder, and Old Stony Phiz. Yes, Ernest, it is my doom.

You must add my name to the illustrious three, and record another failure of your hopes. For—in shame and sadness do I speak it, Ernest—I am not worthy to be typified by yonder benign and majestic image."

"And why?" asked Ernest. He pointed to the volume. "Are not those thoughts divine?"

"They have a strain of the Divinity," replied the poet. "You can hear in them the far-off echo of a heavenly song. But my life, dear Ernest, has not corresponded with my thought. I have had grand dreams, but they have been only dreams, because I have lived—and that, too, by my own choice—among poor and mean realities. Sometimes even—shall I dare to say it?—I lack faith in the grandeur, the beauty, and the goodness which my own works are said to have made more evident in nature and in human life. Why, then, pure seeker of the good and true, shouldst thou hope to find me in yonder image of the divine?"

The poet spoke sadly, and his eyes were dim with tears. So, likewise, were those of Ernest.

At the hour of sunset, as had long been his frequent custom, Ernest was to discourse to an assemblage of the neighboring inhabitants in the open air. He and the poet, arm in arm, still talking together as they went along, proceeded to the spot. It was a small nook among the hills, with a gray precipice behind, the stern front of which was relieved by the pleasant foliage of many creeping plants that made a tapestry for the naked rock by hanging their festoons from all its rugged angles. At a small elevation above the ground, set in a rich framework of verdure, there appeared a niche, spacious enough to admit a human figure, with freedom for such gestures as spontaneously accompany earnest thought and genuine emotion. Into this natural pulpit Ernest ascended, and threw a look of familiar kindness around upon his audience. They stood, or sat, or reclined upon the grass, as seemed good to each, with the departing sunshine falling obliquely over them, and mingling its subdued cheerfulness with the solemnity of a grove of ancient trees, beneath and amid the boughs of which the golden rays were constrained to pass. In another direction was seen the Great Stone Face, with the same cheer, combined with the same solemnity, in its benignant aspect.

Ernest began to speak, giving to the people of what was in his heart and mind. His words had power, because they accorded with his thoughts; and his thoughts had reality and depth, because they harmonized with the life which he had always lived. It was not mere breath that this preacher uttered; they were the words of life, because a life of good deeds and holy love was melted into them. Pearls, pure and rich, had been dissolved into this precious draught. The poet, as he listened, felt that the being and character of Ernest were a nobler strain of poetry than he had ever written. His eyes glistening with tears, he gazed reverentially at the venerable man, and said within himself that never was there an aspect so worthy of a prophet and a sage as that mild, sweet, thoughtful countenance, with the glory of white hair diffused about it. At a distance, but distinctly to be seen, high up in the golden light of the setting sun, appeared the Great Stone Face, with hoary mists around it, like the white hairs around the brow of Ernest. Its look of grand beneficence seemed to embrace the world.

At that moment, in sympathy with a thought which he was about to utter, the face of Ernest assumed a grandeur of expression so imbued with benevolence that the poet, by an irresistible impulse, threw his arms aloft, and shouted:

"Behold! Behold! Ernest is himself the likeness of the Great Stone Face!"

Then all the people looked, and saw that what the deep-sighted poet said was true. The prophecy was fulfilled.

But Ernest, having finished what he had to say, took the poet's arm, and walked slowly homeward, still hoping that some wiser and better man than himself would by and by appear, bearing a resemblance to the Great Stone Face.

ACKNOWLEDGMENTS

For the courteous permission to use the following selections, grateful acknowledgment and thanks are extended to the following authors, publishers, and periodicals.

Samuel Hopkins Adams: "The Centipede."

Mrs. Randolph Bartlett and *The American Girl*: "A Dozen Roses and a Bale of Hay" by Randolph Bartlett.

The Bobbs-Merrill Company: "Out to Old Aunt Mary's" from *The Complete Works of James Whitcomb Riley*, copyright 1913. Used by special permission of the publishers.

Berton Braley: "Opportunity."

Brandt & Brandt: "Johnny Appleseed" and "Wilbur Wright and Orville Wright" from *A Book of Americans*, published by Farrar & Rinehart, Inc., copyright 1933 by Rosemary and Stephen Vincent Benét; "Two Rivers" by Wallace Stegner, copyright 1942 by Wallace Stegner.

Curtis Brown, Ltd.: "Freedom Again at Last" from *Lassie Come Home*, copyright 1940 by The John C. Winston Company, reprinted by permission of the author's estate.

Mrs. Frank Crane: "Boy Wanted" by Frank Crane.

Thomas Y. Crowell Company: "Abe Discovers a New World" from *Abraham Lincoln* by Enid Lamonte Meadowcroft.

Dodd, Mead & Company: "Winter Streams" by Bliss Carman; "A Boy's Summer Song" from *Little Brown Baby* by Paul Laurence Dunbar.

Doubleday, Doran & Company, Inc.: "April" from *The Dreamers and Other Poems* by Theodosia Garrison, copyright 1917 by Doubleday, Doran & Company; "Song of the Nightingale" from *Mother Russia* by Maurice Hindus, copyright 1942, 1943; "Conal and Donal and Taig" from *Donegal Fairy Stories* by Seumas MacManus, copyright 1900, 1928, by Doubleday, Doran & Company.

E. P. Dutton & Co., Inc.: "The Oregon Trail" from *I Sing the Pioneer* by Arthur Guiterman; "Education of Gay-Neck" from *Gay-Neck* by Dhan Gopal Mukerji.

Farrar & Rinehart, Inc.: "The Good Joan," copyright by Lizette Woodworth Reese, and reprinted by permission of Farrar & Rinehart, Inc.

Dr. Clyde Fisher and *This Week Magazine*: "Volcano in His

Cornfield!" copyright 1944 by the United Newspapers Magazine Corporation.

Frances Frost and *The American Girl*: "Runaway."

Henry Holt and Company, Inc.: "The Pasture" from *The Collected Poems of Robert Frost, 1939;* "Oh Fair Enough Are Sky and Plain" from *A Shropshire Lad* by A. E. Housman; "The Snow Witch" from *The Silver Thread and Other Folk Plays for Young People* by Constance d'Arcy Mackay; "Theme in Yellow" from *Chicago Poems* by Carl Sandburg; "Toby Goes to Market" from *The Collected Poems of Lew Sarett*.

Alfred A. Knopf, Inc.: "The Frog" from *Cautionary Verses* by Hilaire Belloc; "Mike Fink" from *America Sings* by Carl Carmer; "Spanish Johnny" from *April Twilights* by Willa Cather; "Dreams" from *The Dream Keeper* by Langston Hughes.

Elizabeth Foreman Lewis—"Freedom For Our Minds."

J. B. Lippincott Company: A selection from *The Birth of a Nation's Song* by Katherine Little Bakeless; "Kelly Courageous" from *The Courage and the Glory* by John J. Floherty; "The Most Dangerous Enemy of All" from *The Last of the Sea Otters* by Harold McCracken.

Little, Brown & Company: "The Snow" from *The Poems of Emily Dickinson* edited by Martha Dickinson and Alfred Leete Hampson. Reprinted by permission of the publishers.

Longmans, Green and Co., Inc.: "The Dog of Montargis" from *Animal Story Book* by Andrew Lang.

The Macmillan Company: "Alas! Poor Annabelle!" from *Caddie Woodlawn* by Carol Ryrie Brink; "The Lobster Marathon" and "Tom Was Just a Little Boy" from *Primer for America* by Robert P. Tristram Coffin; "Something Told the Wild Geese" from *Branches Green* by Rachel Field; "The Broken Note" from *The Trumpeter of Krakow* by Eric P. Kelly.

Macrae-Smith Company: A selection from *Nuvat the Brave* by Radko Doone.

Julian Messner, Inc.: A selection from *The Story of Clara Barton of the Red Cross* by Jeanette Nolan.

Estate of Honoré Morrow and *The Reader's Digest*: "Child Pioneer" by Honoré Morrow, copyright 1925 by International Magazine Company (Hearst's International-Cosmopolitan, January, 1926), by permission of the estate of Honoré Morrow.

Thomas Nelson and Sons: "Mother Volga and Her Child" from *Once Upon a Time* by Agnes Fisher.

William Tyler Page: "The American's Creed."

Rand McNally & Company: A selection from *Wings for Words* by Douglas C. McMurtrie, copyright 1940 by Rand McNally & Company, publishers, and used by their permission.

Liam O'Flaherty, through his agent, A. D. Peters of London, England: "The Wild Goat's Kid."

Katharine D. Riggs: "Mockery."

Row, Peterson & Company: "The Boy Patriot" from *History-Makers,* a collection of radio plays.

The Roycrofters: "A Message to Garcia" by Elbert Hubbard.

Samuel Scoville, Jr.: "The Cleanlys."

Charles Scribner's Sons: "The Pygmies" from *Here Is Africa* by Ellen and Attilio Gatti; "America for Me" by Henry van Dyke.

The L. W. Singer Company: "The Violin-Maker of Cremona" by François Coppee, translated by Mary J. Nelson.

Jesse Stuart: "Another April."

John Burton Tigrett: "A Duck's Best Friend."

The Viking Press, Inc.: "The Siege of Boonesborough from *Daniel Boone* by James Daugherty, copyright 1939 by James Daugherty: "The Peddler of Ballaghadereen" from *The Way of the Storyteller* by Ruth Sawyer, copyright 1942 by Ruth Sawyer.

The John C. Winston Company: A selection from *Give a Man a Horse* by Charles J. Finger.

INDEX OF TITLES

INDEX OF AUTHORS

PROSE AND POETRY JOURNEYS

PART 2

[*If Part 2 is used in the form bound with Part 1 instead of as a separate workbook, no answers should be written in the book itself. Instead, the answers should be written on a separate paper.*]

PROSE AND POETR

JOURNEYS

DONALD MACLEAN TOWER
MARION T. GARRETSON
CORA J. RUSSELL
CHRISTINE W. WEST

ILLUSTRATIONS • GUY BROWN WISER

SYRACUSE • NEW YORK·

THE L. W. SINGER COMPANY

The Prose and Poetry Series

PROSE AND POETRY OF ENGLAND

PROSE AND POETRY OF AMERICA

PROSE AND POETRY FOR APPRECIATION

PROSE AND POETRY FOR ENJOYMENT

PROSE AND POETRY ADVENTURES

PROSE AND POETRY JOURNEYS

PROSE AND POETRY OF TODAY

PROSE AND POETRY OF THE WORLD

CONTENTS

UNIT III · · · JOURNEYS INTO LEGEND AND FANCY

BIOGRAPHIES, READING LESSONS, DISCUSSION QUESTIONS, APPLIED GRAMMAR, WORD STUDY, LIBRARY PROJECTS, CHORAL READING

UNIT IV · · · JOURNEYS WITH INTERESTING PEOPLE

BIOGRAPHIES, READING LESSONS, DISCUSSION QUESTIONS, APPLIED GRAMMAR, WORD STUDY, LIBRARY PROJECTS, CHORAL READING

UNIT V · · · *JOURNEYS INTO OURSELVES*

BIOGRAPHIES, READING LESSONS, DISCUSSION QUESTIONS, APPLIED
GRAMMAR, WORD STUDY, LIBRARY PROJECTS, CHORAL READING

UNIT ACTIVITIES

THE MOST DANGEROUS ENEMY OF ALL
(Part 1, page 1)

CHECK YOUR READING

Supply the correct answer in each blank.

1. Medviedki was the name of a baby   _____.
2. When he tried to leave the little cave which was his home he was always stopped by   _____.
3. One day he escaped and found himself well out in the   _____.
4. One of the first things that he saw was a flock of   _____.
5. He especially enjoyed being carried along in the large   _____.
6. On a ledge of rock above him, he saw a number of huge sea   _____.
7. Some of the animals were shot by native   _____.
8. The natives were riding in a skin boat called a   _____.
9. Medviedki escaped by swimming under water until he reached a   _____.
10. The natives valued Medviedki for his   _____.

DISCUSSING THE STORY

1. Baby animals grow very fast, but like human children, they have to be taught and watched over by their parents. What signs indicated that Medviedki, the baby otter, was growing up? What had he learned to do for himself? How did he sleep?

2. Medviedki was both curious and adventurous. What did he want to do more than anything else? How did he try to make his father think that he was grown-up? When his father paid no attention whatever to him, what did Medviedki decide to do?

3. What kind of world did the little otter find outside his cave? What strange things did he see? What did he find especially delightful?

1

4. Medviedki was both cautious and confident. Why did he not at once fear the strange thing floating on the sea? What was "the most dangerous enemy of all"? What other enemy did he observe?

5. How did his curiosity get Medviedki into trouble? How did the natives hope to wear him out? How did he manage to escape from them?

6. Why did the natives wait so long for another glimpse of the otter? How did Medviedki show that he had learned something? Do you think that, like most runaway children, Medviedki would be glad to get home again? Do you think that sea otters are interesting animals to study? What other facts about their habits or way of living do you know?

APPLIED GRAMMAR

Sometimes people talk so fast that they run their words together in one long breath. They sound as you would if you read the following groups of words without any pauses.

On a separate paper rewrite the paragraphs so that each idea stands by itself. Mark the beginning of each separate thought by capitalizing the first word and mark the end of each thought with a period.

1. each day he became more expert as a swimmer Medviedki could glide through the water with great speed he could even dive under water for food

2. on stormy days he could hear the sound of waves outside their little pool his mother would not let him leave her side he wanted to find out what was beyond

3. one day he decided to swim out he would wait for his father outside soon he was riding waves in the great Pacific whatever would his mother say

WORDS

1. There are few new or difficult words in "The Most Dangerous Enemy of All," but there are several that are often confused or incorrectly used. In the following sentences which of the words in parentheses should you use? Underscore in each case.

2

a. "He was so fascinated that he had (quiet, quite) forgotten he had come out here to wait for his father."

b. "Medviedki's only thought was to get back to the (quiet, quite) cave with his mother."

c. "A fine pair of hunters we are to (leave, let) a small sea otter get away from us."

d. "He could have quickly slipped beneath the surface and (swam, swum) away without being seen."

e. "Instead, he (dived, dove) down to join her."

2. The following words are often found in lists of words most frequently misspelled. Can you spell correctly *several, separate, disappeared, always, completely, traveled, immediately, excitement, unpleasant, hoping?*

THE LIBRARY

Don't break its back! The back of a new book is sometimes broken by forcing it open, and then the leaves near the broken part become loose. Do you know how to open a new book?

Hold your PROSE AND POETRY text so that the back rests on a table, with the leaves upright in your hands. Take a few pages on one side and press them on the inside margin, so that they rest next to the cover. Continue taking a few pages from the front and then the back, until you reach the center of the book. Now examine your book.

1. What is the title? _____

2. By whom is your text edited? _____

_____

3. Who published it? _____

4. Where was it published? _____

5. The date on the back of the title page is the copyright date, which shows when the book was first published. What is the copyright date? _____

6. List the five units in the table of contents.

_____

_____

_____

_____

_____

3

A DUCK'S BEST FRIEND

(Part 1, page 10)

CHECK YOUR READING

Write T (True) or F (False) in the blanks.

_____ 1. An Indian named Justo Montero was the pioneer bird bander of the North American continent.

_____ 2. Jack Miner lives at Kingsville, Ontario.

_____ 3. Jack is still forced to use decoys to lure geese into his trap.

_____ 4. Mr. Miner has great respect for the intelligence of a goose.

_____ 5. Each bird is banded with the same quotation from the Bible each day of the season.

_____ 6. The oldest duck known to Miner was shot down when it was twenty-three years old.

_____ 7. Geese never make a migratory flight against a head wind.

_____ 8. Geese always stop several times for rest during a long flight.

_____ 9. The Eskimos are superstitious and do not like to kill a banded bird.

_____10. Mr. Miner operates a bird hospital, but he never has many patients.

DISCUSSING THE STORY

1. From the story of the Indian hunter we learn that "a duck's best friend" is Jack Miner. What is different about Mr. Miner's way of banding birds? How long has he been interested in bird migration? How did his work begin? What has he learned about Canadian ducks and geese?

2. What method has Jack devised to trap the geese for banding? How is the banding actually done? What is used as a key to the exact date of the marking?

3. Mr. Miner receives letters from many parts of the country. By whom are they answered? How do these letters and returned bands help to show the migratory routes of the birds? What interesting facts has Jack observed about geese?

4

4. Many of the birds are shot down in the cold northern territories. How are the messages received by the Indians and Eskimos? What else does Miner send into these regions?

5. The 400 acres which Jack devotes to the birds is called a sanctuary. Why is that a good name? How does he feed the birds?

6. Why is the Canada goose his favorite bird? To what does he liken the duck? What does the story of "David and Jonathan" indicate about the character of geese? Do you think that such observations require patience and a keen mind?

7. Describe briefly the hospital which Mr. Miner operates. What proof does he have that geese can talk to one another? In what sense is his sanctuary truly a refuge? Why are refuges better than the game-warden system? What is Mr. Miner's greatest hope?

8. Careful observation of animal or bird life requires genuine interest and sympathy. Do you think Mr. Miner possesses those qualities? What other traits of character do you observe in him? Why is his work of real importance? In what ways does he represent the best kind of sportsman?

APPLIED GRAMMAR

How would you answer the following question?

What has Jack Miner done that has made him well known?

If you should say, "Mr. Miner has made homes for ducks" your answer would make sense because the statement is a complete thought. On the other hand, if you were speaking to a friend and you merely said, "made homes for ducks," your friend might wonder what you meant. You might keep him guessing with an unfinished thought.

Do *you* write or speak in this incomplete manner?

The expressions below may keep you guessing because they are not complete thoughts. From what you have learned in reading "A Duck's Best Friend," make each unfinished thought complete by adding necessary words. How do you show the beginning of a complete thought? the end of a complete thought? Rewrite on a separate paper.

5

1. made homes for ducks
2. mending the birds' broken bones
3. 300 birds in a day
4. when the bands are printed
5. fly 1600 miles without stopping
6. a duck's best friend
7. how a goose flies hundreds of miles
8. five ducks in an open patch just ahead
9. a place for protection and shelter

WORDS

1. Find the verb *to migrate* in your dictionary. Explain the meaning of the associated words *migration* and *migratory*.
2. What are *decoys?* How did Jack Miner use them?
3. Explain the word "principal" as used in the phrase, "one of the *principal* sources." Why is the word not spelled *principle?* Which word is used in connection with the _____ of your school?

THE LIBRARY

The table of contents of a book lists the selections or chapters in the order in which they appear in the book. Indexes list information alphabetically.

1. On what page do the indexes begin in your PROSE AND POETRY? _____
2. How many indexes are there? _____
3. By using one of the indexes, find the page number for "Give a Man a Horse." _____
4. On what page will you find a poem by Lew Sarett? _____
5. Arrange the following topics as they would appear in an index: raccoons, zoo animals, sea otters, Eric Knight, colt, calf, Lew Sarett, "The Cleanlys," "The Runaway," "Toby Goes to Market."

_____   _____
_____   _____
_____   _____
_____   _____
_____   _____

6

TOBY GOES TO MARKET

(Part 1, page 20)

LEW SARETT

Birthday: *May 16, 1888*
Birthplace: *Chicago, Illinois*
Poems to Enjoy and Reread:
1. *"Angus McGregor"*
2. *"October Snow"*
3. *"The Lamps of Bracken-Town"*
4. *"Four Little Foxes"*
5. *"God Is At the Anvil"*
6. *"Wailing Lynx"*

Lew Sarett grew to love nature when as a boy he lived on the shores of Lake Superior. He liked to roam along the shore and as he did so he grew to be a keen observer of everything about him. He made friends with the Indians who taught him to handle a canoe skillfully. In later life he was honored by being invited to become a member of the Chippewa tribe.

Although he studied to become a lawyer, he found teaching, lecturing, and writing much more satisfying. His knowledge of wild life and Indian customs makes him an interesting lecturer. His poems, too, tell of life in the woods and of Indian beliefs and legends.

APPRECIATING THE POEM

1. The first line tells the whole story in a single statement. What does the poet tell you in the rest of the poem?

2. How do you know that the poet had an affectionate feeling for Toby? How did Toby show that he feared being roped and led away? What was the "big adventure" he was reluctant to begin?

3. How does the poet make you feel sympathy for the calf? Does he make you understand how the animal felt?

CHORAL READING

When people tap their feet to music, or sing softly while an orchestra plays, or join in group singing, they are saying, "We

7

want to take part." That desire of everyone to take part, rather than to sit and watch or listen to someone else perform is one of the reasons for choral reading. Hearing one person read a poem can be an enjoyable thing, but if that person goes on for hours or days, his voice becomes monotonous to us. This cannot happen in choral speaking because there is such a variety of combinations possible with the group.

You have of course read aloud together lots of times. That is called "unison" reading. Choral reading goes further than unison reading by placing you in a group with voices similar to yours, and giving your group alone certain parts of the material to read. Sometimes all of the boys will read together. Sometimes the girls will read. Occasionally there will be a "solo" part as in music. Occasionally, too, there will be unison reading. As you read, speak clearly in your natural voice.

Imagine you are the boy who is telling the story about Toby. The mood is conversational. Do you think that the boy feels sorry for Toby? Show his attitude in your voices.

Lew Sarett uses descriptive words well. The words "perpetual wonder" make you see the calf and the expression on its face. The words "wallowed in mischief" are very expressive. "Squirmed" makes you see Toby going through the fence. Show these pictures by your voice. Look for other expressive words. Notice the examples of alliteration in the poem: *b*rindle *b*ull, *b*rindle *b*rain, *r*ump himself to the *r*ain, *b*ewildered he *b*awled. Do justice to these with your voice as you read them.

RUNAWAY
(*Part 1, page 22*)
APPRECIATING THE POEM

1. Lying awake on a lovely summer night, what does the poet see? Why does she hurry to look out the window? Describe the "runaway" she sees there. What had made him run away?

2. What beauty does the poet see in the colt? Try to picture the scene—the moonlight, the poised, motionless animal, the madness of the sudden adventure evident in his attitude—and you will see the beauty of him, too.

8

A DOZEN ROSES AND A BALE OF HAY

(Part 1, page 23)

CHECK YOUR READING

Underscore the correct expression.

1. In the New York Zoo there are (500) (1000) (1783) (2500) inmates to be fed.

2. The giant anteater is fed not ants but (ant eggs) (hen's eggs) (hamburger) (chopped horse meat).

3. The parasol ants live on (roses) (dried flies) (honey) (tiny seeds).

4. No substitute has been found for the food of the panda which is (Chinese rice) (bamboo shoots) (brussels sprouts) (sugar syrup).

5. The inmate which is thought to be the most greedy is the (North African wild sheep) (Galapagos tortoise) (humming bird) (elephant).

6. The authorities at the zoo (permit people to feed peanuts to the animals) (furnish packages of suitable food for visitors to purchase) (arrest any person discovered feeding the animals) (give the animals extra food on Sundays).

7. A birthday cake was once prepared for (Alice, the elephant) (Pete, the hippopotamus) (a huge reptile) (the oldest monkey).

8. Snakes are fed (about every two weeks) (once a day) (in the presence of large crowds) (frequently but in small quantities).

9. The animals which require the greatest variety of food are the (birds) (reptiles) (lions) (bears).

10. Lions have been found to be very fond of (grapes) (cod-liver oil) (catnip) (bananas).

DISCUSSING THE STORY

1. What are some of the problems of feeding the animals housed at the New York Zoological Park? What is the first rule which Dr. Goss tries to observe? Why is it not always possible to do this? How is a good substitute found?

2. What problem was presented by the giant anteater?

How was it solved? How did the Zoo attendants show that they understood the animal?

3. The parasol ants are among the most interesting of the inmates of the Zoo. Why are they called "parasol" ants? Describe some of their strange habits. What touches of humor does the author use to describe their life?

4. The panda also requires a special diet. What is its particular food? Why are there not many pandas in this country? What special gift of pandas was made to the New York Zoo?

5. Have you ever seen a humming bird? Describe the method of feeding which has been especially devised for them at the Zoo.

6. What is a glutton? Which of the inmates is called the "prize glutton" of the Zoo? What other animal has strange eating habits?

7. The Zoological Society provides food for the animals which visitors can purchase to feed to them. Why was it necessary to install such machines? Why is it important for visitors to observe feeding regulations?

8. Relate briefly how Alice, the elephant, once lost her appetite. Why did Pete, the hippopotamus, not enjoy the party given for him? What surprising facts did you learn about the digestive system of snakes?

9. The task of feeding twenty-five hundred animals and birds the special foods which they require is a tremendous one. Which items of food impressed you as being particularly large amounts or especially strange food? Which section of the Zoo requires the greatest variety of foods? Which of the animals demands a varied bill of fare?

10. Some of the animals have developed peculiar eating habits and amazing tastes. How does the kinkajou eat grapes? What causes astonishing behavior in the lions? Which group of animals or birds would you especially like to observe on a visit to the Zoo?

APPLIED GRAMMAR

From "A Dozen Roses and a Bale of Hay" supply the name of the person, place, or animal that completes the meaning.

1. The _____ is the biggest boarding house in the world.

2. The _____ eat rose petals!

3. The _____ wants nothing to eat but bamboo shoots.

4. _____ eat or drink almost all the time.

5. Once a North African wild _____ swallowed a glove, three balloons and five rubber balls!

6. One night _____ ate several dozen loaves of bread.

7. _____ would not eat his birthday cake.

8. _____ like many changes in their food.

9. In the winter, the _____ gives the animals cod liver oil.

10. The _____ like a bale of hay each day.

Each word that you have supplied tells *about whom* or *what* the statement is made and is called the "subject" of the sentence.

WORDS

1. In this selection and in others you will meet new words which you will want to add to your own vocabulary. By following the key at the bottom of each page of your dictionary you can learn how to pronounce any unfamiliar word. Following the example below indicate the pronunciation and meaning of these words.

	Pronunciation	*Meaning*
obviously	ŏb'vĭ-ŭs-lĭ	plainly
gesture	_____	_____
compromised	_____	_____
edible	_____	_____
recognize	_____	_____
palatable	_____	_____

2. Many English words have grown out of other languages, particularly Latin. Such words are said to be *derived* from another language and are called *derivatives*. Often a syllable or *prefix* is placed before the main part of a word or *stem* to change its meaning. Some of the common prefixes are *dis* (not or apart), *ex* (from), *in* (in or on), *ob* (against or toward), *per* (through), *pro* (before), *re* (back or again), *sub* (under). Using the English stem *ject* of the Latin verb *jacere* (to throw) show how some of these prefixes have been used to form words of different meanings.

Prefix	*Stem*	*Meaning*
re	ject	throw back or refuse
_____	ject	_____
_____	ject	_____
_____	ject	_____
_____	ject	_____

THE LIBRARY

You will find many exciting stories like "A Dozen Roses and a Bale of Hay" in your school library. You will want to know just where to find books you will enjoy. Before borrowing a book you will, of course, want to know how to sign for it and how long you may keep it. When your class visits the library, find out the answers to the following questions:

1. What hours is the library open?
2. What are fiction books?
3. Where are fiction books kept in your school library?
4. What must you do if you wish to borrow a book? How soon must you return it?
5. Why are you asked to return books promptly?
6. Where are the recent magazines?
7. Are you allowed to borrow recent magazines? If so, for how long?
8. List three ways in which to show courtesy in the library.

Remember, books are like people. *You* wouldn't like to be thrown about, to have your back broken, your clothes torn, or be put on a shelf and forgotten . . . would you?

12

THE CLEANLYS

(Part 1, page 34)

CHECK YOUR READING

Write T (True) or F (False) in the blanks.

_____ 1. The raccoon is known by his black-ringed, cylindrical tail.

_____ 2. Like other animals, the raccoon walks on his toes.

_____ 3. Baby raccoons know how to swim without being taught.

_____ 4. Raccoons are unusually particular about washing their food.

_____ 5. The father coon in this story succeeded in killing a rabbit for their supper.

_____ 6. One night they feasted royally on a large turtle.

_____ 7. One of the baby coons was shot by a farmer.

_____ 8. Another was squeezed to death by a great pine snake.

_____ 9. The youngest coon had a forepaw caught in a trap.

_____10. The father coon saved his family by causing two dogs to drown.

DISCUSSING THE STORY

1. What is the setting of the story—the location, the season, the scene? What colors do you see in the first three paragraphs? To what other senses does the author appeal?

2. Whose was the "funny little face" which appeared first? What do you learn about his family and their home?

3. Like human children, baby animals some day have to venture out alone. What happened to the little raccoon on his first adventure? How did his mother show him both discipline and loving care? How does the author show that he has closely observed animal life and that he understands animal nature?

4. What did the mother coon have for supper? How do her habits explain in part the reason for calling this story "The Cleanlys"?

5 What sound does the big coon's call resemble? What kind of food was secured on the hunt? Why should one not feel sorry when the frogs and the drake are killed?

13

6. How were the little coons taught to eat their first real food? Where were they taken for their first hunting lesson? Describe the events of the night. What important things do you think the little coons learned?

7. As the little coons grew older how did their education advance? What foods did they learn to get for themselves? Why were they usually obedient? What happened to one of them because she was disobedient?

8. What is the difference between an accident in a human family and in a wild folk family? What two accidents were nearly fatal to the little coons? How did the mother coon show courage and love? What task was painful but necessary? How do you think the author feels about people who set traps? What is your own opinion?

9. What farm food makes a delectable dish for the coon? Do you find any reason in this part of the story for farmers to wage war against raccoons? What happened to the coons on this adventure? How did the father show that raccoons are a dangerous enemy in the water? Describe the exciting fight that took place.

10. Do you think the events of the story represent the daily lives of most animals? What, in general, have you learned about animals in the selections of this unit?

APPLIED GRAMMAR

Supply colorful words to tell what the animals did.

1. The baby raccoon _____ slowly down the side of the tree.

2. With a cry of terror, he _____ headlong into the pool below.

3. At the first sound of that SOS the head of Mother Coon _____ at the opening in the tree.

4. Although the shell was dripping, Mrs. Coon _____ down and _____ it.

5. As the turtle _____ slowly up the bank, the coons waited.

6. From behind the fern _____ the brown-and-white pine snake.

14

7. Mother Coon _____ through the bushes at the first cry of her baby in danger.

8. Into the field the raccoons _____ and _____ down stalk after stalk of creamy corn.

9. Then they _____ con- tentedly back toward the woods.

10. Across the field _____ three mongrel hounds!

Words like those you have used above, which show what the subject *does,* are called "predicates."

WORDS

There are many beautiful nature words and phrases in this story. How many can you find which describe out-of-door things?

_____   _____
_____   _____
_____   _____
_____   _____
_____   _____

THE LIBRARY

Perhaps you noticed when you were in the library, how the fiction books are arranged. They are grouped alphabetically first by authors' last names, and then by title, if there are several books by one author.

1. Number the following fiction books in the order in which they would appear on the shelves.

_____ *The Trumpeter of Krakow* by Eric Kelly

_____ *Lassie Come Home* by Eric Knight

_____ *The Adventures of Tom Sawyer* by Mark Twain

_____ *Caddie Woodlawn* by Carol Brink

_____ *Mehitable* by Katherine Adams

_____ *Blacksmith of Vilno* by Eric Kelly

_____ *Mountains Are Free* by Julia Adams

2. As you already know where the fiction books are in your library, find one of the books above and make a note of the number of pages in it.

15

THE SIEGE OF BOONESBOROUGH

(Part 1, page 47)

JAMES DAUGHERTY

Birthday: *June 1, 1889*
Birthplace: *Asheville, North Carolina*
Stories and Illustrations to Enjoy:
1. *Daniel Boone*
2. *Abraham Lincoln*
3. *(Illustrations) John Brown's Body by Stephen Vincent Benét*
4. *(Illustrations) Abe Lincoln Grows Up by Carl Sandburg*

James Daugherty was born in North Carolina, grew up in Indiana and Ohio, and thereafter lived in many widely scattered places. He and his father were inseparable companions, the elder Daugherty often reading aloud from the Bible or the plays of Shakespeare while the younger man played at sketching. After attending the Philadelphia Art Academy and spending some time in Europe, Daugherty wasted several years in New York trying to establish himself as an illustrator. During World War I he found excitement in camouflaging ships at Baltimore and Newport News.

The whole course of his life was unexpectedly changed when he was asked to illustrate Stewart Edward White's book on Daniel Boone. The vigor and dash of his drawings won immediate favor and he has since illustrated scores of children's books, including his own *Daniel Boone, Poor Richard,* and *Abraham Lincoln.* It is easy to see that the leaders and pioneers of America are among his chief interests.

CHECK YOUR READING

In each blank write the letter of the expression which correctly completes the meaning.

———— 1. Boone and his men were on their way to (*a*) French Lick (*b*) Detroit (*c*) Chillicothe (*d*) the fort at Boonesborough.

_____ 2. In 1776 Detroit was (*a*) an American trading post (*b*) an Indian settlement (*c*) a British fort (*d*) a French mission.

_____ 3. Boone (*a*) was sold to General Hamilton for a hundred pounds (*b*) was held as the personal property of Chief Black Fish (*c*) was allowed to return to Boonesborough (*d*) was imprisoned in a rude camp.

_____ 4. It took Boone (*a*) four days (*b*) twelve days (*c*) sixteen days (*d*) twenty days to reach the fort.

_____ 5. Boone delayed the attack hoping to (*a*) trick the Indians (*b*) repair their stockade (*c*) arrange a peaceful agreement (*d*) receive aid from Harrodsburg.

_____ 6. The Indians used the method of (*a*) mass attack (*b*) continuous firing (*c*) intermittent firing (*d*) direct charge against the fort.

_____ 7. Jemima Boone (*a*) was taken captive (*b*) was killed by her father's cannon (*c*) became very ill (*d*) was hit by a sniper.

_____ 8. The defenders feared more than anything else (*a*) a sudden rush on the gates (*b*) an epidemic of illness (*c*) exploding mines in the tunnel (*d*) being scalped.

_____ 9. Once they were saved by (*a*) fire in the Indian camp (*b*) rain (*c*) Black Pompey (*d*) darkness.

_____10. The men from Harrodsburg (*a*) brought strong reinforcements (*b*) had been taken prisoner (*c*) found the fort in ashes (*d*) came in time to celebrate victory.

DISCUSSING THE STORY

1. The story opens with Boone and his party on their way to boil salt at French Lick. What unexpected attack was made on them? How did Boone prevent an attack on Boonesborough?

2. Describe the conditions that existed in and around Detroit in 1776. Why were Boone and his men taken there? What was the outcome of events there?

3. At the Indian camp Boone played a game of pretense. What did he do? Why was he alarmed by the preparations for war which he saw being made? How did he escape?

4. What was remarkable about Boone's journey back to Boonesborough? What had happened there while he had been gone? Why was the Indian attack delayed?

5. How large were the Indian forces? Why did the people in the fort not surrender? Why did Boone agree to sit in council with the Indians? How did he outwit them?

6. What methods of fighting did the Indians use? How did the Americans maintain their resistance? What did they fear most? How were they saved from death by fire? How long did they endure? Who arrived to celebrate with them?

7. What kind of spirit helped these early pioneers to beat off their enemies? What qualities in the character of Daniel Boone are revealed here? How have such men as Boone helped to make our country the proud free nation it is?

APPLIED GRAMMAR

A group of related words which contains neither a subject nor a predicate is called a "phrase." Add subjects and predicates to the following phrases so that they express complete thoughts. Rewrite on a separate paper.

1. near the fort
2. for a powwow
3. squinting at the fire
4. into the woods
5. dancing to pounding drums and shrill war chants

Any group of related words which contains both a subject and a predicate is called a "clause." A clause which expresses a complete thought is a sentence.

Some of the clauses below express complete thoughts and should be punctuated as sentences. Some of the clauses, although they contain both a subject and a predicate, do not express complete ideas. Add words to these clauses, so that all the clauses will be sentences. Rewrite on a separate paper.

6. the Indians had caught the chief of the white men
7. if the fires continued to burn
8. the enemy was driving a tunnel toward the fort
9. who was saving them from attack
10. while the Indians were in close pursuit

18

WORDS

1. An easy way to increase your vocabulary is to learn how to use *synonyms* or words which mean nearly the same as other words; as, *happy* and *joyous; sad* and *sorrowful*. What synonyms could you substitute for the words below?

fictitious	(page 49)	*destiny*	(page 51)
tedious	(page 50)	*parley*	(page 52)
rendezvous	(page 51)	*incessantly*	(page 55)

THE LIBRARY

You can readily understand that some order or system is necessary when you look about a library and see the many, many books and all the people who use these books. Perhaps you have wondered how your librarian finds a certain book so quickly. It all comes from a very carefully planned system for classifying books according to the subject matter and the use of numbers and letters in arranging them on the shelves. The system is known as the "Dewey Decimal System."

Following are the ten main groups of numbers for the various classes of books. After you have learned these classifications find out where in your library each group is located.

GENERAL WORKS	000–099	Books about books and general things.
PHILOSOPHY	100–199	Man thought.
RELIGION	200–299	Man thought about God.
SOCIAL SCIENCES	300–399	Man thought about his neighbors.
LANGUAGE	400–499	Man talked to his neighbors.
SCIENCE	500–599	Man studied the things about him as stars, trees, birds.
USEFUL ARTS	600–699	Man made useful things.
FINE ARTS	700–799	Man made beautiful things.
LITERATURE	800–899	Man wrote.
HISTORY	900–999	Man made records.
		A record of a journey is a travel book.
		A record of a life is a biography.
		A record of events is history.

(From *Library Occurent* v.10:278 Ap-Je '32)

PAUL REVERE'S RIDE

(Part 1, page 56)

APPRECIATING THE POEM

1. Nearly everyone can quote the first three lines of the poem from memory. Why are they worth remembering?

2. What signal had Paul Revere and his friend arranged? How did his friend feel as he heard the soldiers march down to the boats and as he looked down on the scene below him?

3. In what mood was Paul Revere as he waited and watched? How do you think he felt when he saw the signal?

4. Which lines seem to have the rhythm of hurrying hoof beats? Through what villages does Paul Revere pass?

5. Line 111 says, "You know the rest." But *do* you know the rest? Who were the Minute Men? How were they organized? What was the outcome of this first battle of the Revolution?

6. Reread the last stanza carefully. How has World War II shown that the American people have heard the echo of Paul Revere's spirit?

CHORAL READING

Show by your voices the way Paul Revere and his friend felt in lines 6–30. As you grasp the meaning in lines 31–41, you will show your appreciation in the intonation of such words as "stealthy tread," "trembling ladder," "steep and tall."

Feel the change of mood in lines 42–56 before trying to read aloud. Note the change from this mood to that of lines 57–67. The strong rhythm will help you to read these lines well, but putting yourself in Paul's place and feeling as he did will help you more. Note the slight change in mood in line 64. Note how the word "and" repeated between descriptive words helps to emphasize the mood.

Show in your reading the excitement you feel in lines 68–72 and in lines 73–80. Emphasize the time of night (*one* by the village clock, *two* by the village clock) to give a feeling of time's passing. Let your voice express the spirit of the last lines of the poem (119–130).

20

GRANDMOTHER'S STORY OF THE BATTLE OF BUNKER HILL

(Part 1, page 61)

OLIVER WENDELL HOLMES

Birthday: *August 29, 1809*
(Died October 7, 1894)
Birthplace: *Cambridge, Massachusetts*
Poems to Enjoy and Reread:
1. *"The Deacon's Masterpiece"*
2. *"How the Old Horse Won the Bet"*
3. *"The Chambered Nautilus"*
4. *"The Stethoscope Song"*
5. *"Ballad of the Oysterman"*

Very early in his life, Oliver Wendell Holmes became acquainted with books and people. He was perhaps happiest when he was standing on tiptoe reaching for another large volume to read in his father's comfortable library. In fact, he enjoyed these big books more than his school work. However, he was a diligent, faithful, likeable student. At times, like all boys, he was mischievous.

At fifteen he was ready to attend Harvard College under whose shadow he had been born. Several years later, Dr. Oliver Wendell Holmes of Boston was busy visiting patients, inventing better medical instruments, and lecturing to students about medical science. In the meantime his friends had discovered his gift of writing and he was persuaded to write poems for special occasions of every sort. Today he is remembered as a poet rather than as a physician. His friendliness, humor, and kindliness brought him the esteem of people in every nation.

CHECK YOUR READING

Supply the correct answers in the blanks.
1. How old was this grandmother who relates the story? _____
2. What time of year did the battle take place? _____

21

3. How old do you think the grandmother was at the time of the battle? _____

4. Whom did she meet in the street? _____

5. What soldiers were on the hill? _____

6. Who was in command of them? _____

7. What soldiers gathered at the foot of the hill? _____

8. What time did the latter march toward the hill? _____

9. For what king were these soldiers fighting? _____

10. Which side won the first attack? _____

11. What village was burned? _____

12. Which side won the second attack? _____

13. Who won the third attack? _____

14. What method of fighting was used? _____

15. What happened to the grandmother? _____

16. Whom did she see when she regained consciousness? _____

17. Who was killed in the battle? _____

18. Did the wounded blue-eyed soldier live? _____

19. Who took care of him? _____

20. Who was he? _____

APPRECIATING THE POEM

1. It was not long after the first battles of Lexington and Concord that the British plan of action brought troops to Bunker Hill. The red-coated troops crossed the Charles River from Boston on the sultry morning of June 17, 1775, their movements being covered by the fire of the British men-of-war in the Charles River. What was grandma's first opinion about the firing?

2. Without "bodice-lacing or looking-glass grimacing," grandma, then a sweet young girl, started out to discover the cause of the disturbance. Whom did she meet on the way, and where did the little group go? From the steeple, they commanded an excellent view of the battlements, with full sight of the gripping struggle which left them weak and breathless.

22

Can you imagine the dreadful anxiety and stifling terror of watching the advance of the British troops?

3. The colonists had fortified Breed's Hill, which lay in front of Bunker Hill and had hastily constructed a breastwork and prepared themselves to repulse the first attack which was made sometime after three o'clock. The British troops moved forward slowly and the Americans awaited their approach, holding their fire until the British were within ten or twelve rods when they opened on them with terrible execution, forcing them to retreat. But the British commander rallied his troops and ordered another assault. In the meantime what had been set on fire?

4. A second time the British were repulsed, but the struggle was not yet over. Can you imagine the anxiety in waiting to see if your brothers and father, your neighbors, were to be triumphant in that death grapple, or the flag and those you loved wiped out before your very eyes?

5. Exasperated at the repulses of his troops, General Howe resolved on another attack. How was it made and why were the defenders unable to stop the advances? About five o'clock the British troops took possession of Bunker Hill.

6. As if the thrilling story of a great battle were not enough, the poet cleverly gives us a surprise ending. Who was the wounded youth left on grandmother's doorstep? Do you like the last stanza, with its reference to the portrait above the mantelpiece, and the way in which grandmother answers one of the children's questions?

WORDS

1. "These are the times that try men's souls," said Thomas Paine in a famous speech. In what sense is *try* used in that sentence?

2. In line 20 Grandmother says, "I was gone the *livelong* day." Did she mean an *exciting, quickly passing, long in passing,* or *memorable* day?

3. Do you sometimes forget to pronounce final syllables? Make a list of words from the poem ending in "ing." Pronounce each word carefully.

23

THE BOY PATRIOT

(Part 1, page 70)

CHECK YOUR READING

Match the following by supplying each blank at the left with
the number of the correct expression.

_____ an assumed name	1. firing squad
_____ the Commander-in-Chief	2. "Death cometh soon or late"
_____ the Boy Patriot	3. military information
_____ the betrayer	4. Farmer Harrington
_____ the manner of death	5. ". . . one life to lose"
_____ the articles destroyed	6. Patrick Henry
_____ the fate of a spy	7. personal letters
_____ the last words	8. Washington
	9. Nathan Hale
	10. hanging
	11. death without mercy
	12. Stephen Jones
	13. Samuel Adams
	14. life imprisonment

DISCUSSING THE PLAY

1. Every crisis in history produces great leaders and many
heroes. Who are some of the Revolutionary heroes mentioned
by the announcer in the play? Name some others you might
add to this list.

2. What reason do the authors give for including Nathan
Hale among the early heroes of our country?

3. Because the radio play is heard and not seen, the radio
playwright must help you to imagine the setting. He does this
by means of brief explanations and by sound effects. What is
the opening situation of "The Boy Patriot"? Note the sound
effects that are used.

4. How does the writer of radio plays indicate to the listener
the passing of time? What do you learn about Nathan Hale?
What information has he discovered so far?

5. Hale never gets a chance to send his information to

24

Washington. By whom is he betrayed? What is always the fate of a spy?

6. How did Hale pass his last few days? What kind of spirit is revealed in the letters he writes? What happens to the letters? Does the action seem cruel to you? Was the guard justified in his action from his point of view?

7. What were Hale's last words? Why have they not been forgotten? With what kind of spirit did Hale meet death?

8. How does the announcer summarize the character of Nathan Hale? Do you think the quoted lines are a fitting tribute to him?

9. Nathan Hale was a young man when he offered his services to his country in a task which he knew was almost certain to fail. Do you think it was easy for him to give up a brilliant military career? Was it easy to give up his family and friends and the home he had hoped to establish? Do you think you could have made the decision he did?

10. Every nation honors those who die in battle and counts each one a hero. Do we also have our living heroes? Must one be in military service to serve his country or to become a hero? What situations in everyday life call for the quiet courage of Nathan Hale? Do you know anyone who has shown qualities of heroism in his own home?

WORDS

1. Actors in a radio play need to know the meaning of the words in their lines as well as how to pronounce them. How do you pronounce and explain *tyrant, opponents,* and *espionage?*

2. Words are often accented differently according to the way they are used in the sentence. Place the accent mark on the words below to indicate the proper pronunciation.

produce (noun)   proceeds (noun)
produce (verb)   proceeds (verb)

3. Nathan Hale said, "I only regret that I have but one life to (lose, loose) for my country." Explain which word is correct.

THE OREGON TRAIL

(Part 1, page 77)

APPRECIATING THE POEM

1. Between 1839 and 1859 the westward migration from Missouri and Nebraska took place. The Oregon Trail was the route now practically followed by the Union Pacific Railroad from the Bear River. In what kind of vehicles did the pioneers travel? How long was the journey?

2. What hardships did the travelers experience on the way? Which lines tell of their indomitable spirit?

3. Why has the poet made lines 37–42 shorter than the rest of the lines? Does the rhythm change? How do the lines summarize what America has done in all periods of her progress?

CHORAL READING

Read the poem carefully before trying to read it aloud. Those of you who have seen wagons toiling up hills or mountains know how the words of the first stanza apply. Try to imagine the *growling, jolting, grumbling, rumbling* of the wagons. Think of the many places from which they started and of the "long, long trail" they are following. Express these feelings in your voices.

In the fifth stanza show the resolution and courage of the pioneers. In reading the last line of stanza six, remember how the ancestors of these people, thousands of years ago, marched to make new homes also. Notice the excellent choice of words in the next stanza: "creeping down the dark defile," "surging through the brawling stream."

Use the following key for your reading: In stanza 1, let everybody read line 1; all boys line 2; all girls line 3; and everybody line 4. In line 5, let one boy read "From East," two boys read "and South," and three boys continue to the end of line 6. All boys read lines 7 and 8; all girls 9–12; everybody 13–16; all boys 17–24; everybody 25–28; all boys 29–34; everybody 35–36. Let one girl read lines 37–38; a second girl line 39, and third 40; a fourth 41; a fifth 42; and everybody lines 43–46.

26

UNIT ACTIVITIES

SUGGESTIONS FOR FURTHER READING—UNIT I

LAURA ADAMS ARMER, *Waterless Mountain*
JOHN BURROUGHS, *Squirrels and Other Fur-Bearers*
WALTER D. EDMONDS, *Tom Whipple*
WALTER D. EDMONDS, *The Matchlock Gun*
PAUL EIPPER, *Animals Looking at You*
RACHEL FIELD, *Calico Bush*
ALICE GALL and FLEMING CREW, *Ringtail*
AMY HOGEBOOM and JOHN WARE, *One Life to Lose*
HAAKON LIE, *Ekorn*
STEPHEN WARREN MEADER, *Down the Big River*
EZRA MEEKER, *Ox-team Days on the Oregon Trail*
CORNELIA L. MEIGS, *Master Simon's Garden*
ENOS A. MILLS, *In Beaver World*
MILDRED MASTIN PACE, *Early American*
FRANCES ROGERS and ALICE BEARD, *Paul Revere*
FELIX SALTEN, *Perri*
FELIX SALTEN, *Rennie, the Rescuer*
SAMUEL SCOVILLE, JR., *Wild Folk*
ERNEST THOMPSON SETON, *Biography of a Grizzly*
ELEANOR SICKLES, *In Calico and Crinoline*
CONSTANCE LINDSAY SKINNER, *Becky Landers, Frontier Warrior*
CONSTANCE LINDSAY SKINNER, *Silent Scot, Frontier Scout*
CAROLINE DALE SNEDEKER, *Black Arrowhead*
STEWART EDWARD WHITE, *Daniel Boone, Wilderness Scout*
HENRY WILLIAMSON, *Tarka the Otter*

DO YOU REMEMBER FACTS FROM YOUR READING?

In each of the following sentences, underscore the word or phrase which makes the sentence correct.

1. The Cleanlys were a family of (bears) (opossums) (mice) (raccoons).
2. Toby was a (dog) (Persian cat) (brindle bull) (monkey in a zoo).
3. The "Boy Patriot" was (Nathan Hale) (Paul Revere) (Daniel Boone) (Stephen Jones).
4. The "most dangerous enemy of all" to the sea otter is (the sea lion) (Medviedki) (man) (the sea urchin).

5. The "runaway" was (a colt) (a cowardly soldier) (an elephant) (a bear cub).

6. A "duck's best friend" was (a group of Eskimos) (Jack Miner) (a Jesuit missionary) (the veterinarian of the New York Zoo).

7. Daniel Boone was (a Shawnee Indian) (an historian) (a wilderness scout) (a Revolutionary War hero).

8. The Battle of Bunker Hill was fought during (the Revolutionary War) (the War of 1812) (the Civil War) (World War I).

9. At the New York Zoological Park, a dozen roses is the daily food of the (humming bird) (panda) (parasol ants) (tortoise).

10. The "Oregon Trail" was blazed by (Lewis and Clark) (Blackfoot Indians) (railroad leaders) (pioneer families).

CAN YOU IDENTIFY THE SKETCHES?

With what selections do you associate the sketches on the opposite page?

1. _____
2. _____
3. _____
4. _____
5. _____
6. _____
7. _____
8. _____

28

THE PYGMIES
(Part 1, page 81)

CHECK YOUR READING

In each blank write the letter of the phrase which correctly completes the meaning.

_____ 1. The pygmies live in (*a*) the Belgian Congo region (*b*) India (*c*) southern Africa (*d*) Egypt.

_____ 2. The plant and animal life is (*a*) very sparse (*b*) of moderate growth (*c*) of unbelievable proportions (*d*) like that of North America.

_____ 3. The pygmies are a race of (*a*) giant gorillas (*b*) dwarfs (*c*) red-skinned hunters (*d*) cannibals.

_____ 4. To kill the animals which they need for food, the pygmies (*a*) dig deep holes for traps (*b*) shoot them with arrows (*c*) set cleverly made steel traps (*d*) hurl sharp spears at them.

_____ 5. The pygmies use (*a*) skin canoes (*b*) birch canoes (*c*) hemp ropes (*d*) suspension bridges to cross their rivers.

_____ 6. Each clan lives (*a*) in a separate, small clearing (*b*) in one large hut (*c*) in a territory of 50,000 square miles (*d*) in a region determined by its leader.

_____ 7. Makulu-Kulu was chosen as leader of his tribe because he was (*a*) the oldest (*b*) the ablest (*c*) the only unmarried (*d*) the best-educated man.

_____ 8. Besides tracking and trapping, the hunters (*a*) cook the food (*b*) care for the children (*c*) carry the heavy burdens (*d*) make all the equipment.

_____ 9. Most of the clothing is made from (*a*) skins (*b*) grass (*c*) bark (*d*) lianas.

_____ 10. The pygmies are fond of the meat of the (*a*) gorilla (*b*) hippopotamus (*c*) leopard (*d*) antelope.

DISCUSSING THE STORY

1. "The Pygmies" is a chapter taken from an interesting book called *This Is Africa*. What part of Africa are the authors describing in this chapter? What three words seem to sum up the kind of land this region is?

30

2. Why has Central Africa not been explored even by its own people? What examples do the authors cite of excessive growth in plant and animal life? Why are white men poorly equipped to explore the jungle?

3. Who are the "supermen" who successfully fight against the monsters of the jungle? What weapons do they use? How do they provide themselves with meat? By what clever arrangement do they outwit the crocodiles? How does the whole tribe manage to cross a river?

4. The family life of the pygmies is especially interesting. How are the various clans divided? How much territory does each clan possess? Explain briefly in what ways each tribe is a self-sufficient, democratic community.

5. The authors use Makulu-Kulu as an example of a tribe's leader. What are his duties as sultan? What other members make up his tribe? What tasks belong to the men? What special tasks are done by the women and children?

6. Sometimes accidents occur or danger threatens. How does the pygmy often outwit the giant gorilla? What do you learn from this story about the characteristics of the gorilla? How do the dwarfs sometimes celebrate the escape of one of their members?

APPLIED GRAMMAR

What words describe the person, place, or thing spoken of in the following sentence?

The hungry crocodiles snap their horrible jaws.

All the words which tell more about the simple subject of a sentence make the meaning more complete, and therefore with the simple subject form the "complete subject."

What single word in the sentence above shows action? What words add meaning to the predicate? These words with the simple predicate form the "complete predicate."

What words add to the meaning of the subject in the following sentence? to the predicate?

The cavernous mouth of the gorilla raised a blood-curdling yell into the night air.

31

Add colorful words or phrases to the simple subjects and simple predicates listed below.

_____ leopard prowls _____
_____ pygmy swings _____
_____ spiders may grow _____
_____ gorillas rush _____

WORDS

One can see that the authors are not only explorers, but well-read persons of extensive vocabularies.

1. Write a good synonym for each of the following:

epochs: _____   *excavated*: _____
infinite: _____   *durable*: _____

2. Use the following words in good original sentences:

self-sufficient: _____

_____

impassable: _____

_____

unfordable: _____

_____

THE LIBRARY

If you liked "The Pygmies," you will want to read the entire book, *This Is Africa*. As this is a book of travel what number would you expect to find on the back of this book?

Perhaps you have noticed the letters which are below the numbers on the backs of books. Each letter stands for the author's last name. If there are many books about travel in Africa, they are placed on the shelves in alphabetic order, according to each author's last name.

1. What letter would you expect to find under the number of the book *This Is Africa?* _____

2. In the space below, arrange the following numbers in the order in which they would appear on the shelves.

390   796   914.2   520   920   914   914   595   598   595
B   W   E   L   F   H   R   T   A   C

VOLCANO IN HIS CORNFIELD

(Part 1, page 92)

DISCUSSING THE STORY

1. How did the Indian farmer happen to discover the volcano? How fast did it grow? Why are scientists delighted with this phenomenon?

2. What is the name of the new volcano and where is it located? Why do visitors find it difficult to reach?

3. The new volcano already has caused much damage. What has it done to the cornfields? How has it affected the lives of the Indians?

4. Besides the gray ash thrown out by the volcano, what other feature of it is unpleasant? What are the "bombs" that are thrown into the air? Why is the volcano a particularly interesting sight at night?

5. Describe briefly the lava flow. How was the author able to take a picture of it? What wrong idea about volcanoes do most people have? What is the "smoke" that we think we see? From a good encyclopedia find further facts about volcanoes to report to the class.

WORDS

1. What word might you substitute for *obliterated* in the sentence, "If there ever was any road over the last three or four miles . . . it has been completely obliterated"?

2. If the word *spectacle* is defined as "a remarkable or noteworthy sight," how would you explain the sentence, "Our first close view of the volcano was at night, when it is most spectacular"?

3. On page 91 find and explain the meaning of the terms *incandescence* and *incandescent*.

4. What is a *phenomenon*? Show how the word is pronounced and divide it into syllables on the line below.

5. Certain familiar words are often misspelled and mispronounced. Practice writing and saying *traveled* (one *l*); *belief* (*ie*); *actual* (*ua*); *lightning* (*n*ing).

THE LIBRARY

Not all libraries arrange fiction books and biographies in the same manner. Some librarians mark fiction with the letter "F" above the letter for the author's last name; some use just the letter of the author's name. Biographies in some libraries are marked with a "B," while in others they are labeled with the figure 921.

1. How are fiction books marked in your library?
2. How are biographies marked?
3. Can you find how books which are collections of several biographies are numbered?
4. Where are books of short stories in your library?
5. Does your library have a chart of the Dewey Decimal System?

TRAVEL

(Part 1, page 92)

APPRECIATING THE POEM

1. A poet often seems to express the things we all feel but cannot say in words. What longing which all of us have shared is the poet describing in this poem?

2. Name some of the places the poet would like to visit. What scenes would he like to see? If this were your own poem about travel, what places or scenes would you mention?

WORDS

Lines 31 and 32 illustrate how related words may differ slightly in pronunciation and meaning. Explain how *desert* and *deserted* are used. Show how *desert* differs from *dessert*.

THE LIBRARY

Just as you look in a directory for the telephone number of a friend, you can look in a catalog in the library for the number of a book. The number on the book is the "call number" because it is the number by which the book is called. The catalog is known as the "card catalog" because it contains cards for each book, arranged in drawers. Like a telephone book, the card catalog lists names alphabetically.

34

Most of us, like Robert Louis Stevenson, like to travel. You will enjoy the mysteriously exciting adventures which Mr. Stevenson has written. If you look up his name in your card catalog, you may find a card like this:

```
821    Stevenson, Robert Louis
S         A child's garden of verses. Scribner,
       N. Y. c. 1905
          243 p. illus.
```

From the information on the card, can you answer these questions:

1. What is the call number of the book? _____
2. What is the title? _____ _____

_____

3. Who is the publisher? _____
4. When was the book first printed? _____
5. How many pages are there in it? _____
6. Are there any illustrations? _____
7. How many cards are there in your card catalog for Robert Louis Stevenson? _____
8. List the titles of books in your library by Mr. Stevenson.

_____

_____

_____

_____

_____

_____

9. Draw a plan of your school library and mark by letter the following places:
   a. The shelves where you find the fiction books.
   b. The location of the charging desk.
   c. The location of the encyclopedias.
   d. Where the dictionaries are located.
   e. Where the magazines and newspapers can be found.

EDUCATION OF GAY-NECK

(Part 1, page 94)

DHAN GOPAL MUKERJI

Birthday: July 6, 1890
  (Died July 14, 1936)
Birthplace: Calcutta, India
Stories to Enjoy and Reread:
1. *Hari the Jungle Lad*
2. *Gay-Neck*
3. *Ghond the Hunter*
4. *Kari the Elephant*

In a village close to Calcutta, just at the rim of the jungle, Dhan Gopal Mukerji was born. He was taught that the dwellers of the jungles were his brothers and he soon made friends with them.

At fourteen he followed in the footsteps of his ancestors by entering the priesthood, but he was not happy at his duties in the temple. He therefore entered the University of Calcutta, and then went to Japan to study engineering.

Suddenly he decided to make his way to America. Scraping together money earned at all sorts of jobs, he completed his education in California and became a lecturer and teacher.

A number of years later he took a trip to his native land, India. Then it was that he decided to write stories about his jungle friends for American boys and girls. He knew they would enjoy making the acquaintance of Gay-Neck, the pigeon; of Kari, the elephant; and of Hari and Ghond, Hindu boys who understood the jungle animals. He hoped, too, that through his stories American boys and girls would understand India better.

CHECK YOUR READING

Write T (True) or F (False) in the blank spaces.

_____ 1. From the second day of birth young pigeons are fed millet seeds.

_____ 2. When Gay-Neck was five weeks old the author discovered that the bird was blind.

36

_____ 3. The author tried to induce Gay-Neck to fly by placing peanuts on the roof.

_____ 4. Gay-Neck was slow in learning how to fly.

_____ 5. The author pushed Gay-Neck off the roof to teach him to land on his feet.

_____ 6. Gay-Neck liked to fly higher than his parents.

_____ 7. Gay-Neck was once severely injured by a hawk.

_____ 8. His parents saved him from the hawk by flying in outward circles.

_____ 9. Gay-Neck easily learned how to find his home from any direction.

_____10. Gay-Neck's mother perished in a storm.

DISCUSSING THE STORY

1. To a true lover of birds there are "two sweet sights." What are they? Have you ever observed either one of them? Why is "brooding" necessary for young birds?

2. How do parent pigeons feed their young? How was Gay-Neck cared for by his parents? Describe briefly the changes that took place in Gay-Neck as he grew.

3. What discovery did the author make one day which shows how Nature protects her creatures? Would a careless observer have noticed what the author saw?

4. Gay-Neck, like other birds, had to be taught to fly. How did the boy try to make the bird use his wings? Who undertook the education of Gay-Neck and how was it done? What effect did his first flight have upon Gay-Neck?

5. When Gay-Neck had learned to fly fairly well, his parents began to fly much higher above him. What incident explained to the author their reason for flying so high? Were the pigeons as stupid as the author at first thought them to be?

6. How did the author begin to teach Gay-Neck a sense of direction? How did he succeed? What event caused sorrow in the author's house?

7. Even if a person cannot travel in all faraway lands, he can always travel through books. What did you learn about India from this selection? Would you enjoy having pigeons as pets?

APPLIED GRAMMAR

Sentence (*a*) below contains two subjects. The subject is therefore plural and the verb should be plural. In sentence (*b*) the subject is singular so the verb is singular.

a. Gay-Neck's mother and father *were* loving parents.
b. Gay-Neck *was* slow in learning to fly.

Underscore the proper predicate in (*d*) below.

c. Both his mother and his father *were* able to find Gay-Neck food.
d. Both (was, were) happy when he learned to fly.

Underline the correct predicates:

1. (Was, were) his mother and father flying above or below him?
2. (Was, were) Gay-Neck afraid to learn to fly?
3. There (was, were) the hawk heading straight for Gay-Neck.
4. There (was, were) Gay-Neck's parents flying above him.
5. They (was, were) safe at last on their own roof.

What word in the sentences above which contain two subjects, connects the two subjects? Such a word is called a "connecting word" or "conjunction." Conjunctions such as "and," "but" and "or" may join together subjects, predicates, phrases, clauses, or other parts of sentences.

WORDS

1. What word does the author use on page 96 to express his feeling of *alarm* or *horror?* On the same page what word does he use which means *examined closely?*

2. By his careful choice of words, the author helps us to form a mental picture of the bird. If Gay-Neck was a *"nondescript* gray-blue" was his coloring *bright, dull, indescribable,* or *spotted?* If the word *aquamarine* comes from the Latin words *aqua* meaning "water" and *marina* meaning "sea" what color were his "glassy *aquamarine* feathers"?

3. Do you *exasperate* your parents as Gay-Neck *exasperated* his father? Find two synonyms for *exasperate.*

4. The dictionary is a necessary and valuable tool for the student of words, but the meaning of many words can be discovered by their association with other words in a sentence.

For example, reread page 99. Without using a dictionary what meaning would you give to *relenting, alternative, panic, gingerly, preliminary?*

5. "The three flew downwards at a right *angle.*" What word do you often confuse with *angle?* How can correct pronunciation of these words help you to avoid misspelling?

THE LIBRARY

Would you like to read more about Gay-Neck? Look in your card catalog for the author's name, to see if your library has the book *Gay-Neck; the Story of a Pigeon.*

1. What is the call number for this book? _____
2. List any other books which your library owns by Dhan Gopal Mukerji. _____

_____

3. Are any of the books in your library by Dhan Gopal Mukerji non-fiction? _____

You will save time in using the card catalog if you take care to choose the right drawer first. By use of the letters on the drawers, indicate which drawer shown below you would use to find a card for:

4. Oliver Wendell Holmes: _____
5. Henry W. Longfellow: _____
6. Eric Knight: _____
7. James Daugherty: _____
8. Robert Louis Stevenson: _____

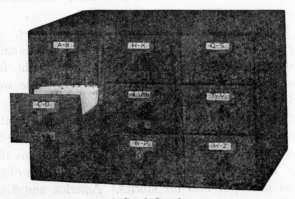

A Card Catalog

FREEDOM AGAIN AT LAST

(Part 1, page 105)

ERIC KNIGHT

Birthday: *April 10, 1897*
          (Died January 15, 1943)
Birthplace: *Yorkshire, England*
Stories to Enjoy and Reread:
  1. *Lassie Come Home*
  2. *Sam Small Flies Again*
  3. *This Above All*
  4. *The Flying Yorkshire Man*
  5. *"Never Come Monday"*

On January 15, 1943, radio and newspapers announced the death of Captain Eric Knight of the United States Army. He had lost his life in a plane crash while he was enroute to duties in North Africa.

In spite of the difficulties thrust upon him from his earliest childhood, Eric Knight achieved his desire to become a writer. From his pen came one of the best-loved dog stories ever written—*Lassie Come Home*.

Perhaps Eric had such a fine friend as Lassie to lessen the loneliness which colored his entire boyhood. The untimely death of his father left his mother and her four sons with no funds. To earn a living for the boys, she left the children with relatives and went to Russia as a governess. She did not see her sons again until they were grown.

Eric lived first with one relative, then with another. At fifteen, he sailed to America. Several years later the family was reunited in Philadelphia. In America Eric sought further education but at the outbreak of World War I, he went to Canada and enlisted for service.

After the war was over, Mr. Knight did cartooning, painting, and newspaper writing. One or two short stories received sufficient recognition to make him decide to spend all his time in writing. In Europe and America he studied the lives of people whom he later put into his stories. America and England mourn the loss of this talented writer.

40

CHECK YOUR READING

Supply words to correctly complete the meaning.

_____ made the mistake of threatening Lassie. As he tugged at her, the _____ slipped. As Lassie waited she knew she should _____ the command. But she also sensed it was time to go for the _____. Approaching the gate were _____ and the _____. When _____ saw Lassie she remembered the _____ and his sad _____ to Lassie. She _____ the gate. Lassie was on her _____.

DISCUSSING THE STORY

1. Read the introduction carefully so that you understand the opening situation. Knowing that Lassie had escaped three times from her new owner, is it natural to expect that she may escape again?

2. On the day of our story, why was Hynes in an impatient mood? How was the dog behaving? How did she get free?

3. If Hynes had been a different kind of man, what might have happened? What mistakes did he make? How did Lassie show the years of training given her by Sam Carraclough?

4. What does the author mean by speaking of a dog's "time sense"? Why did Lassie instinctively keep out of reach of Hynes? What was her "time sense" telling her to do?

5. Hynes was a rather stupid man. How did he make the situation worse? Why did Lassie not return to the kennels? How did Hynes hope to catch her?

6. Priscilla was the granddaughter of the Duke. How did she happen to be near the gate of the estate? In the brief moment that she stood there, what did she remember that caused her to swing wide the gate? Do you feel like cheering for Priscilla? What is your hope for Lassie?

7. If possible, read the book *Lassie Come Home* for yourself. In this brief selection, what do you learn about the intelligence of a fine dog? How does the author reveal his per-

sonal love for dogs? Do you think he understands their thinking processes? Does he also seem to understand people? Explain your opinions on these questions.

APPLIED GRAMMAR

What person is being spoken to in the following sentence?

"Close that gate, Miss Priscilla. Close it."

Words which show what persons are being addressed are called nouns of "direct address" and should be set off from the rest of the sentence by a comma. Punctuate the sentences below.

1. "Here Lassie come here."
2. "I'll open it Grandfather," the girl said.
3. "Good-by Lassie," she said softly.

WORDS

1. Hynes understood that "if he moved *menacingly* again, he might *frighten* the dog even more." How does the word *frighten* help you to understand *menacingly?*

2. Are you always careful to pronounce the "wh" sound in certain words. Practice saying: what, when, where, why, while, whimper, wheedle, wheel.

THE LIBRARY

Have you ever timed yourself to see how quickly you can find a particular word in a dictionary? Perhaps you have already discovered some of the tricks which can help you find words quickly. One such aid is the use of the guide words at the top of each page of a dictionary. Look up the word "fettle."

1. What guide words are at the top of the page which give the word "fettle"? _____

2. What does the abbreviation *"n."* mean? _____

3. What word or phrase would you substitute for "fettle" in the following sentence? _____

Hynes disliked being forced to take exercise himself so that Lassie could be kept in good *fettle.*

42

THE WILD GOAT'S KID

(Part 1, page 111)

LIAM O'FLAHERTY

Year of Birth: *1896*
Birthplace: *Arran Islands, Ireland*
Stories to Enjoy and Reread:
1. *The Fairy Goose and Other Stories*
2. *The Tent and Other Stories*
3. *Spring Sowing*
4. *The Wild Swan and Other Stories*

Liam O'Flaherty, as his name suggests, is an Irishman. He came from a poor family and had to make his own way. As a boy, he was an alert student, interested in many subjects. An intelligent mind, desirous of education, enabled him to earn a scholarship for college.

Out in the world he rocketed through one adventure after another. Probably no other living author has crowded such a variety of adventures into one lifetime. He organized and led groups in religious wars and in Irish revolutionary uprisings. As soon as life grew too quiet to please him, he hurried off to other lands, South America, the United States, Canada, Greece, Turkey, everywhere on the globe. He enjoyed every moment of vagabond days that found him at work in factories, restaurants, lumber camps. He was usually penniless.

While he was roving from place to place, he sometimes paused to write stories. The income from the stories produced just enough to enable him to move on again.

O'Flaherty has written both novels and short stories. They have been published in several countries including France and Russia. His hobby of raising Kerry goats and his love of outdoor life probably brought about the story, "The Wild Goat's Kid."

When he writes he shuts himself away from everyone and writes rapidly until the work is done. He likes to talk for hours, and is noted as an enthusiastic, fiery speaker. When he is not traveling, he is at home either in Dublin or at his cottage in the mountains.

CHECK YOUR READING

Circle T (True) or F (False)

1. On the high cliffs the white goat lived in terror of wild beasts.   T   F
2. She was slender and light, but she could not leap high nor swiftly.   T   F
3. The goat's kid was born at the beginning of winter.   T   F
4. On the first day the kid was taught how to walk.   T   F
5. As the goat grazed she paid no attention to the kid.   T   F
6. The dog's first attempt was to reach the hiding-place of the kid.   T   F
7. The dog hoped to force the kid out into the open.   T   F
8. It was the goat who began the second attack.   T   F
9. The natural weapons of the dog were greater than those of the goat.   T   F
10. At dawn the battle was still raging between the two animals.   T   F

DISCUSSING THE STORY

1. The setting of the story is the mountainous region of Galway County, Ireland, where the author was born. How does the wildness of the region contribute to the character of the white goat? Describe the goat briefly—her appearance and habits.

2. In what season of the year was the goat's kid born? Describe her delight in him. Do you think most animals watch so tenderly over their young? How did the goat care for the little one the first day?

3. On the second day, why did the mother goat graze so carelessly? How do we know that she was constantly alert in spite of her pretense?

4. The fight between the goat and the dog is described in great detail. Are you able to follow closely the movements of each animal? Does this make the struggle seem more real to you? What methods did the dog use in his first attempt to

reach the kid? How did the goat cleverly meet the dog's attack?

5. The second attack of the dog was planned differently. How did it confuse the goat? What natural means of defense did the goat have which the dog did not have? What advantage did the dog have over the goat? What was the outcome of the struggle? What description of natural beauty is a fitting conclusion to the story?

APPLIED GRAMMAR

1. Underline the subject in the sentence below.

This goat was a long, slender thing with short, straight horns.

2. Underline the subject in this sentence.

This goat, she was a long, slender thing with short, straight horns.

If a sentence has two subjects, they should refer to two different persons, places, or things, and be connected by "and." If the sentence has only one subject, no pronoun is necessary to complete the meaning.

Circle the numbers of any sentences below which have two subjects which refer to the same person, place, or thing. Rewrite these sentences on a separate paper.

1. The goat, she was so limber that she could trot on the top of a thin fence.
2. The gallant buck, he was captured and slain by two hungry dogs.
3. The leaves, grasses and herbs served for her meals.
4. The white goat and her kid traveled along the cliff tops.
5. The sleepy sun, it rose slowly from the sea.

WORDS

1. "The Wild Goat's Kid" is full of action and picture words and phrases.

Picture Words

exquisite	delicate	comely	sleek
fragile	gallant	supple	glittering

Action and Picture Phrases

winding horns

nimble hoofs making music

wild, sweet dawn

sleepy sun, golden and soft

infant moon

twitching his snout

wagged his long ears

fierce snort

rattle of claws

peculiar, mournful noises

Choose seven of the words and five of the phrases to use in sentences. Be sure your sentences show the meaning of the words. Just to write "The man was frightened" does not show the meaning of *frightened,* but to say "When the man saw the dreadful thing he had done, he was frightened" shows that the word means *alarmed* and *fearful.*

2. Notice the many words in this selection which contain the "wh" sound. In addition to those which you studied in the previous lesson, practice the following words.

whiskers   whined   white

whispers   whirled   whistling

THE LIBRARY

Dictionaries are helpful in giving information about geography. Sometimes names of places are listed alphabetically with all other words; sometimes they are in a separate list called a "gazetteer." In which place are geographical facts found in the dictionary in your library?

Dictionaries are also helpful in giving information about famous people. Some dictionaries list the names of people with all other words. Others place the names in a separate biographical section at the back of the book. Where do you find biographical information in your dictionary?

Using a large dictionary, find the answers to the questions below.

1. What information can you find about Galway County, the scene of the story?

2. What facts are given about Ireland?

3. Did you find a "see" reference under Ireland? What words were given to find further information?

4. What facts are given about Saint Patrick?

46

THE DOG OF MONTARGIS

(Part 1, page 119)

ANDREW LANG (1844–1912)

Andrew Lang loved books from his earliest childhood days in his home in Scotland.   Best of all, he loved fairy tales.   From the age of four when he taught himself to read, he hunted and searched for these stories.   This interest continued throughout his life.   He translated fairy tales from many languages. These stories were put into books, and for many years a new collection of Andrew Lang's fairy tales would be in the stores each Christmas.   Even today these collections are the favorite fairy-tale reading of most boys and girls.

Lang had other interests also.   He became one of London's most famous journalists.   So many different subjects interested him that he could talk and write endlessly.   His genial kindness brought him many friends who marveled at his versatility and remarkable memory.

CHECK YOUR READING

Renumber the events below in their proper order.

_____ 1. De Narsac is led to the Forest of Bondy.

_____ 2. In the presence of the king the dog springs at Macaire.

_____ 3. De Narsac is awakened by a scratching on his door.

_____ 4. The murderer is executed.

_____ 5. The dog attacks a member of the king's bodyguard.

_____ 6. Macaire confesses his guilt.

_____ 7. Aubrey de Montdidier is missed by his friends.

_____ 8. A trial by judgment is arranged.

_____ 9. De Narsac finds the body of de Montdidier.

_____10. De Narsac finds a starving greyhound.

DISCUSSING THE STORY

1. Why did the young Frenchman suspect that his friend had met with an accident?   What confirmed his suspicions? Why did de Narsac fail to recognize the dog at once?

2. After it had eaten, how did the dog try to convey a message to de Narsac?   Where did the dog lead him?   What dis-

47

covery was made? Do you think that dogs are intelligent enough to act in such a way?

3. To whom did the dog suddenly show unexpected aversion? Was there any apparent reason for the dog's behavior? What did people naturally think after the dog's second attack on Macaire? What other fact was brought to light? Where did the third attack take place?

4. The king took matters into his own hands and devised a test to determine the knight's guilt or innocence. How was it arranged? What was the outcome?

5. How did the dog become known as the Dog of Montargis? What qualities in dogs does the story illustrate? Can you relate the story of a dog's faithfulness or intelligence?

APPLIED GRAMMAR

"A noun is a word which names a person, place, or thing." Using this definition, fill each of the blanks below with a *noun*.

1. The man who so mysteriously disappeared from sight was

   _____.

2. It was _____ who followed the dog into the forest.

3. The forest was infested by bands of _____.

4. This story takes place in and near the city of _____.

5. The dog ran over the Bridge and headed for the forest of

   _____.

6. The combat was carved on a stone mantelpiece which stood for many years in the _____ of

   _____.

7. Stretched beyond the door was a great, gaunt _____.

8. The dog devoured the huge _____ set before it.

9. The dog led him to some freshly turned-up earth, beneath

   a _____.

Some of the names which you have used above referred to *particular* persons and places and are called "proper nouns." The proper nouns used are: _____

48

Nouns which do *not* give such definite reference are "common nouns." The common nouns used are: _____

Can you name a proper noun for each of the common nouns taken from this story?

10. church: _____
11. knight: _____
12. hotel: _____

Name a common noun for each of these proper nouns:

13. Burgundy: _____
14. Aubrey de Montdidier: _____
15. Paris: _____

WORDS

1. By using diacritical and accent marks show how the words below are divided into syllables and pronounced.

	Pronunciation	Meaning
tournament	tŏŏr′ nå mĕnt	_____
emaciated	_____	_____
voracity	_____	_____
combatants	_____	_____
adversary	_____	_____
appeased	_____	_____

2. Words are sometimes used in more than one way—that is, they may serve as different parts of speech. In the dictionary nouns are indicated by the abbreviation *n.*; verbs by *v.*; adjectives by *a.*; adverbs by *adv.*; and so forth. In the previous lesson you learned to use the adjective *gallant*. What change in pronunciation and meaning occurs when this word is used as a noun, as in the phrase "the young *gallants* of Paris"?

3. Do you ever confuse the two words *mantel* and *mantle*? Which refers to a cloak? What is the meaning of the other word?

4. *Post* is a Latin prefix meaning "after." How is that original meaning shown in the sentence, "The dog has been known to posterity as the Dog of Montargis"?

49

THE LIBRARY

1. Does your PROSE AND POETRY book contain another story by the author of "The Dog of Montargis"?
2. Is there another section in your PROSE AND POETRY book about far-away places?
3. Where would you look to find out if your PROSE AND POETRY contains the story, "Child Pioneer"?
4. How many books in the reading list which accompanies Unit II does your library own?
5. What are their call numbers?
6. Arrange the call numbers in the order in which the books appear on the shelves.

THE GOOD JOAN
(Part 1, page 125)
APPRECIATION AND CHORAL READING

1. Read the story of Joan of Arc in an encyclopedia. Try to imagine how the French people feel about the life she lived and about her devotion to France. How does the poet show that the spirit of Joan of Arc is still fresh in the minds and hearts of the French?

2. In your choral reading try to imagine yourself a French boy or girl. Read the poem to show how thoughts of Joan of Arc bring courage to you. Express the feeling that Joan is actually helping France today. Read the refrain (the last line of each stanza) to show the mood expressed by the stanza it follows.

SPANISH JOHNNY
(Part 1, page 126)
APPRECIATING THE POEM

1. The poet writes as if she might have been the child who listened in fascination to the golden songs of Spanish Johnny. Which lines tell you about the sort of person he was? How did he seem to have a two-sided personality?

2. Some of the lines contain vivid pictures. Read aloud some which appeal to you.

NUVAT THE BRAVE

(Part 1, page 129)

CHECK YOUR READING

In each blank write the letter of the correct expression.

_____ 1. Nuvat set out for the sealing grounds (*a*) to exercise his dogs (*b*) with the intention of running away from home (*c*) to prove to himself that he was not a coward (*d*) for the adventure of it.

_____ 2. Seals (*a*) cannot live without air (*b*) live all winter under the ice (*c*) dig large sleeping holes in the snow (*d*) are unfit to eat.

_____ 3. A black stripe on the horizon indicates (*a*) the coming of a storm (*b*) a surface of uncovered water (*c*) a solid ice pan along the shore (*d*) the presence of large numbers of seals.

_____ 4. Nuvat killed the seal with a (*a*) strap (*b*) pistol (*c*) spear (*d*) needle.

_____ 5. Nuvat was astonished to find himself (*a*) close to another village (*b*) lost on the mainland (*c*) adrift on an ice pan (*d*) not far from home.

_____ 6. Nuvat appealed to (*a*) his *tongak* (*b*) Sedna (*c*) the head of the village (*d*) the Storm Spirits.

_____ 7. Preparing for the night, Nuvat (*a*) built a fire to cook his food (*b*) scooped out a snow bank for each dog (*c*) found a sheltered cave (*d*) gave his own sleeping-bag to Kakk.

_____ 8. He was awakened by (*a*) the barking of the dogs (*b*) daylight (*c*) the Aurora Borealis (*d*) a shouting of many voices.

_____ 9. Kakk surprised Nuvat by (*a*) being unusually obedient (*b*) showing that he was a loose leader (*c*) refusing to return with him (*d*) bringing in a seal he had killed.

_____10. The fight ended (*a*) with Unapeek the acknowledged leader (*b*) when Nuvat used his whip (*c*) with the death of Unapeek (*d*) with Kakk as the real leader.

DISCUSSING THE STORY

1. A brief introduction sometimes accompanies a selection in order to acquaint the reader with the characters and to give him necessary information. What do you learn from the introduction about Nuvat and about life in an Eskimo village?

2. On what mission is Nuvat bound as the story opens? What evidences of intelligence and training do his dogs show?

3. What interesting facts do you learn about seals in this selection? What tools are used in seal hunting? Relate how Nuvat caught his first seal. Why did he not fail this time? Why was he so excited over his success?

4. Nuvat's delight is suddenly changed to terror. What discovery does he make? How does an Arctic hunter discover the presence of open water?

5. In what kind of gods or spirits do the Eskimos believe? What is a *tongak?* How did Nuvat appeal to the unseen spirits?

6. Nuvat realized that his safety depended on his own good judgment. How did he avoid the danger of being too close to the edge of the ice pan? Why did he eat raw meat? How did he prepare to spend the night?

7. Nuvat naturally dreamed of his home. What details of the dream showed how lonely Nuvat had been—and how he had longed for the respect and friendship of the villagers?

8. How was Nuvat awakened? What hope was renewed? How did Nuvat discover that Kakk was a "loose leader"? Describe briefly the fight between Kakk and Unapeek. Why did Nuvat not interrupt the fight?

9. What do you imagine will be the outcome of Nuvat's adventure? Do you think he will still be thought a coward?

10. Nuvat was thought a coward for so long that he almost came to believe it himself. To prove his courage to the villagers he first had to prove it to himself. What must anyone do in a similar situation to save his self-respect? What can one do if others think him stupid or awkward or a person of no skill or talent? How can one conquer fear of any kind?

11. As Nuvat waited to kill the seal, his confidence was restored. Why is the fear of failure less when we know that no-

52

one else will learn of it? Why do people find it difficult to be confident of success in the presence of others? How does the knowledge of previous failure or success affect one? What meaning can you find in the saying, "Nothing succeeds like success"?

APPLIED GRAMMAR

Nouns may be used as subjects in sentences. Insert a noun for the subject of each of the sentences below.

1. The continuous polar _____ was over; but it was intensely cold.
2. The hungry _____ were almost exhausted.
3. _____ stopped them in a sheltered spot behind some broken ice.
4. _____ did not lie down with the rest.
5. A _____ is a warm-blooded animal which cannot breathe under water.

Can you supply nouns in the sentences below?

6. The seals must keep _____ open in the ice so that they may breathe.
7. Nuvat pressed the _____ down in the center of the mound.
8. Presently, he saw a black _____ on the horizon.
9. Nuvat hurled the _____ straight down into the seal's neck.
10. He pushed the _____ in his great hurry to return with his prize.

In the sentences above, you told what object the seals must keep open, what object Nuvat used to press down in the mound, what he saw on the horizon. Words that answer *what* or *whom* concerning the predicate are called "objects." Because they tell us directly *what* or *whom* we call these words "direct objects."

Fill in the following blanks and tell whether you have used a subject or a direct object.

11. The _____ on which he stood had been broken loose!
12. Nuvak sang a _____ to his *tongak*.

53

13. He found a _____ sheltered
on three sides by rocks.

14. The _____ went out like a candle
blown out in the dark, leaving them in pitch blackness.

15. He would show the other _____
how clever his dog was.

WORDS

1. The story of a particular locality or region often contains
special words which give *atmosphere* or *local color* to the story.
You will enjoy "Nuvat the Brave" much more if you understand such terms as *floes, ice pan, hummocks, igloo, blubber*.

2. How do you pronounce *Arctic?* Remember the middle *c*
when you spell it.

3. Do you remember the old spelling rhyme about placing *i*
before *e* except after *c?* Review the spelling of such words as
believe, deceive, shriek from this selection.

THE LIBRARY

You will find that there are title cards as well as author cards
in the card catalog. A title card is so called because it has the
title of the book on the top line. Title cards are arranged
alphabetically in the card catalog according to the first word
of the title, except when the title begins with *a, an,* or *the*.

1. What is the title of the book on the card below?

```
916              African game trails
R          Roosevelt, Theodore
```

2. Who is the author?

3. What is the call number?

4. Is there a book in your library by the title of *Nuvat the
Brave?*

5. Arrange the titles of the books in the reading list which accompanies this unit in the order in which they would appear in your card catalog.

54

THE VIOLIN-MAKER OF CREMONA

(Part 1, page 139)

FRANÇOIS COPPEE

Birthday: *January 12, 1842*
(Died May 23, 1908)
Birthplace: *Paris, France*

Each evening a young lad sat in a library in the city of Paris reading and studying. François Coppee was so eager for education that he seized every opportunity and every spare moment to learn.

The people of Paris often saw the young man wandering about the streets and countryside. In his roaming he learned to know the common people of his land. He learned to understand them and to sympathize with their problems. Later when he wrote poems and plays about his countrymen, he won their respect and affection through his appreciation of their lives.

CHECK YOUR READING

Match the phrases of the left-hand column with the characters named in the right-hand column.

_____ The obstinate father	1. Cremona
_____ The hunchback	2. Ferrari
_____ Creator of the secret varnish	3. Sandro
_____ The bride-to-be	4. Filippo
_____ Sponsor of the contest	5. Stradavari
_____ The scene	6. Giannina
_____ The winner of the contest	7. The Mayor
_____ The master of the violin-makers' guild	
_____ The bridegroom-to-be	
_____ The friend of animals	

DISCUSSING THE PLAY

1. As you read the play, imagine that you are looking at the

55

actors, watching their action and listening to their words. Try to visualize the stage scene and keep in mind the time and place of the story. What is the subject of conversation in the opening scene? Explain Ferrari's plan and why he thinks it is an honor to his daughter.

2. How does Giannina feel about her father's plan? What is her own wish in the matter? Of whom is Sandro jealous? Do you think this jealousy is a flaw in Sandro's character or is his envy justified under the circumstances?

3. What is Giannina's feeling for Filippo? What does Filippo's rescue of the dog tell you about his character? What might he envy in Sandro? What is Filippo's consolation? How does he show the nature of the true artist?

4. Filippo feels confident of winning the prize. Why? Why had he not told Giannina that he would enter the contest? Why is he happy to see Giannina weep? What is the real cause of her tears?

5. Filippo is strong enough to make a great sacrifice. Why does he change the violins? Why does he not go to the contest? What is he voluntarily giving up?

6. How does Giannina redeem her friendship with Filippo before the contest? How does Sandro attempt to make up for his injustice to Filippo? Does it take courage to admit one's wrongdoing?

7. Who is the winner of the contest? What plan does Filippo adopt as the best one to follow when the first plan fails? Why is this a greater sacrifice than the first?

8. The title of the play is "The Violin-Maker of Cremona." Who is the hero of the story—Ferrari, Filippo, or Sandro? Give reasons for your opinion.

WORDS

1. From the following multiple choice statements, underline the correct meaning for each italicized word:

a. An *artisan* is (a well) (a foreigner) (an accomplished workman) (a sea-going skiff).

b. A *dowry* is (a tall building) (the gift of money or land which goes with a bride) (a new method of cooking).

c. Harmonies are (wind instruments) (melodious sounds) (blood properties essential to health).

d. A *guild* is (a kind of gold varnish) (an association of persons in the same trade) (the forefin of a fish).

e. A *novice* is (one new in any business) (a man who signs up subscriptions) (a crack in a glacier).

f. Medley means (a neighborhood gossip) (a musical composition of different pieces) (the beauty of the stars).

g. Plaintive refers to (sadness) (the call of a goat) (pattering feet) (peacefulness).

h. Consolation means (companion) (reward) (comfort).

i. Rosin is (an amber turpentine by-product) (the perfume of roses) (rich, oriental incense).

j. The *nightingale* is (a little singing bird) (a fierce storm in the night) (a famous nurse).

2. In casting a play (selecting people to play the parts) the director must take into consideration the voice of each actor. He would not choose a man with the weak voice of a boy for the part of a strong master workman. He must select actors whose voices suggest the personality of the characters they are playing. From the list below select the words that would best describe the kind of voice most suited to each character.

a. Ferrari: *shrill, gentle, hearty, decisive.*

b. Giannina: *pleasing, harsh, nervous, loud.*

c. Sandro: *heavy, lively, monotonous, cultured.*

d. Filippo: *polite, raucous, feeble, quiet.*

THE LIBRARY

An atlas is the best reference book to help one find exact location of cities, rivers, lakes, countries, etc. Using the atlas in your school or public library answer the following questions.

1. What is the title of the atlas?

2. What sections are listed in its table of contents?

3. What information is given in the index to aid readers?

4. What other kinds of information are given in the atlas?

5. Find Cremona in an atlas. Did you need to look in a gazetteer to find out the country in which it is situated?

GIVE A MAN A HORSE

(Part 1, page 156)

CHARLES JOSEPH FINGER

Birthday: *December 25, 1871*
(Died January 7, 1941)
Birthplace: *Willesden, England*
Stories to Enjoy and Reread:
1. *Courageous Companions*
2. *Tales from Silver Lands*
3. *Tales Worth Telling*
4. *Golden Tales from Faraway*
5. *A Dog at His Heels*

It was not until he was fifty years old that Charles Finger decided to give young folks a chance to read stories of his thrilling adventures. Then it was that he began the task of writing the tales and legends he had heard while traveling in Alaska, Canada, Mexico, and South America. He wanted his stories to be very true to life so that boys and girls everywhere could see, hear, and live with these friends as they dreamed over the pages of the stories. Finger expressed himself well in writing because he had been a diligent pupil in his boyhood days in London, where he went to private schools and to college.

Courageous Companions, the story of a boy who sailed with Magellan, tells many of the adventures which Finger himself had when he left England for South America. Many more of his adventures in other lands are told in a collection of stories called *Tales Worth Telling*, great favorites of youth everywhere. His friends liked to hear Finger tell tales of his boyhood days, of shipwrecks, of mountain climbing. Pipe in hand, stories unfolding, he kept guests spellbound for hours. His young friends liked particularly the Indian legends which he has put into a book called *Tales from Silver Lands*.

Finger spent his last years on a farm near Fayetteville, Arkansas, with his family of five children whose activities he shared and enjoyed.

CHECK YOUR READING

Write T (True) or F (False) in the blanks.

_____ 1. Bob was not able to swim, and kept afloat only with the help of a life preserver.

_____ 2. Life as a castaway taught Bob that the white race is indeed a superior race.

_____ 3. Dara and Bob enclosed a pool in which to catch fish.

_____ 4. Bob learned that Dara had no desire to be rescued.

_____ 5. Dara was greatly excited at the prospect of finding large quantities of gold.

_____ 6. Using a shirt for a sail, the boys traveled along the inland sea.

_____ 7. In one of the valleys they found horses of purebred Arabian descent.

_____ 8. Bob was unable to catch the horse he wanted.

_____ 9. Dara's horse was tamed by Bob's expert riding.

_____10. A horse once tamed will never disobey.

DISCUSSING THE STORY

1. Did you read the introduction to the story? Where do you find Bob Honore at the beginning of the selection? What accident was the beginning of an adventure for him and Dara?

2. What details in the second and third paragraphs indicate the severity of the struggle? Which of the boys was the better swimmer? When and how did they reach safety?

3. As Bob lived on the isolated beach with Dara, his respect and admiration for the Indian grew. How did Dara show himself to be more resourceful and self-sufficient than Bob?

4. Bob at first hoped for rescue. Why did he change his mind? What did the boys decide to do? How did Bob make good use of his time? What did the boys learn about the country?

5. Bob was astonished to find gold in abundance. How did Bob and Dara differ in their opinions about gold? Do you think there is some truth in Dara's statement?

6. As the boys paddled along the inland sea what aspects of nature did they enjoy? From the hill on shore what did they discover?

7. How did the boys find the wild horses for which they had been searching? What plan did they devise for keeping the horses in a restricted territory? Why did they need to exercise great caution? Describe the horses which Bob and Dara hoped to secure for themselves.

8. Working together the boys successfully captured the horse Dara had selected. How did they do it? Describe Bob's first ride on the terrified horse. How did Bob show himself to be an expert rider? Why would he have no further trouble with the horse?

9. Which of the experiences seemed most thrilling or delightful to you? What further adventures do you predict for Bob and Dara?

APPLIED GRAMMAR

Can you explain what makes the following sentence sound awkward?

Against the white wave Bob saw Dara and Bob thought some huge thing was bearing down on Dara and Bob.

Reread the sentence substituting other words for some of the proper nouns in the sentence.

Words which are used in the place of nouns are called "pronouns." Like nouns, pronouns are often used as subjects of sentences and are in the nominative case. Listed below are the singular and plural forms of pronouns in the nominative case.

I	we
you	you
he, she, it	they
who	who

Substitute correct pronouns in the following sentences.

1. _____ (Bob and Dara) were discoverers of an uncharted land.

2. While _____ (Bob) was swimming, one of the blankets folded itself about his chest.

3. _____ (The blanket) frightened him for a moment.

60

4. "Dara, _____ are a good scout!" _____
(Bob) exclaimed.

5. _____ (The mare) was chestnut in color.

6. "_____ (Both boys) ought to find a
way to get back to the island," said Bob.

7. _____ (Dara) broke the silence. "If
_____ (Bob) want to go back, Bob, _____
will go too."

Nouns stay the same whether used as subject or object, but
pronouns change in form. The pronouns below are used as
objects and are said to be in the objective case.

me	us
you	you
him, her, it	them
whom	whom

Use the proper pronouns as objects in the following sentences.

8. Dara told _____ (Bob) to swim in a certain
direction.

9. Bob marked _____ (the mare) for his own.

10. Bob wondered if he'd been a fool to leave _____
(the farm).

11. It seemed absurd that two boys with bare hands could
catch _____ (wild horses).

12. "The nugget should bring _____ (Bob and
Dara) good luck," said Bob.

13. "I'll show _____ (speaking to Dara) where I
found it," offered Bob.

14. "You promised _____ (Bob) an adventure,"
Bob reminded Dara.

WORDS

1. The selection makes use of words which you probably
learned in your study of geography. Explain *straits, fjords,
peninsula, isthmus.*

2. In the sentence, "After that Bob and Dara worked fast,
the former running forward . . . the latter preparing as he
ran the long hidestrip. . . ." To whom does *former* refer?
Which of the boys is the *latter?*

"FREEDOM FOR OUR MINDS"

(Part 1, page 169)

CHECK YOUR READING

In each blank write the letter of the expression which correctly completes the meaning.

_____ 1. From all parts of China men were conscripted to work on (*a*) the Burma Road (*b*) the Great Wall (*c*) the rice-filled fields (*d*) the fishing junks.

_____ 2. Prince Cheng had been warned by a fortune teller that (*a*) he could not equal his father's achievements (*b*) he could not conquer neighboring barbarian states (*c*) he would live long but would fail to win the affection of his people (*d*) he would achieve great things but die young.

_____ 3. The scholars (*a*) believed that the Emperor would become as great as some of their former rulers (*b*) advised him to follow the wise ways of Yao and Shun (*c*) urged him to build a larger army (*d*) suggested that he destroy all books.

_____ 4. The Emperor feared only one thing: (*a*) death (*b*) revolution (*c*) pain (*d*) invasion.

_____ 5. One of the hiding places selected by Fu Scholar for his books was (*a*) the lining of the well (*b*) the chimney (*c*) the floor beneath the inner court (*d*) a secret panel in his daughter's room.

_____ 6. The books were written (*a*) on delicate parchment (*b*) in a secret code (*c*) on large sheets of bamboo (*d*) on thick squares of linen.

_____ 7. The Emperor ordered the books to be collected and (*a*) reconverted into paper (*b*) burned (*c*) sent to barbarian missions (*d*) thrown into the Yangtze.

_____ 8. The scholars of the kingdom were invited (*a*) to form a great new university (*b*) to restore the ancient libraries (*c*) to see a rare field of flowering gourds (*d*) to attend a series of lectures.

_____ 9. The people of the kingdom (*a*) prepared to rebel against the Emperor (*b*) planned a great feast for

62

the scholars (*c*) mourned at the death of the Emperor (*d*) rejoiced over the mass murder of the scholars.

_____10. Fu Tze Chien and his daughter (*a*) were put to death (*b*) founded a new Dynasty (*c*) became famous teachers (*d*) revealed the hiding place of the books.

DISCUSSING THE STORY

1. What was the cause of "the cloud of oppression and misery that hung over all China"? Why did the people feel that their fate was bitter?

2. How had the Ch'in dynasty come into power? What prophecy had influenced the life of Prince Cheng? What kind of ruler was he? What title had he given himself?

3. The Prince particularly disliked the scholars. By what complaints did they torment him? What punishments did he give them? What was the best argument of the scholars? By what final decree did the Prince hope to silence them?

4. The Emperor lived in fear all his life. How had he tried to forget the prophecy? How did he hope to overcome it?

5. Fu Tze Chien was a great scholar and philosopher. How did he feel after learning of the Emperor's edict? What suggestion and sacrifice did his daughter offer?

6. How many books did Fu Scholar select to keep? Where were they hidden? What would happen if the books were discovered? Why did Hsi-wo and her father regard the books of more value than their own lives? What might result in any land in which all books were destroyed? Do you think the life of the world today is influenced by the wisdom and learning of thinkers of the past?

7. The Emperor's invitation to the Court came as a surprise to the remaining scholars. Why did not Fu Tze Chien go to the feast? By what trickery were the seven hundred scholars lured to their death?

8. Sometimes a cruel or unkind person brings disaster or unhappiness upon himself by overstepping the bounds of human endurance. What was the natural consequence of the mass murder? How was the destruction of the books used as a weapon against the Emperor?

9. While the rebellion was gathering strength, what was being done in the home of Fu Tze Chien? What further fame came to him and the Lady Hsi-wo after the new dynasty was established? Do you think it is possible for a brilliant scholar to know great books by memory?

10. Discuss the last statement, "Freedom for our minds, O Emperor! For without that—of what value is life?" What events in modern history illustrate the fact that bodies may be conquered while minds remain free?

APPLIED GRAMMAR

Sometimes nouns are used to show ownership or possession of an object or quality. Ownership is shown by adding an apostrophe and "s" to the noun. For example, "the *scholar's* books"; "the *teacher's* wisdom." Sometimes the possessive form shows the relation of one word to another or indicates time, as "each *day's* dawn."

Fill in the blanks with the proper possessive form.

1. It was a problem when a _____ (man) own brother might prove to be a court spy.

2. _____ (Fu Hseng) face lighted with hope for the first time in weeks.

3. The premier managed to keep _____ (Ch'in) son on the throne.

4. The girl had been mistress of the house since her _____ (mother) death.

5. The scholars depended on _____ (China) ancient wisdom.

Pronouns, unlike nouns, change in form when used in the possessive. Study the possessive pronouns listed below and use the correct form in each of the following sentences.

my, mine	our, ours
your, yours	your, yours
his, her, hers, its	their, theirs

6. Engrossed in peaceful pursuits, the people felt _____ resentment change to gratitude.

7. The young girl stayed in _____ room and waited for the books to be hidden.

8. "Can we ask another family to share _____ danger?" she asked.

9. "What of _____ betrothal of Ming's son?" her father asked.

10. "Let this room be _____ as long as I live," she said.

11. Freedom can be _____ only if we strive for it.

The possessive of *it*, which is *its*, does not use an apostrophe. *It's* means *It is*. Underscore the correct words.

12. (Its, It's) a far greater task than building a wall.

13. (Its, It's) well-trained army was rapidly increased.

WORDS

1. After looking up any of the words in the first column whose meanings you do not know, match the words on the left with those on the right.

_____ conscription	1. denied
_____ malignant	2. earnestness
_____ obsessed	3. turned back
_____ contradicted	4. manner of a child toward a parent
_____ seer	5. little known
_____ fervor	6. enforced enrollment
_____ eliminated	7. a prophet
_____ improvised	8. beset by a fixed idea
_____ filial	9. suddenly invented
_____ reverted	10. isolated
	11. evil; threatening
	12. excluded

2. Distinguish between *definitely* and *indefinitely* as used on page 173. See footnote 10.

3. Every nation has its leaders of all kinds—political, military, religious. What did the author mean by calling the scholars "the intellectual leaders"?

THE LIBRARY

Draw a map of China showing the Gobi Desert; the Yangtze River; Tsinan City.

UNIT ACTIVITIES

SUGGESTIONS FOR FURTHER READING—UNIT II

ELEANOR ATKINSON, *Greyfriars Bobby*

OLAF BAKER, *Dusty Star*

HERBERT BEST, *Garram the Hunter*

ARTHUR BOWIE CHRISMAN, *Shen of the Sea*

ARTHUR BOWIE CHRISMAN, *The Wind that Wouldn't Blow*

PHYLLIS CRAWFORD, *Hello, the Boat!*

MARY MAPES DODGE, *Hans Brinker; or, The Silver Skates*

HARRY A. FRANCK, *Marco Polo, Junior*

SARAH IVES, *Dog Heroes of Many Lands*

RUDYARD KIPLING, *Jungle Book*

DHAN GOPAL MUKERJI, *Chief of the Herd*

DHAN GOPAL MUKERJI, *Rama, the Hero of India*

FRANCES JENKINS OLCOTT, *Wonder Tales from China Seas*

ALBERT BIGELOW PAINE, *Girl in White Armor*

LAURA E. RICHARDS, *Joan of Arc*

CAROLINE SINGER, *Boomba Lives in Africa*

CHARLES E. SLAUGHTER, *Hahtibee the Elephant*

VILHJALMAR STEFANSSON, *My Life with the Eskimos*

DOROTHY M. STUART, *Young Folk's Book of Other Lands*

ALBERT PAYSON TERHUNE, *Lad, a Dog*

JANE BREVOORT WALDEN, *Igloo*

LEON F. WHITNEY, *Pigeon City*

CAN YOU IDENTIFY THE SKETCHES?

With what selections do you associate the sketches on the opposite page?

1. _____

2. _____

3. _____

4. _____

5. _____

6. _____

7. _____

8. _____

DO YOU RECOGNIZE THESE CHARACTERS?

In each blank at the left place the number of the character which matches the phrase.

_____ a volcano in Mexico

_____ a South-American Indian

_____ a carrier pigeon

_____ the murderer of Aubrey de Montdidier

_____ a youthful seal-hunter

_____ a dog-trainer

_____ a girl patriot of France

_____ a man who played a mandolin

_____ author of "The Wild Goat's Kid"

_____ an Eskimo dog

_____ a great scholar

_____ chief of a pygmy tribe

_____ an intelligent collie

_____ a crippled violin-maker

_____ friend of a murdered man

1. Nuvat
2. Lassie
3. Spanish Johnny
4. Makulu-Kulu
5. Joan of Arc
6. Filippo
7. De Narsac
8. Paricutin
9. Fu Tze Chien
10. Dara
11. Sandro
12. Prince Cheng
13. Hynes
14. Chevalier Macaire
15. Gay-Neck
16. Priscilla
17. Liam O'Flaherty
18. Bob
19. Giannini
20. Kakk

RIP VAN WINKLE

(Part 1, page 183)

WASHINGTON IRVING

Birthday: *April 3, 1783*
      (Died November 28, 1859)
Birthplace: *New York City*
Stories to Enjoy and Reread:
1. *"The Legend of Sleepy Hollow"*
2. *"The Specter Bridegroom"*
3. *The Bold Dragoon and Other Ghostly Tales* *(edited by Anne Carroll Moore)*

Washington Irving was named for General George Washington under whom his father had served in the Revolutionary War. Although he was born one hundred sixty years ago, his stories are still read and loved.

Because he was frail as a child, he spent much of his time out of doors, rambling about the country with his dog and his gun like Rip Van Winkle about whom he later wrote. When he was grown he spent many years in Europe, and was for several years our ambassador to Spain. Upon his return to America he bought a home called "Sunnyside" which still stands overlooking the Hudson River at Tarrytown, New York.

CHECK YOUR READING

Complete the meaning by filling in the blanks.
1. Rip was a good-natured man, but he disliked any form of _____.
2. His wife was notorious for her _____.
3. Rip's closest companion was _____.
4. Led by the stranger, Rip found a queer group of persons playing _____.
5. Rip slept for _____ years.
6. On waking, Rip thought it was merely next morning and blamed the _____ for his slumber.
7. When Rip left home the portrait of _____ hung before the village inn; when he returned the portrait of _____ hung there.

69

8. The day on which Rip reappeared was _____ day.

9. Among the strange crowd Rip finally discovered his

_____.

10. According to neighborhood tradition, the strangers who lured Rip off to the mountains were _____ _____ and his crew of the *Half Moon*.

DISCUSSING THE STORY

1. America, like other countries, has her legends. "Rip Van Winkle" is one of those tales told "once upon a time" by the fat and jolly Hollanders who came to live in what is now southeastern New York State. Long after the English conquest of New Amsterdam destroyed the pure Dutch customs, Washington Irving discovered the legends and told them again in all their full and imaginative color. With what description does Irving begin the story? Why is the setting important in a legend?

2. When an author tells how a character looks he is *describing* him; when he tells how he acts he is *characterizing* him. Which of these methods does Irving use? What kind of person was Rip Van Winkle? What do you learn about his family?

3. What habits had Rip fallen into to escape from the wrath of his wife? Who were his companions? Why does Irving describe the character of persons unimportant to the story? Why was Rip forced to give up his visits to the inn?

4. Rip's life took a strange turn one day. What queer adventure befell him on the mountain? What strange effect was caused by the sound of the rolling ninepins? What caused Rip to fall into a deep sleep?

5. What was Rip's first thought when he awoke? What things seemed strange to him? How had he himself changed? What changes did he find in his home and in the village?

6. How did Rip almost get into trouble on his first visit to the inn? What news did he learn of his friends? How did he recognize his daughter?

7. Some of the villagers accepted Rip's story of his twenty-year absence. What explanation did they give for it? How

did Rip reëstablish himself in the community? Why was he naturally popular with the young people?

8. Do you know any older people who seem to be living in the past—who fail to keep up interest in new improvements, new methods of doing things, new changes in political life? Do you think that one who fails to keep up with his own times is mentally asleep? How can one avoid being a "Rip Van Winkle"?

APPLIED GRAMMAR

Name the person, place, or thing in the story which each group of words describes.

1. blue, purple, gray   _____
2. good-natured, henpecked, meek   _____
3. fiery, termagant, riotous   _____
4. wild, lonely, shagged, dark   _____
5. odd, quaint, peculiar, outlandish _____

Words which describe a person, place, or thing are called "adjectives." List three adjectives which accurately describe the following persons:

6. Rip Van Winkle: _____
7. Dame Van Winkle: _____
8. Wolf: _____
9. Derrick Van Brummel: _____
10. Washington Irving: _____

WORDS

1. Irving had a distinctive way of using words to make them picture just what he meant to say. Try putting into your own words what he means by the following phrases:

fiery furnace of domestic tribulation

dodging about the village

pestilent piece of ground

foolish, well-oiled disposition

torrent of household eloquence

uncouth, lack-lustre countenances

lean, bilious-looking fellow

white sugar-loaf hat

petticoat government

2. Many of the phrases above contain adjectives—that is, descriptive words that help to create *exact* pictures in one's

71

mind. Reread the first paragraph noting these adjectives: *magical* hues; *good* wives; *bold* outlines; *clear evening* sky. From the rest of the story make a list of ten such phrases.

_____   _____

_____   _____

_____   _____

_____   _____

THE LIBRARY

Imagine that you fell asleep like Rip Van Winkle, sometime about 1910. How would you feel some sunshiny morning to awake and find yourself in the midst of the world's radio communication; its airplanes, streamline trains, and automobiles; its skyscrapers; and the wonders of electricity? Wouldn't you also be bewildered and amazed?

Now, how much do *you* know about the wonders of our present-day world and the changes which have come about in the last quarter of a century? A good encyclopedia will furnish the most available information in the most concise form.

Plan a visit to your school or public library and answer the following questions.

1. Does your library own Compton's *Pictured Encyclopedia?*

2. Can you find *The World Book* in your library?

3. What aid on the backbone of an encyclopedia corresponds to the letters on the drawers of the card catalog?

4. Are there guide words in your encyclopedia?

5. Research in the library will give you the history and interesting facts about each of the following topics. Choose one on which to make a complete report, including what you can find on the developments during the last twenty years.

The Radio	Moving and Talking Pictures
Automobile Transportation	Education
Train Transportation	Electricity
Ships of the Sea	(*a*) In the home
Ships of the Air	(*b*) In the factory
Photography	(*c*) In the laboratory
Television	(*d*) On the farm

THE COURTSHIP OF MILES STANDISH

(*Part 1, page 203*)

HENRY W. LONGFELLOW

Birthday: *February 27, 1807*
   (*Died March 24, 1882*)
Birthplace: *Portland, Maine*
Poems to Enjoy and Reread:
1. *"The Song of Hiawatha"*
2. *"The Children's Hour"*
3. *"The Village Blacksmith"*
4. *"The Arrow and the Song"*
5. *"Evangeline"*

If you have read "The Song of Hiawatha," you are already acquainted with Henry Wadsworth Longfellow, "The Children's Poet."

Longfellow grew up in a little seaport town in Maine. He liked to walk by the trim wooden houses and to hear the surging of the sea against the shore. He liked, too, to visit his grandfather's farm. But best of all, he liked to put his thoughts on paper. He was only thirteen when his first bit of poetry was published; and he was only fourteen when he went to college. At college he became interested in foreign languages. After graduation he spent several years of study in Europe. There he became acquainted with Washington Irving who was serving as Ambassador to Spain.

Back home he became a professor of languages at Harvard University. While at Harvard he lived in "Craigie House"—a large, old-fashioned, colonial house which had once been the headquarters of General George Washington. There he wrote the poems that are read in every corner of the earth. Some of the best loved ones are translations from the German, the Spanish, and the Italian.

CHECK YOUR READING

Underline the correct expressions.

1. The scene of the poem is the colony at (*a*) Plymouth (*b*) Jamestown (*c*) Providence (*d*) Boston.

73

2. The military leader of the colony was (*a*) John Smith (*b*) John Adams (*c*) John Alden (*d*) Miles Standish.

3. The letters which John wrote were full of the name of (*a*) the *Mayflower* (*b*) Bertha, the Beautiful Spinner (*c*) Priscilla (*d*) Rose.

4. The Captain commissioned John to bear (*a*) a threat of war to the Indians (*b*) a message of praise to the Elder (*c*) a proposal of marriage (*d*) a bouquet of flowers.

5. The Captain accused John of (*a*) treachery to the colony (*b*) treachery to their friendship (*c*) cowardice (*d*) duplicity.

6. The Captain's answer to the Indians' challenge of warfare was the snake skin filled with (*a*) arrows (*b*) powder and bullets (*c*) Indian corn (*d*) wampum.

7. The *Mayflower* sailed back to England (*a*) as soon as the colonists had reached America (*b*) after waiting six weeks for return cargo (*c*) in the spring (*d*) after the first harvest.

8. The Puritan maiden was an accomplished (*a*) spinner (*b*) scholar (*c*) musician (*d*) cook.

9. News came back to the village of (*a*) the death of the Captain (*b*) the marriage of the Captain (*c*) the wreck of the *Mayflower* (*d*) the death of the king.

10. The wedding was disturbed by (*a*) what the people thought was a ghost (*b*) a sudden storm (*c*) an Indian attack (*d*) the approach of a vessel.

APPRECIATING THE POEM

1. It is at the close of the terrible first winter of 1620 that we find the Puritans of our story. A commanding figure is to be seen pacing up and down in one of the dwellings with martial air, past a table where a young man is writing. Describe the companions, showing how they are different in age and appearance. What is the pride of Miles Standish? Who was Rose Standish, and why does the thought of her make the Captain pensive? How are the three books of the Captain in keeping with his character?

2. How does the poet introduce the character of Priscilla? What is the special talent of the "stripling," as the poet calls him?

Lines 87–184

1. What abilities does Standish admire in Caesar? Of what adage is he particularly fond? How does the young man show deep respect and friendship for the Captain? Find two lines in this part which show his feeling.

2. What thoughts did the Captain confide to John? How does the young man respond? What arguments finally persuade John to serve as a messenger to Priscilla?

Lines 185–338

1. Tumbling, contending feelings accompany John Alden through the woods to the home of Priscilla. In his thoughts and words we catch our first picture of the Puritan maiden. What kind of person are you expecting to meet?

2. Describe the natural beauty which the young man passes on his way. When he comes within sight of the newly-built house, what is he thinking?

3. Describe the scene as Priscilla sings and spins in her home. How does she greet her guest? Why is she lonely? How does John take advantage of this part of the conversation to tell her of his message? What reasons has Priscilla for refusing the Captain's offer of marriage? What astonishing remark does she make?

Lines 339–481

1. Without a word, out into the open air rushes John Alden; triumph and torment possess him, then the voice of his Puritan conscience, "It hath displeased the Lord!" What sight at sea decides him upon a course of action?

2. Confident, assured, Miles Standish greets his messenger. Was John justified in thinking that this incident would end their friendship? What interrupts the angry scene? Do you think it a fortunate or an unfortunate interruption? If the Captain had stayed, might they have made up their quarrel?

3. Was Standish in a proper mood to answer the war challenge of the Indians? What happened at the council meeting?

Lines 482–626

1. At dawn, the Captain and his companions in war march north from Plymouth to meet the red men. In the bay lies the

Mayflower, rigged to sail that day back to its English home. Morning prayer over, the colonists pour onto the shore to wave good-by to their gallant ship, the last link of communication with their native land. Who is the first to reach the shore?

2. What had happened in the cabin of the Captain the previous night? How did the friends part, the one to war, the other with the intention of returning to England? How many Puritans went back on the *Mayflower?* What caused John to change his plans?

Lines 627–724

1. As John watches the *Mayflower* sail from view, he muses a while on things that have passed, and most of all on Priscilla. Turning, he finds her beside him. What apology does she offer for her words of yesterday? Do they agree on who was to blame for the happening? How much does John tell Priscilla of what happened between himself and the Captain? Do you think that Priscilla has a sense of humor? Why or why not?

2. This part belongs exclusively to John and Priscilla. Side by side, the lovers walk in the morning sun, confide their friendship, and establish a deeper and firmer kinship. Do you like this part of the story?

Lines 725–824

1. Meanwhile, Miles Standish is on the trail of the Indians. He continues to recall John's "betrayal," and stirs anew the flames of his anger. What thought finally stills the feverish recital of his "wrong"?

2. What do the soldiers encounter at the Indian encampment? Give an account of the battle with Wattawamat's Indians. Who was Hobomok, and why was he interested in the white man's victory? Was Priscilla pleased with the trophy of war nailed to the fortress? How did she connect it with Miles Standish?

Lines 825–925

1. Spring has passed into summer, and summer into autumn. There is the bustle of peaceful activity—building, harvesting, fishing, and hunting. How is John Alden faring in the midst of the growing prosperity of the village? Describe his new house. Where does the path through the woods often lead him in

"pleasure disguised as duty, love in the semblance of friendship"?. How does he constantly think of Priscilla?

2. Relate the incident of Priscilla, John, and the spinning
wheel. What interrupts the quiet scene? Suddenly released
from the bondage of unhappy friendship, how does John feel?

Lines 926–1018

1. In glorious splendor rose the sun on the wedding day of
Priscilla and John. Friends gather together for the simple,
beautiful service, but outside a strange, armor-clad figure appears, silently witnessing the service at the altar. Why do the
bride and groom suddenly grow pale? What lines tell you
that the Captain purposely waited until after the ceremony before appearing? How does he assure John of increased friendship? What adages does he quote to prove his sincerity?

2. Why are the people so very glad to see the Captain?
What does he laughingly declare is preferable to coming thus
uninvited to a wedding?

3. Describe in detail the wedding procession, headed by
Priscilla mounted on Raghorn. Would this be a satisfactory
closing scene for a movie version of the story?

APPRECIATING QUOTATIONS

Each of the following passages was spoken by an important
person in the poem. Fill in the name of the speaker in the
blank provided.

Passage	Speaker
1. "Why don't you speak for yourself, John?"	_____
2. "Serve yourself, would you be well served."	_____
3. "Such a message as that, I am sure I should mangle and mar it."	_____
4. "I almost wish myself back in Old England, I feel so lonely and wretched."	_____
5. "Let there be nothing between us save war, and implacable hatred!"	_____
6. "Here I remain!"	_____

7. "Yes, we must ever be friends; and of all who offer you friendship let me be ever first, the truest, the nearest and dearest." _____

8. "He is a little man; let him go and work with the women." _____

9. "No man can gather cherries in Kent at the season of Christmas!" _____

10. "Those whom the Lord hath united, let no man put them asunder!" _____

APPLIED GRAMMAR

Sometimes poetry is difficult to understand because poets often use an inverted word order, that is, they may place phrases, adjectives, or the complete predicate before the subject of a sentence. Rewrite the sentences below so that the subjects come before the predicates.

1. To and fro in his room of simple dwelling strode Miles Standish. _____

2. Buried in thought he seemed. _____

3. Short of stature he was, but strongly built and athletic. _____

4. Brown as a nut was his face. _____

5. Near him was seated John Alden. _____

6. Long at the window he stood and wistfully gazed at the landscape. _____

Find five adjectives to describe each of the following:

7. Priscilla: _____

8. Miles Standish: _____

9. John Alden: _____

WORDS

Can you determine the meaning of the italicized words from the following lines from the poem? See how many you can decide upon without checking with the dictionary. Then arrange the words alphabetically and look up all the meanings.

1. "In the old colony days . . . in a room of his simple and *primitive* dwelling."
2. "Short of *stature* he was, but strongly built and athletic."
3. "The sword . . . once saved my life in a *skirmish*."
4. "Sadly his face he *averted,* and strode up and down."
5. "To and fro . . . his thoughts were heaving and dashing, as in a *floundering* ship washes the bitter sea."
6. "Stouter hearts than a woman's have *quailed* in this terrible winter."
7. "Bringing in utmost haste a message of *urgent* importance."
8. "The village awoke from its sleep, and arose intent on its *manifold* labors."
9. "Meekly the prayer was begun, but ended in *fervent* entreaty."
10. "After the Puritan way, and the *laudable* custom of Holland."

THE LIBRARY

Some encyclopedias have indexes at the end of each volume; others have a separate volume which contains one index for the entire set. Then, too, there are encyclopedias with no indexes, but with long topics which are divided into sub-topics.

1. How is the encyclopedia in your library indexed?

2. In your school encyclopedia look up one of the following tribes of Indians: Samoset, Corbitant, Squanto.

3. What can you find about the Narraganset Indians who are mentioned in note 450?

4. What does the encyclopedia say about the *Mayflower?* Does it give anything you do not already know about this famous ship?

5. What can you find in an encyclopedia about Miles Standish? John Alden? Plymouth, Massachusetts? the Puritans?

CHORAL READING

Although "The Courtship of Miles Standish" has not been marked for choral reading, it is a poem which can well be used for chorus work. It is written in Longfellow's characteristic rhythm, which is so strong that it is a pleasure to read it aloud. Let this rhythm carry your voice along, but be careful to keep it from interfering with the thought in any way. This will call for careful planning of the way you read. Talk together about parts of the poem where, if you give attention to the rhythm alone, you will not give the thought. An example of this is in lines 13–14. Rhythm alone would give a ridiculous effect here and make you say his "beard was already" when the poet meant, of course, that it was "already flaked with snow." Experiment with different ways of reading these lines and agree on an interpretation. Other such lines are 54–55, 187–189, and 101–102. Watch for other such places in the poem.

A key for reading the poem is given on the opposite page. The part marked 1B(#1), the part of Miles Standish, should be read by a boy with a strong, decisive voice. Alden's part, 1B(#2), should be read by a boy who has not only a clear voice but who has imagination and who can put himself into the part so well that he can show Alden's conflicting emotions. Another boy, 1B(#3), reads the part of the Elder of Plymouth. Still another single boy's voice, 1B(#4), reads the part of the Indian, Wattawamat; and a fifth boy's voice, 1B(#5) reads the part of the other Indian, Pecksuot. The part of Hobomok, the Indian friend of the white men, is read by a boy whose part is marked 1B(#6). A single girl's voice reads Priscilla's part. Other parts are read by all boys (B), or all girls (G), or by everybody together (U).

In the key which follows, only the beginning line of each voice is indicated. That is, all boys (B) begin reading at line 1 and continue until another voice is indicated, which in this case is at line 15. At line 15 all girls (G) pick up the reading and continue through line 20. At line 21 all boys (B) pick up the reading again. At line 23 one boy (#1) reads the part of Miles Standish. In this manner, the reading can be continued throughout the entire poem.

80

Lines 1–86

Line						
1	B	23	1B(#1)	45	1B(#2)	66 B
15	G	31	1B(#2)	54	B	81 U
21	B	34	1B(#1)	61	1B(#1)	

Lines 87–184

Line						
87	U	98	1B(#1)	128	1B(#2)	165 1B(#1)
92	1B(#1)	116	U	132	1B(#1)	181 1B(#2)
94	1B(#2)	123	1B(#1)	156	1B(#2)	183 G

Lines 185–338

Line						
185	U	227	G	254	B	297 B
195	1B(#2)	239	B	267	1G	300 1G
207	B	245	1B(#2)	280	1B(#2)	315 B
213	1B(#1)	249	B	285	B	335 G
219	B	252	1G	293	1G	

Lines 339–481

Line						
339	B	389	B	424	B	466 1B(#3)
359	1B(#2)	397	1B(#1)	432	G	470 1B(#1)
361	B	403	B	438	B	479 B
376	1B(#1)	413	1B(#1)	459	1B(#1)	

Lines 482–626

Line						
482	U	512	B	552	U	589 U
496	B	516	G	564	G	601 B
504	G	523	B	573	1B(#2)	609 G

Lines 627–724

Line						
627	B	662	1B(#2)	695	1B(#2)	713 1G
632	1G	667	1G	700	U	714 G
650	1B(#2)	681	G	706	1G	718 1G
653	1G	687	1G	710	G	719 U

Lines 725–824

Line						
725	B	745	B	782	1B(#5)	810 1B(#6)
735	1B(#1)	771	1B(#4)	788	B	816 B

Lines 825–1018

Line						
825	G	876	1B(#2)	926	U	967 1B(#1)
840	B	885	G	932	G	974 B
851	G	889	1G	943	B	982 G
869	1B(#2)	901	B	959	1B(#1)	993 1B(#2)
873	G	918	G	965	1B(#2)	1005 U

MIKE FINK

(Part 1, page 260)

CARL CARMER

Birthday: *October 16, 1893*
Birthplace: *Cortland, New York*
Stories to Enjoy and Reread:
1. *"Stormalong"*
2. *"John Henry"*
3. *"Davy Crockett"*

Carl Carmer's father was a superintendent of schools, his mother a teacher, yet he says that in his own school days he learned two of the three r's, but no "rithmetic." However, he gained enough knowledge of mathematics to enable him to figure out how much he would need to save to buy a much longed-for fiddle. He still enjoys fiddling.

In college days he won several prizes for writing, and was recognized as the fastest half-miler of his time. He served in World War I, after which he was a professor in universities in New York and in Alabama. While he was in the South he continued his hobby of studying and collecting folklore.

CHECK YOUR READING

Complete the summary of the story by filling in the blanks with the proper words.

Mike Fink was an expert ＿＿＿＿＿＿＿＿＿ and ＿＿＿＿＿＿＿＿＿. One day Mike boasted that he could ＿＿＿＿＿＿＿ across the ＿＿＿＿＿＿＿ river from ＿＿＿＿＿＿＿＿＿, Illinois to ＿＿＿＿＿＿＿＿＿ point. To get a start Mike ran down ＿＿＿＿＿＿＿, but a little ＿＿＿＿＿＿＿ got in his way. When he knew that he would fail, Mike ＿＿＿＿＿＿＿＿＿ and landed on the ＿＿＿ ＿＿＿＿＿ shore. To get back upstream Mike and his crew had to use a system called ＿＿＿＿＿＿＿＿＿ and as they went they sang "＿＿＿＿＿＿＿＿＿."

82

DISCUSSING THE STORY

1. Mike Fink, like Paul Bunyan, Pecos Bill, and John Henry, is one of America's favorite legendary characters. Each of them has grown out of our fondness for exaggerated stories, particularly tales of extraordinary physical prowess. For what two skills was Mike Fink famous? What examples of each skill does the author give?

2. The best of the jumping stories grew out of a boast. What did Mike claim that he could do? What prevented him from getting a good start? What decision did Mike make when he saw that he would fall into the river? What is ridiculous about this famous leap?

3. What is meant by the term "bushwhacking"? Sing the song the boatmen sang on their way upstream.

APPLIED GRAMMAR

If you want to show possession or relation by using the possessive, you have learned to add an apostrophe and "s." However, the possessive form of plural nouns is formed in two different ways.

If the plural form of the noun ends in "s," an apostrophe is placed after the "s." For example,

    Plural arguers   *Plural Possessive* arguers'

When the plural form of a noun does not end in "s," an apostrophe and "s" are added to the plural form—

    Plural men   *Plural Possessive* men's

Supply the correct possessive form of the words in the parentheses.

1. Some pigs have straight tails due to Mike's having shot the curl out of their (parent) _____ tails.

2. The (children) _____ holiday was planned to watch (Mike) _____ jump.

3. The (judges) _____ decisions did not agree.

4. Mike could see the (people) _____ houses grow larger and larger.

5. The (boatmen) _____ eyes grew wide in astonishment.

83

On the lines below write four sentences of your own in which you use the possessive plural of nouns.

_____

_____

_____

_____

WORDS

Words that have the same sound but differ in meaning and spelling are called *homonyms*—for example, *their, there; dear, deer; aloud, allowed.* What homonyms do you know for the following words selected from the story?

tail	_____	some	_____
so	_____	seen	_____
straight	_____	bear	_____
due	_____	right	_____
too	_____	not	_____
real	_____	sense	_____
current	_____	great	_____
hear	_____	break	_____
sun	_____	one	_____
see	_____	knew	_____
air	_____	would	_____

THE LIBRARY

Just as you may find information in an encyclopedia under a certain subject such as "Legends" or "Folk Tales," you may find cards in the card catalog under a *subject* heading, usually printed in red. Under *"Legends"* you would probably find a card like this:

```
        LEGENDS,                    see also
    FOLK TALES
    FOLKLORE
```

Under what subject would you then look? Continuing your search you may then find a card like the one on the next page.

398.1
C

FOLKLORE
Carmer, Carl
America sings.
Knopf, N. Y. c. 1942
243 p. illus.

1. What is the title? _____
2. Who is the author? _____
3. Who is the publisher? _____
4. When was the book published? _____
5. How many pages are there in this book? _____
6. Does this book contain pictures? _____
7. What is the call number? _____

What folk tales and legends surround the country where you live?   Report on one of the following groups of legends.

8. If you live in the East, do you know
   a. whether Captain Kidd's treasure was ever found?
   b. why Alfred Bulltop Stormalong tied an octopus into knots?
   c. how John Darling made up his mind faster than Jersey mosquitoes?

9. If you live in the Midwest, do you know
   a. how Johnny Appleseed was given his name?
   b. how Davy Crockett happened to hang his powderhorn on the moon?
   c. how Jim Higgins' bear sped his flatboat down the Mississippi?

10. If you can claim a home in the South, can you tell
    a. how Daniel Boone outwitted a bear?
    b. how Brer Rabbit caused it to rain pancakes and persimmons?
    c. what happened to John Henry, the steel-drivin' man?

11. If the Far West is where you live, do you know about
    a. Pecos Bill and the Rio Grande?
    b. Paul Bunyan's remarkable deeds with his blue ox, Babe?
    c. Wild Bill Corlett's looking for a gold mine along the Sacramento?

WALTZING MATILDA

(Part 1, page 264)

APPRECIATION AND CHORAL READING

1. "Waltzing Matilda" is a folk song—that is, a song handed down from one generation to another by word of mouth. Folklore is the literature of the common people and is seldom written down. Ballads and other folk songs generally tell a story. What story is told in this song?

2. The strange words add humor to the song. Which are especially humorous? Be sure to sing the song in class.

3. The poem is also effective for choral reading. The strongly accented beat adds to the pleasure of reading it and to the effect produced. Use a light tone and practice until you can pronounce easily the words which are not familiar to you but which give a rollicking sound.

MOTHER VOLGA AND HER CHILD

(Part 1, page 265)

CHECK YOUR READING

Complete the meaning of each sentence by filling in the correct word.

1. People living along the Volga were wakened by a great
   _____.

2. Everyone feared a _____ would come.

3. The Volga and the _____ were quarreling.

4. The Volga claimed to be the _____ of all rivers in _____.

5. The other claimed to be the most dearly _____.

6. A man suggested that they _____ together and see which first reached the _____ Sea.

7. The _____ changed her course in the night.

8. At _____ the rivers met.

9. There the _____ admitted that the other was the greater.

10. Each spring the _____ is first to break the bonds of the winter ice.

DISCUSSING THE STORY

1. In legends and folk tales people often endow animals, objects of nature, or inanimate things with traits of human personality. What human weakness did the people attribute to the river Volga? In what country is the Volga? Locate it on a map.

2. How did the people discover the cause of the noise? Why were the rivers quarreling? What suggestion was made to them as a way to end the argument?

3. The Vazuza was young and inexperienced. She thought that she could outwit the older and stronger river by a bit of cleverness. How did her plan work out? What characteristics of the Volga are shown by the story?

4. How could the Volga take the Vazuza in her arms? What special task belongs to the Vazuza? Why do you think this story is a favorite one of the Russian people? In what way do the rivers behave like real persons?

APPLIED GRAMMAR

When we wish to describe just *one* thing, we use the simple or positive form of adjective.

When we wish to describe *two* objects by comparing them with each other, we must use the comparative degree of the adjective, formed by adding *er* to the positive form.

However, if we want to compare *one* object with *two or more* other objects, we must use the superlative degree of the adjective which is formed by adding *est* to the positive.

> The *wise* Volga flowed quietly to the sea. (*Positive*)
> The Volga is *wiser* than the Vazuza. (*Comparative*)
> The Volga is the *wisest* river in the world. (*Superlative*)

With longer words, *more* and *most* are usually used.

> The Volga is *more* turbulent than the Vazuza.

Underline the proper form of adjective in the sentences below.

1. The noise was (louder, loudest) than thunder.
2. It was the (louder, loudest) noise they had ever heard.

3. "I am the (stronger, strongest) river in Russia," cried the Volga.

4. "I took a (straighter, straightest) path than you," the Vazuza cried.

5. Whichever one reaches the Caspian Sea first will be the (wiser, wisest), (mightier, mightiest) and (more, most) highly respected of the two.

WORDS

1. Do you ever *wrangle* with your friends? What synonyms for wrangle do you often use? _____

_____

2. "The people called a *council* of the wisest men." Distinguish between the two words *council* and *counsel* by using each in a sentence.

council: _____

_____

counsel: _____

_____

3. Have you ever noticed that a good writer achieves variety in his work by using synonyms to avoid repeating an overworked word? What synonyms do you find throughout the story for the word *said?* Find at least six.

_____   _____

_____   _____

_____   _____

THE LIBRARY

Probably you were already familiar with the Volga through the song, "The Volga Boatman." Using library reference books, find the answers to these questions:

1. In what direction does the Volga flow _____

_____

2. What other rivers flow into the Caspian Sea? _____

_____

_____

3. Is the Vazuza River one of the chief rivers of Russia?

_____

THE PEDDLER OF BALLAGHADEREEN

(Part 1, page 268)

CHECK YOUR READING

Write T (True) or F (False) in the blanks.

_____ 1. The peddler lived with his family in a large house at the crossroads.

_____ 2. He made a good living by catching rabbits and other animals in home-made traps.

_____ 3. He often gave away trinkets from his pack.

_____ 4. The peddler told delightful stories of England's kings and queens.

_____ 5. Misfortune came upon him because he was selfish and unkind.

_____ 6. Saint Patrick appeared to him in a dream.

_____ 7. The landlord of the Head Inn gave him an old sea chest.

_____ 8. The landlord had never heard of Ballaghadereen.

_____ 9. The peddler changed his home at the crossroads into a fine inn.

_____ 10. His neighbors had a statue made of him after his death.

DISCUSSING THE STORY

1. As you grow older and your reading experience deepens, you will discover that Ireland is a rich source of folk tales and legends. Perhaps already you have learned that certain words or expressions are typical of the Irish people. Mention some of the characteristic expressions you find in this story.

2. The character of the peddler is revealed in little stories about him. How do you learn that he loved animals? How do you learn that he was kind and generous? That he was unselfish and delighted in giving pleasure to others?

3. The peddler was especially fond of children. What good advice did he often give them? Did he follow his own teachings? What did the neighbors say about him? Do you agree with them? Did they prophesy correctly?

4. Irish literature is full of stories of strange dreams and

89

mystic characters. Who appeared to the peddler in a dream? What strange message was he given? Why did he not do as he was told until after the third night?

5. The peddler did indeed "hear what he was meant to hear." How did he know that the landlord's words were meant for him? What did he find upon carrying out the directions?

6. We are told that the peddler used the gold wisely and for great good. Besides building the chapel, how do you imagine he used it? Which of his own words were prophetic?

7. Few of us will ever find a chest of gold beneath a tree in our gardens. Do you think there are other rewards for living a simple, humble life? What qualities of character do you observe in men and women who seem to find the most happiness in life?

APPLIED GRAMMAR

Most adjectives show the comparative and superlative degrees by the addition of *er* or *est* to the word, but certain adjectives require completely different words. Notice the changes in the adjectives below.

good, well	better	best
bad, evil, ill	worse	worst
little	less	least
much, many	more	most

It is incorrect to use the words "more" or "most" with an adjective already ending in "er" or "est," such as *more* rich*er* or *most* happi*est*. Use either *richer* or *more rich; happiest* or *most happy*.

Underline the proper form in the sentences below.

1. The kerchief looked (prettier, prettiest) in her curls than in the peddler's pack.
2. Each day the peddler grew (hungrier, more hungrier) than before.
3. He was a (more, most) generous peddler than any one they had ever known.
4. He was the (best, most best) known peddler in the country.
5. Which of the two stories do you think it is (better, best) to believe?

6. The song of the blackbirds on yonder cherry tree is the (most sweetest, sweetest) in all Ballaghadereen.
7. His pockets are (more, most) empty than his pack.
8. He is (foolisher, more foolish) than the blackbirds.
9. An empty stomach and weak legs are the (most bad, worst) companions a man can have.
10. He dug a (deeper, more deeper) hole beneath the tree.

WORDS

1. In the first paragraph of the story, what word meaning *grass* or *sod* also means a *kind of fuel?*
2. From the context of the story what do you think *dolefully* on page 270 means? Check your answer with the dictionary.
3. Several references are made to English terms of money. Find out the value in American money of *half a crown;* a *shilling; sixpence;* a *farthing;* a *pound.*
4. There are many expressions in the story that are peculiar to the people of Ireland, such as "a bit of a" and "faith." Name three other similar expressions.

_____
_____
_____

THE LIBRARY

Perhaps you will want to keep a list of the legends you have read that you liked best, so that your friends may read them too. The author's *last* name should come first on your list, then his first name. Next give the title of the story. On the next line, write one or two sentences telling what you liked about the story.

After you have arranged the authors' names in alphabetical order, your list should look like this:

Colum, Padraic. "The Golden Fleece"
Jason learns to hunt and fight while looking for the Golden Fleece.
Sawyer, Ruth. "The Peddler of Ballaghadereen"
A peddler in Ireland gave all his wares away to children. Later he had a strange dream.

91

THE PIED PIPER OF HAMELIN

(Part 1, page 275)

ROBERT BROWNING

Birthday: *May 7, 1812*
    (Died December 12, 1889)
Birthplace: *Camberwell, England*
Poems to Enjoy and Reread:
1. *"How They Brought the Good News from Ghent to Aix"*
2. *"The Boy and the Angel"*
3. *"Incident of the French Camp"*
4. *"Home Thoughts from Abroad"*

Robert Browning wrote poems when he was a mere boy living in a London suburb. He received his education from his parents and tutors, and since his parents were well-to-do, he had many opportunities. He became recognized as one of the best educated men of his day. Besides being an accomplished musician, a scientist, and an amateur artist, he enjoyed many sports.

In later years he became acquainted with Elizabeth Barrett, a semi-invalid poet who had already won fame for her work. The story of their romance and its happy climax has been told repeatedly in books and plays. Because Mrs. Browning's health was delicate, the couple went to live in the sunshine of Italy. Mrs. Browning died fifteen years later, but Browning lived to be an old man. His entire life was spent in writing poetry. He believed that life is beautiful and worth living. The world is richer because of his poems.

APPRECIATING THE POEM

This charming legend was written for Willy Macready, the son of a famous actor of Browning's day. Willy was sick and confined to the house, and Browning wrote the poem to amuse the boy and give him subjects for illustrative drawings. He never intended that it be published, but the world would have missed a most enjoyable piece of literature had the poem never gone beyond Willy's hands.

1. Almost five hundred years before Browning wrote the poem the pleasant little German town of Hamelin was overrun with rats. The people were frantic and naturally looked to their leaders for help. What threats did the people make against these "civic servants"?

2. Describe the Piper as he advanced to the table where the puzzled Corporation sat. What story did he tell? What agreement was reached with the Mayor and the Corporation?

3. How did the Piper carry out his part of the agreement? How did the rats perish? Were the townspeople grateful? Were the Mayor and the Corporation grateful?

4. What threat did the Piper fling at the council? What was the consequence of the Mayor's failure to keep his promise?

5. Carefully read the report of the lame boy, and then go back to the tale of the rat who also remained to tell of the fascinating music of the Piper. What was the secret of the fascination of the Piper's song?

6. Hamelin, like selfish people, learned its lesson too late. What explanation is given in the next-to-the-last stanza of what happened to the children?

7. Do you know any people who like to make big promises and then never make good what they promise? Why is it better to promise less but make sure that one's promise is kept?

CHORAL READING

As you read the poem chorally, listen carefully to the words to hear the pleasing combinations of sounds that they contain. In II notice the effect of *alliteration* (repetition of the same sounds at the beginnings of words) in "*b*it the *b*abies" "*s*alted *s*prats," etc. This poem gives many examples also of words in which the sound suggests the meaning. Some of them are "shrieking and squeaking," and "grumbling grew to a mighty rumbling." Find other examples.

THE LIBRARY

In an atlas, locate the following places which are mentioned in the poem: Hamelin, Hanover, Weser River, Bagdad, Transylvania.

THE SNOW WITCH

(Part 1, page 287)

HOW TO READ A PLAY

Plays differ from the short stories you have been reading in two important respects. In stories, the author describes much that happens in detail, but the dramatist cannot do this. Instead, he relies on *stage directions* for his descriptions. These are usually printed in italics or in different type and occur at the beginning of the play and in parentheses along through the play. These should always be read very carefully.

The second great difference to be noted is that plays are not written in solid paragraph form, but in what is known as *dialogue* form. The author merely indicates who is speaking by using the name of the character, then indicates the conversation of all those present on the stage. If you enjoy books which contain considerable conversation, you should enjoy reading plays.

CHECK YOUR READING

Match the phrases on the left with the names on the right.

_____ 1. the Snow Witch	Foma
_____ 2. the sledge-driver	Ivan
_____ 3. one who fears robbers	Valeska
_____ 4. a peasant woman	Paul
_____ 5. the soldier	Marya Topliff
_____ 6. the Princess	Silver-Sonia
_____ 7. the dancer	Marina
_____ 8. one whose life is bewitched	
_____ 9. one who suffers frozen feet	
_____10. the giver of the charm	

DISCUSSING THE STORY

1. The scene of the story is Russia. How does the stage setting give the effect of a cold winter night? What do you learn about Marina as she talks to herself in the opening speech?

2. How do you know early in the play that the story is a

folk tale? What powers does the Snow Witch possess? Do most people still believe in witches? Is it easy to understand that such beliefs grow out of the imagination?

3. Why had Silver-Sonia stopped at the home of Marina? What complaints does she hear from her? What power does the Snow Witch give Marina?

4. Marina is delighted at the prospect of changing her personality. Why does she have difficulty in deciding at once with whom to change places? Why does she say that she would not be the Princess Valeska for a thousand rubles?

5. Marina learns that other people's lives, like her own, are a mixture of sunshine and shadow, of happiness and unhappiness. Why would she not care to change lives with Ivan or with Foma? Do you agree with Marina's decision that "it is better to be just one's self, with one's own burdens"?

6. Learn the little jingle which was inscribed on the ring. Think carefully of the people with whom you have perhaps wished to change lives at one time or another. What part of their lives would you not wish for yourself? Do you think that the jingle is true?

WORDS

1. Sometimes the stage directions of a play indicate how certain lines should be spoken. Many lines are left to the interpretation of the actor. Marina, for instance, speaks *hesitantly, timidly, bitterly, joyfully.*

a. Explain how you think Silver-Sonia would say her first long speech on page 288.

b. How would Marina's voice and manner change as she "suits her action to the word" on page 290?

c. Would the Princess speak *humbly, sharply, fearfully, quietly, rudely,* or *softly?*

d. Would Ivan's tone of voice be *firm, loud, shrill, weak, tremulous, hearty, mild* or *gruff?*

2. If you were to be an actor in the play, how would you pronounce the words below?

wander	prophecy	hearth	jest
enlightening	windows	warmth	pelf

THE BROKEN NOTE

(Part 1, page 293)

ERIC P. KELLY

Birthday: March 16, 1884
Birthplace: Amesbury, Massachusetts
Stories to Enjoy and Reread:
1. *The Christmas Nightingale: Three Christmas Stories from Poland*
2. *The Blacksmith of Vilno*
3. *The Golden Star of Halich*

Leaving the traditional home of their ancestors in New England, Eric Kelly's family moved westward to Colorado, when he was five years old. The boy was delighted with the freedom and vastness of his new home and enjoyed every moment he spent exploring the mountains and canyons.

It was a great disappointment to Eric when his family moved back to New York. There he completed his high school course. After graduating from Dartmouth College, he spent the next years working on the staffs of several different newspapers. His spare moments found him writing stories for young people. Success came when several stories were accepted by magazines.

While in France during World War I, he met many Polish exiles and patriots. After a meeting with Paderewski, the world famous pianist and statesman who worked ceaselessly for his people, Kelly determined to go to Poland after the signing of the Armistice. While he was studying at the University of Krakow, he roomed near a church tower from which he could hear each hour being announced by a beautiful trumpet call. This was the inspiration for his well known story, *The Trumpeter of Krakow,* from which "The Broken Note" is taken.

Kelly was honored on many occasions by the Polish people, who felt his affection and loved him in return. Later he returned to America to teach journalism at Dartmouth.

Write T (True) or F (False) in the blanks.

———— 1. The Tartars were a quiet, peaceful people living in southwest Poland.

———— 2. To escape a savage band of warriors, the peasant people fled to Krakow.

———— 3. In 1241 the city was entirely destroyed by fires set by the barbarians.

———— 4. The Heynal was a hymn to Our Lady Mary sung by a group of choristers from the balcony of the church.

———— 5. In the midst of the terror and destruction the trumpeter kept his vow to sound the trumpet every hour.

———— 6. Two hundred years later young Joseph Charnetski became the trumpeter.

———— 7. It was the duty of the trumpeter to sound an alarm when fire or danger threatened the city.

———— 8. The trumpeter's official clock was a large hourglass.

———— 9. The trumpeter always ends the Hymn on a broken note.

————10. The traditional Heynal was last played in 1461.

DISCUSSING THE STORY

1. Folk tales and legends often develop from purely imaginative sources. Others sometimes grow from stories of heroic action or from simple historic events which gain in importance as the years pass. When and where did the story of the young trumpeter originate?

2. Why did the author liken the Tartars to a horde of wild beasts? Where did the people seek refuge?

3. Describe the attack upon Krakow. What remained in the morning outside the gates of the castle? Who alone remained alive outside the castle walls?

4. What was the "Heynal"? What thoughts passed through the mind of the young trumpeter as he waited for death? What reasons prompted him to remain at his post in the hour of confusion and terror? How was he able to make the hymn sound triumphant and joyous? Why did it end on a broken note?

5. How many years passed between the story of the trumpeter and the story of Pan Andrew? In what respect were the situations the same? What oath did Pan Andrew take?

6. Describe briefly the Church of Our Lady Mary in Krakow. How did Joseph and his father reach the high tower? What duties were exacted of the trumpeter? What instruments were used to tell time?

7. Besides playing upon the trumpet every hour what did the trumpeter do? What sights and sounds did Pan Andrew see and hear as he played? What story did Joseph hear? What tradition had been added to the original hymn? Do you understand the "thrill of pride" with which Joseph listened to the song of the trumpet?

8. How many years elapse between the second and third parts of the story? How have the years added to the beauty of the church and to the tradition that still lives even today? What has the Heynal come to mean to its hearers? Do you think the custom may have had special significance for the people of Poland in recent years? Why?

APPLIED GRAMMAR

Stories which tell of savage warriors and noble deeds are naturally filled with action. Such action is expressed by words which we call "verbs." Besides expressing action, verbs also declare or express a state of being. Many verbs are used too often and therefore become uninteresting. Learn to use colorful verbs to make your writing and speech more vivid. In each of the sentences below substitute a strong verb for the word in parentheses. For example,

"The arrow *pierced* the breast of the young trumpeter when he was near the end of his song; it *quivered* there a moment and the song *ceased*."

1. On their horses they carried shields, and long spears (hung) ———————————— from their saddles.
2. Behind the army (moved) ————————————
carts with slaves, provisions, and booty.
3. Children (walked) ———————————— wearily along.

4. Refugees from all about the country (ran) _____ into the fortification and were housed inside its walls.

5. As morning (came) _____ the watchers (looked over) _____ the town and saw only three churches not already in flames.

6. Here and there they could see clouds of black smoke which (came from) _____ the roof-tops.

7. A Tartar below (knelt) _____ with his bow and drew back the arrow.

8. The arrow (passed through the air) _____ _____ with lightning speed.

WORDS

From each group of italized words chosen from the story, underline the one which is similar in meaning to the first word of the line. When in doubt, use a dictionary.

1. pillaged (*fortified; plundered; defended*)
2. ruthlessness (*cruelty; suffering; kindliness*)
3. oath (*debt; agreement; vow*)
4. conflagration (*smoke; fire; fumes*)
5. ecstatic (*beyond reason; destructive; everlasting*)
6. heritage (*hermit; inheritance; ill fortune*)
7. aperture (*wall; tower; opening*)
8. magnificence (*great size; great beauty; great power*)
9. veritable (*true; wise; capable*)
10. epoch (*change of heart; knowledge; age*)

THE LIBRARY

There are many persons about whom legends still linger to-day. Find the answer to one of the questions below, and add more to the story for the class to hear.

1. Was there a real Robinson Crusoe?
2. Did George Washington actually cut down a cherry tree?
3. What story do you know about Robin Hood?
4. Did the Pilgrims really land on Plymouth Rock?
5. How did Joan of Arc return to the soldiers in battle?
6. How did William Tell show his skill as an archer?
7. Where is Davey Jones's locker?

HOW TOM SAWYER WHITEWASHED THE FENCE

(Part 1, page 308)

MARK TWAIN

Birthday: *November 30, 1835*
(Died April 21, 1910)

Birthplace: *Florida, Missouri*
Stories to Enjoy and Reread:
1. *The Adventures of Tom Sawyer*
2. *The Adventures of Huckleberry Finn*
3. *Life on the Mississippi*
4. *The Prince and the Pauper*

Samuel Clemens' boyhood in Hannibal, Missouri, was full of fun and mischief. Those carefree years came to a sudden end when he was twelve, for at the death of his father, he had to start earning a living. He learned the printing trade, remaining in this occupation for several years. His dream of becoming a river pilot materialized at twenty, but the Civil War ended that job. Next he ventured West and tried his hand at newspaper reporting. His articles were signed "Mark Twain," meaning in a river-pilot's language "two fathoms deep." From then on he became known as Mark Twain and his own name, Samuel Clemens, was almost forgotten.

His popularity as an author began when, just for fun, he wrote a story about a trained jumping frog, which had been told him by an old river pilot. It was printed everywhere and jobs were offered to its author. Audiences begged for Mark Twain's humorous lectures. He was sent abroad to gather material for articles and on this journey, a fellow traveler happened to show him a picture of his sister. Mark Twain fell in love "at first sight" and upon his return he married the girl in the picture, Olivia Langdon. The story of the voyage— *Innocents Abroad*—brought him further popularity and wealth.

His creations, Tom Sawyer and Huckleberry Finn, are two of the best loved friends of thousands of boys and girls. The movies have shared the adventures of these boys with every one who wished to live again favorite moments in reading.

CHECK YOUR READING

Write T (True) or F (False) in the blanks.

_____ 1. Tom was delighted that Aunt Polly told him to white-wash the fence.

_____ 2. He offered Jim a white marble in exchange for letting him see Jim's sore toe.

_____ 3. Aunt Polly gave Jim a whack with her slipper.

_____ 4. Ben pretended to be a railroad engineer.

_____ 5. Tom began to whitewash the fence with extreme care.

_____ 6. Ben took over the whitewashing after giving Tom his kite.

_____ 7. Tom went swimming while the other boys worked.

_____ 8. Tom lost a good many treasures during one afternoon.

_____ 9. Tom learned that anything which is difficult to attain is desirable.

_____ 10. Work consists of whatever a person is not obliged to do.

DISCUSSING THE STORY

1. Most boys and girls look forward to Saturday morning as a time to sleep late or to do something especially delightful. Why was Tom Sawyer in a melancholy mood on this particular Saturday? Why would he have preferred to carry water from the town pump?

2. Tom almost persuaded Jim to change tasks with him. What did he offer Jim? What prevented the carrying out of the plans?

3. Ben Rogers was playing the favorite game of boys who lived along the Mississippi. Was his pretense very realistic? How did he begin to tease Tom?

4. Tom had had an "inspiration." How did his attitude toward his assigned task change? How did he manage to get Ben to take over the whitewashing? How did Tom profit during the afternoon by his shrewdness?

5. What great law of human nature had Tom discovered? What is the difference between work and play? Is it possible for anyone to turn play into work? How can you turn some of your work into play?

APPLIED GRAMMAR

When you are telling a story, it is important that you relate it clearly by explaining events in the order in which they happened. One way of indicating when action takes place is through the use of different forms of verbs. If you were relating a part of this story to a friend, and you wanted to say that Tom was at that moment whitewashing the fence, you would say: "Tom *is whitewashing* the fence now," or "Tom *whitewashes* the fence with ease."

But if, in relation to the rest of your story, you wanted to indicate that he had finished whitewashing the fence, you would say: "Tom *whitewashed* the fence yesterday."

However, if you wanted to show that Tom had already painted part of the fence *before* the other boys worked on it, you would say: "Tom *had* whitewashed a part of the fence before the boys arrived to finish it."

Rewrite the paragraphs below correcting the verbs which give the wrong impression of the time when the action took place. Be able to explain the changes you make.

Tom appeared on the sidewalk with a bucket and a brush. He surveys the fence and all gladness left him. Life to him seemed hollow. Bringing water from the pump is always hateful to him. Now it seemed a pleasure.

By the time Ben was tired out, Tom trades the next change to Billy Fisher for a kite. By the time the fence was finished, Tom spent a lazy day. Tom said to himself that it isn't such a hollow world, after all.

WORDS

1. In the dictionary, find the meanings of *vegetation, melancholy, tranquilly, covet.* Use each word in a sentence.

2. From the context, that is, from the story itself, explain *delicious expeditions.* Is this the usual meaning of *delicious?* Also explain *personating a steamboat; continent of unwhitewashed fence; swept daintily back and forth.*

3. Distinguish between *starboard* and *larboard.* Are these synonyms or antonyms? Modern usage is discarding *larboard* and using *port* instead. Can you see why *port* is a better word?

4. Sometimes an author deliberately uses incorrect expressions like "it don't" or overworks words commonly used in conversation like "awful" and "ain't." Make a list of such words or expressions. Why should one not use these words in his daily speech?

_____   _____

_____   _____

_____   _____

5. List six colorful verbs used by Mark Twain.

_____   _____   _____

_____   _____   _____

THE LIBRARY

If you look in the card catalog to see what books your library owns by Mark Twain, you may find a card like this:

```
TWAIN, MARK, pseud.    see
   CLEMENS, SAMUEL LANGHORNE
```

1. What reference book would you use to find what the abbreviation "pseud." means? _____

2. What does "pseud." mean? _____
_____

3. What author card will lead you to the books in your library by Mark Twain? _____

4. What are the titles of five of the books?
_____
_____
_____
_____

5. Find some interesting fact about Mark Twain in an encyclopedia. _____
_____
_____

GODFREY GORDON GUSTAVUS GORE

(Part 1, page 314)

APPRECIATING THE POEM

1. The constant, clever repetition of the same sounds and theme throughout the poem accounts for its humorous effect. What vowel predominates?

2. Godfrey Gordon Gustavus Gore wouldn't shut the door, and eight stanzas of amusing poetry carry this refrain. Every time Godfrey went forth, what combination of sounds flew after him? What did his mother beg, his father implore? To what purpose were the plans for the voyage to Singapore? Do you think Godfrey Gordon Gustavus Gore always remembered to shut doors thereafter?

CHORAL READING

The alliteration in the boy's name gives an opportunity to enjoy speaking it in unison. You might like to try dividing into two groups for this unison speaking of the name and have the two groups speak on different pitches—one for the deeper voices and one for the lighter voices in your group.

Notice that people grow more and more impatient with Godfrey Gordon Gustavus Gore and that finally a climax is reached. Try to show this progress by your voice. In the last two stanzas, especially, be careful not to allow the rhythm to destroy the thought.

THE MODERN HIAWATHA

(Part 1, page 315)

APPRECIATION AND CHORAL READING

1. Hiawatha had his troubles in the forest, you will admit, but they were nothing compared to this figuring out which side's outside so that the warm side's inside. The poem is a clever bit of word twisting, rhymed to match Longfellow's "Hiawatha." Surely you have seen fur-lined mittens? Read the poem again with those fur-lined mittens pictured in your imagination.

2. One secret of effective reading of this amusing poem is to

104

read it rather rapidly, but to enunciate very, very plainly.
Learn to know the poem so well that you can read it rapidly
with no apparent effort. Read as though you are really trying
to explain the matter. This will add to the amusing effect. An
alternative to the division of voices suggested would be to give
the entire poem in unison.

THE LOBSTER MARATHON

(Part 1, page 316)

APPRECIATION AND CHORAL READING

1. Do you think that love of racing is characteristic of
Americans? What examples of racing does the poet name?
What other kinds of races can you add to the list?

2. What kind of race did Dan'l Prince and Hen McCue arrange for their sons? How many bowls of stew did each boy
eat? How did the contest end?

3. Everybody enjoys such a poem as this one which exag-
gerates a commonplace experience. What kind of "eating"
contests have you seen? Which lines of the poem present the
most humorous aspect of the situation?

4. In your choral reading, read the first two lines briskly
to set the nonsensical mood of the poem. Boys' voices will lead
up to the climax of the race. The humorous anticlimax of the
last stanza may well be given by girls' voices as they emphasize
in their reading the veto of the race by the boys' mothers.

THE CENTIPEDE

(Part 1, page 317)

APPRECIATING THE POEM

1. What is a centipede? What thought occurs to the author
as he observes a centipede?

2. In a similar fashion write a little four-line jingle of your
own on an interesting insect or animal—the caterpillar, the bat,
the bee, the bear.

THE FROG

(Part 1, page 317)

APPRECIATION AND CHORAL READING

1. What names are frogs often called? Do you know any others besides those mentioned by the poet?

2. What is amusing about the poet's praise of the frog?

3. Write a four-line poem in praise of a fish.

4. If you read the poem aloud as though you felt it to be very serious, it will add to the amusement of your listeners. Speak the names of the frog very distinctly. The parentheses give opportunity for a pause and a different intonation of the words inclosed in the parentheses.

A LIMERICK

(Part 1, page 318)

APPRECIATING THE POEM

Limericks are fun to read and to write. They are always humorous in thought and have an unexpected climax in the last line. Notice that lines 1, 2, and 5 rhyme; also 3 and 4. Can you complete the limerick below?

There was a young lady who said,
"Oh, how I hate butter and bread!
Next time I eat dinner,
I'll surely be thinner,

Can you write a limerick which will rhyme the following way?

_____ Jones,
_____ bones.
_____ snore,
_____ more,
_____ stones.

Can you write a limerick of your own?

_____
_____
_____
_____

CONAL AND DONAL AND TAIG

(Part 1, page 319)

SEUMAS MACMANUS

Year of Birth: *1869*
Birthplace: *Donegal, Ireland*
Stories to Enjoy and Reread:
  1. *Donegal Fairy Stories*
  2. *In Chimney Corners*
  3. *Well o' the World's End*
  4. *Ballads of a Country Boy*
  5. *The Bewitched Fiddle*

Of himself, Seumas MacManus writes: "As a barefoot boy I herded cattle and sheep on the hills, labored on the farms, and attended the mountain school. By the time I was seven, I could tell a hundred of the old tales, as I had learned them by a hundred firesides." Years later while earning a meager living as a schoolmaster, he retold the tales he had heard as a child and set sail for America. His stories sold rapidly and soon he was making annual lecture tours to American colleges. Every summer, however, he returns to his native Donegal hills and people.

CHECK YOUR READING

Write T (True) or F (False) in the blanks.

_____ 1. Three brothers fell into an argument as to which of them should inherit their father's estate.

_____ 2. Each one claimed to be the laziest man in the world.

_____ 3. None of them was willing to admit that he was the youngest among them.

_____ 4. Each one claimed to have the best memory.

_____ 5. Each one claimed to have the keenest hearing.

_____ 6. None liked physical exercise.

_____ 7. Conal boasted that he could make a man a suit if he knew only the color of his eyes.

_____ 8. Donal bragged that he could fit a man with clothes without knowing the very slightest thing about him.

107

_____ 9. Taig said that he would be too clever to admit that he was stupid.

_____10. The Judge decided in favor of Donal.

DISCUSSING THE STORY

1. What disagreement arose among the three brothers? Why was the argument difficult to settle? How soon do you learn that the story is going to be a "tall tale"?

2. Even the wisest judge found it hard to make a decision. How did he first attempt to solve the puzzle? Do you agree that the brothers are equally lazy?

3. What clever answers do the brothers give as to which is the oldest of them? Which of the brothers seems to you to have the best memory? Which of the answers as to their sight is the most absurd? How did each claim to be the supplest?

4. The argument might never have ended if the Judge had not asked which of the brothers was the cleverest. Who was awarded the field? Do you think the winning answer was indeed the most clever?

5. Much of the humor of the story lies in the repetition of the questions and in the exaggeration of the answers. What else did you like about the story?

APPLIED GRAMMAR

Underline the correct word in each sentence below.

1. One of them (has, have) as good a claim as the other.
2. None of the judges (was, were) able to decide the case.
3. I doubt if Donal or Taig (is, are) (lazier, laziest) than that.
4. I'll give the field to whichever one of the three of you (is, are) the (lazier, laziest).
5. Which one of you (is, are) the (older, oldest) is hard to decide.
6. Which of you (has, have) the (greater, greatest) memory is difficult to say.
7. There (was, were) several trials before the case was settled.
8. You are the three (more, most) wonderful men in the world.
9. The cleverness of you two boys (is, are) hard to beat.
10. I'll give the field to the (supplest, most supplest).

UNIT ACTIVITIES

SUGGESTIONS FOR FURTHER READING—UNIT III

RALPH S. BOGGS AND MARY GOULD DAVIS, *The Three Golden Oranges and Other Spanish Folk Tales*

LUCIA MERECKA BORSKI AND KATE B. MILLER, *The Jolly Tailor and Other Fairy Tales*

MILDRED CRISS, *Malou*

ALEXANDER DUMAS, PÈRE, *The Nutcracker of Nuremberg*

AGNES FISHER, *Once Upon a Time—Folk Tales, Myths, and Legends of the United Nations*

MIKKJEL FONHUS, *Northern Lights*

HARRY W. FRENCH, *The Lance of Kanana*

FRANCES FROST, *Legends of the United Nations*

MARIE HAMSUM, *A Norwegian Farm*

EDWARD LEAR, *Nonsense Books*

SELDEN LORING, *Mighty Magic*

ANNE MALCOLMSON, (ed.), *Yankee Doodle's Cousins*

ANNE MERRIMAN PECK, *Roundabout Europe*

GLEN ROUNDS, *Ol' Paul, the Mighty Logger*

JULIA SAUER, *Fog Magic*

RUTH SAWYER, *The Way of the Storyteller*

MONICA SHANNON, *Dobry*

IDA ZEITLIN, *Skazki: Tales and Legends of Old Russia*

DO YOU RECOGNIZE LITERARY CHARACTERS?

In the blanks at the left, write the names of the characters which correctly answer the questions.

_____ 1. Who lured away all the children of a village by his magic music?

_____ 2. Who made a proposal of marriage for a friend?

_____ 3. Who became the trumpeter of Krakow in the year 1461?

_____ 4. Who was clever enough to win a field for himself?

_____ 5. Who found gold under a cherry tree?

_____ 6. Who always neglected to shut a door?

_____ 7. Who awoke from sleep to find himself an old man?

_____ 8. Who was given a magic charm by a snow witch?

_____ 9. Who learned at an early age the main difference between work and play?

_____ 10. Who made her husband's life miserable by scolding?

_____ 11. Who carried the Vazuza in her arms?

_____ 12. Who wore his mittens fur side inside?

_____ 13. Who regretted his failure to keep a promise?

_____ 14. Who leaped almost across the Mississippi River and back again?

_____ 15. Who was fond of studying the campaigns of Julius Caesar?

CAN YOU IDENTIFY THE SKETCHES?

With what character do you associate each of the objects pictured on the opposite page?

1. _____

2. _____

3. _____

4. _____

5. _____

6. _____

7. _____

8. _____

ABE DISCOVERS A NEW WORLD
(Part 1, page 327)

CHECK YOUR READING

Underscore the correct expressions.

1. Abe's stepmother was (*a*) lazy (*b*) unkind (*c*) full of fun (*d*) stingy.

2. Everyone thought that Abe was too big to go to school except his (*a*) father (*b*) stepmother (*c*) cousin Dennis (*d*) grandmother.

3. Abe was especially good in (*a*) reading (*b*) writing (*c*) arithmetic (*d*) spelling.

4. Mrs. Carter discovered that Abe would rather read a book than (*a*) go fishing (*b*) eat (*c*) work for cash (*d*) go to town.

5. The first book Abe ever read, excepting the Bible, was (*a*) *Aesop's Fables* (*b*) *Pilgrim's Progress* (*c*) *Arabian Nights* (*d*) *The Life of George Washington.*

6. Working for Josiah Crawford, Abe earned (*a*) a dollar a day (*b*) a dollar a week (*c*) twenty-five cents a day (*d*) twenty-five dollars a month.

7. Abe once teased his stepmother by marking up the ceiling with (*a*) green paint (*b*) muddy footprints (*c*) soot (*d*) charcoal.

8. To pay for a borrowed book which rain had damaged, Abe (*a*) pulled fodder for three days (*b*) walked six miles to a store (*c*) gave up all his savings (*d*) went to jail for a week.

9. Abe was (*a*) a poor farm hand (*b*) an unwilling worker (*c*) an excellent worker (*d*) a splendid carpenter.

10. Everyone found Abe (*a*) too sober and serious (*b*) very dull in conversation (*c*) extremely religious (*d*) full of fun and good spirits.

DISCUSSING THE STORY

1. Abraham Lincoln was fortunate in having two good mothers—his own mother and his stepmother. What kind of woman was Sarah Lincoln? What comforts had she brought to the cabin home? How did she help to unify her own family and Tom's?

2. In Lincoln's day, educational opportunities were scarce. Who insisted on Abe's getting all the schooling that he could? How did Abe show that he recognized the value of education? In what subject was he especially proficient?

3. Working at the Carter farm one day, Abe did indeed discover a new world. How was this new world of books made known to him? How did he astonish Mrs. Carter? Have you read any of the books which Lincoln read? If so, why do you think Abe found them fascinating? How did Abe's father and stepmother feel about his sudden absorption in books?

4. As Abe grew older, how did he set himself to the task of studying without such usual equipment as pencil and paper? To what extent did he grow in physical strength? How did Mr. Crawford attempt to teach him to stick to his work? What kind of reputation was Abe acquiring?

5. In spite of his studiousness Abe was full of fun. What practical joke did he play on his stepmother? How do we know that she was full of fun, too, and that she and Abe had much in common?

6. What book was to have a profound influence on Abe's life? How did he pay for the book when it was damaged?

7. The Crawfords grew very fond of Abe. What qualities in him did they admire? What laughing remark did Abe make one day? Do you think he had any such personal ambition at that time? Have you ever read a good account of Lincoln's whole life?

8. Imagine for the moment that you were living in Lincoln's day when there were few schools and few opportunities to learn. Would you have been, like Lincoln, eager to learn all that you could? Would you have preferred to work on your father's farm or set yourself to the tasks at hand? Even today, if America had no compulsory education laws and you were free to make a choice, would you choose to go to school or to find your place in the working world?

9. Imagine too, for the moment, that you have never learned to read or to write. How would your life right now be affected by that fact? In other words, does education help you to live a more secure and happy life? If not, why do we not

abolish compulsory education? If so, why do pupils fail to appreciate modern schools and their splendid equipment of laboratories, gymnasiums, workshops? Why are you not eager, curious, or excited about the wonderful world of learning?

10. Perseverance and initiative are not abstract ideals—they are definite qualities of personality. Anyone can possess them. Do you know the precise meaning of each term? Look them up in a dictionary to be sure. What evidence of these qualities do you find in Lincoln's life? In what phases of your daily life do you need to persevere or to show initiative?

APPLIED GRAMMAR

What word tells *how* Abe carried the milk?

Abe carried the pail of milk carefully.

Words that tell *how* are "adverbs," and usually end in "ly." Adverbs are used to modify or to describe verbs, adjectives, and other adverbs.

In each of the sentences below underline the adverb once and the verb twice.

1. Abe suddenly spied a large book on a shelf.
2. He turned the pages of the book carefully.
3. The winter passed swiftly, and before they knew it, school was closed.
4. Sarah Lincoln agreed cheerfully that Abe would work at Mr. Crawford's farm.
5. Abe slowly and sorrowfully told how the rain had ruined the book.

Some adverbs tell *how* or *to what extent* but do not end in "ly," such as: *fast, well, aloud, hard, very, almost,* and *too.* In the sentences below supply such adverbs.

6. The Lincoln children studied their lessons _____.
7. Abe learned to read and write _____.
8. The boys ran _____ across the snowy field to the school.
9. Abe worked _____ on Mr. Crawford's farm.
10. Sarah Lincoln agreed that it was a _____ cold day.

114

WORDS

1. The Latin prefix *trans* meaning "across" or "over" may be used with many verb stems to make new words. What meaning does *transformed* have in the sentence, "She had *transformed* it into a comfortable home"? What other words do you know that use the prefix *trans?*

2. Explain the sentence, "Abe scrubbed away at the *grime* of the day's work." How do you pronounce *grimy?*

3. Find the word *reluctantly* near the top of page 331. From the surrounding context, what meaning do you apply to *reluctantly?* What is a good synonym for it?

4. When you are *oblivious* to everything about you, are you *keenly observant, attentive, forgetful,* or *indifferent?*

5. *Exclude* comes from the Latin prefix *ex* meaning "out" or "from" and the Latin verb *claudere* meaning "to shut." Explain the thought of the sentence, "The schoolmaster was forced to *exclude* Abe from the spelling matches." Make a list of ten words using the prefix *ex.*

6. In your dictionary find the meaning and pronunciation of *chagrin*. In a sentence of your own, use the word in the same sense as that in which it is used on page 334.

THE LIBRARY

There are many interesting stories about Abraham Lincoln. You will want to have one ready to tell to your class or to your friends.

1. How many books does your library own about Abe Lincoln?

2. Find an interesting story about Lincoln in an encyclopedia.

3. Under what other topics would you be likely to find facts about Lincoln's career?

4. Have you read any of the books Abe Lincoln read when he was a boy? What can you find in an encyclopedia about one of these titles?

   a. Aesop's Fables

   b. Arabian Nights

   c. Pilgrim's Progress

WINGS FOR WORDS
(*Part 1, page 338*)

CHECK YOUR READING

Write T (True) or F (False) in the blanks.

_____ 1. Johann and his two friends worked in the scriptorium as copyists of handwritten books.

_____ 2. For a long time the partners had been working on the problem of finding a better mold for their type.

_____ 3. Herr Riffe suddenly discovered how to make a perfect mold from two L shaped pieces of wood.

_____ 4. Johann redesigned the type faces to match the work of the monks.

_____ 5. The first book which Johann attempted to print was the Bible.

_____ 6. To work quickly the men had to memorize the appearance of the letters in reverse.

_____ 7. Johann was so excited that he printed only ten lines on his first attempt.

_____ 8. The first printing venture was to make five hundred copies of the Donatus.

_____ 9. The first finished copy was given to the mayor of Strasbourg.

_____ 10. Only the great universities protested against the printing of books.

DISCUSSING THE STORY

1. Did you ever wonder how the miracle of the printed book came into being? Somewhere, sometime, some one had a vision of "wings for words" and devised a method of printing so fundamentally perfect that after five hundred years its basic principles are still unchanged. To whom does the world owe thanks for this invention? When and where did he live? How did the dream which became his life work originate?

2. Few important discoveries or inventions are made without years of patient, persistent work. Why had Johann and his friends become discouraged? What suggestion did the bishop make?

3. During their visits to the scriptorium, what did the three partners learn? Why did Johann call the books the "labor of love"? How did the cathedral and the monk inspire the men to continue their work?

4. What particular problem were the partners working on at this time? How was it unexpectedly solved? What difficulties were smoothed out by Johann's discovery? What did he mean by saying "the work of any man, if it is good, will help the work of other men"?

5. What book did Johann select as the one on which to test his invention? Why had the men learned to recognize the type in reverse? How did Johann show the strain of the excitement? Do you understand the suspense and intense emotion of the final moments of the experiment?

6. The Bishop of Strasbourg had always encouraged Johann. What hope did he express when he learned that the invention was successful? To what did Johann liken the task of printing the Bible?

7. What reasons prompted Johann to continue with the printing of the Donatus? How was the printing actually done? In spite of difficulties encountered, what did the first hundred copies prove?

8. Why was it fitting that the bishop receive the first finished copy? To whom were other copies sent? Why was the work thought by some people to be "magic"? What is the "secret magic" of any such invention?

9. Johann Gutenberg's dream had come true. Was it worth all his years of work and sacrifice? How did his invention change men's thinking? Can you think of any invention which has had more influence on the life of the world than that of printing?

APPLIED GRAMMAR

What word in the sentence below tells *when* Herr Heilmann would arrive?

Herr Heilmann will be here soon to help you.

Words that tell *when* are adverbs as well as words that tell

117

how. Using adverbs that tell *when* may improve your writing because they explain to the reader whether the event happened *early, now, again, often, never, yesterday, last.* It is often wise to place the word telling *when* at the beginning of a sentence so that it will be given a place of importance.

Rewrite the sentences below so that the adverbs telling *when* will be given a place of importance.

1. We know now that men want our books.
2. The soft lead types wore down often.
3. The types were then taken out of the frame and sorted.
4. There was still a slight difference in the height of the type.
5. Gutenberg worked on his invention early in 1440.
6. His mind began to race suddenly.
7. Each type was now exactly the same as the others.
8. It is only afterward that we know whether or not a thing is important.
9. Johann Gutenberg labored over the types again and again.
10. We shall give copies to a few boys tomorrow.

WORDS

1. In a sentence at the top of page 340 appear the verbs *produce* and *reproduce.* From this context, what is the meaning of the Latin prefix *re?* Besides this meaning, *re* may also mean "back." Using your dictionary, apply these two meanings to the following words chosen from the selection: *reverse, retreated, released, remember, revived, revising, refining.* Use each word in a sentence.

2. The Bishop of Strasbourg praised Johann for his *courage.* What other words might he have used for "courage"? Which of the synonyms found in your dictionary applies to Johann's particular kind of *courage?*

THE LIBRARY

Using your school encyclopedia or other reference books find information about one of the following: the history of printing; the history of books; Johann Gutenberg; the development of the use of paper; the history and making of ink; papyrus; parchment; libraries; the Gutenberg Bible.

WILBUR WRIGHT AND ORVILLE WRIGHT

(Part 1, page 348)

APPRECIATION AND CHORAL READING

1. Everyone knows that the Wright brothers were the pioneers of aviation. Do you think they really said the words quoted in the first stanza? Do you think their idea grew from watching birds in flight? If so, why had not someone long before observed the flight of birds and invented a plane? What does an inventor need besides the ability to observe?

2. How did the Wright brothers begin as youthful mechanics? What difficulties did they encounter? When did they achieve success? What facts besides those given in the poem can you add to the discussion? Why is it unlikely that men will ever forget the Wrights?

3. The dialogue provides opportunity for excellent choral reading. Try to show exactly how Wilbur and Orville felt about what they were trying to do. In the last stanza, express the excitement that they felt when the plane flew.

JOHNNY APPLESEED

(Part 1, page 350)

APPRECIATION AND CHORAL READING

1. Jonathan Chapman was a real person who for many years crossed and re-crossed the thriving pioneer land of Ohio and Indiana. His self-appointed task was a strange one. What was it?

2. What do the poets tell us about Johnny Appleseed's work? About his personality? Why was he never harmed by man or beast? What simple wish governed his whole life? What is a more fitting tribute to his memory than any monument could be?

3. Before reading the poem chorally, try to remember or imagine the beauty of an apple orchard in bloom. Show your feeling as you read the words "ruddy and sound as a good apple tree." Let your voice show the passing of a long time when you read "for fifty years." Read stanza 8 to show that Johnny Appleseed's heart was light and that his step was still skipping

TOM WAS JUST A LITTLE BOY

(Part 1, page 352)

ROBERT COFFIN

Birthday: March 18, 1892
Birthplace: Brunswick, Maine
Poems to Enjoy and Reread:
1. *Collected Poems*
2. *Maine Ballads*
3. *Primer for America*
4. *Saltwater Farm*

Robert Peter Tristram Coffin was born with the taste of salt water in his mouth. His ancestors and parents knew intimately the sea that lashed the Maine coast and took the boats out to the fishing grounds.

Robert was a scholarly boy who in early school years won prizes for his essays and short stories. College years brought him many more honors. Like many young men of the past and present, his career was interrupted by a World War. When war years ceased, he returned to his writing and entered the field of teaching. He is well known because he often makes appearances before audiences to whom he reads his own poetry.

APPRECIATION AND CHORAL READING

1. Ideas grow and thrive in fertile young minds. What simple childhood pleasure set small Thomas Edison to thinking? What similarities did he see in the lightning from the sky and in the lightning bug? What ambition was born in him by that experience?

2. What facts do you know about Edison's life? What other inventions did he give to the world? How is his life an example of perseverance and initiative?

3. The poet's feeling for beauty in nature helps us to see the pictures. Notice how he makes Tom seem little by speaking of the white flowers around him looking "tall as towers." As you read the last stanza, let your voice express the wonder of what this boy accomplished.

KELLY COURAGEOUS

(Part 1, page 354)

CHECK YOUR READING

Underscore the correct expressions.

1. The scene of the action is the (*a*) Aleutians (*b*) North Atlantic (*c*) South Pacific (*d*) Mediterranean.

2. Captain Kelly was a (*a*) flight surgeon (*b*) flight engineer (*c*) graduate of West Point (*d*) graduate of Annapolis.

3. Kelly was ordered to destroy (*a*) an aircraft carrier (*b*) a battleship (*c*) a fleet of transports (*d*) a submarine.

4. Before taking off Kelly (*a*) made a careful inspection of the plane (*b*) loaded a full quota of bombs (*c*) neglected to secure sufficient gasoline (*d*) studied his maps carefully.

5. The first vessels sighted (*a*) were sunk by three bombs (*b*) were discovered to be American transports (*c*) were passed by as unimportant (*d*) were able to get away.

6. The bombardier requested the captain to fly over the (*a*) flight deck (*b*) smoke stack (*c*) port side (*d*) bow.

7. On the way back the B-17 was attacked by (*a*) an enemy bomber (*b*) enemy pursuit planes (*c*) antiaircraft fire (*d*) planes from the demolished carrier.

8. The first to lose his life was (*a*) Kelly (*b*) the bombardier (*c*) the sergeant (*d*) the co-pilot.

9. The only one who failed to obey the order to bail out was (*a*) the lieutenant (*b*) Levin (*c*) Mac (*d*) the gunner.

10. Kelly had great courage but also (*a*) a great fear of death (*b*) poor control over his men (*c*) a high sense of duty (*d*) a strong personal hatred of the enemy.

DISCUSSING THE STORY

1. Colin Kelly was one of the first of America's heroes to lose his life in World War II. What do you learn about him from the first incident that the author relates? What kind of relationship existed between Kelly and his men?

2. Arriving at Clark Field, Kelly received a new assignment. On what mission was he sent? Why was the take-off made so hurriedly? What kind of plane was Kelly using? How did the plane prove itself worthy of his confidence in it?

3. In spite of his eagerness to learn the outcome of the mission, the reader is impressed with the unusual descriptive pictures the author has painted. What was "resting on a pillow of morning mist"? What looked like "a handful of hemp seed"? What was a "dome of indigo"?

4. Captain Kelly, although recognizing and accepting his own responsibility, relied on the cooperation and alertness of each of his men. How did he encourage his bombardier? How did he surprise the crew when the two transports were sighted?

5. Excitement rose when the real target was seen a little later. How did the men show that they could work in perfect coordination? What sentence tells you that Kelly's orders were the expression of deep emotion and a keen sense of patriotism? How did he react to the news that his target was a battleship rather than a carrier? What is the comparative value of a carrier and a battleship today?

6. How did the captain and the bombardier work together to achieve success? How accurately did the bombs hit? What did the bombardier say in praise of Kelly?

7. Kelly felt the great personal satisfaction that comes from a job well done. Did the successful completion of his mission make him careless? What dangers threatened the men now? How were Kelly's fears justified?

8. The active combat called for courage and resourcefulness from every one of the crew. How did they respond to the attack? In what way was this attack more savage than any Kelly had experienced? What casualties occurred? Why did Kelly order the men to bail out? Why did he not bail out himself? How can we best honor men like Kelly who live and die so heroically?

APPLIED GRAMMAR

Which word in the following sentence tells *where?*

They realized an enemy plane was flying near.

Words that tell *where* are adverbs, as well as words that tell *how* and *when*. Change the sentences below so that each adverb telling *where* will give an opposite meaning.

1. The plane kept flying high.
2. A tractor rolled out, hauling a train of trucks loaded with bombs.
3. The quarry might have sailed north.
4. The lieutenant shouted, "Fleet of vessels sighted ahead."
5. Kelly reached back for the stick.
6. The nose of the plane shot upward.
7. The planes were seen three and a half miles below.
8. The plane dived back into a cloud.
9. He saw one of the planes roll and then fly down.
10. The plane responded and leaped skyward.

WORDS

Shorten each sentence by substituting one of the following words for each phrase in parentheses: *disintegrate; pulverized; simultaneously; irritable.*

1. The third burst began and ended almost (at the same time) _____.
2. This showing-off made him (angry) _____.
3. A flight of bullets (reduced to a fine powder) _____ _____ half a dozen of his instruments.
4. The warship seemed to (fall to pieces) _____ in a blast of fire.

THE LIBRARY

If you want to know about world records in aviation or if you want to find facts about any subject of national interest use the *World Almanac*. The index is in the front of the *World Almanac*. Look up the word "Aviation" in the index and find answers to the questions below.

1. On what pages is information given about Atlantic crossings? _____
2. What is the air line distance between Buffalo, New York and San Francisco? _____
3. What is the air line distance between London and Moscow? _____
4. What is the highest altitude a plane has reached in world air records? _____

CHILD PIONEER

(Part 1, page 370)

HONORÉ WILLSIE MORROW

Year of Birth: 1880
Birthplace: Ottumwa, Iowa
Stories to Enjoy and Reread:
1. *On to Oregon! The Story of a Pioneer Boy*
2. *We Must March*
3. *Forever Free*
4. *With Malice Toward None*
5. *The Last Full Measure*

From early childhood Honoré Willsie Morrow wanted to write. Upon graduating from the University of Wisconsin she went to visit friends at a mining camp in Arizona and there found material for excellent western stories. Her historical novels show earnest, painstaking work. Ten years of research were spent in the writing of the three books on the life of Abraham Lincoln, her most popular work.

CHECK YOUR READING

Write **T** (True) or **F** (False) in the blanks.

_____ 1. John Sager, with his five young sisters and a brother, walked a hundred miles over the Oregon Trail.

_____ 2. His father and mother were killed by Indians.

_____ 3. At Fort Hall the Sager orphans were allowed to join a caravan going to California.

_____ 4. After several weeks on the road they arrived at Fort Boise ill-clothed and half-starved.

_____ 5. John's only hope for the little sister was to reach Dr. Whitman.

_____ 6. The oldest sister suffered a broken arm.

_____ 7. John was forced to kill the oxen.

_____ 8. One of the sisters drowned on the way.

_____ 9. The baby was saved by Narcissa Whitman.

_____ 10. The Whitmans adopted the Sager orphans.

DISCUSSING THE STORY

1. "Child Pioneer" is the story of a thirteen-year-old hero. For what extraordinary achievement do Americans remember John Sager? When and where did his struggle take place?

2. How did Kit Carson become acquainted with John? What does Carson's description tell you of the responsibility John had already accepted? How were his responsibilities enormously increased? Why did he not accept the circumstances and accompany the caravan into California? How did he prevent the others from learning his plans?

3. Nearly two months were consumed in the painful journey from Fort Hall to Fort Boise. What hardships had the children endured? In what condition were they when they arrived at Fort Boise? How was John showing the strain? Was it necessary for him to demand implicit obedience from the other children?

4. The crossing of the Blue Mountains was the worst of their experiences. What accident befell the oldest sister? What frightful physical hardships did the children suffer? Is it difficult to believe that seven children could survive such an ordeal?

5. Where did John at last find help? When did he finally yield the little sister to the care of some one else? What dream had come true for John?

WORDS

1. Certain foreign words and phrases have been so widely used that they have become a part of our own language. Find the meaning in your dictionary of the French expression, *en route*.

2. "The factor . . . was trying to prevent American emigrants from entering the Columbia Valley." Explain how *emigrants* differs from the related word, *immigrants*.

THE LIBRARY

Using an atlas, locate the following places which were part of John Sager's pioneer world: the Columbia River; the Blue Mountains; the Snake River; (Fort) Boise, Idaho.

SONG OF THE NIGHTINGALE

(Part 1, page 377)

MAURICE HINDUS

Birthday: February 27, 1891
Birthplace: Bolshaye Bikovo, Russia
Stories to Enjoy and Reread:
1. *Green Worlds*
2. *Moscow Skies*
3. *We Shall Live Again*
4. *Sons and Fathers*
5. *To Sing with the Angels*
6. *Mother Russia*

Maurice Hindus has written many books about his native Russia and his early experiences in America. In *Green Worlds* he tells the fascinating story of his adventures as a newcomer to the United States. Working and studying in this country, he graduated from Colgate University and became a free-lance writer for various magazines. In recent years he has been a lecturer and war correspondent. His many visits to Russia give him authentic information and a wealth of material for his books. "Song of the Nightingale" appears in one of his most recent books, *Mother Russia*.

CHECK YOUR READING

Complete the summary of the story by filling in the blanks.

The story concerns a _____ year-old boy who lived in a _____ village. A company of _____ troops came upon the boy as he sat _____ and _____. He agreed to lead them to a certain _____.
When the officer inquired if there were any _____ in the woods he pretended that the officer meant _____. As they marched along, the boy called _____ times like a _____. All of the _____ were _____ by _____.

126

DISCUSSING THE STORY

1. Although the date of the year is not given, how do we know that this selection is a story of World War II? Who is the hero of it?

2. What sound attracted the attention of the German troops? Do you think the boy whistled deliberately? Was he really frightened or merely a good actor? Why did he wish to show his skill in imitating the cuckoo also?

3. The boy gave further evidence of being quick-witted. How did he deceive the officer? How did he bring about the destruction of the whole company?

4. Do you think that, young as the boy was, he was rendering an important service to his country? Are heroes necessarily adult fighting men? What stories of the courage and daring of youth have you heard or read?

WORDS

1. It is often interesting to trace the history of a word, that is, to learn from what original source it came into the English language. For example, in your dictionary you will find that *devastate* came from the Latin prefix *de* plus the Latin verb *vastare* meaning *to lay waste*. What is the correct pronunciation and meaning of *devastated* as used on page 377?

_____

_____

2. By further use of the dictionary, discover the history and pronunciation of *binoculars*. _____

_____

_____

3. The author refers to the *ingenuity* and *joviality* of the boy. What synonyms can you supply for these characteristics?
ingenuity: _____
joviality: _____

4. How do you pronounce *mien?* _____
What is "an innocent mien"? _____

_____

5. Look up the pronunciation of the word *partisan*:

_____

CLARA BARTON OF THE RED CROSS

(Part 1, page 381)

CHECK YOUR READING

Underscore the correct expression.

1. On the way to Falmouth, Clara (*a*) had to drive the ambulance herself (*b*) won the friendship of her drivers (*c*) made an enemy of George (*d*) became ill.

2. Clara's real work began with General Burnside's attack on (*a*) Falmouth (*b*) the Lacy House (*c*) Washington (*d*) Fredericksburg.

3. Clara helped a young Confederate soldier by (*a*) lending him money to return to his home (*b*) having him exchanged for a Union prisoner (*c*) promising to communicate with his family (*d*) singing an old Southern melody.

4. In the twelve-room Lacy House Clara cared for (*a*) 100 (*b*) 440 (*c*) 872 (*d*) 1200 people.

5. Riley Faulkner was saved by (*a*) Mrs. Fales (*b*) Clara's milk punch (*c*) a transfusion (*d*) an amputation.

6. On the day Fredericksburg fell, Clara was warned not to go into the city by (*a*) the Union authorities (*b*) a Confederate officer (*c*) a mysterious letter (*d*) a premonition.

7. The night that Clara returned to Washington she was (*a*) particularly unhappy (*b*) exceedingly gay (*c*) planning to return to her old job (*d*) injured in a railroad accident.

8. In her room she found a large box of (*a*) clothing (*b*) bandages (*c*) food (*d*) unopened mail.

9. At the Lincoln Hospital she rejoiced to see (*a*) Donald (*b*) George (*c*) Faulkner (*d*) President Lincoln.

10. Clara's success was due to her (*a*) large personal fortune (*b*) beauty of face and figure (*c*) unfailing hard work (*d*) friends in the South.

DISCUSSING THE STORY

1. Long before the Red Cross organization came into being, Clara Barton was doing the work which that organization now sponsors. What work was taking her to Falmouth as we first meet her? What caused the little "tiff" between Clara and her

drivers? How did she win the respect of the men without yielding her authority? What does the incident tell you about the character and spirit of Miss Barton?

2. How close was the Lacy House to the battle area? Where were the opposing forces stationed? How did General Burnside plan the attack on Fredericksburg? What incident illustrated Clara's determination and fearlessness?

3. The winter at Falmouth was a period of incessant work and responsibility for Clara. Name some of the many duties which she had to assume. What incident proved that her work was appreciated by the men?

4. What was the chief worry of the young Confederate lad, Donald? How did Clara reassure him? What phase of modern Red Cross service perhaps originated with that promise?

5. In spite of the enormous load of work there were little incidents which cheered Clara. How did George provide more bunks? How did Mrs. Fales help? How was Clara encouraged by the amazing recovery of Riley Faulkner? How did the Confederate lieutenant try to thank Miss Barton for her kindness to him?

6. Clara returned to her home in Washington tired and worn and in low spirits. What gave her just the kind of personal and practical lift which she needed? What final incident showed the worth of her work?

7. Clara Barton lived in the difficult days of the Civil War and at a time when women had not yet gone into public life. What criticism did she have to face? Why was her work more difficult if not more dangerous than the work of the Red Cross nurse of today? What abilities and qualities of character did Miss Barton display? In what sense was she a pioneer?

APPLIED GRAMMAR

Can you supply a word in the following sentence so that the meaning will be clear?

Clara Barton rode _____ an ambulance.

The word you supplied joins the word "ambulance" with the verb "rode." Words which join nouns with a subject or predicate are called "prepositions." In the sentence below under-line each preposition and supply a noun which the preposition may join to the sentence.

1. She trailed troops through Maryland and later went to

_____.

2. Clara spread a cloth on the _____.

3. The drivers sauntered into the _____ _____
   away from _____.

4. Next morning, Clara was awakened by muffled _____.

5. George was walking from the _____,
   a bucket in his _____.

6. Union soldiers were to storm Fredericksburg, but there was no bridge over the _____.

A preposition and the words which it joins to the rest of a sentence make what is called a "prepositional phrase." Un-derline the prepositional phrases in the following sentences.

7. Clara kept fires on every hearth of the big house.

8. On one day, Clara had twelve hundred people under one roof.

9. The boy had milk punch tucked into his blouse under the blankets.

WORDS

1. Clara was to learn that "the men could be both *sullen* and *fractious*." Were they kind, friendly, sulky, jovial, unsociable, helpful, cheerful, cross, polite, lazy or irritable? Underline your choice.

2. What is a *spit* upon which cooking can be done? Explain its construction. Perhaps your dictionary will give an illustra-tion of it.

3. The Northern forces crossed the Rappahannock by means of a pontoon bridge. What is a *pontoon?* Illustrate by a drawing on the blackboard how a pontoon bridge is con-structed.

4. The word *superfluous* originally meant "overflowing." How is it interpreted today as in the sentence on page 388, "Why not dismember the superfluous things"? What is the correct pronunciation of *superfluous?*

A MESSAGE TO GARCIA

(Part 1, page 392)

THE HISTORICAL BACKGROUND

In 1895 the island of Cuba revolted from Spain. She was faring badly in her struggle for independence when in 1898 the United States came to her rescue. It was news of the United States' declaration of war on Spain and an appeal for cooperation in routing the enemy which President McKinley sent by the American army officer, Rowan, to Garcia, the Cuban leader.

CHECK YOUR READING

Write T (True) or F (False) in the blanks.

_____ 1. The man who carried the message was "a fellow by the name of Hubbard."

_____ 2. The message was from President Washington to General Garcia.

_____ 3. The messenger wisely asked for all necessary information before starting out.

_____ 4. Another messenger was sent to Corregio.

_____ 5. The average man cannot be trusted to do a task promptly and correctly.

_____ 6. In all business organizations, the employer has difficulty in finding competent and trustworthy help.

_____ 7. When first asked to carry the message Rowan answered, "Take it yourself."

_____ 8. The author thinks that the man who works when the "boss" is away is a coward.

_____ 9. Any man who can carry a message to Garcia will never be "laid off."

_____10. Not all poor men are virtuous.

DISCUSSING THE STORY

1. Why was the writer not interested in telling the story of Rowan's difficult journey to Garcia? Why was the journey to Garcia necessary, and why was it difficult? How did the journey require courage? resourcefulness?

2. How did Rowan show that he knew it was his job to find Garcia without asking silly questions? When an order is given,

131

or a request made, is all questioning silly and useless? Can you think of any circumstances where questioning would be intelligent and wise?

3. What do young men need to be like Rowan? What is it that the average man lacks? What is likely to happen when the average man is asked to "carry a message to Garcia"?

4. Why is the sincere worker in any job highly desirable? Would such a one have all the assurance there ever could be of finding and holding a place in the world's work?

5. How can you, every day, carry small messages to Garcia?

WORDS

Underline the correct meaning of each of the following words.

1. cooperating: (speaking out of turn) (acting together in harmony) (being in several businesses)
2. mountain fastnesses: (lonely spots) (places difficult of approach) (desert areas)
3. traverse: (to cross in traveling) (to be afraid of) (to ridicule)
4. inability: (a headache) (a state of insufficient power) (unhappy event)
5. assistant: (a union worker) (a friend) (a helper)
6. memorandum: (a statue) (a brief note) (a song to the memory of one mourned)
7. entrust: (to commit something to another's care) (to borrow from a bank) (to intrude upon another's privacy)
8. maudlin: (a kind of malt) (gushing and sentimental) (not important)
9. intelligent: (highly understanding) (widely read) (well educated)
10. brilliant: (sprightly) (sparkling) (distinguished)

THE LIBRARY

What library assignment was given in "The Message to Garcia"? Would you have needed to ask any questions of your employer about which encyclopedia, had you been the clerk? Without asking help from *anyone*, make the memo requested in the story, and hand it in to your teacher.

UNIT ACTIVITIES

SUGGESTIONS FOR FURTHER READING—UNIT IV

RICHARD EVELYN BYRD, *Skyward*
MITCHELL V. CHARNLEY, *Boys' Life of the Wright Brothers*
IRMEGARDE EBERLE, *Radium Treasure and the Curies*
CHELSEA FRASER, *Famous American Flyers*
FITZHUGH GREENE, *Dick Byrd—Air Explorer*
WILLIAM HENRY MEADOWCROFT, *Boy's Life of Edison*
CORNELIA MEIGS, *Young Americans*
MILDRED MASTIN PACE, *Clara Barton*
FRANKLIN M. AND CLAIRE RECK, *Power from Start to Finish*
CARL SANDBURG, *Abe Lincoln Grows Up*
IRENE COOPER WILLIS, *Florence Nightingale*
W. E. WISE, *Thomas Alva Edison, The Youth and His Times*

A BOOK REPORT

In the spaces below write briefly about one of the books in the list above, or about some biography of your own choice.

Title of Book: _____

Author: _____

CAN YOU REMEMBER FACTS ABOUT YOUR READING?

Write T (True) or F (False) in the blanks.

_____ 1. Abraham Lincoln disliked his stepmother.

_____ 2. Abe wanted to study law, but he didn't like to read.

_____ 3. The first book printed by Johann Gutenberg was a Latin grammar.

_____ 4. Johann gave up printing to become a monk.

_____ 5. Johnny Appleseed's real name was Jonathan Chapman.

_____ 6. The first plane built by the Wright brothers was a glider.

_____ 7. Thomas Edison invented the electric light by accident.

_____ 8. Captain Kelly was ordered to destroy an enemy aircraft carrier.

_____ 9. Kelly died of wounds in a California hospital.

_____ 10. Clara Barton nursed both Union and Confederate soldiers.

_____ 11. Miss Barton was wounded in the battle of Fredericksburg.

_____ 12. "The Song of the Nightingale" relates the story of a child pioneer.

_____ 13. John Sager's greatest desire was to reach California.

_____ 14. General Garcia was an American general stationed at Cuba.

_____ 15. Elbert Hubbard carried a message to Garcia.

CAN YOU IDENTIFY THE CHARACTERS?

With what characters do you associate the sketches on the opposite page?

1. _____

2. _____

3. _____

4. _____

5. _____

6. _____

7. _____

8. _____

OH FAIR ENOUGH ARE SKY AND PLAIN

(Part 1, page 399)

A. E. HOUSMAN

Birthday: March 26, 1859
(Died May 1, 1936)
Birthplace: Shropshire, England
Poems to Enjoy and Reread:
1. *"Loveliest of Trees"*
2. *"I Lay Me Down and Slumber"*
3. *"When I Was One-and-Twenty"*
4. *"When I Was in Love"*
5. *"When Green Buds Hang"*

Alfred Edward Housman, English poet and critic, preferred to be known for the quality of his writing rather than by the quantity of it. He wrote almost continually from the time he was twenty until his death, yet published only two slim volumes: *A Shropshire Lad* and *Last Poems*. He despised careless and slipshod work in himself and every one else.

Mr. Housman's life was curiously lonely. He never married and he made few friendships. Many of his poems reflect the melancholy tone of his life and express the sadness he felt in the passing of beauty, in the shortness of life, and in the cruelty of time.

APPRECIATING THE POEM

1. Poets are not the only persons who enjoy the beauty of flowers, the song of birds, or the delight of a fine day. All of us find rich rewards in many aspects of nature, but it takes the skill and imagination of a poet to describe these experiences in words. What natural beauty is Mr. Housman admiring? To what does "those" in the third line refer?

2. How do the pools and rivers wash the trees and clouds and air? Do you agree that the clouds are as beautiful in the reflection as in the sky?

3. What thoughts come to the poet as he stands on the edge of the water? Have you ever had those same thoughts?

MOCKERY

(Part 1, page 399)

APPRECIATING THE POEM

1. When you were a small child did you ever see the moon glow in such amazing beauty that you wanted to reach out and touch it? Perhaps you have had an experience something like that about which Katherine Riggs tells us. What kind of night was it? Which lines tell you of the lateness of the hour, of the fragrance of the night, and of the radiance of the moon?

2. Why did the poet not find the moon when she reached the hilltop? Was she naturally disappointed? How did the moon "mock" the poet? Can *you* write a little poem about the moon?

WINTER STREAMS

(Part 1, page 400)

BLISS CARMAN (1861–1929)

Bliss Carman, poet of the open road, was born and educated in New Brunswick, Canada. A shy, yet friendly man, he enjoyed a vagabond life which took him from place to place. For several years he lived and worked in the United States. His fame and success mounted until he was recognized as one of Canada's popular lecturers and poets. Many of his poems express his love for roaming, his devotion to outdoor life, and his belief that life is exciting and good.

APPRECIATION AND CHORAL READING

1. Like the flowers that sleep through the long winter, perhaps the streams sleep and dream beneath their icy blankets. What does the poet tell us about the thoughts of the snow-bound brooks? Have you ever heard their "muffled" sound?

2. When will the snowy bands burst? Is the thought of an eager little stream, waiting for the spring sunshine like a sick child kept in the house, a pleasant one?

3. Read the poem to yourself, several times if necessary, to absorb the mood before you try to read it aloud. Show by your voices the contrast between the streams in winter and the streams as spring approaches.

137

THEME IN YELLOW

(Part 1, page 401)

CARL SANDBURG

Birthday: January 6, 1878
Birthplace: Galesburg, Illinois
Stories and Poems to Enjoy:
1. *Early Moon*
2. *Abe Lincoln Grows Up*
3. *Rootabaga Stories*
4. *The American Songbag*
5. *"Fog"*

In a deep, sonorous voice, to the accompaniment of his guitar, Carl Sandburg sings folksongs and ballads gathered from mountaineers, cowboys, steel workers, hoboes, all kinds of people whom he has met in his wanderings. His audiences of young and old are captivated by this man whose gray hair falling over his forehead frames a sensitive face.

Carl's father and mother were Swedish immigrants who, though meagerly educated, were capable craftsmen. Carl's father, August Johnson, worked in a railroad shop. The fact that there were several workers of the same name sometimes brought about confusion when pay envelopes were given out. So Mr. August Johnson changed his name to Mr. August Sandburg.

Carl Sandburg's youth was filled with all kinds of jobs—as dish-washer, porter, farm-hand, milk wagon driver. His poems reflect his many experiences.

APPRECIATING THE POEM

1. Spring and summer are not the only seasons in which we find rewards in nature. What sight in autumn gladdens the poet? Even if line 5 were omitted would you know the subject of his poem?

2. What holiday in autumn always provides fun for children? How do pumpkins contribute to the fun? Do you like a poem written from the viewpoint of the pumpkin?

THE PASTURE

(Part 1, page 402)

ROBERT LEE FROST

Birthday: March 26, 1875
Birthplace: San Francisco, California
Poems to Enjoy and Reread:

1. *"The Tuft of Flowers"*
2. *"A Time to Talk"*
3. *"Stopping By Woods on a Snowy Evening"*
4. *"Spring Pools"*
5. *"The Road Not Taken"*

Robert Frost is a poet of the New England countryside and people. His poems picture scenes he knows well and express his thoughts and feelings about these surroundings.

Though Robert did not care for the routine of school days, he was an outstanding scholar and a poet at fourteen. College subjects did not appeal to him greatly. After a few months he left Dartmouth to take a job in a textile mill. Later on, after his marriage, he went back to college again, but soon turned to newspaper work, teaching, and farming. His poetry is now widely acclaimed.

The Frosts lead a simple, enjoyable life in a stone farmhouse in Shaftesbury, Vermont. Mr. Frost likes neighbors and long walks through the countryside.

APPRECIATING THE POEM

1. Even the simple little chores of farm life give great rewards in pleasure. What pleasure did Robert Frost find in clearing the leaves away from the spring? Which words show that he wanted to share his delight with some one else? Do you think that he meant *you*, the reader?

2. What picture does Frost draw for you in the second stanza? How do you know that the sight of the calf and its mother gives him pleasure? Write a four-line verse about something you have observed and remembered.

139

ROBERT OF LINCOLN

(Part 1, page 404)

WILLIAM CULLEN BRYANT

Birthday: November 3, 1794
    (Died June 12, 1878)
Birthplace: Cummington, Massachusetts
Poems to Enjoy and Reread:
1. *"To a Waterfowl"*
2. *"To the Fringed Gentian"*
3. *"O Fairest of the Rural Maids"*
4. *"A Forest Hymn"*
5. *"The Yellow Violet"*

Born in the Berkshire Hills of New England, William Cullen Bryant grew up in a stern religious atmosphere. His Puritan parents were poor but they were keenly interested in affairs of their world. Bryant was ready for college at the age of fifteen, and there he studied law. From law he worked gradually into journalism, which was much more to his liking. For forty-nine years he was editor of the New York *Evening Post*. On the side he wrote the poems for which he is remembered today. Curiously, although his life was spent in the city, his poems deal largely with nature. Death and patriotism were also favorite subjects with him.

APPRECIATION AND CHORAL READING

1. William Cullen Bryant had a special fondness for birds. What does he tell us in the first stanza about the habits of the bobolink? How does the bird get its name?

2. Describe the appearance of the bobolink. How does the mother bird differ from the male in coloring? Why does the poet call her a Quaker? How do the two birds differ in the quality of their song?

3. Both birds share in the care of young ones in the nest. What changes take place in the older birds? How does the bird family resemble the human family?

4. Bryant's love of nature makes his poems tender—notice how he says, "snug and safe in this nest of ours." If you know

140

and love birds, you can think and feel the way the poet does. Then you will read beautifully.

A BOY'S SUMMER SONG

(Part 1, page 402)

APPRECIATION AND CHORAL READING

1. Perhaps you live on a farm or at least have visited in the country. Which of the pleasures that the poet mentions have you experienced? Might the poem apply just as well to girls?

2. What two things seem the "best of joy" to the poet? What delights of summer in the country can you add to the poem?

3. The rollicking rhythm of the poem is almost like music. Enjoy the pictures the poet paints with his well-chosen words and try to recreate his gay, happy spirit.

APRIL

(Part 1, page 403)

APPRECIATING THE POEM

1. What sights and sounds of spring might the poet be describing in the first stanza? Do you think most people wait eagerly each year for the coming of spring?

2. Sometimes it is fun to think of the seasons as persons who come and go. How does the poet personify April?

THE SNOW

(Part 1, page 406)

APPRECIATION AND CHORAL READING

1. What is "it" that sifts from leaden sieves? What are the "leaden sieves"? At what kind of scene is the poet looking? Can you remember seeing a very quiet snowstorm that covered everything the way this one did?

2. Some poets have a special talent for delicate, imaginative description. Emily Dickinson is such a poet. How does she describe the road, the fence, and the field? Which picture do you like best?

3. Read the poem very carefully to absorb the poet's mood

141

before attempting choral reading. When you can feel your-self a part of the scene and have grasped the almost unearthly beauty of it,—then and not till then, read it aloud and let your voice express what you feel.

Two interpretations for reading are given. The one in-dicated in the left margin is the easier one. In the interpreta-tion shown in the right margin, the readers of the separate lines can produce a beautiful effect if they will work together, following one another closely and in perfect time and not allowing any one voice to dominate the others. In this way they can preserve the unity of the poem.

SOMETHING TOLD THE WILD GEESE
(Part 1, page 407)
APPRECIATION AND CHORAL READING

1. What do we call the "something" that told the wild geese that winter was coming? What was the appearance of the countryside?

2. Why were the wild geese not deceived? Where do they go for the winter? Do you remember what you learned about the flight of geese in "A Duck's Best Friend"? Did the poet find any reward in watching the geese?

3. This poem could be read antiphonally with good effect. Two-part or responsive reading is usually called *antiphonal* reading. In the poem is a series of groups of two lines each that seem to belong together. The first two lines (B) introduce the theme. Then the next two lines (G) partly explain it. The next two (B) speak of the last part of summer which can still be seen. Then the contrast in the next two lines, read by the girls, seems like a response as it tells that the wild geese know winter is coming. Again (B) the late summer orchards are pictured, followed by (G) the memory of winter by the wild geese. Thus all through the poem we have a series of inter-esting pictures with responses which use two lines each. Be-cause of the pleasing balance you will enjoy the contrasts of these lines if they are read well; but good reading takes careful practice.

142

ANOTHER APRIL

(Part 1, page 408)

CHECK YOUR READING

Complete the sentences below by filling in the blanks.

1. The boy in the story thought Grandpa looked like a picture of _____.

2. Grandpa had been a _____ _____ in his youth.

3. Grandpa stopped to pick up and play with a _____ _____.

4. Grandpa was _____ _____ years old.

5. He stooped to pat the heads of seven _____.

6. He pulled sprays of _____ and _____ blossoms and tore them apart.

7. He couldn't tear apart the _____.

8. Down by the smokehouse Grandpa found his old friend, the _____.

9. The date on the shell was _____.

10. Grandpa _____ to his friend and stroked his _____.

DISCUSSING THE STORY

1. Grandpa was held in great affection by his family. How did Mom show her concern for him? Even before you learn his age, how do you know that Grandpa was a very old man?

2. From Mom's conversation with the boy the reader learns something of Grandpa in his younger days. What kind of work had he done? How do you know that he was proud of his physical strength? What interested Grandpa first as he started his walk?

3. Grandpa had lived and worked in the outdoors. How do you know that he loved nature? What did he especially enjoy on this April day? Why did Mom insist that the boy stay inside? What did the boy begin to understand about Grandpa?

4. Who was the "old friend" that Grandpa had set out to see? What kind of understanding seemed to exist between Grandpa and the terrapin? Describe how a terrapin looks.

What did Grandpa and the terrapin have in common? Why did Mom cry softly for a moment? Do you think that Grandpa had been finding great rewards in nature all his life?

APPLIED GRAMMAR

Rewrite the sentences below, adding an adjective and an adverb to each:
1. Grandpa laughed.
2. The sun was shining.
3. The blossoms swayed from a bough overhead.
4. The terrapin twisted his neck.

Add a prepositional phrase to each of the following sentences:
5. He wore a heavy overcoat.
6. I watched Grandpa stop.
7. Then he pulled pine needles.
8. He put the terrapin back.

WORDS

1. The characters in Mr. Stuart's stories speak the way the hill people do in his native Kentucky. Make a list of six words and pronunciations that mark the speakers as hill people.

2. Much of your ability to appreciate description depends upon your knowledge of the terms used. For instance, do you recognize a *dogwood* tree when you see it? What kind of leaves and flowers has the *redbud* tree? What is a *cocoon?* What do you know about the size or habits of a *terrapin?* Report to the class on one of these questions.

THE LIBRARY

The authors of the selections in your PROSE AND POETRY are interesting people. The *Junior Book of Authors* will enable you to peek into their private lives and gain a glimpse of their personalities. Brief biographies of well-known illustrators of juvenile books are also given in this book.

Using the *Junior Book of Authors*, what can you discover about the life of one of the following persons: Samuel Scoville, Jr.; Robert Louis Stevenson; Elizabeth Foreman Lewis; Constance D. Mackay.

ALAS! POOR ANNABELLE

(Part 1, page 417)

CHECK YOUR READING

Write T (True) or F (False) in the blanks.

_____ 1. Annabelle Grey, like her western cousins, was a tom-boy.

_____ 2. Caddie was intensely interested in Annabelle's chatter.

_____ 3. One of Annabelle's new dresses was trimmed with eighty-eight buttons.

_____ 4. Caddie and the boys allowed Annabelle to ride Pete, the gentlest horse in the stable.

_____ 5. Annabelle showed that she was a skillful rider.

_____ 6. The sheep ate the buttons off her dress.

_____ 7. Caddie slipped a rock down the back of Annabelle's blouse as she turned a somersault.

_____ 8. The boys were punished but Caddie was not.

_____ 9. Caddie planned to run away to Boston to live with Annabelle.

_____10. Father convinced Caddie that growing up to be a lady could be thrilling.

DISCUSSING THE STORY

1. Clara and Caddie Woodlawn were sisters, but they were not at all alike in personality. Describe each of the girls. Which one was like her mother?

2. Annabelle was definitely a city girl. What impressions did she make on her cousins? What were her chief interests? What was her opinion of Dunnville? Did she expect to enjoy her visit in the country? What incident showed that Caddie, although younger than Annabelle, was a more understanding person?

3. Caddie, Tom, and Warren planned to introduce Annabelle to farm life. How did the riding lesson turn out? What happened when Annabelle tried to salt the sheep? How did Annabelle take the practical jokes played on her?

4. Why did Caddie consent to play the third trick on Annabelle? Do you think they took unfair advantage of Annabelle?

How did Annabelle react this time? Who told Mrs. Wood-lawn? What punishment did she give Caddie?

5. Caddie seldom resented punishment but on this occasion her anger flared high. Why did she think her mother had been unjust? What plans did she make?

6. Before Caddie could put her plans into action, her father came to see her. Do his words show tenderness, kindness, wisdom, and understanding? How did Caddie learn the difference between a superficial "lady" and a real woman? Why was she no longer afraid of growing up?

7. Sometimes it is fun to imagine how we would behave in certain situations. If you were a city girl or boy going to visit in the country, what attitude would you take toward your hosts? Should you try to impress them with the superiority of your home in the city? How could you best learn something about a kind of life very different from your own?

8. If you were host or hostess to a city guest, how could you show your friend that you were proud of your home? Why are practical jokes almost always unkind?

9. Have you ever felt that your family didn't understand you? Have you ever planned to run away from home? Is there usually, as in Caddie's case, a real reason for some punishment which seems unjust to you? If you have no understanding parent or friend to talk things over with, what is the next best thing to do? Is it helpful to postpone hasty action until you have time to think things out for yourself? Is it good to try to see someone else's point of view?

10. What problems are you facing as you grow up? Are you afraid of growing up or are you looking forward to the responsibilities of your place in the family and the community?

APPLIED GRAMMAR

Throughout this story, Annabelle has many chances to express strong or sudden feeling at the newness of farm life and at the pranks of her cousins.

Underline the words or groups of words which show such feeling. Change commas or periods to exclamation points as necessary.

1. "Oh, lots of things," said Tom and there was a twinkle in his eye.
2. "Dear me," said Annabelle, "are these all your children?"
3. "Golly, what fun," chirped Warren.
4. "Oh, my buttons," cried Annabelle. "They're gone."
5. "What an experience," she said.
6. "Dear me," said Annabelle. "How quaint and rustic."
7. "Oh, it's squishy," she sobbed.

WORDS

1. One of Annabelle's favorite expressions was *"quaint* and *rustic."* Explain what she meant by these terms.

2. Have you ever heard a "perfect *pandemonium"?* Look up the pronunciation and origin of the word.

3. Annabelle talked a great deal about the *superiority* of her native city over other cities. Was she speaking of its *architecture, wealth, excellence,* or *geographical position?*

4. Caddie experienced a feeling of *remorse* after playing the tricks on Annabelle. Did she feel *delight, satisfaction, disgust* or *regret?*

5. Is an *affected* person one who *is ill with a serious disease, puts on airs, is greatly loved* or *is a poor student?*

THE LIBRARY

There are two reference books in your library that tell about the lives of present-day authors. One is called *Living Authors.* It contains brief biographies of authors who were living when the book was published in 1931. The other book, *Authors Today and Yesterday,* tells about authors who are now living and authors who have lived recently. Another excellent reference book is *Twentieth Century Authors.* What other biographical reference books does your library own?

The persons named below are the authors of selections in your PROSE AND POETRY. What can you find about the life of one of them?

Rachel Field	Hilaire Belloc
Stephen Vincent Benét	Arthur Guiterman
Willa Cather	Jesse Stuart

147

TWO RIVERS
(Part 1, page 432)

WALLACE STEGNER

Birthday: February 18, 1909
Birthplace: Lake Mills, Iowa

Wallace Stegner was born in Iowa, but his family moved about so much that he calls himself the "original homeless and footloose American." He has lived in North Dakota, Washington, Saskatchewan, Montana, Utah, Nevada, and California. His hobbies are playing tennis and picking wild berries. His writings are filled with stories of his own childhood and are welcomed everywhere by readers of the *Atlantic, Collier's* and *Story*. In recent years he has been a teacher at Harvard University. He lives with his wife and son at Greensboro Bend, Vermont.

CHECK YOUR READING

Underline the correct expressions.

1. The boy woke up (*a*) planning to go fishing (*b*) in a bad mood (*c*) eager to see the parade (*d*) after a frightful nightmare.

2. While he had been asleep his parents had (*a*) gone to Chinook (*b*) had an accident (*c*) prepared for a picnic (*d*) gone to a neighbor's farm.

3. As they set out (*a*) the Ford broke down (*b*) a storm came up (*c*) the father drove rapidly (*d*) the lunch fell out.

4. On the way they saw (*a*) a milk snake (*b*) a rattler (*c*) a bear (*d*) a rabbit.

5. The boy tried to remember (*a*) when he had last gone hunting (*b*) where he had left his cap (*c*) what the sea looked like (*d*) an early childhood experience in the mountains.

6. The boy's father (*a*) was ill (*b*) was in gay spirits (*c*) had forgotten a spare tire (*d*) was unusually quiet.

148

7. The boy's memory was stirred by (*a*) the blackberries in the lunch box (*b*) the shells they found (*c*) cold water on his skin (*d*) the smell of pine cones.

8. They all remembered that the river (*a*) had two channels of hot and cold water (*b*) had dried up that year (*c*) had contained many fish (*d*) had been dotted with sailboats.

9. The father was skillful at (*a*) catching trout (*b*) repairing cars (*c*) making up rhymes (*d*) finding trails.

10. They had all had a (*a*) disappointing (*b*) tiresome (*c*) strange (*d*) happy day.

DISCUSSING THE STORY

1. As you read the story you probably noticed that there was little action other than the ride the family took. Most of the story is concerned with the thoughts and feelings of the boy as they varied throughout the day. In what kind of mood did he awaken? What was the cause of it? What experience of your own helps you to understand the boy's disappointment?

2. What caused a quick change in the boy's mood? Why do you think the parents had arranged the trip? Why were they all in a mood to enjoy every small detail? What slight incidents gave them pleasure as the ride began?

3. Have you ever had the experience of dimly remembering an incident of your early childhood? What did the boy remember? What happened to interrupt the chain of memory? Why do you like the way the author describes the boy's efforts to remember the past?

4. If you live near the mountains or have made trips there you can appreciate how the three people enjoyed the fresh cool air and the majestic beauty of the trees. What did they look down upon from their high ledge? What set the boy to thinking again of that earlier picnic?

5. As his mother said, "Everything means something different to everybody." What did his parents remember about that long-ago picnic? Why would a little child remember only such physical sensations as sticky blackberries and hot and cold water? Did the parents recall things that a man or a woman would be most likely to remember?

149

6. The picnic had been a wonderful adventure. How had the parents contributed to the fun of the outing? Is it good for families to enjoy such outings together? What do you think each one will remember about that day? What personal experience similar to the story can you relate?

APPLIED GRAMMAR

It is important to remember that the conjunctions *and, but, or,* and *nor* must always join equal parts of a sentence such as subjects, predicates, objects, phrases, clauses, adverbs, or adjectives. In the sentences below underline the equal parts so connected. Underline the conjunctions twice.

1. He lay on his back and watched a spider.
2. He ran out of his room and down the stairs.
3. His mother and father tried to cheer him.
4. The bacon was snapping and curling in the pan.
5. He had wanted to go to Chinook, but the car wouldn't run.
6. They passed a team pulling an old and empty wagon.
7. They found a stream winding here and there.
8. He saw wheat fields and the red peaks of barns.
9. Did you hear about him and her?
10. Neither his mother nor his father seemed to remember the day.

Add phrases, clauses, subjects, objects, etc., so that the conjunction will join equal parts.

11. His father *stopped* singing and _____

_____

12. Bruce wanted to get *out of the house* and _____

_____

13. His father drove *quickly* and _____
14. They enjoyed *the golden-green wheat* and _____

_____

15. *They hated to leave the beautiful scenery* but _____

_____

WORDS

1. Mr. Stegner uses a simple, homely vocabulary which is more suitable to his characters than high-sounding, scholarly

words would be. His use of strong verbs and especially vivid descriptive terms makes the story memorable. Notice *dangled, yanked, poking around, snapping, mumbled.* What other good verbs do you find in the rest of the story? List them below.

_____	_____
_____	_____
_____	_____
_____	_____
_____	_____

2. Descriptive words like *mashed* blackberries, *stiff* finger, *toothed* rocks, *reddish* gravel help you to understand the boy's feeling and to visualize the changing scenes. Make a list below of ten such phrases.

_____	_____
_____	_____
_____	_____
_____	_____
_____	_____

THE LIBRARY

A Review

1. Is the selection "Two Rivers" fiction or non-fiction?

2. In which part of your history book would you look to locate a paragraph about Daniel Boone?

3. In which part of your history would you find the page numbers of a section about life in colonial America?

4. Why is it important to notice the copyright date of books about science?

5. On what page in your PROSE AND POETRY can you find a story by Maurice Hindus?

6. What three indexes may a book of poetry contain?

7. As a telephone book is an index to your friends' phone numbers, what is an index to books in a library?

8. The initial for whose name is given in the call number of a book of biography?

9. What four kinds of cards does the card catalog contain?

10. Which card in the card catalog often has the first line printed in red? Why?

OUT TO OLD AUNT MARY'S

(Part 1, page 446)

JAMES WHITCOMB RILEY

Birthday: October 7, 1849
      (Died July 22, 1916)
Birthplace: Greenfield, Indiana
Poems to Enjoy and Reread:

1. *"When the Frost Is on the Punkin"*
2. *The Old Swimmin' Hole and 'Leven Other Poems*
3. *Rhymes of Childhood*
4. *Book of Joyous Children*

James Whitcomb Riley, the "Hoosier poet," is so well loved that October 7th, his birthday, is celebrated as a special holiday by the school boys and girls of Indiana.

Riley poured into verse memories of his favorite moments in boyhood. He joined a band of entertainers, toured many country towns and villages, acted and recited, and made friends with every one. These adventures led Riley to a decision—to become a poet. He mailed several poems to Longfellow who immediately replied in terms of praise and encouragement.

Riley's good nature, humor, and appreciation of simple things have endeared both the man and his poems to every boy and girl in America. He put into his writing much about simple joys and sorrows and the way of life of ordinary folk.

APPRECIATING THE POEM

1. It is said that the older people grow the more they remember the gay happy times of their childhood. What pleasant days is the poet recalling? What did the boys enjoy on their way to Aunt Mary's?

2. Mention some of the things that delighted the boys at Aunt Mary's home. What kind of person was Aunt Mary? How do you know that she loved the boys? What message is the poet giving his brother? Why is any child fortunate who has known an "Aunt Mary"?

152

A CHRISTMAS CAROL

(Part 1, page 448)

CHARLES DICKENS

Birthday: *February 7, 1812*
  (Died June 9, 1870)
Birthplace: *Portsea, England*
Stories to Enjoy and Reread:
1. *Old Curiosity Shop*
2. *Oliver Twist*
3. *David Copperfield*
4. *Nicholas Nickleby*
5. *Great Expectations*

From dire poverty to fortune and fame before he was thirty—such is the story of the world—renowned author, Charles Dickens.

Charles was one of a large family whose father drifted easily into debt and was tossed into a debtors' prison, the customary treatment in those times for failure to pay one's bills. Better days arrived when the father received a small inheritance which released him from prison and allowed him to support his family for a few years. At last Charles could go to school again, read all the books he longed to know.

His happiness was short lived for at fourteen he was again seeking jobs. Years followed as office boy, newspaper reporter, writer in leisure moments. Within a few years he wrote several successful novels, married, and became famous both as an author and a lecturer. Shortly after his first tour to the United States, he wrote the most popular of all his stories—"A Christmas Carol."

His death occurred suddenly when he was fifty-five. He was given one of the highest honors bestowed upon men of unusual literary achievement—burial in the Poets' Corner of Westminster Abbey. Charles Dickens will never be forgotten. Many improved conditions of today are the result of his stories which told people of the situations in need of correction. His fresh and novel style of writing made him the most popular author of his day.

Stave One

CHECK YOUR READING

In each blank write the letter of the correct expression.

_____ 1. Marley, Scrooge's partner, was (*a*) away on a visit (*b*) dead (*c*) ill with pneumonia (*d*) insane.

_____ 2. Scrooge, who managed the business, was (*a*) friendly (*b*) lovable (*c*) stingy (*d*) generous.

_____ 3. His clerk was forced to warm himself by (*a*) putting on a comforter (*b*) building up the fire (*c*) drinking hot tea (*d*) chopping wood.

_____ 4. Scrooge's nephew stopped in to wish his uncle (*a*) good day (*b*) a Merry Christmas (*c*) a happy Easter (*d*) a happy birthday.

_____ 5. The two gentlemen asked Scrooge for a (*a*) loan (*b*) gift (*c*) job (*d*) mortgage.

_____ 6. Scrooge gave (*a*) grudgingly (*b*) bountifully (*c*) nothing at all.

_____ 7. Because the clerk wanted (*a*) more pay (*b*) a day off (*c*) a new desk (*d*) two weeks' vacation, Scrooge was provoked.

_____ 8. When Scrooge went home he saw a (*a*) note (*b*) spot of blood (*c*) face (*d*) shining handle, on the knocker.

_____ 9. In the evening, Marley came to him, dragging (*a*) a chain of mortgages (*b*) a child's cart (*c*) a half dozen balls on a string (*d*) a sheet.

_____10. Marley promised that Scrooge would be visited by (*a*) three spirits (*b*) his long-lost aunt (*c*) several friends (*d*) death.

DISCUSSING STAVE ONE

1. The central character of "A Christmas Carol" is Ebenezer Scrooge. What sort of person is he? Find a sentence which seems to sum up his characteristics.

2. At what season of the year do we find Scrooge in his office? What kind of day is it? What details tell you that the time of the story is in the past? What do the open door of the office and the size of the fires prove?

154

3. In spite of the season, Scrooge is not in a merry mood. With what two words does he express his opinion of Christmas? How do the views of Scrooge and his nephew differ? With which one do you agree? With which did the clerk agree?

4. On what errand had the two gentlemen come to call on Scrooge? How did Scrooge answer their appeal? What organizations today carry on the same relief work?

5. Dickens is known as a master of the art of description. How does he make you feel the cold and the fog?

6. What further incident proves Scrooge's ill nature? How do you know that the clerk was a much happier man than Scrooge?

7. Where did Scrooge live? What words used in the description of his rooms seem to fit Scrooge himself? What unusual circumstance startled Scrooge on this particular night? Why did he search the rooms? What further evidence of Scrooge's miserliness do you find in his rooms?

8. Even Scrooge could know fear. What sounds astonished him and filled him with dread? Who was his visitor? Describe the apparition. By what explanation did Scrooge try to persuade himself that he did not believe in ghosts?

9. What caused Scrooge to change his mind? Why was the spirit condemned to walk the earth? What lessons had the phantom learned? Why had he come to Scrooge? What events did he foretell?

WORDS

In years to come you will very likely read many of the famous stories by Charles Dickens. You will want to know then why his stories have been so well loved and why they have continued to be popular over a long period of years. One of the reasons for his popularity is his ability to make a character seem like a real person. Notice that in the first four paragraphs of the story Dickens introduces the chief character, Scrooge, and that, although you may not learn just how he looks, you do learn what kind of person he is. In the fourth paragraph find at least ten good words that describe Scrooge. List them on a separate paper.

Stave Two

CHECK YOUR READING

In the blank at the left place the number of the matching phrase on the right.

_____ The time when Scrooge awoke

_____ When the Spirit was expected

_____ How the figure of Christmas Past looked

_____ What the Spirit and Scrooge first saw on their journey

_____ Who sat alone in the schoolhouse

_____ Whom Scrooge remembered

_____ The sweet youngster who came to take Scrooge home for Christmas

_____ The old gentleman to whom Scrooge was apprenticed

_____ What they enjoyed on Christmas Eve

_____ What surged in the heart of Scrooge as he watched this celebration

_____ With whom Scrooge next saw his former self speaking

_____ What he had loved more than the fair young girl

_____ Where Scrooge and the Spirit next found themselves

_____ How the children were behaving

_____ How Scrooge regarded the scene

1. regretfully
2. a happy Christmas feeling
3. 2 o'clock
4. gold
5. Marley
6. 1 o'clock
7. his sister, Fan
8. a grand ball in the warehouse
9. the sweetheart of days gone by
10. the schoolteacher
11. 12 o'clock
12. the scenes of Scrooge's childhood
13. his nephew
14. little boy singing a carol
15. a concert
16. the forgotten little Scrooge
17. home of his former sweetheart
18. childlike in beauty, yet old
19. jovial old Fezziwig
20. uproariously
21. his clerk

DISCUSSING STAVE TWO

1. As Marley had predicted, the first of the three spirits appeared promptly at one o'clock. Describe the strange form of the visitor. What did it represent? Why did Scrooge offer no resistance?

2. It is good for older people to now and then recall the days of their youth. What scenes of his boyhood was Scrooge first shown? What kind of childhood had Scrooge known? Scrooge shows his first sign of human sympathy. What is this sign?

3. Describe the second scene. What was the purpose of the Spirit in showing this scene to Scrooge? Did it have the desired effect?

4. As a young man Scrooge had been a business apprentice. What kind of person had his employer been? How had Christmas Eve been spent then? What words make you think that Scrooge has been comparing himselt with Fezziwig?

5. As a child Scrooge had missed the friendly companionship of other children and had not known the care of a tender mother. What scenes show that as a man he had also missed great happiness? What happiness might he have known if the love of gold had not possessed him? What do you think Scrooge has learned by these four visions?

WORDS

1. Scrooge clasped the robe in *supplication*. Did he clasp it in (fear) (haste) (entreaty) or (anger)?

2. Twice on page 469 appears the word *conscious*. What synonym could be substituted for it in each case? _____

Learn to spell *conscious* correctly.

3. What is an *apprentice?* What shortened form of the word does the author sometimes use? _____

4. Notice the description of Mrs. Fezziwig on page 474. What does the phrase "one vast substantial smile" tell you about her appearance and personality?

157

Stave Three

CHECK YOUR READING

Complete the meaning of each sentence by filling in the blanks.

1. When Scrooge awakened, he found himself the center of a blaze of _____.

2. Upon opening the door into his room, he found it decorated with _____, _____, and _____.

3. The visitor, who said he was the Ghost of _____ _____, was dressed in a _____ robe, bordered with _____ fur.

4. The streets to which the Spirit conducted Scrooge were _____ and filled with people going to _____.

5. At the Cratchit home, Scrooge saw _____, home for Christmas; the other little _____; the father, _____, and _____ _____.

6. For Christmas dinner, they had _____ and _____.

7. Every one in the house was _____, and the celebration was most hearty.

8. The family drank the health of _____, notwithstanding his stingy meanness.

9. Scrooge and the Spirit went, then, to the home of _____ _____.

10. The _____ spread his cheer far and wide, before he left _____.

DISCUSSING STAVE THREE

1. What "surprising transformation" had occurred in Scrooge's rooms? What was the second spirit? What qualities seemed to characterize it?

2. Do you think most people awaken on Christmas Day in a glad, joyful mood, full of good will, and kindly thoughts? How did the Spirit show Scrooge that the true spirit of Christmas can change men's hearts for the better?

3. Even the poor can know the blessing of Christmas happi-

ness. By what incidents did Scrooge learn that Bob Cratchit and his family were rich in contentment and love? What simple holiday festivities did they enjoy? What prediction did the Spirit make about Tiny Tim?

4. Wherever the Spirit of Christmas Present visited, Scrooge found gayety, joy, good will, and contentment. What strange places did they visit? At whose home did they stop? How was Scrooge included in the celebration?

5. Why did the Christmas Spirit grow visibly older? Why did it vanish so suddenly?

WORDS

1. Dickens' descriptions of appetizing foods are famous. Select six terms from page 483 that make the Christmas luxuries especially tempting.

_____	_____
_____	_____
_____	_____

2. From the descriptive paragraphs on page 492, list six especially vivid verbs or adverbs with which Dickens describes the action of the sea.

_____	_____
_____	_____
_____	_____

Stave Four
CHECK YOUR READING

Write T (True) or F (False) in the blanks.

_____ 1. The spirit which next came to Scrooge was the Ghost of Christmas Past.

_____ 2. The merchant group in the market was the mainstay of British business.

_____ 3. The man who died was friendless and alone.

_____ 4. The people who came to the den were thieves.

_____ 5. When he saw the drama in the Den of Crime, Scrooge understood that the dead man was his partner.

_____ 6. The only emotion caused by the passing of the unkind man was that of pleasure.

_____ 7. Tiny Tim had died, and the Cratchits were sorrowful indeed.

_____ 8. Scrooge was glad at not finding himself among the business men of the city, nor in his own chair at the office.

_____ 9. Scrooge pleaded tremulously with the Good Spirit that he might die at once.

_____10. If Scrooge had been past all hope, the vision would not have been given him.

DISCUSSING STAVE FOUR

1. The last of the spirits was very different in appearance and manner from the others. Describe it. What did it symbolize? Why did it not speak?

2. What was the subject of conversation among the business men? How was the scene at the filthy pawnshop connected with the previous conversation? What lesson did Scrooge see in the tragedy of the lone man?

3. The scene at the little home showed Scrooge the only persons who felt any emotion at the man's death. What emotion did they feel?

4. For the second time, Scrooge looked in upon the family of his clerk. What had happened there? Who showed compassion to Bob Cratchit? What different effects were caused by the death of the man and by that of Tiny Tim?

5. Why did Scrooge wish to know whether these visions were shadows of things that "*will* be" or "*may* be"? What final realization came like a blow to Scrooge? What plea did he make? Do you think Scrooge was sincere in his remorse?

WORDS

1. Throughout the story the author has used several synonyms for the *apparitions* that visited Scrooge. Name at least four other terms.

_____   _____

_____   _____

2. One section of the city was known to Scrooge by "bad *repute*." Explain the meaning of the italicized word. What

related noun is more frequently used? May the words also be used with the adjective "good"?

3. Many adjectives are formed by adding the suffix *ful* meaning "full of" to the original noun as in *wonderful, delightful, fearful, awful*. In this sense, *awful* is not to be confused with the slang term often used, but is meant to describe a feeling *full of awe* or *fear*. Reread the paragraph on page 505 beginning "He recoiled in terror . . ." and explain orally the phrase "*awful* language."

Stave Five

CHECK YOUR READING

Complete the meaning of each sentence by filling in the blanks.

1. Scrooge awoke in a _____ mood.
2. He was glad to know that he hadn't slept through _____
   _____.
3. He sent a _____ to the home of his _____.
4. He sent the Poulterer's man in a _____.
5. Dressed in his best he went to _____.
6. He contributed a generous sum to _____.
7. He dined with his _____.
8. He gave Bob Cratchit an _____ in _____.
9. In after years he led a _____ life.
10. _____ _____ did not die.

DISCUSSING STAVE FIVE

1. How did Scrooge feel when he awakened? Do you think it had all been a dream? What was Scrooge's first act of celebration? How did he regard the knocker, the boy, the turkey, and the cab?

2. The new Scrooge was indeed filled with the spirit of Christmas. In what excellent ways did he celebrate the day? How did he carry the spirit over into the next day? Is it possible for one to carry the spirit of Christmas good will with him all through the year?

3. Did Scrooge, after all, change the shadows of Christmas-Yet-to-Come into joyful days? Why was he truly happy thereafter?

4. Have you ever known a "Scrooge" in real life? What qualities should one cultivate to avoid becoming a person like Scrooge? Is it enough to be loving and giving on Christmas Day alone?

WORDS

1. On page 518 the author allows you to guess a word which he left unfinished. From the context we imagine that the word means *generosity* or *liberality*. Searching your dictionary, complete the word beginning *munifi* _____.

2. What word on the last page describes the *change* which had taken place in Scrooge? _____
What is the verb from which it comes? _____
What other word meaning "a place of sacrifice" is pronounced in the same way? _____.

APPLIED GRAMMAR

Rewrite the sentences below, correcting all errors.

1. Even the blind mens' dogs appeared to know Scrooge.

_____
_____

2. Although the court was the most narrowest, the houses opposite were dimmed by the fog.

_____
_____

3. The door of Scrooges' countinghouse was open.

_____

4. "You don't think *me* ill-used, when I pay a days' wages for no work." _____
_____

5. "A poor excuse for picking a mans' pocket!"

_____

6. "Its humbug still," said Scrooge.

_____

7. Scrooge had laid until the chimes rang again.

_____

8. The ghost held up its chains at arms length.

_____

9. Every one of the ghosts were wearing chains.

10. Scrooge resolved to lay awake until an hour passed.

11. Sitting up in bed to get his thoughts together.

12. The poulterer's shops were still half open.

13. Martha warn't as late last Christmas Day by half an hour!

14. By the time Scrooge and the Spirit left, it was getting dark and snowing pretty heavy.

15. Scrooge's niece laughed as hearty as him.

THE LIBRARY

1. Christmas in other lands is a fascinating subject on which to find information. Choose a country in which you are particularly interested and take notes on what you can learn from reference books about its Christmas celebration. The story of these customs may be written as a paragraph or longer theme, or given orally before the class.

2. If some one should give you a new copy of "A Christmas Carol" for your personal library, how would you proceed to open the book? Demonstrate this with any book you have, before the class.

3. Look up the complete listing of Dickens' novels at the library. Have you read any of them? From one which interests you most, write down the copyright date, the dedication, and the publisher.

4. In what reference book will you find a friendly, "chatty" account of Charles Dickens' life, with a picture of him included?

5. What reference book would you use to find a more detailed account of Dickens' life?

AMERICA FOR ME

(Part 1, page 522)

APPRECIATION AND CHORAL READING

1. Do you think that living for a while far away helps one to really appreciate his home or country?

2. Henry van Dyke enjoyed his first trip abroad in 1909. What cities did he visit? What sights did he admire? What did he feel was lacking in Europe? How has World War II affected these cities?

3. What present-day significance do you find in line 19? How do you think the men and women in service in foreign lands feel about returning home? Do you think that Europeans, like Americans, love their own land best? Explain why you would choose either America or Europe as your home.

4. All parts of this poem except the refrain should be read by single individuals (or by the same person throughout). Then the refrains may be read in unison because, even though written as though spoken by one person, they express a feeling that is common to all people.

THE FLAG GOES BY

(Part 1, page 523)

APPRECIATION AND CHORAL READING

1. In this poem, the poet shows us the glorious scenes he sees behind and in the flag. What are some of the things he makes clear to us? When you watch the flag are you impressed with the great ideals which belong to our American republic? What gesture of respect does the good American make?

2. Study the stanzas to catch their spirit before trying to read them aloud. Recall the feeling of pride and happiness which you experienced at the sight of the flag in a procession. Think of the bugles, the drums, the flash of color, the orderly lines of marching soldiers. In the third stanza let different boys and girls interpret the lines telling of things for which our flag stands. For the last stanza, let every one join in a closing tribute to the flag.

164

THE BIRTH OF A NATION'S SONG

(*Part 1, page 524*)

CHECK YOUR READING

Write T (True) or F (False) in the blanks.

_____ 1. Francis Scott Key was the commander of Fort McHenry.

_____ 2. The British planned an attack on Baltimore.

_____ 3. Dr. Beanes had to give medical aid to the captain.

_____ 4. Key and Skinner knew by the sound of the rockets that the Fort still held.

_____ 5. During the night the Fort surrendered.

_____ 6. The enemy set fire to the cartel boat.

_____ 7. Key and Skinner could see that the boats were sailing past the Fort.

_____ 8. The enemy ships were caught in the sunken barrier.

_____ 9. At dawn Key could see the white stripe of the flag.

_____10. Key jotted down his thoughts on an old envelope.

DISCUSSING THE STORY

1. Have you ever wondered how Francis Scott Key happened to write the stirring words which later became America's national anthem? The experience which prompted his thoughts was a thrilling one indeed. Explain the chain of events by which he found himself an unexpected observer of the British attack on Fort McHenry.

2. With what emotions did the three men on the cartel boat follow the attack? As night came on, how did Key and Skinner know that "the flag was still there"?

3. Imagine yourself there on the boat with Mr. Key and Mr. Skinner. Can you understand their suspense when darkness and silence surrounded them? Why were they not kept informed of the progress of the battle?

4. What trap had been set for the British in the event of their trying to pass by the Fort? Was it effective?

5. Waiting for daylight, Mr. Key and Mr. Skinner were consumed with impatience and anxiety. What were they waiting to see? How could they tell that dawn was approaching?

165

6. The huge flag flying above Fort McHenry was 36 feet long and 29 feet wide with fifteen stars and fifteen stripes. What states besides the original thirteen colonies made up the Union? With what feelings did Mr. Key at last see that great flag still flying above the Fort?

7. Francis Scott Key was a lawyer, but he found time to write in odd moments of leisure. Do you think he was wise to write down his thoughts on this occasion? Do the words seem truly inspired? Whenever you see "the broad stripes and bright stars," think of the poet's prayer and whisper to yourself, "Oh, long may it wave!"

APPLIED GRAMMAR

Can you match singular predicates with singular subjects, plural predicates with plural subjects? Underline the correct verb.

1. All he could see amid the invader's bombs (was, were) the great star-bespangled banner.

2. When a volley of shells (was, were) hurled at one time, the sound was deafening.

3. Cries and screams of the wounded (was, were) breaking through the night.

4. The big guns of the frigates (was, were) booming.

5. The swaying of many boats (was, were) added to the thundering noise.

WORDS

1. Do you know the exact meaning of words often used in descriptions of battles? Explain:

broadsides: _____

concussion: _____

bombardment: _____

2. On a separate paper use each of the words below in an original sentence, first making sure of each meaning by checking with the dictionary.

accented	perceived	pacing
abandoned	assail	intense
suspense	subsided	fervent

166

THE LIBRARY

How well do you find information in the library?

1. Before you could locate Fort McHenry on a map, you would need to know in what state it is. Where would you look to find this? _____

2. In what book would you first look to find the dates of the life of Francis Scott Key? _____

3. What aids should you use when looking in a dictionary?

_____

_____

4. What do the following abbreviations mean?

vol. _____

c. _____

p. _____

ff. _____

pseud. _____

5. In what book would you look to find how many persons became naturalized citizens in 1940? _____

6. What aids should you use when looking in an encyclopedia? _____

_____

7. In what part of a book does an author give his purpose in writing the book? _____

8. In what book would you expect to find an article about Francis Scott Key? _____

THE STAR-SPANGLED BANNER

(Part 1, page 530)

APPRECIATING THE POEM

1. You have often sung America's national anthem, but have you given real thought to the words? Now that you know the story behind the song, what new meaning do the words take on?

2. Although the poem was inspired by a battle in a long-ago war, which lines do we sing with special significance today? Which lines will ever state the heart-felt prayer of the nation?

3. Do you really know, without stumbling, the words of our national anthem? If you don't, learn them today and sing them with pride.

AMERICA

(*Part 1, page 531*)

APPRECIATING THE POEM

Generations ago, America lived in bondage to her mother country. There was no free schooling; there was no democratic government. Americans belonged not to themselves, but to a king who lived across the sea, and who many times proved unfair in his dealing with his colonies. Then came the Revolution; "Give me liberty, or give me death," was the battle cry. And death it was for many, before liberty was finally won. This liberty, then, of which we think so little because it exacts no payment, was once upon a time earned by the spirit, the death, the sacrifice, of thirteen fighting colonies. When you realize these things, you will not wonder why the poet calls America "sweet land of liberty."

1. "America" has one pure purpose in its lines—to sing the praise of its country in simple, grateful tones. "My country, 'tis of thee . . . I sing" the poet says, and goes on to tell how very much he loves his country. Upon what things does he call to fling the music of sweet freedom's song across and back throughout the land?

2. From God Himself the poet seeks protection for this land where the holy light of Freedom must ever reign. Read the poem again, this time really getting the meaning of the words and sentences. In recent years how has America seemed more than ever "a sweet land of liberty"?

THE AMERICAN'S CREED

(*Part 1, page 532*)

HISTORICAL BACKGROUND

A descendant of President Tyler, and a page boy and clerk in the United States House of Representatives, William Tyler Page seemed destined by ancestry and career for the writing of "The American's Creed."

From his youth he had been interested in the great documents of the nation and in the lives of the makers and scribes of these documents. When he was a young man, he began the custom of spending each Fourth of July in his library reading many of America's documents. He learned to know each word of the "Declaration of Independence," of the "Constitution," of the "Mayflower Compact," of the "Articles of Confederation," of speeches and debates of great statesmen. All these works he called his "American Bible."

In May 1917 a friend told him about a contest calling for the writing of a National Creed. Page thought little about it until one Sunday just after church service. As he strolled along, he was thinking about the Apostles' Creed recited that morning—what it expressed, how brief and complete it was. It occurred to him that a creed for Americans, a civic creed, could be written like that, stating things Americans had been believing and building for years, echoing the ideals of a free people from ocean to ocean.

Turning to his "American Bible" as a source, he worked out a creed. In August 1917, after writing, rewriting, changing phrases, words, and their order, he slipped his creed into an envelope, and mailed it.

In March 1918 a brief note informed William Tyler Page that he had won the award of $1000 for the prize-winning National Creed. The award was presented by the Mayor of Baltimore. The Creed was accepted by the United States Government so that it might become part of every citizen's life. The record of this ceremony can be read in the Congressional Record of April 13, 1918.

IN APPRECIATION

1. A "creed" is sometimes defined as a summary of principles or opinions. It is a simple, concise expression of faith or belief. What are the chief principles of Mr. Page's creed?

2. How many words are there in this "American's Creed"? How does any creed gain in effect by simplicity and brevity?

3. Repeat the pledge of allegiance with which you salute the flag. Consider carefully the meaning of the words. In what respects are the pledge and "The American's Creed" alike? Can you repeat from memory the last paragraph of the creed?

DREAMS
(Part 1, page 533)

LANGSTON HUGHES

Birthday: *February 1, 1902*
Birthplace: *Joplin, Missouri*
Poems to Enjoy and Reread:
1. *"Youth"*
2. *The Big Sea*
3. *The Weary Blues*
4. *"Minstrel Man"*
5. *"Mother to Son"*

Though Langston Hughes had never written a poem, he was elected class poet in the eighth grade. That, he says, is how he began writing poetry. His first poems were published in the high school paper.

The story of his life, told in *The Big Sea,* is one of hard work and struggle, and of making the most of every opportunity. His work in writing has been devoted to picturing the lives, thoughts, and feelings of the Negro people. In his poems he uses their folklore and legends.

APPRECIATING THE POEM

1. Boys and girls growing up into young adults are learning to understand the thoughts and feelings of other people—and through others are beginning to understand themselves. One of the ways of learning is by sharing the thoughts of others as expressed in written form through story or poem. How can a reader share in the thought of a poet?

2. What thought is Langston Hughes offering his readers in "Dreams"? To what kind of dreams does he mean we should hold fast? How is a person without dreams like a "broken-winged bird"?

3. What bright dreams do you hold of your own future? If all hope of the fulfillment of your dreams were to be suddenly snatched away, how would you feel? To what does the poet compare life without dreams?

OPPORTUNITY

(Part 1, page 533)

APPRECIATION AND CHORAL READING

1. Did you ever hear of a prize in composition being won by a boy or girl who had never studied grammar? Did you ever hear of a race being won by a boy or girl who had never learned to walk or run? Can a person who has never seized small opportunities grasp great ones?

2. What does the poem offer as great deeds yet to be done? Which of these would you choose as *your* opportunity? Or have you a thought different from any in the poem?

3. Has it occurred to you before that when we say that "this is the best book that has ever been written" we mean it is the best only up to this time—that we cannot say that it is the best that ever *will* be written?

4. If you like the message which the poet gives us, it will be a pleasure to read this poem chorally and to give the message to someone else by your reading. Two interpretations are suggested. In the interpretation given in the left margin, the question is asked by one boy who must be able to express the meaning very clearly. Then the answers are given by groups.

In the interpretation suggested in the right margin the response is by several individual voices, each one emphasizing some one part of the answer.

OPPORTUNITY

(Part 1, page 534)

APPRECIATION AND CHORAL READING

1. How does the poem illustrate that our opportunity lies not so much in what we have, as in what we do with what we have?

2. What opportunities do you have right now which you are neglecting to use?

3. Notice how vividly the words "a craven hung along the battle's edge" show you the picture. Notice also the way the poet makes us see clearly how the two men felt. Try to show these two moods in your choral reading.

TODAY

(Part 1, page 535)

APPRECIATING THE POEM

1. The poet gives us something to think about in the first stanza. What question does he put to us? How does he enlarge on the thought in the second and third stanzas?

2. Think of the day as having ended. Did you let it "slip useless away"? What do you consider a day wasted?

BOY WANTED

(Part 1, page 536)

IN APPRECIATION

1. "Boy Wanted" is written in sentence-paragraph form. Do you like this style of writing? Why is it likely to leave definite thoughts with you?

2. A paragraph should contain one main thought. What is the central thought in the second paragraph? in the third paragraph? in the fifth paragraph?

3. This selection is an excellent code of conduct. Characterize yourself by listing the numbers 1–21 which correspond to the qualities you are making real in your own life. In taking this inventory of yourself, be honest in your evaluation. Your best friend will help you answer 16, 18, and 20, as these would be difficult for you to decide alone.

4. Has Dr. Crane left out any point which you would add? If so, what?

WORDS

Properly divide each word into syllables. Place the accent mark over the correct syllable for proper pronunciation. After you have accented those you are sure you know, consult the dictionary for all the words to be sure each one is right.

respectful ———————	advertisement ———————
mistake ———————	intimate ———————
immediately ———————	necessary ———————
expelled ———————	secretary ———————
respectable ———————	business ———————

172

THE GREAT STONE FACE

(Part 1, page 538)

NATHANIEL HAWTHORNE

Birthday: *July 4, 1804*
 (Died May 18, 1864)
Birthplace: *Salem, Massachusetts*
Stories to Enjoy and Reread:
1. *Grandfather's Chair*
2. *"The Gray Champion"*
3. *"David Swan"*
4. *"The Pine Tree Shillings"*
5. *Twice-Told Tales*

Nathaniel Hawthorne began his career as a famous American on Independence Day, July 4th, 1804, in the historic village of Salem, Massachusetts. When he was four years old his father died, and the little boy and his mother went to live with relatives in Maine. His boyhood days were spent in fishing, hunting, roaming in the woods, skating, and reading. Soon it was time for him to prepare for college, and he returned to Salem where a private tutor was engaged. Later he entered Bowdoin College at Brunswick, Maine.

After graduation, Hawthorne's college friendships followed him and when his labors as an author brought in little income, his college friend, Franklin Pierce, then President of the United States, appointed him as consul to Liverpool, England. Rescued from actual need, he took his family to England where they lived comfortably.

When his task as a statesman was finished, Hawthorne returned to "Wayside," in Concord, Massachusetts. He again devoted himself to writing and now his stories were well received. *Grandfather's Chair,* stories from history which he wrote for his grandchildren, is still a favorite book today.

Hawthorne's death occurred as he was returning to Bowdoin College with Franklin Pierce for a visit to scenes of his youth. Sorrowfully his family and friend accompanied the body of this lover of children to its resting place in Sleepy Hollow Cemetery, in Concord.

CHECK YOUR READING

Underline the expression which correctly completes the meaning.

1. The Great Stone Face looked down upon a (*a*) wide plain (*b*) spacious valley (*c*) winding river (*d*) shining lake.

2. The villagers believed in a prophecy that (*a*) the Face would some day fall (*b*) someone would one day climb to its high peak (*c*) a great person from the valley should some day resemble the Stone Face (*d*) the weather would wear away the features of the Face.

3. A rumor went around that (*a*) a great doctor (*b*) a great merchant (*c*) a congressman (*d*) a preacher was coming to live in the village.

4. This person built a magnificent (*a*) church (*b*) library (*c*) hospital (*d*) mansion.

5. He was known as Mr. (*a*) Gathergold (*b*) Scattercopper (*c*) Dogood (*d*) Plentyman.

6. The second famous person to come to the village was a great (*a*) architect (*b*) sea captain (*c*) soldier (*d*) aviator.

7. Old Stony Phiz was a well-known (*a*) politician (*b*) author (*c*) sportsman (*d*) artist.

8. Among Ernest's visitors came (*a*) a musician (*b*) the President of the United States (*c*) his brother (*d*) a poet.

9. The visitor asked for (*a*) advice (*b*) charity (*c*) a night's lodging (*d*) an autograph.

10. Ernest's face reflected (*a*) greed (*b*) nobility (*c*) vanity (*d*) cruelty.

DISCUSSING THE STORY

1. If we could visit Franconia Notch in the White Mountains of New Hampshire and place ourselves at the proper spot on the southern side of Cannon Mountain we might behold "The Old Man of the Mountain." The "Old Man" is about 1,200 feet above beautiful Profile Lake at the foot of the mountain. Jutting rocks on the side of Cannon Mountain form that which appears much like the side view of a man's face. The rocks have been gradually worn away by the weather until it has become necessary to chain them in place in order to

prevent the "Old Man" from falling into the valley below. What do you learn about the effect of the Great Stone Face upon the inhabitants of the valley?

2. The child Ernest was early influenced by the Great Stone Face. What prophecy about it did he learn from his mother? What qualities of character did the growing boy seem to absorb from his affection for the Great Stone Face?

3. Simple, plain people are often deceived by a great show of wealth. How is this fact illustrated by the story of Mr. Gathergold? Why do you think the author gave the character that particular name? Describe the rich merchant and the home he built in the valley. How was Ernest disappointed by the appearance of the great man? What incident revealed the true nature of Mr. Gathergold?

4. As a young man, Ernest is described as "industrious, kind, and neighborly." Do you think those traits of character are desirable? How had the Great Stone Face taught him honesty, kindness, and sympathy? Have you ever known a person whose face expressed these qualities?

5. What happened to Mr. Gathergold? Who was the next person to be acclaimed as the one who fulfilled the prophecy? In what way was his nickname especially appropriate? In what foolish ways did the crowd behave? Who alone was not deceived? By what was he comforted?

6. Nearly every community has its men and women of such high and noble character that all others turn to them for guidance and wisdom. How had Ernest become an influence for good in his native valley? Why was he still thought an ordinary man?

7. Still another was hailed as the long-awaited image of the Great Stone Face. Describe Old Stony Phiz and the reasons for his fame. In what respects did he resemble the "Old Man"? To Ernest, what was lacking in the statesman's face? Why was Ernest saddened by this disappointment?

8. Late in life fame came to Ernest, though not through his own seeking. For what had he become known? How do you learn that Ernest himself has grown in resemblance to the Great Stone Face?

9. Ernest particularly enjoyed the work of a great poet. On what subjects and with what skill did the poet write? Why did the poet come to talk with Ernest? When Ernest at last learned the identity of his guest, what hope was destroyed? Why was the poet not worthy of representing the noble face of stone?

10. How was it at last discovered that Ernest was himself the likeness of the Great Stone Face? Describe the scene as Ernest talked to the people. What qualities of the Great Stone Face were reflected in Ernest's face?

11. Can anyone, like Ernest, shape and mold his life about an ideal? Do you know a real person who represents your ideal man or woman? How can you grow like that ideal person? What great persons in history are worthy ideals? Is it important to have an ideal to follow as you grow up? What is the meaning of the phrase "to hitch one's wagon to a star"?

APPLIED GRAMMAR

A Review

Rewrite each of the sentences below, correcting all errors.

1. When the sun was going down and they were talking about the Great Stone Face.

_____

2. The expression of the Great Stone Face, with all the features, were grand and sweet.

_____

3. It's face was so kindly that its voice must be pleasant.

_____

4. Ernest, as well as his mother, were impressed by its beauty.

_____

5. Mr. Gathergold, he was said to look like the Great Stone Face.

_____

6. This Mr. Gathergold was more richer than other men in the valley. _____

7. "Won't you tell the story to him and I?"

8. The Face may have looked no more kind at Ernest than at all the world.

9. Ernest laid by the hour to watch the Face.

10. The old prophecy was sure true!

WORDS

1. "The Great Stone Face" contains many words which you will encounter in your reading as you advance in school. From the words below select ten which are new and unfamiliar to you. Consult your dictionary for pronunciations and meanings.

destined	edifice	inevitably
pensive	sordid	illustrious
unobtrusive	meditate	discourse
veneration	communed	imbued
shrewd	imbibed	majestic

2. Explain how the story deals with *ideals* rather than with *deeds*. What difference can you distinguish between *knowledge* and *wisdom*? Explain such characteristics as *simplicity, sincerity, dignity,* and *grandeur*.

A TEST ON LIBRARY USAGE

Group I

Underline the correct word or phrase in each sentence.

1. A title page is (usually the first printed page in a book) (on the cover of the book) (in the back of the book).

2. The copyright date tells you (the date of the information in the book) (the date the book was written) (the date of the author's birth).

3. The table of contents is arranged (alphabetically by topic) (chronologically by subject) (in chapter order).

4. A book which has been written about a man is called his (bibliography) (biography) (biology).

5. An index is usually in the (front of the book) (middle of the book) (back of the book).

6. A book of poetry usually has (several indexes) (one index) (no index).

7. A library is a good place (to visit with one's friends) (to study one's lessons) (to read for pleasure and information).

8. Fiction in a library is on a shelf (by itself) (with the classified books) (with the reference books).

9. When you are through using a library book, you should (put it back on the nearest shelf) (leave it on the reading table) (return it to the charging desk).

10. The index to the books in a library is called (a book list) (a card catalog) (a vertical file).

11. All the cards in a card catalog are arranged (in one alphabet) (in several alphabets) (by call number).

12. An author card gives (the copyright date of a book) (the printing date of the book) (the date the card was made).

13. A call number is found (in the upper right hand corner of a catalog card) (in the upper left hand corner of the card) (at the bottom of the card).

14. The initial of the author's first name (is used in the call number) (is used in the classification number) (is not used).

15. A cross reference card (gives information about books) (tells you to look for another subject which means the same) (tells you the name of the author of the book).

16. A subject card usually has the subject written on the top line of the card (in red) (in black).

17. The call number $\frac{398}{T}$ would come (before) (after) the call number $\frac{398.1}{C}$

18. If a word has several different meanings (only the one that is used most is printed in the dictionary) (the one used most is printed first) (all the different meanings are given).

19. Maps can be found in (an atlas) (a dictionary) (an almanac).

20. The almanac can be used to find (statistics) (biographies) (poems).

21. The gazetteer contains (maps) (geographical information) (newspaper articles).

22. A dictionary may contain (a gazetteer) (an almanac) (an encyclopedia).

23. Reference books are found (in all school libraries) (in large school libraries) (only in high school libraries).

24. The *Junior Book of Authors* tells about (only living authors) (only authors) (authors and illustrators).

25. Special care should be taken of library books because (they cost money) (they are public property) (they are needed for class work).

26. The *World Almanac* gives (a map) (a story) (the population) of India.

27. *Living Authors* tells about authors (living only in America) (living in many countries) (who have lived recently).

28. The chief work of a school librarian is (to keep pupils in order) (to buy books for the library) (to see that pupils get the right books at the right time).

29. When you go into a new library, you may expect to find (a new system of arrangement) (a system similar to other libraries) (no system at all).

30. *Authors Today and Yesterday* (does) (does not) contain pictures of the authors.

Group II

Complete the meaning of the following sentences by supplying the proper words.

1. A title page contains the following information about a book: _____, _____, and _____.

2. To tell how recent the information in a book may be, look for the _____ date.

3. "To my friend, John Brown" in the front of a book is called the _____ of the book.

4. The purpose of a book is told by the author in the
_____ of the book.

5. A list of books at the end of a chapter for further reading
is called a _____.

6. To show that information is on several pages, an index
makes use of the following abbreviation: _____.

7. The three ways to find information in a card catalog are
to look for the _____ card, the
_____ card, and the _____ card.

8. The book *What Bird Is That?* by Chapman will have a
card in each of the card catalog drawers marked with the letters _____, _____, and _____ on the outside.

9. A card which says "Toads, see also Frogs" is called a
_____ card.

10. A book which gives the meaning of common words is
called a _____.

11. A book which gives information about all sorts of persons, places, and things is called an _____.

12. A reference book which tells you quickly in what state
a city is located is _____.

13. A book of miscellaneous facts and statistics which is
revised every year is called an _____.

14. The letter in the call number for a book of biography
stands for _____.

15. Two important encyclopedias are _____
and _____.

16. Two alphabetical aids in finding a word in a dictionary
are a _____ and _____.

17. Three common uses of a dictionary are to find _____
_____, _____, and
_____.

18. A word which means almost the same thing as another
word is called a _____ for that word.

19. Two alphabetical aids in finding a topic in an encyclopedia are _____ and _____.

20. The best known almanac in this country is the _____
_____ Almanac.

180

UNIT ACTIVITIES

DO YOU REMEMBER FACTS ABOUT YOUR READING?

1. "Theme in Yellow" is a poem about (the moon) (a dandelion) (pumpkins) (sunshine).
2. Robert of Lincoln is a (robin) (meadow lark) (thrush) (bobolink).
3. Every spring Grandpa went out to see his old friend (the neighbor on the next farm) (the colt in the pasture) (Aunt Mary) (the terrapin).
4. Something told the wild geese that (spring had arrived) (winter was coming) (hunters were close) (a refuge was near).
5. Annabelle (planned to run away and live with Indians) (agreed to play tricks on Caddie) (became a tomboy like Caddie) (remained a perfect lady).
6. "Two Rivers" is a story about a (fishing adventure) (family picnic) (boy and his grandfather) (a summer vacation at Aunt Mary's).
7. The words "God bless us, every one" were spoken by (Scrooge) (Ernest) (Tiny Tim) (Francis Scott Key).
8. "The Star-Spangled Banner" was written during the (Civil War) (War of 1812) (Spanish-American War).
9. "America" was written by (Samuel Francis Smith) (Francis Scott Key) (William Tyler Page) (Henry van Dyke).
10. The Great Stone Face greatly inspired (the poet) (Nathaniel Hawthorne) (Ernest) (Scrooge).

CAN YOU ASSOCIATE TITLES OF POEMS WITH THE SKETCHES?

1. _____
2. _____
3. _____
4. _____
5. _____
6. _____

CAN YOU IDENTIFY THE CHARACTERS?

1. _____
2. _____
3. _____
4. _____
5. _____
6. _____

CAN YOU RECOGNIZE QUOTATIONS?

Match the quotations of the left-hand column with the titles of the selections in the right-hand column.

___ "Long may our land be bright
With Freedom's holy light."

___ "Oh, thus be it ever when free-men shall stand
Between their loved homes and the war's desolation."

___ "I therefore believe it is my duty to my country to love it; to support its constitution; to respect its flag."

___ "Think, wilt thou let it
Slip useless away"

___ "For the best jobs haven't been started,
The best work hasn't been done."

___ "I shan't be gone long.—You come too."

___ "It sifts from leaden sieves,
It powders all the wood."

___ "Along the street there comes
A blare of bugles, a ruffle of drums,
A flash of color beneath the sky."

___ "To the blessed Land of Room Enough beyond the ocean bars,
Where the air is full of sunlight and the flag is full of stars"

___ "And poking through the window was her bald gold head"

1. "America"
2. "April"
3. "The American's Creed"
4. "Opportunity"
5. "The Star-Spangled Banner"
6. "The Snow"
7. "Theme in Yellow"
8. "America for Me"
9. "Winter Streams"
10. "The Flag Goes By"
11. "Dreams"
12. "Mockery"
13. "Today"
14. "Robert of Lincoln"
15. "The Pasture"